AF689258

CEDIA™

ADVANCED RESIDENTIAL ELECTRONIC SYSTEMS

V 3.0

Published by the Custom Electronic Design and Installation Association (CEDIA)

CEDIA would like to acknowledge the following contract service providers for this project:

Book Design and Layout
Anthony Sclavi

Graphic Services
Erikk Lee, Thunderlight Studios

Technical Writing
Writing Assistance, Inc.

ISBN: 9817394-3-4

THIRD EDITION

To purchase bulk quantities of this book please contact
CEDIA, attn: Certification Dept., 7150 Winton Drive, Suite 300
Indianapolis, IN 46268 (317-328-4336)

CEDIA would like to thank the following subject matter experts for their contributions to this text:

Robert Archer	*EH Publishing*
Peter Aylett, ESC-N	*Archimedia*
Tyrel Boehm	*Milestone AV Technologies*
Michael Bridwell	*Digital Projection, Inc.*
Ryan Brown	*Media Environment Design*
Simon Buddle, ESC-D	*Future Ready Homes, Ltd.*
Ryan Burnish	*Lutron Electronics, Inc.*
Ian Bryant, ESC-T	*Simplified Concepts*
Dean Callis, ESC-T	*CS Media, Inc.*
Sam Cavitt, ESC-D	*Paradise Theater*
James Chen	*Kords Pty Ltd*
Colin Clark	*Russound*
Henry Clifford	*Livewire, LLC*
Joel Crane, ESC-N	*MetaGeek LLC*
Vic Cypher	*Cypher Communications*
Ken Erdmann, ESC-T, ESC-D, HTDS	*Erdmann Electric*
James Forthman	*Labor Saving Devices, Inc.*
Jay Franetovich	*Middle Atlantic Products*
Lewis Franke, ESC-T, ESC-D, ESC-N	*Texadia Systems*
Jeffrey Gardner, ESC-T, ESC-D	*CEDIA*
Alan Grambo, B.E.E.	*Indianapolis Public Schools (Retired)*
Rich Green, ESC-T, ESC-D, HTDS	*Rich Green Design*
Scott Goldfine	*EH Publishing*
Patrick Hartman, ESC-T	*Diversified Systems Intl.*
Gavin Haverstick	*Haverstick Designs*
Dave Hunt	*Intuitive Integration*
Rich Huttick	*Interlogix*
Bjorn Jensen, ESC-N	*Why Reboot*
Jason Knott	*EH Publishing*
Ben Komar, ESC-T, ESC-D	*Komar Associates, Inc.*
Richard Kwasneski	*WyreStorm Technologies Ltd.*
Eric Lee, ESC-D	*Integrated Control Experts*
Gerry Lemay	*Home Acoustics Alliance*
Michael Maniscalco, ESC-N	*ihiji*
Geoff Meads, ESC-T, ESC-D	*Presto A/V*
David Meyer	*Kords Pty Ltd*
Laura Mitchell	*Laura Mitchell Consulting*
Mike Moon	*Milestone AV Technologies*
Ken Nelson	*Interlogix*
David Pedigo, ESC-T, ESC-D	*CEDIA*
Charlie Porritt	*Russound*
Steven Rissi, ESC-T	*Sensory Technologies*
Stuart Robertson	*Sound Integration*
Bob Schluter	*Middle Atlantic Products*
Joel Silver	*Imaging Science Foundation*
Steven Sumners, ESC-D	*Sound Insights, Inc.*
Dave Tkachuk, ESC-D	*Symbol Logic*
Floyd Toole, PhD	*Harman Intl. (Retired)*
Tim Troast	*Middle Atlantic Products*
Gordon van Zuiden	*cyberManor, Inc.*
Brannon Young, ESC-N	*Luxul*

The following young professionals from Indiana University Purdue University Indianapolis (IUPUI) contributed by writing, organizing data, and proofreading:

Kimberly Curry
Anastasia Khudoyarova
Fred Kukra
Danielle McDougal
Aaron Stroude

CHAPTER 12

CHAPTER 13

CHAPTER 14

CHAPTER 15

CHAPTER 16

CHAPTER 17

CEDIA™

ADVANCED RESIDENTIAL ELECTRONIC SYSTEMS

V 3.0

About CEDIA

The Custom Electronic Design & Installation Association (CEDIA) is an international trade association of companies that specialize in planning and installing electronic systems for the home. CEDIA provides top-ranked educational conferences, industry professional training, and certification focused on the installation and integration of residential electronic systems that consumers use to enhance their lifestyles. CEDIA's purpose is to build recognition and acceptance for this specialized field, and to speak up for its interests in addressing the industry, government, and the marketplace.

Comments Requested

Our industry is constantly evolving. No printed reference can remain current for long. In order to keep up with these changes, we invite comments from members of our industry. Please address them to:

CEDIA
Attn: Certification Dept.
7150 Winton Drive, Suite 300
Indianapolis, IN 46268

When you send comments to CEDIA, you grant CEDIA a non-exclusive right to use or distribute your comments in any way it believes appropriate without incurring any obligation to you.

FOREWORD

The systems integration industry is evolving rapidly, and so are the ways that CEDIA trains and certifies the professionals who design and install these systems. In 2014, a new general certification was launched (ESC), as well as a new book to serve as an introduction to the industry (Fundamentals of Residential Electronic Systems). Also in recent years, dozens of CEDIA's top courses have been converted for eCourse delivery online, along with many other online resources.

This book represents another of these major initiatives; a substantial overhaul of the highly successful Technical Reference Manual, which was introduced in 2009 and revised in 2012. Since it is so closely tied to the legacy of that publication, it is designated as the Third Edition. This time it has been completely reworked, made even more advanced, and now more fully supports CEDIA's higher certifications; ESC-T, ESC-D and ESC-N. The two books together serve as comprehensive body of knowledge for home technology professionals, both in the U.S. and internationally.

All of the technologies and standards have been updated, networking content has been greatly expanded, and many new sections have been added which address retrofit installation, subsystems integration, the role of the designer, and more.

This book represents hundreds of hours of work by many great volunteers, from the creation of the First Edition of the Technical Reference Manual, to the extensive revisions, and new content, found in this volume. The Advanced Residential Electronic Systems book is perfect for any industry professional who wants to be sure their projects are done to the highest standards, and for any individual seeking any of CEDIA's professional certifications.

Ken Erdmann

Certification Working Group Chair

Larry Pexton

CEDIA Chairman of the Board

CHAPTER 1

BASIC ELECTRONICS AND ELECTRICITY

The field of electronics is huge and complex and can take years of study to fully understand. Electricians serve substantial apprenticeships before becoming licensed. Electrical engineers generally spend four or more years acquiring a degree. Electronic systems contractors and technicians also need to have a basic understanding of the terms and theories that govern the electrical power running electronic equipment. This need for knowledge of electricity is true for anyone working with residential or commercial electronic equipment. A working knowledge of basic electricity is critical for everyone's personal safety.

Contractors and technicians also need to be aware that incorrectly installed electronics may result in personal injury or death and can cause damage to the equipment and property. Proper training is one of the best ways for electronic system contractors to provide a safe workspace and reduce liability.

ELECTRICAL CURRENT

Figure 1-1. *Simple Circuit*

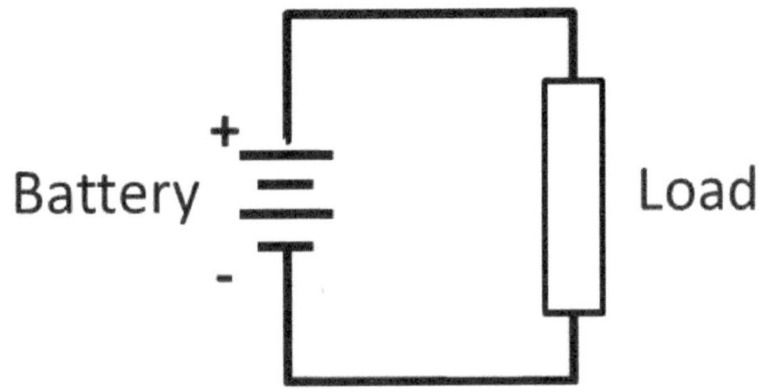

Direct Current

Direct Current (DC) refers to current that flows in one direction and does not change direction of flow. It is the key to the operation of most electronic components and is the "familiar" electricity that is found in batteries, cell phones, and cars. A battery is a group of electrochemical cells whose function is to convert chemical energy to electrical energy. Traditional batteries (also called a primary cell) are "use once" devices exemplified by the common zinc/carbon dry battery.

A secondary cell is a rechargeable device in which the chemical reactions that result in the generation of electricity can be reversed. An automobile battery is an example of a secondary cell. DC can also be created by rectifying and filtering an AC source. In fact, most DC power supplies do just that; they receive input from standard AC power line outlets, transform the voltage from 120 VAC to a low voltage amount like 6, 12 or 24 volts, rectify the AC voltage into a pulsating DC voltage, and then filter it to a smooth DC voltage output that can be delivered to the load.

Alternating Current

Alternating current (AC) is the electricity that comes into our homes. It is an electric current that constantly changes its amplitude and reverses its direction of flow (polarity) in a sinusoidal cycle at a frequency that is measured in hertz (Hz), or sine wave cycles per second.

The elapsed time for one complete cycle is known as the period of the wave. A sine wave is a waveform where the time is divided into degrees of rotation, with zero degrees being the starting point at the zero level, 90 degrees the positive peak, 270 degrees the negative peak, and a complete rotation is 360 degrees. Figure 1-5 shows a sine wave and the relationship of the amplitude, where the peak amplitude is measured from the zero level to a positive peak. The peak-to-peak measurement is from the negative peak to the positive peak.

The Root mean squared (RMS) value of an AC waveform is calculated by dividing the peak value of the wave by the square root of 2. The RMS value of an AC sine wave is the wave's effective value, the value equal to the work done by an equivalent amount of DC current. The RMS value can also be found by multiplying the wave's peak value times 0.707. It is the RMS voltage of 120 VAC RMS that we commonly refer to as household voltage.

In the United States, the AC to a home changes direction at 60 Hz, or 60 cycles per second. In Europe and many other parts of the world, AC to a home typically alternates at 50 Hz. Today, electrical power distribution is nearly all alternating current because of the advantages alternating current has over direct current in the ease of transmission from power generation source to the end-user.

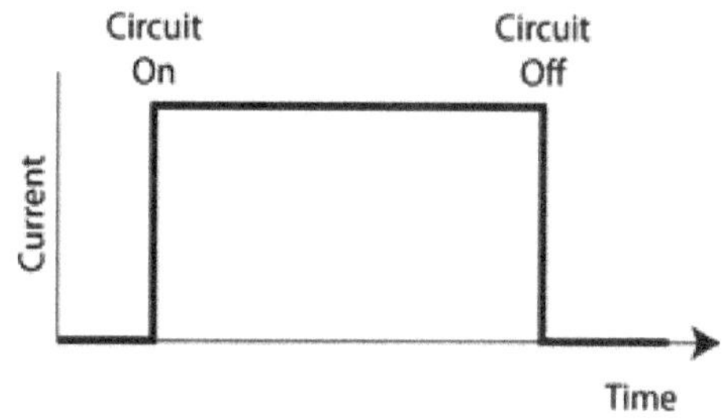

Figure 1-2. Direct Current

STANDARD TERMS

Coulomb — A coulomb is a measurement of a quantity of electrons. One coulomb contains 6.242×10^{18} (about 6,242,000,000,000,000,000) electrons. Although you will never directly measure a coulomb, knowing what it is helps in the understanding of the next term which you will need to measure and understand: the ampere.

Ampere — The Ampere or amp is a quantity measurement combined with a time measurement to define the number of electrons flowing through a circuit in one second. One amp is equal to one coulomb of electrons per second flowing past a point in an electrical circuit. In electrical equations, current is represented by the capital letter I and the unit of the Ampere is represented by a capital A.

Volt — Voltage is also known as electromotive force or EMF. It is the force that pushes the electrons through a wire and is referred to as electrical pressure. Voltage exists when there is a difference of potential between two points in a circuit. This difference of potential, or voltage, creates the electric field which causes electrons to move toward the terminal with a more positive potential due to electro-magnetic attraction. In electrical equations, voltage is commonly represented by the capital letter E and the unit of the volt is shown with a capital letter V.

Ohm — An ohm is the measure of the resistance to the flow of current within a conductor or load. Before voltage can cause electrons to flow, it must first overcome the resistance in the circuit.

Figure 1-3. *Amplitude Relationships of AC*

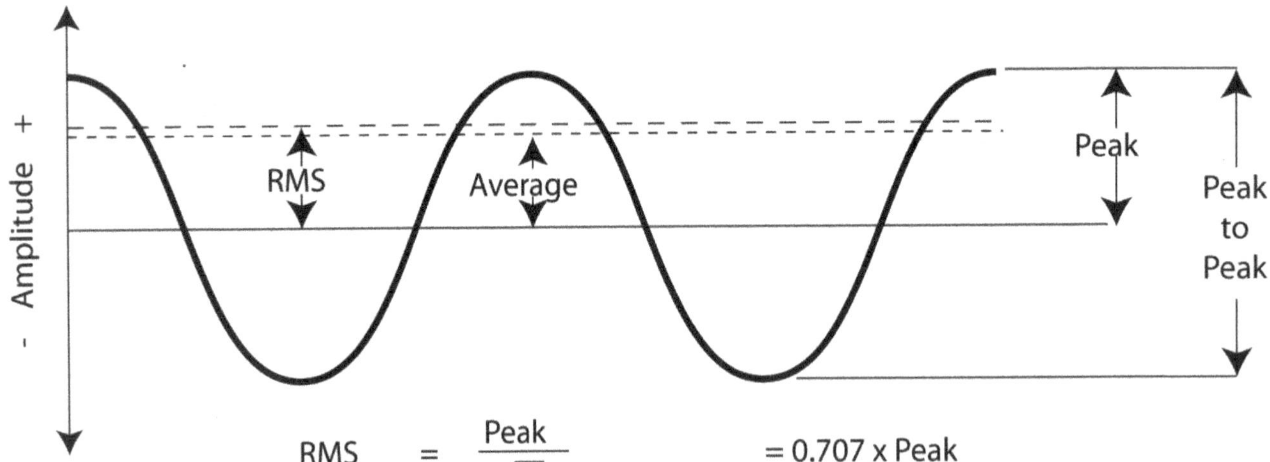

$$\text{RMS} = \frac{\text{Peak}}{\sqrt{2}} = 0.707 \times \text{Peak}$$

$$\text{Average} = \frac{\text{Peak-to-Peak}}{\pi} = 0.637 \times \text{Peak}$$

All electrical loads are measured in ohms, and it is symbolized by the Greek omega symbol (Ω). However, in electrical equations, resistance is commonly represented by the capital letter R.

Watt — Wattage is the measure of the amount of power that is being used in the circuit. It is proportional to the amount of voltage present and the amount of current flow. In electrical equations, a watt is represented by the capital letter P, while the unit of the watt is represented by the capital letter W. Power is the energy used to operate an electrical device. Power has two components, voltage (E) measured in volts and current (I) measured in Amperes. The amount of power or wattage is measured as the amount of voltage multiplied by the amount of current. Thus, one watt is equal to one volt times one amp.

BASIC ELECTRONIC COMPONENTS

A typical electronic circuit has several components. Each component is responsible for a different task (delivering, storing, regulating or controlling power). The most basic examples of these components include:

- Resistors
- Capacitors
- Inductors

Resistors

A resistor is a component that opposes the flow of an electrical current and produces a voltage drop between its terminals in proportion to the current flowing through it. The amount of resistance with which it opposes current flow is measured in ohms. All components in an electrical circuit have some level of resistance and changing a circuit resistance is a way of modifying a circuit's current and voltage parameters.

While we like to minimize resistance of circuit conductors, resistors are often placed into a circuit to reduce current or voltage for proper system operation.

In addition to the resistance of a resistor, you need to be aware of its power requirement. Every resistor dissipates electrical energy in the form of heat as current flows through it. The current flowing through the resistor multiplied by the voltage drop produced equals the power that will be dissipated by the resistor. The resistor must have a power rating greater than the power it will dissipate or it is likely that the resistor will simply burn up and open the circuit.

Figure 1-4 shows the symbol for a fixed resistor. They are common parts of electrical networks and circuits.

Figure 1-4 *Resistor Symbol*

Resistor Color Code

The most commonly used color coding scheme on all resistors is a four-band identification scheme, as shown in Table 1-1.

The scheme consists of four colored bands applied around the body of the resistor. The first two colors represent the first two digits of the resistance value, the third represents a multiplier, and the fourth represents the tolerance, or the percentage of change a resistor value may display and still be considered the nominal value indicated. Each color corresponds to a certain number (digit) or factor in the case of the fourth band.

For example, if a resistor was labeled with the colors brown, red, orange, and gold, its value would be 12,000 ohms ±5% as follows:

- brown = 1
- red = 2
- orange = 3 (indicating the number of zeroes or decimal places)
- gold = tolerance of ±5%

If the resistance was measured with a multimeter, that resistor should have a value somewhere between 11,400 and 12,600 ohms. If there is no fourth band present, a tolerance of ±20% is assumed. It should also be noted that if the third band is either gold or silver, the multiplying factor moves the decimal point one or two places to the left respectively; thus giving a resistance value less than one ohm.

In addition to a resistor's resistance value, a technician will need to know how much power the resistor is rated to dissipate. A resistor's power rating is given in watts.

For small carbon resistors from 1/8th watt to 2 watts, the power capability of the resistor is usually indicated by the size or diameter of the resistor. The larger the resistor, the more power it will dissipate. Resistors above 2 watts will often have their power rating printed on the body of the resistor or on its enclosing package.

Choosing the correct power rating for a resistor is as important as choosing the correct resistance value.

The use of a resistor is a circuit will often dictate what tolerance can be used without causing a circuit to malfunction. When replacing resistors, it is recommended that a resistor of equal or less tolerance be used to ensure proper operation.

Table 1-1. *Resistor Color Code*

Color	First Band	Second Band	Third Band (multiplier)	Fourth Band (tolerance)
Black	0	0	$\times 10^0$	
Brown	1	1	$\times 10^1$	±1%
Red	2	2	$\times 10^2$	±2%
Orange	3	3	$\times 10^3$	
Yellow	4	4	$\times 10^4$	
Green	5	5	$\times 10^5$	±0.5%
Blue	6	6	$\times 10^6$	±0.25%
Violet	7	7	$\times 10^7$	±0.1%
Gray	8	8	$\times 10^8$	±.05%
White	9	9	$\times 10^9$	
Gold			$\times 10^{-1}$	±5%
Silver			$\times 10^{-2}$	±10%
None				±20%

Capacitors

In consumer electronics, capacitors are often used as energy storage or power conditioning devices, and also as filters and signal processors. Common devices relying on capacitors are high pass filters in speaker crossover networks and power storage and filtering devices in amplifier power supplies. Figure 1-5 shows the symbol for a polarized capacitor. The straight line indicates the positive plate and is sometimes marked with a + symbol, while the curved line represents the negative plate. Applying voltage of reverse polarity to a polarized capacitor can result in catastrophic damage to the capacitor. Non-polarized capacitors are usually shown as a symbol with two straight lines with no polarity markers.

Capacitance

The amount of capacitance a capacitor exhibits is directly proportional to the size of the overlap of the plates and inversely proportional to the distance that separates the plates. The capacitance is also directly affected by the type of material used as the dielectric. The formula for finding the capacitance of a capacitor is:

$$C = \frac{kA}{d}$$

Where: C = the capacitance in picofarads
k = the dielectric constant of the material between the plates
A = the area of the one plate in square inches
d = the distance between the plates in inches

Capacitance is measured in units called farads (F); however since the unit of a farad is quite large, most capacitors are labeled in microfarads (μF) or picofarads (pF). Besides a capacitor's capacitance value, they are also rated by the amount of voltage that can be safely applied to a capacitor before the dielectric will break down, and this is called the capacitor's working voltage. It is generally considered a good rule-of-thumb to choose a capacitor with a working voltage that is at least twice the voltage you expect to be applied across the capacitor. Some capacitors are also marked with the frequency range they are expected to work in. All these factors must be considered by the technician when choosing the proper capacitor.

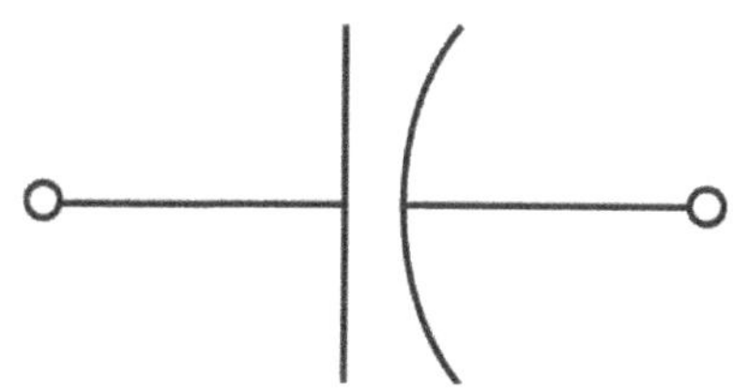

Figure 1-5. *Capacitor Symbol*

Inductors

The inductance of a coil is measured in a unit called a henry (H), though you will most often see inductors with units of henries, millihenries (mH) or micro-henries (μH). A coil's inductance is directly proportional to the square of the number of turns in the coil, the permeability of the material in the core of the coil, and to the cross-sectional area of the coil. It is also inversely proportional to the length of the coil. The formula for determining a coil's inductance would be:

$$L = \frac{N^2 mA}{l}$$

Where: L = inductance of the coil in henrys
N = the number of turns in the coil
m = is the permeability of the material in the coil's core
A = is the cross-sectional area of the coil
l = the length of the coil

A change in the current applied to the inductor creates a change in the magnetic field in each turn. The charges in each turn fight against each other to oppose the original field. This action opposes the initial change in current. As such, inductors only react to circuits that use alternating current (AC). Figure 1-6 shows the symbol for an air-core inductor.

Figure 1-6. *Inductor Symbol*

Inductors are used extensively in analog circuits When combined with capacitors and other components, inductors form tuned circuits that can emphasize or filter out specific signal frequencies. Smaller inductor/capacitor combinations provide the tuned circuits used in radio reception and broadcasting.

Any coil of wire can be considered an inductor and can create inductive reactance in a circuit. Technicians should avoid leaving large coils of spare cable as the inductive reactance created can adversely affect some circuits, particularly high-speed data and video circuits.

Transformers

A transformer is made up of two (or more) inductors that have coupled magnetic fields. Changing current in the primary circuit creates a dynamic magnetic field that triggers a changing voltage in the secondary circuit. Adding a load to the secondary circuit makes current flow and transfers energy from one circuit to the other.

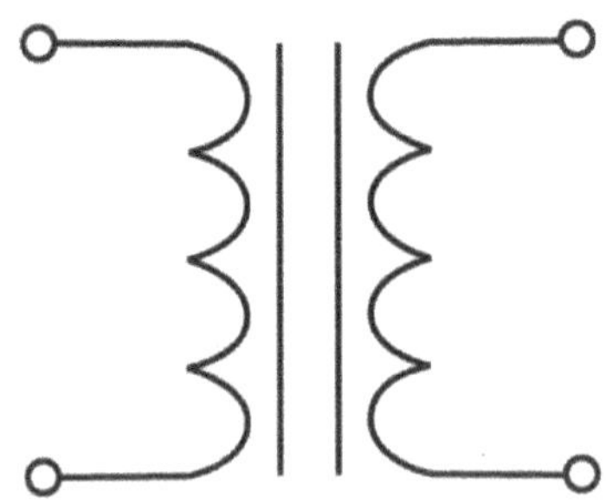

Figure 1-7. *Transformer Symbol*

Changing the number of turns (or windings) of the primary or secondary inductor enables the transformer to output either increased or decreased voltage compared to its input. It should be noted that the increase or decrease in voltage in the secondary comes with an inversely proportional change in current.

A transformer that has a higher voltage on its secondary winding than its primary winding is called a "step up" transformer; when the inverse is true the transformer is known as a "step down" transformer. For example, a transformer operating at 120 volts and with 500 turns on its primary winding and 100 turns on its secondary winding will output 24 volts. Since voltage and current are inversely proportional, if there were 1 amp available to supply the load on the primary side at 120 volts, there would now be 5 amps available to the load at 24 volts.

A typical transformer found in the power supply of many common electronic components might have a number of secondary windings sharing a single primary winding. This allows for different voltage values from a single transformer, thus saving space, weight, and cost.

Transformers are extremely efficient at managing electrical current. They come in sizes from extremely large units weighing hundreds of pounds (e.g., components of large national power grids) to tiny coupling transformers used in portable microphones. Figure 1-7 shows a symbol of an iron-core transformer.

RESISTIVE NETWORKS

The current through resistors in series stays the same, but the voltage drop occurring across each resistor can be different and is dependent on the value of the resistors. The sum of the voltage drops across all resistors is equal to the total voltage being applied to the circuit. The calculation for total resistance in a series-resistive network is shown in Figure 1-8.

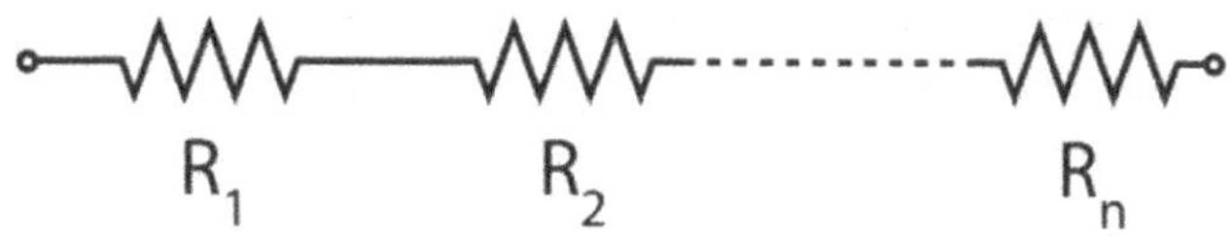

$$R_{eq} = R_1 + R_2 + \dots + R_n$$

Figure 1-8. *Series Calculation*

Resistors in a parallel configuration each have the same potential difference (voltage) across them, since they are all connected directly across the common power source. The current flowing through each resistor will equal the total current present in the circuit, although the current through each resistor will vary according to its resistance value. The common calculation for total resistance in a parallel-resistive network is shown in Figure 1-9.

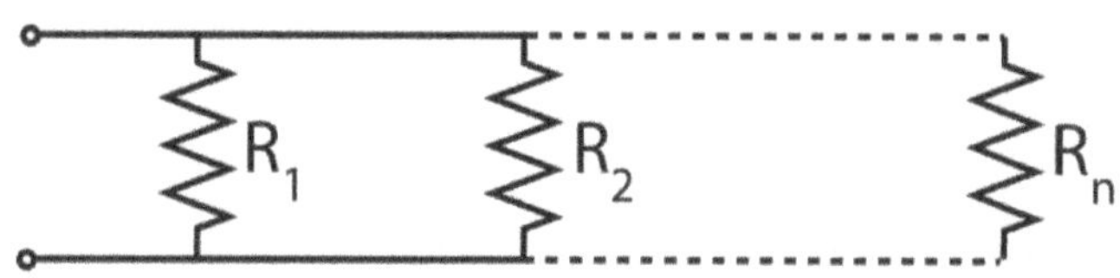

$$\frac{1}{R_{eq}} = \frac{1}{R_1} + \frac{1}{R_2} + \dots + \frac{1}{R_n}$$

Figure 1-9. *Parallel Calculation*

A resistor network that is a combination of parallel and series can sometimes be broken up into smaller parts that are either one or the other. The total resistance calculation for a simple combination-resistive network is shown in Figure 1-10. You will note another method of calculating parallel resistance is used in the formula. With only two resistors in parallel, (e.g. R1 and R2) the parallel resistance can be calculated by dividing the product of the two resistances by the sum of the two resistances. Adding the result to the series resistance of R3 will give the total resistance of the network.

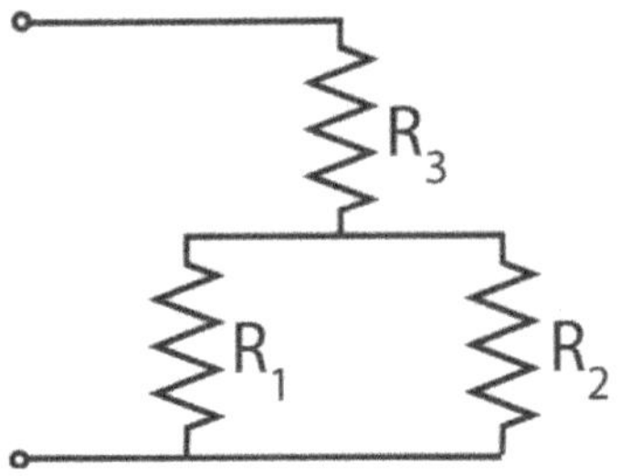

$$R_{eq} = \frac{R_1 R_2}{R_1 + R_2} + R_3$$

Figure 1-10. *Combination Calculation*

In certain instances, where all the resistors in a parallel circuit are of the same value, the total resistance can be found by dividing the value of one resistor by the number of resistors. In most cases, series-parallel circuits can be broken up into their constituent series and parallel paths and solved individually, then combined for an overall total resistance. Re-drawing a complicated circuit into groupings of series and parallel components can greatly simplify the solving of total resistance.

Networks, or combinations of resistances, draw current when they are hooked up to a source of voltage. The total amount of current they draw is calculated by determining the total resistance of the combination and then looking at the network as a single resistor. If the resistive value is the same for all of the resistances on the network, the power from the sources is evenly distributed. In this case, it does not matter whether they are in series or parallel. If the resistive value is not the same, the power is divided up unevenly and the power in each resistor is determined by using the applicable power formula based on the current running through it and the voltage across it.

Current and Voltage in Series Circuits

In a series DC circuit, the current is the same at every point in the circuit even if the components have different resistances. The voltage is divided up among each of the resistances and the sum of the voltage drops across each resistance equals the supply voltage. Series circuits are sometimes called voltage dividers.

Current and Voltage in Parallel Circuits

In a parallel circuit, each of the components receives the same voltage, which is determined by the power source, while the current is divided up among the resistances. When wired in parallel, each resistor functions independently and the current drawn by each depends on its individual resistance value. The total current equals the sum of the currents through all the resistances in the circuit. Parallel circuits are sometimes called current dividers.

Kirchhoff 's Current Law (KCL) — This law is also called Kirchhoff 's First Law, Kirchhoff 's Point Rule, Kirchhoff 's Junction Rule (or Nodal Rule), and Kirchhoff 's First Rule, and is shown in Figure 1-11. This rule states that the sum of all currents entering a node must equal the sum of all currents leaving the node. The principle of conservation of electric charge implies that at any point in an electrical circuit where charge density is not changing in time, the sum of currents flowing towards that point is equal to the sum of currents flowing away from that point.

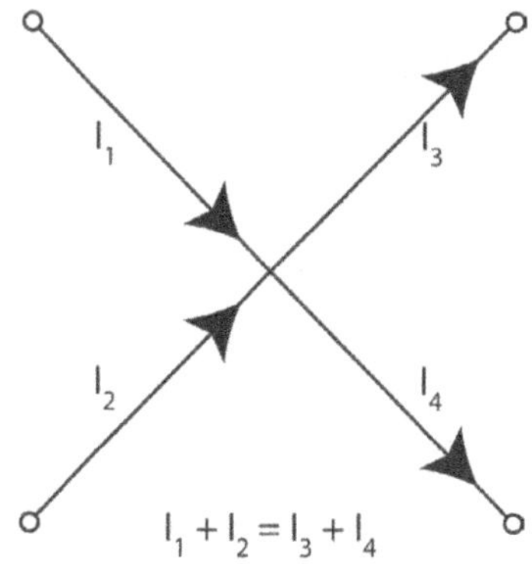

Figure 1-11. *Kirchhoff's Current Law*

Kirchhoff's Voltage Law (KVL) — Kirchhoff's Voltage Law (KVL), also called Kirchhoff's Second Law, Kirchhoff's Loop (or Mesh Rule), and Kirchhoff's Second Rule, is shown in Figure 1-12. This law states that the directed sum of all the voltages around a loop must equal zero (V1 + V2 + V3 + V4 = 0). This means that voltage can never simply appear or disappear. For example, if there is a 12-volt power source and three resistors in series, they can be arranged in any order and the sum of the voltage drop across all three will always add up to 12. If instead the three resistors are in parallel with the same power source, each one will be an individual circuit and each one will have 12 volts across it.

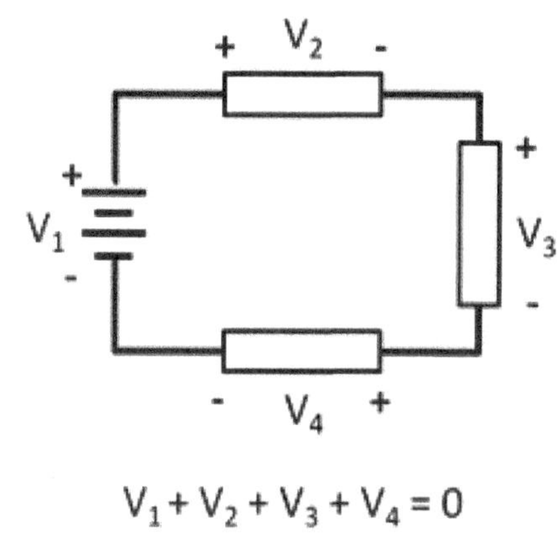

Figure 1-12. *Kirchhoff's Voltage Law*

The net result of these two laws is simply that all power must be accounted for in any DC circuit, whether it is parallel or series. This means that every volt, amp, or watt that enters a circuit must be passed through the circuit and dissipated by the components of the circuit for a net result of zero.

Ohm's Law

All DC circuits are made up of three parts: a source of voltage, a set of conductors to carry the current, and a resistance, or load. As mentioned earlier, the symbol for the voltage used in formulas is E. The current through the circuit is represented by I, and the resistance of the circuit is represented by R. In the late 1820's, Georg Ohm developed several formulas or laws about the interdependence of voltage, current flow, and resistance.

Figure 1-13. *Ohm's Law*

Ohm's law states that the voltage (E) across a circuit is equal to the product of the current (I) flowing through it and the resistance (R) of the circuit (E = I × R). The other derivations of Ohm's law are I = E÷R and R = E÷I. Figure 1-13 shows the relationship between these elements in the form of a circle chart. The circle chart provides a handy way to determine the correct formula to use when two quantities are known and you wish to find the third. By placing your finger over the unknown quantity, the circle reveals the relationship between the remaining quantities. For example, if you wish to find current, place your finger on the "I" symbol. The circle shows that E is above the "R" symbol, so volts must be divided by ohms to find the current in amps. When finding voltage, the circle indicates that amps must be multiplied by ohms. This is one of the most fundamental equations used in calculating any unknown or immeasurable aspect of an electrical circuit.

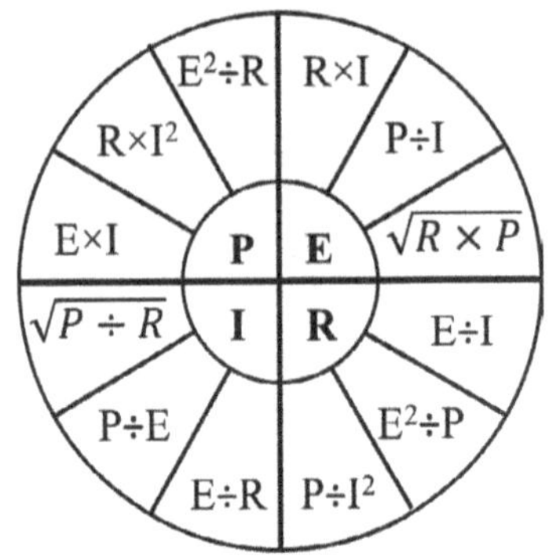

Figure 1-14. *Ohm's Law & Watt's Law*

Ohm's Law and Power Relationships

Another electrical unit we need understand, in addition to those in Ohm's law, is power. Power, designated in formulas as a capital P, is a measure of the capability of the electrical circuit to do work. More specifically, it is the amount of work done by one volt of electricity at a rate of one coulomb per second (one amp of current) for a period of one second. The amount of electrical power used is typically expressed in watts (W), which are usually calculated in a DC circuit by multiplying the voltage (E) by the current (I).

P = E × I, so one watt equals one volt times one amp. Figure 1-14 shows the relationship between power, voltage, current and resistance in the form of an equation wheel. For example, to solve for voltage (E) in a circuit where power (P) and current (I) are known values, the upper right quadrant of the equation wheel is used, and the formula chosen is E = P ÷ I. Be sure all values are shown in their base units of watts, volts, amps or ohms.

Power Distribution

The amount of power that a particular resistor dissipates is calculated by the formula:

$$P = I^2 \times Rn$$

Where: P is the power in Watts
I is the current in Amps
R is a particular resistors value in Ohms

The wattage, or total power, dissipated in a series circuit is equal to the sum of the wattages dissipated in each resistor similar to the distribution of voltage.

In parallel-wired circuits, where the current in each resistance is not the same, you can use the formula:

$$P= E^2 \div Rn$$

E is the voltage of the power supply or battery supply that is the same across all resistors in parallel. The total dissipated wattage in a parallel circuit is equal to the sum of the wattages dissipated by the individual resistances.

Measurements in DC Circuits

Measurements in DC circuits are usually accomplished using a multimeter of some type.

Multimeter features will be discussed later in this chapter under test equipment. Multimeters are used with circuits to typically measure voltage, current and resistance.

There are many safety issues involved with using a multimeter, so a technician should seek proper training before using a multimeter for the first time.

DC MAGNETISM

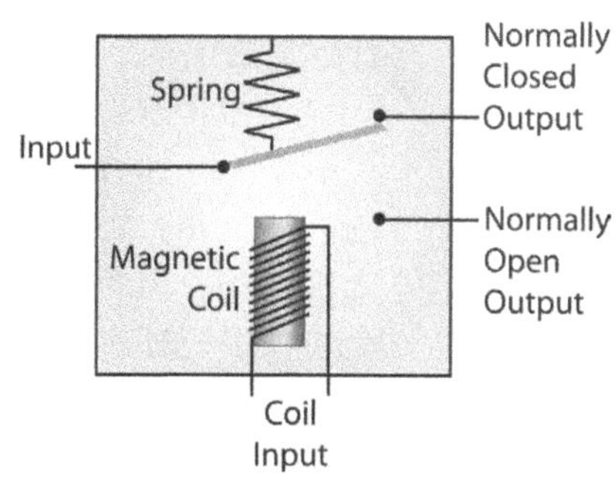

Figure 1-15.
Simple SPDT Relay

A magnetic field results when atoms in a material are aligned in a particular way. The motion of electrons or other electric charge carriers can also create a magnetic field either in a wire or in space. Engineers describe magnetic fields in terms of flux lines, which are imaginary curved lines that represent quantities of magnetism.

The amount of magnetism produced by a device is measured in webers (Wb). It is also discussed in terms of flux density. Permeability is a measure of the way a particular substance affects magnetic flux density. Materials, such as iron, that concentrate magnetic lines of flux are called ferromagnetic, have high permeability, and can be magnetized. Substances, such as wax or wood, that dilute magnetic flux are called diamagnetic, have low permeability, and are used to keep magnetic objects apart.

Relays

Electromagnets, such as a magnetic coil, are used in a relay to move contacts for remote control switching. A movable lever, called the armature, is pulled to one side by a spring when no current is flowing in the relay's magnetic coil and is pulled over to the other side by electromagnetism when current is flowing. Figure 1-15 shows a diagram of a simple relay. Relay contacts can be normally open, normally closed or both depending on contact arrangement.

Normally Open and Normally Closed Relay Switches

Relays come in many shapes, sizes, and configurations. Common nomenclature used to describe relays is SPST, DPDT, 4PDT, etc. SPST is an abbreviation for single-pole single-throw. DPDT is an abbreviation for Double-Pole Double-Throw. Beyond these names, numbers are used, such as 4PDT to designate a Four-Pole Double-Throw relay or set of contacts.

A four-pole relay can switch four separate circuits all at once, while a single-pole relay can switch only one. The throws, or contacts of a relay, are what the circuits are connected to. Most relays are single-throw or double-throw. The normally open (NO) contacts on a relay are open (or disconnected) from the common contacts (C) when the relay is at rest and has no current applied to the coil. While the relay is still at rest, the normally closed (NC) contacts are connected to the common contacts (C). The coil is the electromagnet that switches the state of the relay when it is energized.

Relays with both NO contacts and NC contacts operated by a common coil are often used to provide a safety interlock when controlling motors in shades, screens or lifts. When the contacts are closed for one direction the circuit providing power to the opposite direction is held open thus, preventing accidental connection to the power source.

Relays are typically non-directional. This means that a double-throw relay can be used to switch one power source between two different loads. It can also be used to provide one load with two different power sources. A single-throw relay, however, is always an on/off switch because each circuit only has two contacts, a common and either a normally open or a normally closed contact.

Some relays switch several times per second, while others are designed to stay in the same state for a very long time. Even though there is a limit to how fast relay switches can work (and they can experience corrosion and pitting), relay switches are still used in many applications because they are more capable of adapting to unexpected voltage spikes. However, in most situations they have been replaced by semiconductor switches. Figure 1-16 shows the symbols used for various types of relays.

Relay coils can be designed to work with either AC or DC current, but a technician should be aware of which type is needed as they are not directly replaceable for one another. Likewise, the relay's contacts can switch both AC and DC circuits, but care must be taken to not exceed the current and voltage limitations of the switching contacts.

Inductors

The opposition to current change exhibited by a coil of wire is due to the magnetic field that is constantly building and collapsing as the AC wave moves through its cycle. Inductors store energy in the magnetic field during part of the cycle and release it during another part. This ability to store energy in a magnetic field is called the coils inductance (L) and is measured by a unit called a henry (H). Inductors are commonly rated in henries, milli-henries and micro-henries.

The inductive reactance (XL) of an inductor is directly proportional to the inductor's inductance and the frequency of the AC wave. As the frequency of the AC signal or the inductance of the inductor increases, the inductor's inductive reactance increases proportionally. The formula for determining an inductor's inductive reactance is:

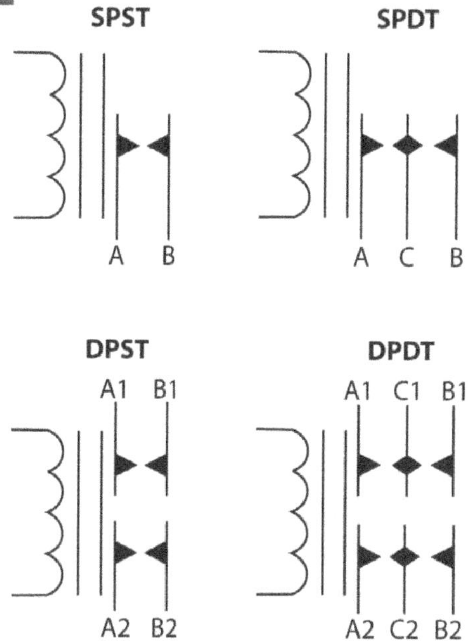

Figure 1-16. *Relay Symbols*

$$X_L = 2\Pi fl$$

Where: XL is capacitive reactance in ohms, Ω
f is frequency is hertz, Hz
L is the inductance in henries, H

Total inductance in series and parallel AC circuits is found using the same methods as those used to calculate total resistance in DC circuits.

Capacitors

Capacitors have an ability to store voltage in an electro-static field that is created between the plates of the capacitor. This ability is known as the capacitor's capacitance (C) and it is measured in units of farads (F). The farad is a fairly large unit, so most often capacitors are rated in microfarads, nanofarads and picofarads.

Capacitors create an opposition to the change of voltage in an AC circuit and that opposition is called capacitive reactance (XC). The amount of capacitive reactance a capacitor exhibits is inversely proportional to the frequency of the AC current and the capacitance of the capacitor. As the frequency of the AC signal increases or the capacitance increases, the capacitive reactance decreases proportionally. The formula for finding the capacitive reactance of a capacitor is:

$$X_C = \frac{1}{2\Pi fC}$$

Where: XC = capacitive reactance in ohms, Ω
f = frequency in hertz, Hz
C = capacitance in farads, F

Total capacitance of a series circuit is found using the formulas like those used in finding total resistance of resistors in parallel, while finding total capacitance in a parallel circuit is found by adding the capacitances, like we do resistors in series. Just the opposite of what we do for inductors.

Impedance

Impedance is the total opposition that a component or circuit offers to alternating current. Impedance is not as simple to calculate as DC resistance, although resistance is one component of the equation. Impedance consists of two independent components: resistance (R) and total reactance (XT). Total reactance in a circuit is found by adding the inductive and capacitive reactances together. However, both inductive and capacitive reactances have a 90° phase relationship to resistance in a circuit. Inductors have a +90° phase shift, meaning voltage leads current through an inductor by 90°; while a capacitor has a -90° phase shift meaning voltage lags current by 90°. By convention, capacitive reactance is assigned a negative value due to the negative phase shift, so that when inductive and capacitive reactances are added together, we are in fact subtracting the circuit's capacitive reactance from its inductive reactance and taking the absolute value of the result.

$$X_T = X_L + (-Xc)$$

Resistance is the same for AC and DC circuits. A circuit's impedance is a complex quantity that must take into account the phase relationships between resistance and total reactance. The formula for finding a circuit's impedance is:

$$Z = X_T^2 + R^2$$

Where: Z = impedance in ohms, Ω
XT = total reactance in ohms, Ω
R = resistance in ohms, Ω

The formula is the same formula used to find the hypotenuse of a right triangle, according to the Pythagorean Theorem. It this case, the hypotenuse is the circuit's impedance and the legs of the right triangle are the circuit's resistance and total reactance.

Resistance, inductive reactance, capacitive reactance, total reactance and impedance are all measured in units of ohms.

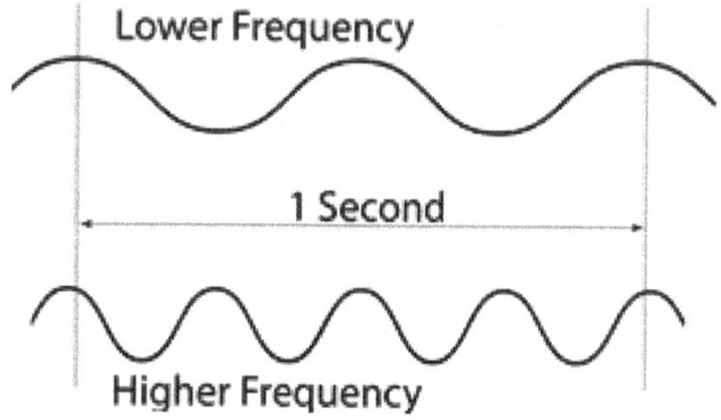

Figure 1-17. *Sine Wave Frequencies*

Sine Waves

As mentioned earlier, the sine wave, or sinusoidal wave form, is the classic AC wave. This wave pattern occurs often in nature, including ocean waves, sound waves, and light waves. In a periodic AC wave, the length of time between a particular point in the cycle and the same point in the next cycle is the period of the wave, and the distance a wave travels during its period is the wave's wavelength. The inverse of a wave's period is the wave's frequency, which measures the number of complete repetitions or cycles that occurred in one second. Figure 1-17 shows two sine waves, one with a frequency of 2 Hz and the other at 4 Hz. Though in theory, a wave's period can range anywhere from a fraction of a second to many years, in electronics, we generally talk about audible frequency (AF) ranges and radio frequency (RF) ranges.

In AF ranges, the wave reverses polarity from around 20 times per second to about 20,000 times per second (20 Hz to 20 kHz), with periods of 50ms to 50μs, respectively. In RF ranges, the timeframe is from a few thousand times per second (kHz) up to billions of times per second (GHz).

Each sine wave cycle starts with the voltage at the zero level. The voltage rises until it reaches a positive maximum value, then it decreases until it passes the zero level and becomes negative. The voltage continues in a negative direction until it attains a maximum negative value. It then changes direction and becomes less negative until it again reaches the zero level, completing one full cycle.

Electricity is brought to a home by power lines in the form of alternating current. Power transformers can change the voltage of an AC power source. The transformer can either "step up" to increase the voltage or "step down" to decrease the voltage. High voltage transmission is more efficient than low voltage transmission over long distances because the power loss caused by conductor resistance decreases as the voltage increases. Looking back at the relationship circle in Figure 1-16, we find that power (P) equals current squared (I2) times the resistance (R). Using transformers to increase the transmitted voltage decreases the current proportionally, and since we have a squared relationship between power and current, as we decrease current we also decrease power loss by inverse of the square. If we double the voltage we decrease current by half and we effectively decrease power loss by a factor of four.

Non-Sinusoidal Waveforms

Non-sinusoidal waveforms are waveforms that are not pure sine waves. Any non-sinusoidal waveform, such as a square wave or even the irregular sound waves made by human speech, can be represented as a collection of sinusoidal waves of different periods and frequencies blended together. They are usually derived from simple mathematical functions.

Although a pure sine wave consists of a single frequency, non-sinusoidal waveforms contain multiple sine waves of different frequencies.

These "component" sine waves may or may not be multiples of a fundamental or "lowest" frequency. The frequency and amplitude of each component can be found using a mathematical technique known as Fourier analysis.

Square Waves

In illustrations, the transitions for a square wave are shown as vertical lines, resulting in the squared-off wave shown in Figure 1-18. On a oscilloscope, a perfect square wave looks like a pair of parallel dashed lines. One of the lines has a positive polarity and the other has a negative polarity.

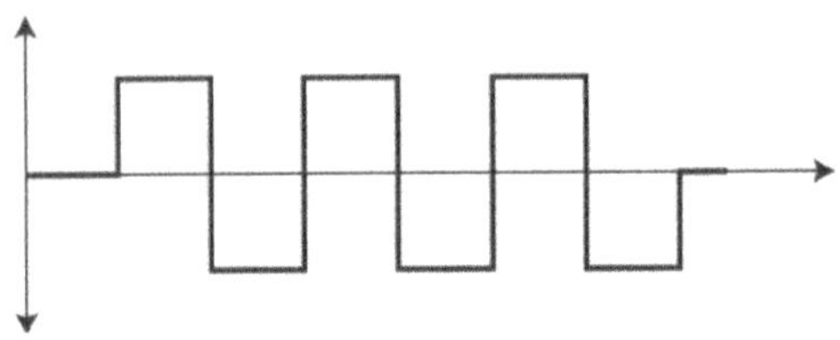

Figure 1-18. *Square Wave*

If a square AC wave has equal negative and positive peaks, it is called a symmetrical square wave. An asymmetrical square wave has positive and negative amplitudes that are not the same. This wave is not truly square and is called a rectangular wave.

Sawtooth Waves

In addition to sine and square waves, the sawtooth wave, shown in Figure 1-19, is also a common type of wave. The positive slope, called the rise or attack, occurs instantly. The negative slope, or the decay, is gradual. The period of the wave is the time between points at identical positions on two successive pulses. The sawtooth wave can also take the opposite form, with a gradual rise and a rapid fall. This is also called a ramp. Sawtooth waves can contain an infinite number of combinations. If the rise and fall are equal, the wave is called a triangular wave.

Figure 1-19. *Sawtooth (Triangular) Wave*

Irregular Waves

Irregular or complex waves have specific and measurable frequencies. Although the shape appears irregular, it is repetitive. The period is the time between points on adjacent, succeeding repetitions of the wave form. Irregular waves can produce a variety of strange frequency-domain displays.

Measurements

An instrument commonly used to measure and display frequency-based electrical information such as the waveforms mentioned above is an oscilloscope, often called a scope. An oscilloscope shows voltage on the vertical y-axis and time on the horizontal x-axis. A scope, unlike a multi-meter, will display the peak and peak-to-peak value of a waveform. RMS and average values must then be calculated by interpreting the peak value shown and applying the correct formula. Some scopes have a built-in voltmeter that displays the wave's RMS voltage without the need to calculate it from the scope's display.

Standard commercial power frequency varies in different countries. In the U.S., standard commercial power frequency is 60 hertz or 60 sine waves cycles per second. However, the AC current is not quite perfect. Sometimes the imperfections are so small that they cannot be measured. The imperfections are the cause of the electromagnetic noise that is sometimes radiated by AC power lines.

An instrument called a spectrum analyzer shows frequency on a horizontal scale, shows amplitude on a vertical scale, and depicts amplitude as a function of frequency. This display is called a frequency-domain display. These are frequently used to measure video signals, RF broadcast, or CATV (community antennae television) signals.

BASIC ELECTRIC SWITCHES

The light switch is the most familiar electrical control device. It works by making a physical break in the electrical circuit. There are a large variety of switches for residential electrical applications. Most switches are rated at 15 amps or 1800 watts.

Dimmers are special purpose switches that operate by reducing the amount of time, during the AC cycle, that voltage is delivered to the bulb. The most common type of dimmer is the triac-based electronic dimmer rated at 600-watt to 1000-watt maximum load at 120 volts.

Locations of dimmers and switches are dependent upon the code requirements, future system integration plans, and the requirements of the homeowner. Underwriters Laboratories (UL) lists switches that are used for general-purpose lighting control as general-use snap switches or toggle switches. They are limited to use with AC current only.

Switches are classified according to the arrangements of the contacts in the switch. The terminology used to describe switches is identical to the relay terminology covered earlier. In some switches, the contacts are normally closed and they are opened by the switch action. Others are normally open and subsequently closed by the switch action.

When switches are closed, there is no space between the contacts and electricity can flow through them. When switches are open the contacts are separated and the current is stopped.

Pole and throw are terms used to describe different types of switch contacts. A throw is one of the positions of a switch. A pole is a set of contacts belonging to a single circuit.

Toggle Switch

Toggle switches are electrical switches that use a mechanical lever or handle to open/close the electrical contacts or control the flow of electrical current. Toggle switches usually have a short handle and a positive snap action.

Slide Switch

Slide switches function like toggle switches but operate using a sliding button or bar, either from left to right or up and down, to control the flow of electrical current. These are often used in dimmers to provide steps of dimming.

DIP (Dual In-Line Package) Switch

DIP switches can be thought of as miniature, ganged, slide switches (but also come in the rocker variety). This type of switch is designed to be used on a printed circuit board along with other electronic components and is commonly used to customize the behavior of an electronic device for specific situations. DIP switches would be considered a collection of single pole, single throw switches.

Rotary Switch

A rotary switch works like a slide switch except that the control is a knob that rotates instead of moving in a line. They are used in circuits with two or more different "states" or modes of operation, such as a ceiling fan or volume control. These are multi-throw switches that can have one or more poles.

HIGH VOLTAGE AND SAFETY

Even though electronic systems technicians work with low voltage wiring, it is important to know and respect the power of high voltage electricity. Something as simple as a circuit failure could result in exposure to high voltage power.

Basic electrical safety rules:

Unusual Circumstances — keep an eye out for unusual circumstances like circuit breaker boxes with the covers removed, frayed or loose cords, and damaged equipment.

Workers — pay particular attention to other devices and workers in the work area. In the workplace, cables might have to run in areas with heavy motors, compressors, or other equipment that can draw considerable current causing the overall voltage to decrease.

Test — test any cable that might be live with a multimeter or other voltage-measuring device before touching it. . If using a multimeter, make sure the meter is set to AC Volts and not DC Volts if measuring AC power circuits. If using a wand or pen style tester that is battery operated, make sure the battery is operating properly.

One Hand Rule — never touch a possibly live cable with both hands because a complete circuit could be formed through the body, causing electricity to run through the heart. Even after testing for voltage, the one hand rule is a safe work habit.

Drilling — be particularly careful when cutting or drilling. Drilling into a live wire or a gas pipe can have fatal consequences. Drilling or cutting into telecom cables or water pipes isn't fatal, but can lead to costly repairs. Use blueprints to verify existing locations and make small trial holes to check for obstructions before cutting.

Respect Lightning — don't install or connect copper wiring during electrical storms. Improperly installed copper wires can carry a fatal lightning surge for many miles.

Boots — Always wear rubber-soled insulated boots when working around electricity.

Calculating Electrical Loads

Average-size homes constructed before 1950 were typically wired for electric service of 60 to 100 amps. There were usually five or six circuits of 15 amps (at 110 volts) or 30 amps (at 240 volts). The stove was on the 240-volt circuit and with the exception of a few electric dryers or air conditioners all other appliances had adequate capacity.

CIRCUITS

A simple electrical circuit is made up of a voltage source and a resistor. An electrical circuit is a network that has a closed loop. There is a return path for the flow of current. A network is an interconnection of electrical elements including:

- Voltage sources
- Current sources
- Resistors

- Inductors
- Capacitors
- Semiconductors
- Transmission lines
- Switches

If the network contains these active electronic components, it is called an electronic circuit.

Types of Electrical Circuits

Electrical wiring in a large, technology-intensive home may often include any or all of the following kinds of circuits:

- Electric light and power
- Motor control
- Instrumentation signaling
- Process control
- Thermocouple or temperature sensing
- Communication systems

Circuit Breakers

The size of the circuit breakers or fuses in a residential electrical distribution panel is determined by the load requirements of the circuits in the home. Load requirements also indicate the appropriate gauge of the wire going to the outlets and switches. A 15-amp breaker requires a minimum of 14-gauge wire, and a 20-amp breaker requires a minimum of 12-gauge wire.

This is due to the amount of heat that is dissipated by the wire as current is flowing through it. Therefore care must be used when matching the gauge of the cable with the breaker.

Two factors determine the size of a breaker:

- The number of high amperage devices plugged into the circuit
- The assumption that it is unlikely that all devices will be in use at the same time

It is possible to exceed the load of a circuit for a short period of time, but dimming lights are an indication that the circuit is overloaded. Most lighting and utility outlets in a home will be 15-amp or 20-amp circuits. The amperage of the circuit is defined by the rating of the breaker. If an appliance does not have the amperage listed, the wattage is usually listed. A quick rule-of-thumb to determine the amperage from the listed wattage is to divide the wattage by the nominal voltage. Any circuit that is (operating at maximum current for 3 hours or more) shall be derated by 20%; therefore a 20-amp 2,400-watt breaker has a continuous load of 16 amps or 1920 watts, and a 15-amp breaker has a continuous load rating of 12 amps or 1440 watts.

Calculating AC Load Requirements

AC is the type of load that almost all homes receive from the electric utility company. Load requirements refer to the amount of electrical power that a circuit must have to meet the maximum needs of all electrical devices wired to that circuit. It is very important to understand how load requirements can affect the function of home networks.

The average power consumption of a home can be calculated from the electric bill or as a percentage of the available maximum service. However, this "average use" calculation isn't a good method of determining whether a home needs more electrical service capacity or additional wiring. Average use is usually only about five percent of peak use. Peak use is when all electrical devices in the home are operating at the same time.

Importance of Residential Load Calculations

Computers, peripherals, and network hardware all work best on clean power that is at or very close to the recommended voltage. The more strain there is on the load, the more vulnerable the power supply is to voltage drops, spikes, power surges, and outright blackouts.

Even if the total power consumption in a home is well within normal limits, individual circuits might be at or above their rated capacity. The performance of any motors or processor-controlled equipment running on those circuits will likely be affected.

Some electronic equipment that might experience problems are:

Wireless Connections — Wireless connections are more likely to pick up noise or interference.

Computers — Computers or computer-controlled devices (such as printers or scanners) might operate sporadically.

Televisions — Televisions might have vertically scrolling horizontal bands across the image and audio systems might have an audible buzz.

New circuits might be needed before installing home electronic system equipment in order to avoid these scenarios. The advice of a licensed electrician might be needed to determine the best solution.

POWER QUALITY

When power utility companies were originally constructed, there was no need to worry about the quality of electrical signals delivered to consumers. The appliances of the day (lamps, washing machines, and so on) were not sensitive to signal problems such as noise, surges, and sags. The equipment only needed the voltage to operate. How much noise or interference the voltage emitted did not usually affect the performance of the equipment it powered.

Today, however, technology demands a more efficient energy flow to operate sensitive equipment effectively. For instance, audio/video components and computer networks require cleaner voltages than household appliances.

Noise

Electrical noise is any kind of unwanted signal that causes undesirable effects in the circuits of the systems in which it occurs. It is unwanted distortion to the power signal that is not considered as harmonic distortions or transients. This disruption of electronic equipment can come from within the system or from external sources, through either conduction or radiation.

Noise can be caused by any of the following:

- Arcing equipment
- Control circuits
- Electronic devices
- Improper grounding
- Power supply switching
- Solid-state rectifiers with loads

Harmonics

Harmonics are distortions to signals caused by nonlinear loads. These loads use current draws to vary with voltage during each half cycle. This variation in current causes the AC waveform to have multiple waveforms imposed upon it, causing multiple frequencies within the sine wave. These multiple frequencies are harmonics of the original frequency. See Chapter 6, Home Theater Room Design, for more information on harmonics.

Examples of nonlinear loads are:

- Battery chargers
- Electronic ballasts
- Switching mode power supplies
- Inverters and rectifiers found in common UPSs

These loads found inside the home can create electrical distortion for sensitive electronic equipment. Additional harmonics can enter the system from the electrical utility company, or from nearby commercial and industrial facilities.

Harmonics are harmful to electronics because they can:

- Overload wiring
- Trip circuit breakers
- Heat up neutral and phase conductors
- Cause damage to motors and transformers

Avoiding Harmonic Problems

Harmonics is much more of a problem in business applications because energy demand is significantly higher than in residential applications. It is best to avoid residential harmonic problems by purchasing:

- A UPS system
- Electronics that follows IEC regulations
- Computers and peripherals that have lower overall power draws

Overvoltages

Overvoltages are conditions where voltage is above normal for extended periods of time. The American National Standards Institute (ANSI) classifies overvoltages as long-duration voltage variations that last longer than 1 minute. They are usually caused from load switching. Load switching is the switching off of a large load or energizing a capacitor bank, which results in temporary increased voltage.

Overvoltages result from weak equipment that cannot regulate the desired voltage or from inadequate voltage controls. Incorrect tap settings on transformers can also cause overvoltages.

Undervoltages

Undervoltages are conditions where voltage is below normal for extended periods of time (usually longer than 1 minute). Undervoltages can also be caused by load switching, except in the reverse scenario. For instance, when a load is switched on a capacitor bank, it could cause the system to use extra power to switch off the load. This extra power usage could then cause a decrease in voltage until voltage regulation equipment could bring the voltage back within its limits. Overloaded circuits can also cause undervoltages.

Brownouts

Brownouts occur when power grids are overstressed. They can last anywhere from a few minutes to several hours. They are generally caused by greater demand on the system due to extreme hot or cold weather. They can also be caused by temporary damage to local subsystems from lightning or overstressed transformers. A more localized cause can be from inadequate wiring within a building.

Surges

Surges (also known as transient voltages) generally occur in systems when power at the generating source fluctuates, causing a voltage increase between 10% and 35% that lasts anywhere from 15 milliseconds to several minutes. Surges can also be caused by temporary anomalies, such as open neutral lines or shorts between low voltage and high voltage distribution lines. When surges last longer than one minute, they are considered an overvoltage.

In layman's terms, surges occur when something causes the electrical charge to increase at some point in the power lines. The most recognizable cause of surges is lightning, even though it is the least common cause. When lightning strikes near a power line, electrical energy from the lightning can increase the electrical pressure by millions of volts.

A more common, but lesser known, cause of surges is voltage increases from high-powered electrical devices like air conditioners and refrigerators. These devices require a lot of electricity to power on and off compressors and motors. This switching of power causes sudden, brief demands for power that upsets the steady voltage flow in the power lines.

Many other points of failure in power lines could possibly cause electrical surges. Just a few of these other possibilities include:

- Faulty wiring
- Problems with utility companies' equipment
- Downed power lines

Spikes

Spikes are severe surges that last for a short period. They are short pulses of energy with voltage as high as 6,000 V but only lasting a few milliseconds. Spikes are strong enough, however, that they often cause immediate damage to sensitive, solid state equipment. One common cause of a spike is a lightning strike.

Sags

Sags are brief drops in voltage that last from 0.5 cycles to 1 minute. They are the most common kind of power disturbance and are caused by many of the same phenomena as spikes and surges. They might be caused by abrupt changes in loads, such as short circuits or faults, or by the starting of motors. They can also be caused by a loose connection.

Voltage sags are usually localized conditions. They do not happen at the power utility's site, but within the building where the disturbance occurs. For example, refrigerator motors turning on and off can cause sags to occur in the home. Sags do not usually disturb less sensitive equipment (such as fluorescent lighting, motors, or heaters), but they do interfere with more sensitive equipment (such as audio/video components and computer networks).

Transients

Another term that is commonly used to denote both surges and spikes is transients. Transient is the term used to describe an undesirable but momentary event in nature. A transient occurs any time an unexpected change happens in current.

Impact of Power Surges on the System

Power surges can cause serious problems with equipment, but the damage generally occurs over a prolonged period of time rather than immediately.

This is because surges are mild enough to allow the equipment to still function, but slight damage still occurs with each surge.

Many lower cost surge protectors burn out after one or two surges but will still function properly as cord extensions. As a result, they might appear to work properly even after they have stopped protecting sensitive equipment from power surges.

Damage to Equipment from Transients

Even though surges and spikes differ in intensity and duration of time, both can damage equipment. Spikes can cause immediate damage, and surges can cause cumulative damage. The damage varies from occasional annoyances to unexpected catastrophic failures. Other problems that might occur are:

- Failure of switch contacts
- Degradation of wire insulation
- Unexplained behavior in semiconductor-based (IC) equipment

Factors in Transient Damage

A number of factors contribute to the susceptibility of electronic equipment. For example, weather affects the chance of power spikes during storms due to lightning strikes.

Anomalies that occur due to problems with appliances also cause transients. Even though these anomalies are less severe than lightning strikes, they can also be damaging to sensitive equipment. In general, the greater pull a piece of equipment has on the power system, the greater the chance that it will cause transients like spikes, surges, and sags.

GROUNDING AND BONDING

NEC Article 250 covers the "general requirements for grounding and bonding of electrical installations, and specific requirements" related to the following:

- Systems, circuits, and equipment required, permitted, or not permitted to be grounded
- Circuit conductors to be ground on grounded systems
- Locations of grounding connections
- Types and sizes of grounding and bonding conductors and electrodes
- Methods of grounding and bonding
- Conditions under which guards, isolation, or insulation may be substituted for grounding. (NFPA, NEC 2005, NFPA, 2004, 70-92)

NEC Article 250 also requires that an effective grounding path (path to ground from circuits, equipment, and conductor enclosures):

- Be permanent and continuous
- Have capacity to conduct safely any fault current likely to be imposed on it
- Have sufficiently low impedance to limit the voltage to ground and to facilitate the operation of the circuit protective devices in the circuit
- Not use the earth as the sole equipment ground conductor

Key Points in Grounding

The purpose of grounding is to provide a low impedance path for unintended ground-fault currents to travel unimpeded to the ground. The grounding conductor, typically green or bare, is different from the grounded neutral, current-carrying conductor (typically white or gray or with three continuous white stripes). All grounds must originate from a single point at the supply side of the electrical service. The NEC requires that separate system grounds be bonded together to equalize potentials between each point.

TESTING EQUIPMENT

In the past, technicians have traditionally used analog meters for field testing and troubleshooting. The most common analog meters are:

- Ammeter
- Voltmeter
- Ohmmeter

These analog meters are usually limited to a single function so to broaden the efficiency of testing, but all three of these meter functions have been combined into a multifunctional tester called the multimeter. Multimeters can be either analog or digital in design.

Ammeters

Ammeters are instruments used to detect and to measure electrical current. To measure current using traditional ammeters, the ammeter must be connected in series with the current path being measured. This could be dangerous in high-voltage applications, and requires very expensive meters for high-current applications. It also requires that the circuit be disconnected to install the meter in line with the load being measured, which can be difficult to do. The proper polarity of connection must also be observed when measuring a DC circuit with an analog ammeter to avoid damage to the meter movement. The meter used for measurement must have enough current capacity to measure the current without causing damage to the meter.

Clamp-On Ammeters

A popular type of ammeter is the clamp-on ammeter, as shown in Figure 1-20. A clamp-on ammeter has a movable set of jaws that are used to open and clamp around the wires to be measured, one wire at a time. The advantage of this type of ammeter is that current measurements can be taken without interrupting the circuit by fastening the ammeter clamps directly around the wire. This method also works better for taking higher current measurements because the current isn't actually flowing through the meter. A clamp-on ammeter inductively samples the current flowing through the wire.

Voltmeters

Voltmeters are instruments used to detect and to measure electrical voltage. To measure it correctly, the voltmeter must be connected in parallel with the load being measured. Test probe polarity must also be observed when measuring a DC circuit or there will be no reading on an analog meter and a negative voltage reading will be indicated on a digital meter. It is a best practice to measure unknown voltages using the meter's highest scale and then dropping down to the scale that give the best resolution of display.

Using Ammeters and Voltmeters

Voltmeters work very similarly to ammeters. The difference is that ammeters are placed in series with the circuit so that all of the current must flow through an ammeter. Because of this, they typically have a very low resistance in order to have a minimal effect on the circuit being measured (remember, resistors in series are additive). Voltmeters are placed in parallel with the circuit because the value being measured is the voltage drop across a resistance. Because two resistors in parallel always have a net value smaller than the smallest resistor in the circuit, voltmeters have a very high resistance in order to have a minimal effect on the circuit being measured. Most analog voltmeters are rated at 20K ohms/volt or higher, while digital voltmeters have rating of 10 Megohms or more.

Figure 1-20.
Clamp-on Ammeter

If the meter is accidentally set to measure amperage, and it is connected in parallel, the fuse will be blown or the circuit will be damaged. Conversely, connecting the meter in series and setting it to measure voltage will provide unpredictable results, but will most likely not damage anything, including the meter.

Ohmmeters

Ohmmeters measure the electrical resistance of circuits in ohms, which is the measure of electrical friction as electrons move through conductors. Ohmmeters can also be used to locate open circuits (which will show an abnormally high reading), or shorted circuits (which will show an abnormally low reading). Ohmmeters can only be used on circuits with no voltage or current flowing through them because they apply their own internal voltage and measure resistance based on the voltage drop across the resistance being measured. Even though ohmmeters are rarely found as separate meters, all standard Multimeters have an ohmmeter setting.

Digital Multimeters (DMM)

Digital Multimeters (DMM), like the one shown in Figure 1-21, come in various models and are generally used for the same functions as analog Multimeters. DMMs, however, display digital numbers on a liquid crystal display (LCD) rather than moving needle pointers to display their measurements. Due to their built-in microprocessing power, DMMs are more precise than their analog counterparts, often have accessory adaptors for additional measurement capabilities, and sometimes have data-handling and storage capabilities as well. However, analog meters still provide better visibility when measuring constantly changing signals, like the voltage level on a speaker line.

Figure 1-21. *Multimeter*

Continuity Testers

Continuity testers measure the capability of a circuit to conduct electrical current. They indicate whether or not the wires have the capability to conduct electricity. These instruments can also indicate if a circuit is wired correctly or has a short. Continuity testers are simple instruments that are easy to understand and include audible tones and/or indicator lights to denote when continuity has been found. Unlike an ohmmeter, they do not give an indication of a circuit actual resistance.

Frequency Meters

Frequency meters measure the frequency of signals being produced, by electronic equipment, by measuring the number of cycles completed each second at a given AC voltage. Most frequency meters can measure from DC up to 40 GHz. Many have features that allow period averaging, time-interval measurements, and scaling. Frequency meter accuracy can be extended by using an external frequency standard instead of its internal frequency standard.

Watt Meters

A watt meter is an instrument used to measure total power consumption in watts. The watt meter is connected to a circuit to measure direct power, which is displayed on its meter scales. The advantages of digital watt meters are that they indicate true (not apparent) power, and compensate for power losses when measuring by clearly indicating lost power on the meter. Typically, they can automatically calculate the power factor (PF) to within one percent accuracy.

AC Line Quality Monitor

AC Line Quality Monitors are used to detect problems in the AC line. They monitor the minimum and maximum frequency and voltage as well as count the number of drops and surges during the monitoring time. These monitors can be either analog or digital. They are essential in finding AC power line anomalies that happen intermittently. These meters either have the capability to store data for later retrieval, or output data to a chart recorder for later analysis.

Specifications and Calibration Considerations

No matter what type of test instrument is used, care must be taken to understand its specifications (specs) and calibration needs because each instrument will have different values depending on both the kind and the brand of the instrument.

Many test instruments require calibration procedures to be performed periodically to ensure the following:

- Effectiveness of the instrument
- Compliance with standards
- Safety of the equipment

CHAPTER 2

CABLING AND INFRASTRUCTURE

Almost all electronic systems depend upon cabling of some type to carry information and power to, from and between system components. Use of the proper cable (properly terminated) can be the difference between great system performance and complete system failure. Many of the systems used for networking, security, audio and home automation benefit from standards developed to ease the selection and installation of the proper cable for the application. The Electronics Industries Association (EIA) has published a number of joint standards with the Telecommunication Industries Association (TIA) regarding structured cabling systems for residential and commercial markets. These standards were written for the US but have been widely adopted internationally. For the residential market, the most recognized standard is EIA/TIA-570-C (2012 Revision), which describes minimum requirements for the selection, installation, and testing of communication cabling systems using coaxial, and unshielded twisted pair cable, as well as fiber optic cable. Figure 2-1 shows the components of a residential structured cabling system, according to the EIA/TIA-570-C cabling standard, often referred to as simply TIA-570C.

This chapter will relate to all aspects of structured cabling, as well as reviewing other types of cabling an electronic systems technician may be required to install to support various systems that are part of the residential infrastructure.

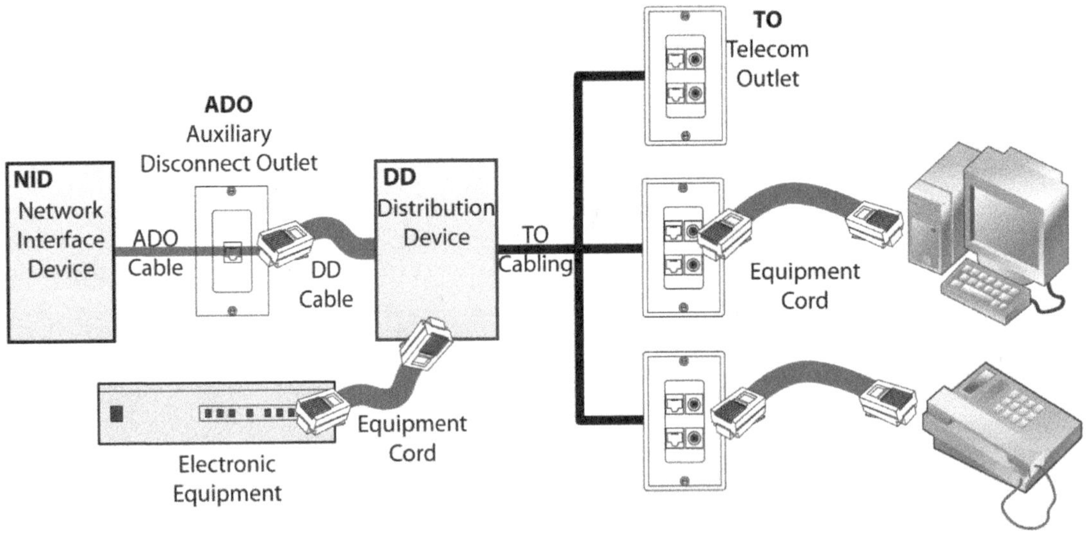

Figure 2-1. *EIA/TIA 570-C Cabling System*

There are numerous ways to describe and categorize wire and even more when we start looking at all the various types and configurations of cable. From how they are constructed; to how they are installed, tested and used; this chapter will provide information needed to make the proper selection.

First, the distinction between wire and cable; wire is a single conductor of conductive metal that is either insulated with a non-conductive jacket material or un-insulated, bare metal. A cable is one or more insulated wires covered by an overall jacket. The terms wire and cable are often used interchangeably. For instance, when someone refers to "speaker wire," they really mean "speaker cable," since it consists of two insulated conductors under a common jacket.

Although we commonly think of wire and cable as having metal conductors for electrical current, we must also include cable used to conduct signals using light. A single optical fiber can be thought of as an optical wire, while a group of two or more fibers will be a cable. Optical fiber does not conduct electrical current, but rather allows for the transmission of analog and digital information using light as the carrier. Optical fiber has its own characteristics which will be addressed later in this chapter.

Conductor Material

In almost all cases, when we speak of wire or cable conductors, we are talking about an annealed copper conductor. Although copper is second to silver in having low resistance, silver is more expensive and more brittle than copper, making copper the more appropriate metal to use for electrical conduction. Aluminum and gold are also acceptable conductors, although they offer more resistance than copper, and are only used in special applications where the cost or special properties of these metals are beneficial. Gold is particularly good as a coating for contacts and connectors, since it does not oxidize or tarnish when exposed to air. It also has self-burnishing properties that keep contacts clean as the contacts move against each other.

Copper is annealed using a heating process that makes it more ductile or flexible. Copper wire will consist of a single strand of bare copper or a grouping of multiple strands; the more individual strands making up a wire of the same gauge, the more flexible the wire will be. Bare copper is sometimes coated with tin to reduce the oxidation that takes place when copper is exposed to air. Oxidation of the metal reduces conductivity and impedes current flow. It is a good idea to terminate wires onto terminals as soon as possible after removing the insulating jacket to avoid the build-up of oxidation.

Wire Size

One of the characteristics of a wire or cable is the size of the conductor(s). Conductor size is inversely related to the resistance of the conductor and directly related to amount of current it can safely conduct.

AmericanWire Gauge

American Wire Gauge (AWG), also known as the Brown & Sharpe wire gauge, is a North American system used primarily in the U.S.A. and Canada to define the size of copper wire, specifically for the diameters of round, solid, nonferrous, electrically conductive wire. This standard assigns a numeric value to a specific size of cross-sectional area of a wire, with larger numbers applying to thinner wires. (Note that stranded wire size corresponds to solid wire with an equivalent metal cross section, not the diameter of the bundle of strands.) In this system, 22-AWG wire is thinner than 18 AWG. American Wire Gauge starts with 4/0 (0000), pronounced four-ought, at the largest size, going to 3/0 (000), 2/0 (00), 1/0 (0), 1, 2, and up to 40 and beyond for the smallest sizes.

This is derived from the fact that the gauge number is related to the number of times the wire must pass through the wire drawing dies (a tool made of a polished, shaped hole to draw wire through to reduce its diameter). The more passes, the thinner the wire. Table 2-1 shows the diameter and resistance for each AWG size down to size 30.

Resistance and Wire Size

Because AWG is specifically for electrical conductors, the cross-sectional area of each gauge is an important factor for determining its current-carrying capacity. The AWG size is one of the essential specifications that are printed on electrical wires and data/communication cables.

Table 2.1. *American Wire Gauge Table*

AWE	Diameter (inch)	Copper (mm)	Resistance (Ω/km)	(m Ω/ft)
0000(4/0)	0.46	11.68	0.16	0.05
000 (3/0)	0.41	10.40	0.20	0.06
00(2/0)	0.36	9.27	0.26	0.08
0 (1/0)	0.32	8.25	0.32	0.10
1	0.29	7.35	0.41	0.12
2	0.26	6.54	0.51	0.16
3	0.23	5.83	0.65	0.20
4	0.20	5.19	0.82	0.25
5	0.18	4.62	1.03	0.31
6	0.16	4.12	1.30	0.40
7	0.14	3.67	1.65	0.50
8	0.13	3.26	2.06	0.63
9	0.11	2.91	2.60	0.79
10	0.10	2.59	3.28	1.00
11	0.09	2.31	4.13	1.26
12	0.08	2.05	5.21	4.59
13	0.07	1.88	6.57	2.00
14	0.06	1.63	8.29	2.53
15	0.06	1.45	10.45	3.18
16	0.05	1.29	13.17	4.02
17	0.05	1.15	16.61	5.06
18	0.04	1.02	20.95	6.39
19	0.04	0.91	26.42	8.05
20	0.03	0.81	33.31	10.15
21	0.03	0.72	42.00	12.80
22	0.03	0.64	52.96	16.14
23	0.02	0.57	66.79	20.36
24	0.02	0.51	84.22	25.67
25	0.02	0.46	106.20	32.37
26	0.02	0.41	133.90	40.81
27	0.01	0.36	168.90	51.47
28	0.01	0.32	212.90	64.90
29	0.01	0.29	268.50	81.84
30	0.01	0.26	338.60	103.20

As you reviewed Table 2-1, you may have noticed that a wire's resistance is inversely proportional the wire's cross-sectional area. In fact, if you double the area of a wire, you reduce it resistance by one-half. On the AWG chart, this equates to a change of three AWG sizes. For example, going from an

18 gauge wire to a 15 gauge wire reduces the wire resistance from 6.39 milliohms per foot to 3.18 milliohms, or about half. In addition, wire resistance is directly related to wire length, so that if you double the length of a wire, you double the resistance the wire presents to the circuit. Knowing these relationships, you can see that long cable runs will require larger diameter cables in order to function efficiently.

Metric Wire Gauge

For most of the world, wire is sized using common metric sizes that are numbers equal to the actual area of the wire in square millimeters. Table 2-2 shows a comparison between AWG sizes and commonly used Metric wire sizes. You will notice that there are few, if any, direct one-to-one comparison between AWG and Metric wire sizes. With metric sizes it is easy to see when you are doubling the area of a wire and thus lowering the wire's resistance by one-half.

Table 2-2. *AWG vs. Metric Wire Sizes*

AWG Size	Metric Wire Size mm^2	AWG Size	Metric Wire Size mm^2
-	0.50	-	16
20	-	5	-
-	0.75	4	-
18	-	-	25
-	1.0	3	-
16	-	2	-
-	1.5	-	35
14	-	1	-
-	2.5	-	50
12	-	1/0	-
-	4	2/0	-
10	-	-	70
-	6	3/0	-
9	-	-	95
8	-	4/0	-
7	10	-	120
6	-	-	150

Cable Construction

What a cable is to be used for greatly impacts how a cable will be constructed. Cable conductors can be the same size or different sizes, solid or stranded, shielded or un-shielded, paired or un-paired. Likewise, pairs of cable conductors can be twisted or un-twisted.

Solid versus Stranded

As mentioned earlier, wire gauge is based on the diameter of round, solid, nonferrous, electrically conducting wire. Wire and cable made using solid conductors are stiff, hard to install and subject to breaking if exposed to repeated bending. To overcome these shortcomings, stranded conductors were developed using numerous small strands that are bundled together to form the conductor. For installed cables not subject to repetitive bending, solid copper conductors of 18 AWG are preferred since they are smaller, less expensive and still fairly easy to install.

A typical AWG stranded conductor might be designated as 7/32, indicating the conductor is made up of seven strands of 32 gauge wire. As the strand size gets smaller, more stands are required to give the equivalent cross-sectional area of the solid conductor. More strands equate to more flexibility, but care must be taken not to cut or break these small stands when terminating the conductor. Loss of strands during termination will raise the resistance of the cable, which can be detrimental to system performance. Stranded conductors will have slightly larger diameters than the equivalent solid conductor.

Stranded conductors also exhibit additional attenuation at high frequencies due to skin effect on the smaller strands in the conductor. Stranded conductors used in data networks offer about 20% more attenuation than the equivalent solid conductors.

Skin Effect

The skin effect describes how, when using alternating current (AC), the signal migrates from the middle of the center conductor out toward the skin of the cable as frequency increases. In reality, as the signal frequency increases above 10 MHz (approximately), the signal is flowing on the outer skin of the cable. The skin depth for copper at various frequencies is shown in Table 2-3. A graphical representation of the skin effect is shown in Figure 2-2.

Table 2-3. *Skin Depth for Copper*

Frequency	Depth
60 Hz	0.337 in (8.57 mm)
10 kHz	0.026 in (0.66 mm)
100 kHz	0.008 in (0.21 mm)
1 MHz	0.003 in (66 μm)
10 MHz	0.001 in (21 μm)

Figure 2-2. *Skin Effect*

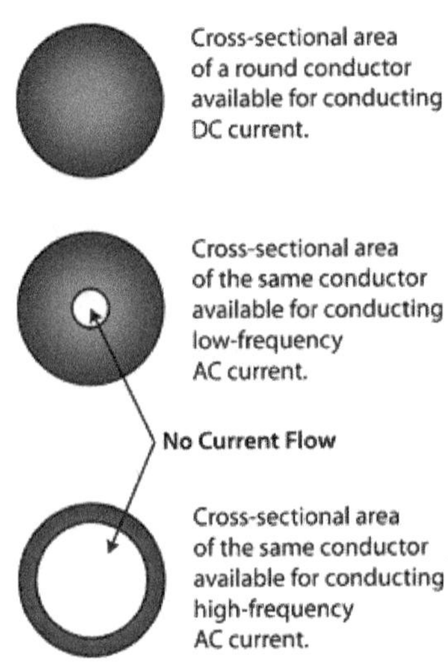

Coaxial cables meant for transmission of high frequency signals (50 MHz or more) will often be built with a center conductor having a copper or silver coating over a core of steel or aluminum, since the signal will only be traveling in the lower resistance outer coating. This makes a strong, less expensive cable with very good transmission characteristics.

Pairing Conductors

Conductors within a cable may be paired to delineate a specific signal path within a cable. Most often, conductors that are paired within a cable are twisted together to show the pairing, although color coding of conductors may also be used to show paired conductors. Paired conductors offer no specific benefit over other conductors within a cable, other than easy identification, until they are twisted together.

Twisted-pair conductors benefit in a number of ways, the most important way being a reduction in outside interference known as common mode noise. The twisting of the conductors in a cable, when used with balanced circuits, can practically eliminate common mode noise from being picked up by the cable. The twisting of the conductors within a cable with multiple twisted pairs will also reduce the possibilities of cross talk between pairs.

Crosstalk occurs when the electrical signal on one signal path induces current flow into a nearby signal path. When multiple pairs of conductors are to be placed inside a common jacket, the pairs must be designed with different twist-rates, or pitches, to reduce crosstalk. Pair pitch is usually rated in twists per foot or twist per meter.

Twisted pairs also benefit from a more predictable and constant capacitance between paired conductors.

Shielding Conductors

Another method of protecting a signal path within a cable is the use of shielding. Shielding can be applied to a signal conductor, individual pairs, over all conductors, or to more than one level at the same time. Shielded cable can also be call screened cable, although screening is a term usually applied to shielding applied to individual pairs within a cable.

Cable shielding is usually in one of three forms:

- *Spiral wrapped shield:* consisting of multiple small wires wrapped around a conductor or group of conductors in a spiraling method.
- *Braided shield:* consisting of multiple small wires that a braided together, enclosing one or more conductors within the braid.
- *Foil shield:* consisting of aluminum or a conductive polymer foil placed around the cable's signal conductors and includes a drain wire which is in physical contact with the conductive foil along the entire length of the cable. The drain wire, usually made of tinned copper, serves as the attachment point for the ground connection to the foil shield.

The type and number of shields used is based upon the application for which the cable is designed to be used. Table 2-4 details how each type of shielding compares to each other. It must be noted that for any shield to be effective in blocking unwanted interference, the shield must be connected to a good ground, usually the equipment chassis, on at least one end of the cable. Grounding both ends at each chassis offers the best protection, but if only one end is to be grounded it should be the sending end.

Table 2-4. *Cable Shielding Compares*

Type	Cost	Resistance	Flexibility	Flex Like	Frequency <10 MHz	Performance >10 MHz
Spiral Wrap	Moderate	Excellent	Excellent	Excellent	Fair	Poor
Braided	High	Excellent	Good	Very Good	Good	Fair
Foil	Low	Fair	Good	Fair	Fair	Good
Foil/Braid	Hig	Excellent	Good	Good	Good	Good

Unbalanced and Balanced

Certain cable types are used for balanced or unbalanced signals. Some cables are used to carry both. It is not the cable that makes a balanced signal, it is the inputs and outputs on which the cable is terminated.

Unbalanced Signals

An unbalanced signal path uses one conductor of a cable to carry the signal from output to input, and the signal is returned back to the source on the signal ground which is normally the shielding conductor that encloses the signal conductor. Twisted pair cables can serve as unbalanced cables, but because of susceptibility for intrusion by radio frequency interference (RFI) and electromagnetic interference (EMI), most unbalanced cables consist of a shielded single conductor cable. Unbalanced outputs and inputs are more inexpensive to build and cabling and connectors are inexpensive as well. They allow for quick interconnection and termination. Even with the shielding, unbalanced audio cables are much more susceptible to outside interference than balance audio cable and should be restricted for use in distances of 6 meters (20 ft.) or less. In addition, the unbalanced design is more likely to develop ground loops and introduce hum and buzz into the audio signal.

Coaxial cable is a good example of unbalanced cable design. Both the center conductor and the braid play a part in carrying the signal.

Balanced Signals

With balanced signals, the signal path is isolated from ground and has equal impedance from each side of the path to ground. This balanced configuration provides a natural immunity to noise which is cancelled out at the input.

The two conductors used with balanced signals carry the signal with opposite polarity. While one conductor has a positive polarity with respect to ground, the other has an opposite and equal polarity, this is known as differential signaling.

At the balanced input, the difference in the two voltages is extracted as the signal. Outside noise that enters into the cable is coupled equally into both conductors with the same polarity. Voltages of the same polarity are cancelled out at the balanced input, if equal impedance balance to ground is maintained. This cancellation is known as Common Mode Rejection (CMR), and balanced inputs are rated with a Common Mode Rejection Ratio (CMMR) that shows how effective they are at rejecting common mode noise. CMMR is specified in decibels (dB) and the higher the CMMR, the better the input is at rejecting common mode noise.

Cables used for balanced signals are almost always twisted-pair copper cables with or without an enclosing shield. If the cable is shielded, the shield is not part of the signal path, but must be grounded on at least one end to be effective. Balanced cables are used predominately in telecom and professional/broadcast audio applications, or anywhere electrical signals must be transported for long distances with minimal interference.

Cables used to transport telephone and data circuits are good examples of unshielded cables using balanced or differential signaling. Microphone cables commonly consist of shielded, twisted-pair cables for connecting the balanced microphone output to the pre-amplifier input.

Code Compliance

In most countries, electrical, building or other safety-related codes are created and adopted to define the construction and installation of low-voltage cables. These codes center on safety issues related to shock, fire and smoke hazards.

In the United States, electrical installations, including low voltage systems, are regulated by various community, county or state governing entities. For the most part, these entities fulfill their rules and regulation making responsibilities by adopting as a whole or in part the National Electric Code as its own regulations. Internationally, each country will either create or adopt rules and regulations to provide minimum safety standards for the installation of electrical systems. We will be reviewing the pertinent provisions of the U.S. NEC with the understanding that each country will have their own Electrical Code that may or may not have similar provisions as the U.S. NEC. It is the responsibility of each industry professional to know the codes in effect where their projects are taking place.

The National Electric Code (NEC) is a book, NFPA70, published by the National Fire Protection Association (NFPA). This book is revised every three years and provides guidance for the industry but is not an established national code. State and local municipalities have the option to pass a law adopting NFPA70 as their regulatory code and even if they do, they will often make changes and additions based on their local regional conditions. The NEC manual includes:

- Guidelines for installing and working with high-voltage and low-voltage systems

- Safety precautions for high-voltage wiring
- Fire-resistance standards for cables
- Conduit capacities and fill percentages
- Allowable wiring installation and routing methods

Voltage Levels

The NEC specifies the cable voltage rating on many of the low-voltage cables. Class 2 cables must have a voltage rating of at least 150 volts, while Class 3 and Communication cables must have a voltage rating of at least 300 volts. If the code allows various low-voltage cables to occupy the same raceway, all cables must have the voltage rating of the highest voltage cable.

Most of the time, the NEC stipulates that the voltage rating shall not appear on the cable jacket. This is to avoid confusion where someone misinterprets that the voltage rating means the cable is suitable for use in Class 1 electric light and power application. Except for a very few instances, low-voltage cabling is not allowed to occupy the same box or raceway as Class 1 cabling. For almost all applications, low-voltage cables must maintain a minimum separation of 50mm (2") from any Class 1 type cabling.

Note: this minimum separation is established for safety reasons. Larger distances are required to ensure acceptable performance.

Jacket Materials

In the US, low-voltage cabling is categorized into the following five basic groups within the National Electrical Code (NEC) as shown in Table 2-5.

Table 2-5. NEC Cable Ratings

Cable Type	Use
CL2, CL3 (Class 2, Class 3)	Remote-control, signaling, and power-limited cables
CM	Communications
FPL	Power-limited fire protective signaling cables
MP	Multi-purpose cable
PLTC	Power-limited tray cable

Fire safety ratings under the NEC are conducted according to a common group of flame retardancy tests, which makes the cable markings similar across all of these designations. Video, audio, and low-voltage control cables fall into Class 2 typically due to the available power limits set by the NEC. All computer network and telecommunications cabling falls into the CM class. CM and CL2 categories of cabling are of primary concern in the A/V industry.

Plenum-rated cables (suffix "P") are constructed of materials that have very low "fire load." Fire load is the term used to describe how much fuel a given material provides to an active fire. A lower fire load rating means that the material is more fire-resistant and produces less smoke, which accounts for most fire-related deaths.

Plenum is a commonly used term in the construction and system installation industries. In most cases, plenum-rated cables may be installed in air handling spaces (air plenums) without expensive metallic conduit.

Riser (suffix "R") describes cables having a lesser degree of flame retardancy than plenum, but may be used to convey signals vertically in non-plenum shafts without requirement for metallic conduit. General-purpose (no suffix) cables may be used in conduit, behind walls, or other enclosed locations where the cable is protected but not in an air plenum or traveling between floors.

CL2X and CL3X are the lowest-rated cable and must comply with the UL VW-1 Vertical- Specimen Flame Test. Cables with this rating may be used in residential dwellings, PLTC (power-limited tray cable) complies with a 70,000 BTU/hr. vertical-tray flame test. The cable is not marked VW-1. Instead, cables of this type are marked with "PLTC" with ink or marker tape.

The cable rating to use on a project is, first and foremost, dictated by the local building authorities. Always check local codes before committing to a proposed design. Generally speaking (for the U.S.), general-purpose cable, like CL2, is acceptable in enclosed raceways and protected areas no used as air plenums.

Cables that run between floors must be a minimum of riser-grade or else run within metal conduit. Cables run in horizontal air plenums must be plenum-rated, or run in metal conduit. Some of the more typical cable types used in the electronic systems contracting industry and their permitted uses are listed in Table 2-6.

Once again, it is imperative that the designer and technician know and understand local and regional codes as they apply to cable jacket materials.

Twisted-Pair Cable

Twisted pair cable is used more than any other cable in residential systems. It can be seen in telephone and home networking and as a general communication cable for keypads, thermostats, and other integrated devices. The cable is formed by twisting two insulated wires around each other and combining them with other pairs to form a complete cable. Although any cable with on one or more pairs of twisted insulated conductor in a jacket can be called a twisted pair cable, we are most often referring to a four-pair cable.

There are two forms of twisted pair cable:

- STP (shielded twisted pair)
- UTP (unshielded twisted pair)

Anatomy of STP and UTP

Shielded twisted pair (STP) cable is wrapped in a grounded shield which protects the signal from interference due to external sources. For this reason, STP cable provides less signal degradation than UTP cable. Unshielded twisted pair (UTP) cable does not have a shield. As shown in Figure 2-3, within a pair, one conductor has a solid colored insulation (the "Ring") while the other has a white insulation with a same color stripe (the "tip").

Table 2-6. *NEC Communication Cable Classifications*

Cable Type	Description	Permitted Uses	Allowable Substitutions
CMP	Communications Plenum	Anywhere, including air ducts and plenums	None
CMR	Communications Riser	General use and in vertical shafts	CMP
CMG, CM	Communications General Purpose	General use, except for risers and plenums	CMP or CMR
CMX	Communications Limited Use	Only in raceways and dwellings	CMP, CMP, CMG or CM
CMUC	Communications Under-carpet	For Under-carpet use only	None

Unshielded Twisted Pair (UTP) Cable

Unshielded twisted pair (UTP) cable is the preferred choice for most residential applications, including telephone, data, and control. However, some manufacturers recommend STP cable for certain environments where high levels of radio frequency interference may be present.

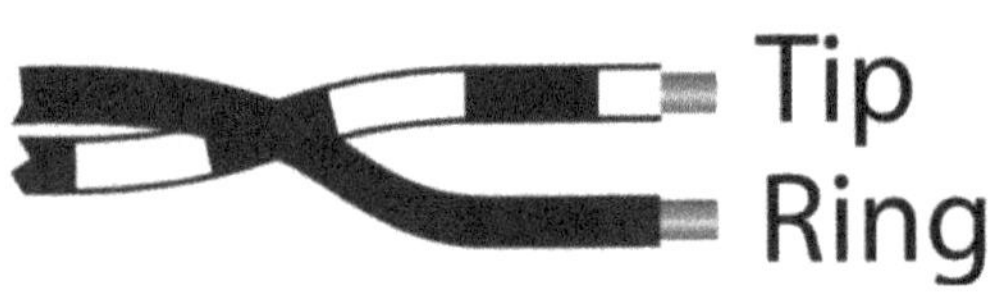

Figure 2-3. *A Single Twisted Pair*

UTP cable requirements are covered by the ANSI/TIA/EIA 568-C.2 standard for commercial cable installation. The cable that residential integrators are familiar with is a 4-pair UTP cable, as shown in Figure 2-4, with a category 5e (abbreviated Cat 5e or cat 5e) or greater rating. The same configuration is found in Cat6 and Cat6a cable.

Each conductor consists of either a single solid core of wire or a stranded core of several small gauge wires surrounded by a coating of insulating material, commonly polyvinyl chloride (PVC). Solid conductor UTP cables are used predominately as telecommunications

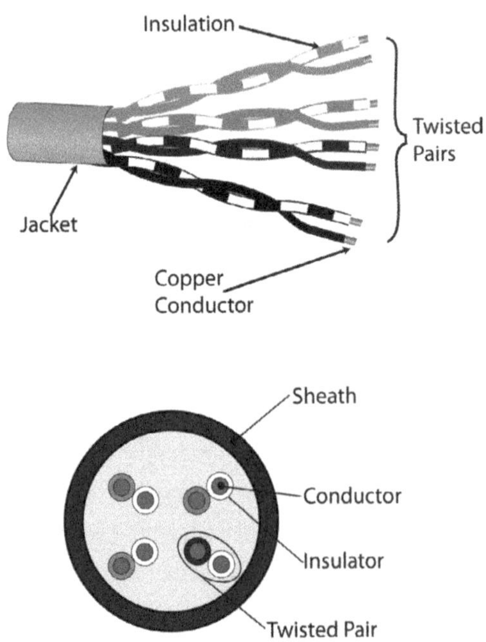

Figure 2-4.
Unshielded Twisted Pair Cable

outlet (TO) cables within the home. Stranded conductors have superior flexibility and are used mainly for patch and equipment connection cords. Stranded conductors have about 20% more loss than an equal gauge of solid wire, this is the main reason why solid conductor UTP cables are used for the horizontal/TO cable runs.

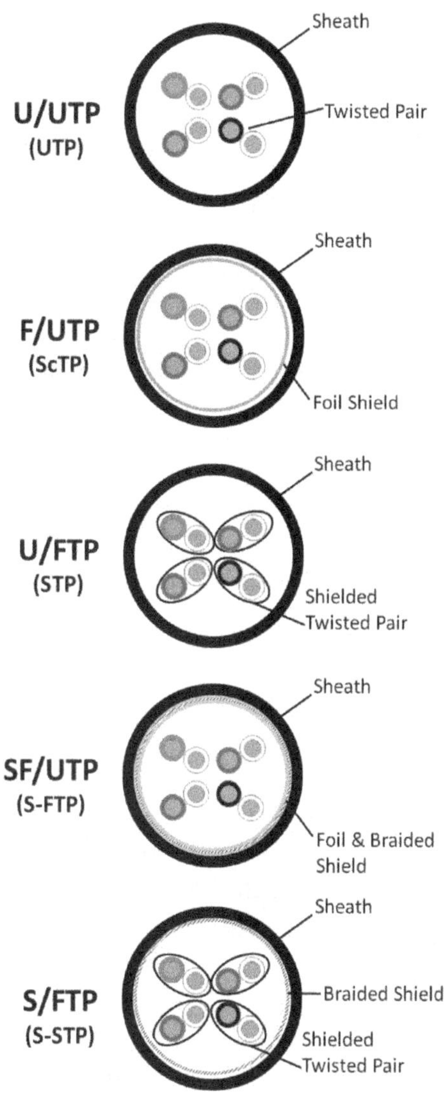

Figure 2-5. *Twisted Pair Cable*

Shielded Twisted Pair (STP) Cable

Shielded Twisted Pair cable is what we generally call all twisted-pair cable that has a shield protecting the four twisted pairs. However, there are actually several more accurate names used to describe the cables and how they are shielded.

STP originally referred to a twisted-pair cable where each individual pair was shielded. In particular, it referred to the IBM STP-A cable that was a two-pair cable with 150-ohm impedance per pair used in IBM token ring networks. When the original TIA/EIA 568 specification was released, they used the term ScTP, or Screened Twisted Pair, in order to avoid confusion. ScTP cable was a four twisted-pair cable with an overall foil shield. As needs have changed and cable types have developed, cable designations have evolved as well.

S/UTP, also known as fully shielded or foiled twisted pair (FTP) and formally ScTP, has a foil shield placed around all four pairs of cables rather than the individual pairs.

Screened shielded twisted pair (S/STP also known as S/F TP) has both individually shielded pairs (such as the original STP cabling) and also has an outer metal shielding covering the entire group of shielded copper pairs (such as S/UTP). This type of cabling offers the best protection from interference from external sources and also minimizes alien crosstalk.

Note that different vendors and authors use different terminology (e.g., STP has been used to denote both STP-A, S/STP, and S/UTP). Figure 2-5 shows the construction of the five main types of twisted pair cabling.

The ISO/IEC has attempted to internationalize the cable designations in its 11801 document. Figure 2-5 shows the old names, the new names and how the cable is shielded.

Table 2-7. *Twisted Pair Categories*

Category	Bandwidth (MHz)	Data Rate (MB/s)	Application	Status per TIA 570-C
3	16	10	Telephone, 10Base-T	Obsolete
4	20	16	Telephone, 10Base-T	Obsolete
5	100	100	10Base T, 100Base-T	Obsolete
5e	100	1,000	100Base-T	Compliant
6	250	1,000	1000Base-TX, 10GBase-T	Recommended, 35-55m (1000Base-T) 100m (10GBase-T)
6A	500	10,000 (1Gb/s)	1000Base-TX, 10GBase-T	Recommended: 100m (10GBase-T) Lower crosstalk

The code before the slash designates the shielding for the cable itself, while the code after the slash determines the shielding for the individual pairs:

- TP = twisted pair
- U = unshielded
- F = foil shielding
- S = braided shielding

UTP Categories

The original TIA-568 Standard contained a specification for a single 4-pair UTP cable. However, when increased network speeds created the need for better cables, the TIA 568-A Standard was created. This standard addresses: category 3 (Cat 3), category 4 (Cat 4), category 5 (Cat 5), and category 6 (Cat 6), as shown in Table 2-8.

In May 2001, the TIA568-B Standard designated the use of Category 5e with LANs that transmit on all 4 pairs. Category 5e is the same as Category 5 for many specifications, but S-STPS/FTP braiding foil tightens the specifications for crosstalk between pairs. The residential structured cabling standard, TIA 570-C specifies the use of Category 5e as a minimum requirement.

Category 5e Cable

Category 5e cable is used to transport balanced signals and is primarily designed for preserving high-signal integrity. The "e" or enhanced version added tighter specifications for far-end crosstalk. Horizontal cable paths are installed using solid, 4-pair UTP cable. The patch cable, used to interconnect equipment is sometimes stranded for ease of connection and because it is less likely to be damaged by movement. Because this type of wire is twisted, the actual wire length will be longer than the cable length. Category 5e cable is typically used at 100 Mbps (megabytes per second—using two of the four pairs), but is capable of transmitting data for short distances over an Ethernet network at 1 Gbps (gigabytes per second — using all four pairs) under the right conditions, and has a current rating of 500 mA per conductor.

Category 6 Cable

In June 2002, the TIA 568-B.2-1 introduced Category 6, which represented a major improvement in performance, yielding 2.5 times the bandwidth of Category 5e.

Category 6 cable is designed to be used as a higher frequency carrier than Category 5e. The next step up from a gigabit Ethernet is a 10GB Ethernet (IEEE 802.3an 10GBASE-T). Category 6 supports 10 GB Ethernet up to approximately 40 meters, while augmented Category 6 (called Category 6a) supports 10GB Ethernet up to the full 100 meter Ethernet channel length.

Cat6A offers higher bandwidth and improved alien crosstalk performance, as well as compatibility with future 10GBaseT Ethernet networks. Category 6 cable requires special handling and termination techniques, patch panels, and modules, which make it more expensive to use than Category 5e. Its physical construction is different that Cat5e, with heavier gauge conductors, a plastic center spline, and a different twist configuration. The TIA/EIA 570-B specification for residential networking allows Cat 5e cabling as the minimum, but recommends using Cat 6 to allow for future applications that may require additional bandwidth.

Category 6A Cable

Category 6A cable augments the performance of Category 6 cable by extending the useable length from 35-55 meters to 100 meters for 10GBase-T data. It also provides reduced alien crosstalk (AXT), the crosstalk which occurs between separate cables in a run. To ensure that Cat6A runs are delivering the expected performance, comprehensive qualification/certification testing should always be done.

Coaxial Cable

Coaxial cable is used for satellite, cable TV (CATV), television antenna, and baseband video as well as both analog and digital audio. Satellite, cable, and antenna uses RG6 (Series 6) cable. Outside of the Americas, this cable type is known as CT100/WF100, and for new installations, HD100 is recommended. RG11 (which has a larger center conductor than RG6) is often used to distribute long cable runs, and to serve as a backbone for sophisticated RF and DBS (satellite) distribution designs. RG59 (Series 59) coaxial cable (which has a smaller center conductor than RG6, and thus greater loss at higher frequencies) is used only for baseband video distribution (such as CCTV systems and component video distribution) and for patch and equipment cords.

When using RG59 for baseband video, it is a good idea to use solid copper conductor instead of copper clad steel, because baseband videos (lower frequencies) tend to propagate through the center of the conductor.

It is very important to understand the frequency rating on a coaxial cable used for CATV or DBS (Direct Broadcast Satellite) distribution as referenced in ANSI/SCTE 74 2003 and ANSI/ SCTE 15 2006 standards. Coaxial cables used for CATV should be sweet tested to at least 1,000 MHz (1 GHz) and DBS cables should be sweep tested to at least 2.3 GHz.

Each of these cables will now exceed their maximum required bandwidth by approximately 150 MHz, (CATV runs to approximately 850 MHz and DBS to 2150 MHz). This extra bandwidth allows for "rolloff ", additional attenuation, which occurs at the upper frequencies. It is best that all cables installed in the home be sweep tested to 2.3 GHz, which will ensure that the customer has the ability to choose any service provider he wishes. The characteristic impedance (nominal impedance) of these cables is 75 ohms +/- 3 ohms.

CABLE DESIGNATIONS

RG/Series

The military classified coaxial cable as RG-x or RG-x/U, where the RG stood for Radio Guide and the U for Universal. Common 75 ohm coaxial cables used for RF distribution were, RG-59/U, RG-6/U and RG-11/U. Common 50 ohm coaxial cables used for transmission were; RG-58/U and RG-8/U. The RG designation is obsolete, so many manufacturers are replacing the old RG designation with a Series prefix on cables like Series 59, Series 6, and Series 11.

Anatomy of Coaxial Cable

A coaxial cable is made up of four components: the center conductor, dielectric, shield, and jacket, as shown in Figure 2-6. The coaxial cable shown is a quad-shielded cable which has four separate shields instead of just one. The center conductor consists of one of three elements:

- Copper
- Copper-clad steel (CCS)
- Copper-clad aluminum (CCA)

Although copper-clad steel is the most commonly used conductor, copper-clad aluminum is more often used for semi-rigid distribution cables. Bare copper is typically used for DBS (satellite) and baseband video because it has lower direct current (DC) resistance than the other two types.

Core Construction

The conductor wire runs through the center of a polymeric material called the dielectric. The dielectric protects the center conductor from the ground shields that are wrapped around the dielectric material. Dielectric material, typically made of foamed polyethylene, is comprised mostly of air, which makes it rather soft or "spongy." Most quality cables have a very soft dielectric.

The most important job of the dielectric is to provide the proper distance between the center conductor and the braid and foil. This distance, along with the characteristics of the dielectric, is what gives a cable its nominal impedance.

Due to its rather soft pliability, it is important to ensure that a coaxial cable always maintains its shape. For this reason, electrical staples should never be used to attach a cable to a stud, and care should be taken to avoid kinking when pulling cable. Kinking can cause the center conductor to drift into the dielectric material and cause a change in the cable's characteristic impedance.

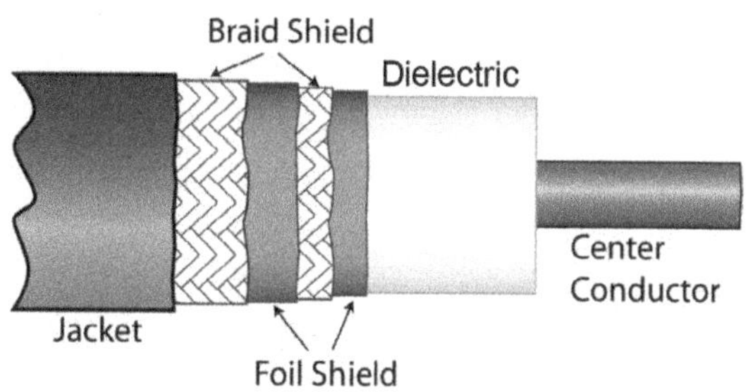

Figure 2-6 *Anatomy of a Coaxial Cable*

Shielding

The shielding layer is placed between the core and the outer jacket of the cable to contain the RF signal and to keep out most interference. Cable shielding is offered in a wide range of designs and configurations, with each type offering distinct advantages and disadvantages. In quad-shielded coaxial cable, the shielding layer consists of a laminated foil tape covered by a metallic braid, a second foil tape, and the final metallic braid.

Foil shields consist of aluminum foil typically laminated to a polyester or polypropylene film. Foil shields should provide 100 percent cable or component coverage (realistically, good cables will overlap the foil on the cable somewhere between 18% and 35%), improving protection against radiated emission and ingress of audio and radio frequencies. Because of their small size, foil shields are commonly used to shield individual pairs of multi-pair cables to reduce crosstalk. Foil shields may also be bonded to a coaxial cable insulation or cable jacket with a layer of adhesive, allowing for faster, easier, and more reliable termination. They have less weight, bulk, and cost less than braided shields and are generally more effective at higher frequencies.

The best results are derived from cables that use the foil in conjunction with the braid. All coaxial cable should have a minimum of a 60% braided shield. The two components work together to protect against low and high frequency RFI and Radio Frequency Emissions. Also, when trying to decrease lower frequency or DC loss for satellite, one may use solid copper braid and foil, which will reduce the DCLR (Direct Current Loop Resistance) that substantially reduces the loss per 100 feet.

Finally, the cable is covered with a sheath known as the cable jacket. The jacket, made of a continuous polymeric material, functions as the exterior coating of the cable. Its job is to hold the other cable components together. RG 6 and 11 cables are capable of being installed at temperatures ranging from -20° C to +60° C, while certain plenum cables have a lower temperature limit of 0° C.

Impedance

Coaxial cable is designed to be a transmission line for radio frequency signals. The dimensions of the center conductor, dielectric and shielding are tightly controlled to create a characteristic impedance for the cable. For best operation, coaxial cable is always terminated with its characteristic impedance.

Experimentation determined that a characteristic impedance of 76.7 ohms gave the lowest signal attenuation of any cable design, while best power transfer happens at about 30 ohms. 75 ohm coaxial cable became the standard for receiving antenna designs and 50 ohm cables, a compromise between attenuation and power handling, where used to output transmitter signals to antennas. While coaxial cables of other impedances exist, these two standard impedances account for the bulk of the coaxial cable in use with RG-6 cable being the most used cable for RF distribution networks.

Attenuation

Signal attenuation, or loss, in coaxial cable is a function of the cables core diameter, distance and signal frequency. Attenuation decreases as core size increases. Attenuation increases with cable length and the frequency of the signal. Each cable experiences various levels of attenuation over distance and varying frequencies.

Figure 2-7 shows that RG 11 has substantially lower attenuation than RG 6 and RG 59 coaxial cable at all frequencies. Because backbone cables are longer than the outlet cables, it follows that RG 11, which retains more of its signal strength over greater distances, should be selected for this purpose.

When determining which cable to choose, the three main factors to consider are:

- Frequency of signals to transmit
- Length of cable required
- Amount of power loss that can be tolerated

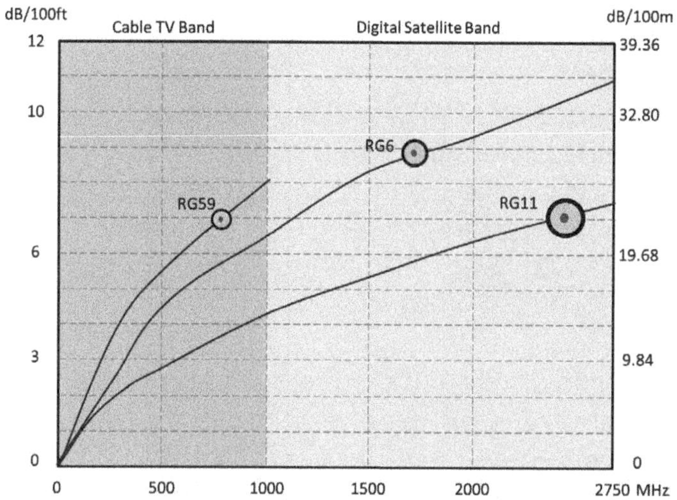

Figure 2-7 *Attentuation of RG 59, RG 6, RG 11*

Each of these factors involves relationships among the type of signal being distributed, the distance to the farthest device, and the minimum signal level at the receiving end.

For example, when designing an RF distribution system, all televisions must receive an analog signal between 15 dBmV and 0 dBmV or a digital signal between +5 dBmV and dBmV. If the calculations indicate that there is too much loss, one can either insert an amplifier (which will also amplify the noise floor) or increase the cable size (which is passive, and thus reduces loss without increasing the noise floor).

COAXIAL CABLE APPLICATIONS

Although coaxial cable is used in a number of applications, the most common applications in our industry is transporting video and RF signals.

Video

Video signals, typically generated by closed-circuit television cameras and DVD players, are baseband analog signals with a bandwidth from zero up to 6 MHz. The term baseband means the signal is a discrete analog voltage varying in amplitude and frequency.

RG 59 coaxial cable is frequently used for baseband applications, such as CCTV. It may also be used for broadcast frequencies, but its high-frequency losses are too great to allow its use over long distances. In these applications, RG 6 or RG 11 is used instead. RG 59 coaxial cable is commonly packaged with consumer equipment, such as VCRs and digital cable/ satellite receivers. This cable is also used as Serial Digital audio cable for HDTV and DTV applications.

Manufacturers tend to include only RG 59 interconnection cables with their equipment because of its low cost (as compared to RG 6, which is more expensive).

RG 6, with a solid copper core, is also used for baseband applications such as CCTV, video projectors, component video, or plasma TVs due its type of shielding, which should be 60% braid.

RF Distribution

Coaxial cable used in RF distribution networks must be able to carry modulated RF signals that range from about 50 MHz up to 2.5 GHz. Proper cable shielding is essential for these high-frequency signals.

RG 6 Dual or Quad Shield is manufactured using foil shields and braided aluminum shields. The makeup of the shields differs between models. The effective range of operation for foil shields is above 50 MHz, which makes them suitable for rejection of radio frequency interference (RFI). Foil shields are not effective at frequencies below 50 MHz.

CATV

The frequency band of CATV extends to approximately 1000 MHz. As shown in Figure 2-7, RG 6 cables have approximately 5.5 dB greater loss per 100' at 1000 MHz (the highest channel) than at 55 MHz (the lowest channel). Cable companies account for this change by boosting the signal level of higher frequency channels over the lower frequency channels.

Satellite

Digital satellite systems utilize very high-frequency signals, around 12 GHZ, that are converted to the range of 950 MHz to 2200 MHz at the dish and carried to the satellite receiver over the coaxial cable. As with CATV, RG-6 cable is most often used to carry the signal to the receiver.

Optical Fiber

Fiber optic cable offers a totally different technology for signal transmission than copper-based cabling. Fiber optic cables carry signals in the form of light (photons) through their hair-thin fibers, whereas coaxial and other copper cables carry electrons through their copper conductors. Use of fiber optic cable is increasing due to its immunity to outside interference, like EMI and RFI. Using fiber based interconnections also eliminates possible ground loop issues that are common with copper cables. The distance an optical signal can be sent is a big benefit for long-haul applications, such as telecom inter-office links and wide area networks.

Anatomy of Fiber Optic Cable

Fiber-optic cables consist of the following parts:

- *Core* – Thin glass center of the fiber where the light travels.
- *Cladding* – Outer optical material surrounding the core that reflects the light back into the core.
- *Buffer coating* – Plastic coating that protects the fiber from damage and moisture.

Mode of Operation

The term mode pertains to how light propagates within the fiber core. You can think of a mode as a path a light ray follows as it travels down the fiber. How many modes, or paths, a ray may take relates to the size of the fiber's core and the directionality of the light entering the fiber. For example, a small core has fewer modes.

There are two general types of optical fiber, Multi-mode Fiber (MMF) and Single-mode Fiber (SMF)

Multi-Mode Fiber

Multi-mode fiber is a fiber that has a relatively large core and offers light many paths (modes) in which to travel. It is designed to carry potentially thousands of light rays concurrently, each with a slightly different reflection angle within the optical fiber core.

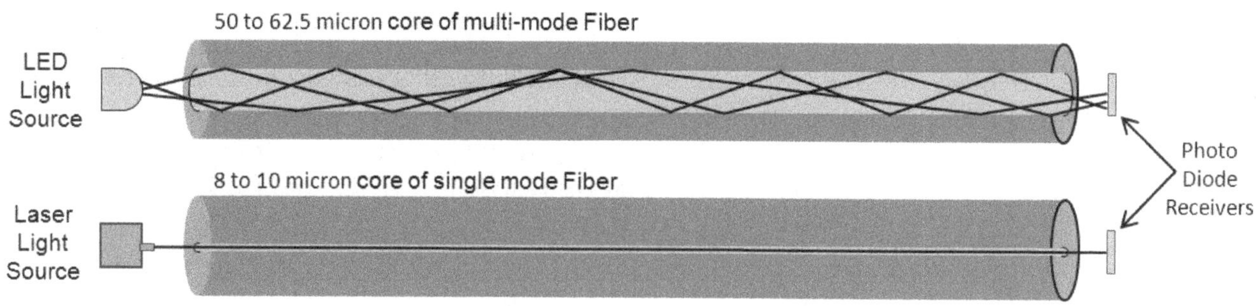

Figure 2-8. *Transmission Characteristics of Optical Fiber*

Unfortunately, the large number of internal reflections increases signal attenuation and the varying lengths of the multiple paths tends to smear high-frequency signals. These factors translate to lower bandwidth and a shorter distance of operation. On the other hand, multi-mode fiber uses less expensive LED light sources, making multi-mode fiber more cost effective for shorter runs of limited bandwidth.

Two types of multi-mode fiber are Step-index multi-mode fiber and Graded-index multi-mode fiber

Step-Index Multi-mode Fiber has a core with uniform optical properties. However, due to its high dispersion, it offers the lowest bandwidth capability.

Graded-Index Multi-mode Fiber has a core with varying optical properties that allows the light to travel faster and with less dispersion. This results in better bandwidth capability, making it a popular choice for networking and data communications that do not require long network links.

For very short runs of a few meters, plastic optical fiber (POF) is very cost effective. POF uses high quality plastic instead of glass so it is more rugged, but it does not have the clarity needed for long distance, high bandwidth links.

POF is commonly used to interconnect consumer AV equipment to transfer digital audio signals (Toslink). POF, with a core size sometimes 100 times that of glass fiber, is considered a multi-mode fiber.

Single-Mode Fiber

Single-mode fibers have relatively small cores and use a laser light source that transmits light on a single path (mode) straight through its core, making it more suitable for long-distance applications. Since it experiences negligible reflections and low dispersion, there is a lower amount of signal loss and smearing than with multi-mode fiber. Even though the fiber is not that much more expensive than multi-mode, the laser transmitters and receivers are more costly then the multi-mode LED based equipment. Cost for terminating and splicing single-mode fiber is higher than multi-mode also.

Core Size

As we have seen, the size of an optical fiber's core directly relates to how light travels through the fiber. Over the years, since the introduction of optical fiber for signal transmission, many different core diameters have been used. Today, core diameters for single-mode fiber are between 8.3 and 10 microns in diameter. One micron, also called one micrometer, is one millionth of a meter. A single-mode fiber is smaller than a human hair, which ranges between 17 and 180 microns in diameter.

There are three common sizes of multi-mode fiber; 50 microns, 62.5 microns and 100 microns. Multi-mode fiber with a core diameter of 62.5 microns has been the standard for local area network for many years. However, 50 micron fiber is now increasing in use since the smaller fiber core allows high-bandwidth capabilities than the larger 62.5 core.

Plastic optical fibers have core diameters of about 900 microns and are built to conduct light in the visible spectrum instead of the infrared light used with glass fibers. POFs are much easier to terminate and less prone to physical damage, making them the fiber of choice for short interconnections of consumer audio equipment.

Each glass fiber core is surrounded by a coating of glass called the cladding. The cladding is used to keep the light in the core by reflecting of refracting the light back into the core as it travels down the fiber. For both single-mode and multi-mode fibers, the cladding is commonly 125 microns in diameter. In fact, you will often see fiber designated as 62.5/125 showing both the fiber's core and cladding dimensions.

The fiber cladding is covered with an acrylic coating for strength and protection and then placed inside a buffer material for additional protection.

Buffer Type

Another way to classify optical fiber is by its buffer. There are two types of optical fiber buffers, Loose-tube (or loose-buffer) and Tight-buffer.

Loose Tube

Loose tube buffered cable is essentially a plastic tube with one or more fibers running through it. A gel is often used to fill the empty space within the tube and provide protection from water infiltration. Because the fibers are protected from the hazards of expansion and contraction, this type of cable is preferred for outdoor applications. In some cables, each tube contains only one fiber and the tube color is used to designate the fiber.

In cables where multiple fibers are contained in each loose tube buffer, the fiber's acrylic coating is tinted to indicate the fiber color designation.

Tight-Buffer

By applying a polymer coating of 900 microns over the fiber acrylic coating, the fiber can be mechanically protected and easily identified by the buffer color.

Tight-buffered cables work well in indoor applications, due to their crush and impact resistance. Variations of tight-buffered cables are used in riser applications due to their additional outer strength.

Table 2-8. *Optical Fiber Attenuation*

Cable Type	Wavelength (nm)	Max Attenuation (dB/km)
50/125 μm Multi-mode	850 1300	3.5 1.5
62.5/125 μm Multi-mode	850 1300	3.5 1.5
Single-mode inside plant cable	1310 1550	1.0 1.0
Single-mode outside plant cable	1310 1550	0.5 0.5

Attenuation

Just like copper cables, optical fiber also suffers from signal loss or attenuation as the light travels down the fiber. The amount of loss varies with the type of fiber, mode of transmission and the wavelength of the light being used. The loss that occurs is measured in decibels per kilometer (dB/km).

Various impurities in the fiber increase light attenuation at different wavelengths. Multi-mode fiber has two windows of minimal attenuation centered on light wavelengths of 850 nanometers (nm) and 1300 nm, while single-mode fiber has windows at 1310 nm and 1550 nm.

Table 2-9 shows the acceptable attenuation of the various types of fiber-optic cable, given in dB loss per kilometer at each wavelength of interest.

In addition to the cable loss, losses are also incurred by connector insertion and splice insertion. Typical losses can be added together to create a cable link loss budget for a particular cable path. The specifications for the optical transceiver will specify the acceptable link loss budget needed for a particular application. Generally, overall link loss must be held to 12 dB or less for acceptable link performance.

Fiber Disadvantages

Although fiber optic cabling has become widely used in recent years, there are some disadvantages which sometimes result in higher labor costs and the necessity of more training.

Transceivers — The interface between fiber optic cable and terminal equipment is handled by transceivers, which convert optical signals to electrical signals (O-E), and vice-versa (E-O). Their cost is relatively high and can be very high

Maintenance — Fiber optic systems are subject to performance problems from dust and dirt, making routine maintenance a higher priority than in copper-cabling systems.

AUDIO CABLING

For the most part, copper cables are used to interconnect audio components. A number of different styles of cable are used based on the levels being sent, susceptibility to interference and the length of the path between components.

Speaker Level

This type of cable is used to connect the output of a power amplifier to a loudspeaker:

Installation Process — Speaker cable is perhaps the least complex, and one of the easiest to install and terminate. Amplifier outputs are chosen for their ability to transfer the required power to the speaker with minimal loss, and except for some unusual RF intensive locations, they are not required to be shielded. The biggest factor to consider when choosing a speaker cable is conductor size. A large conductor size equates to less power being dissipated in the cable and more power being transferred to the speaker.

Speaker cable conductor polarity is typically indicated on one of the conductors with a colored line, jacket ribbing, or, for clear jacket cable, by conductor color.

For some stereo or 2-channel applications, a cable containing four unpaired conductors is used. This type of cable will generally contain a red, black, white and green conductor of equal gauge. The cable gauge must be at least 16 AWG or larger depending on distance to the volume control or speakers. The red and black conductors serve as the positive and negative connections for the right speaker in a pair, while the white and green conductors serve as the positive and negative connections for the left speaker in the pair. Other colors may be used, but all connections must be consistent to avoid changes in a speaker output polarity.

Most residential and commercially installed speaker cable consists of a two-conductor, twisted-pair cable that is jacketed with stranded copper conductors that are 16 gauge or larger. Some commercial applications make use of smaller 18 to 20 gauge cable that is either solid or stranded.

Conductor polarity is indicated by the color of the conductor insulation. Two conductor speaker cable generally contains red and black insulated conductors, with red used for signal positive and black used for signal negative. Again, other conductor colors may be used, but all connections must be consistent to avoid changes in a speaker output polarity. Best practice indicates that the lighter of the two colored conductors be assigned as positive, with the darker used for negative.

Table 2-9. *Power Loss Due to Attentuation (4 Ω Speaker)*

Loss (dB)	Power Loss (%)	16 AWG Run m (ft)	14 AWG Run m (ft)	12 AWG Run m (Ft)
0.5	11	17 (56)	27 (89)	43 (143)
1	21	36 (119)	58 (190)	92 (303)
2	37	82 (269)	131 (428)	209 (684)
3	50	139 (458)	222 (729)	355 (1164)

Table 2-10. *Power Loss Due to Attentuation (8 Ω Speaker)*

Loss (dB)	Power Loss (%)	16 AWG Run m (ft)	14 AWG Run m (ft)	12 AWG Run m (Ft)
0.5	11	34 (112)	54 (179)	87 (285)
1	21	73 (238)	116 (379)	185 (606)
2	37	164 (538)	261 (857)	417 (1358)
3	50	279 (915)	444 (1458)	710 (2328)

Attenuation

As mentioned, when determining how much power reaches the speaker, the resistance of the cable connecting the speakers to the amplifier becomes relevant. For example, a 30 meter (100ft) cable run of 16 AWG speaker cable will have a loop resistance of 0.8 ohms. If this cable is used with a 4 ohm speaker, then approximately 17 percent of the power from the amplifier will be dissipated within the cable. Although high, this is acceptable because the CEA-2030 standard recommends no more than 20 percent power loss for the speaker cabling. A 20 percent loss of power is a power loss of approximately 1 dB.

Power losses for speaker cables, when they are used to connect to 4 ohm and 8 ohm speakers, are shown in Table 2-9 and Table 2-10. These tables assume the resistance used was 4.35 ohms/1000 ft. for 16 AWG,

2.73 ohms/1000 ft. for 14 AWG, and 1.71 ohms/1000 ft. for 12 AWG. These values come from the maximum resistance of stranded copper wire at 68° F given in the CEA-2030 standard.

Line Level

Line level analog audio connections are used to interface between components in a system. Most residential and commercial audio equipment uses unbalanced cables terminated in RCA style connectors for line level interconnections that span a short distance, such as within a rack or cabinet.

However, for professional audio installations and very long analog audio runs balanced audio cabling is usually specified. This configuration utilizes two conductors for signal (+ and -) and a third, braided conductor to act as a shield and ground wire. This provides excellent protection from interference due to the shield being tied to ground, and the fact that the signal conductors are always out of phase, causing noise to cancel at the destination (Common Mode Rejection or CMR). It is also easier to troubleshoot and correct grounding problems with this type of signal.

It should be noted that while we mentioned high-impedance and low-impedance connections, these descriptors do not pertain to the cables being used, but to the input and output circuitry to which the cables are attached. While it is true that most high-impedance connections use unbalanced cables and most low-impedance connections use balanced cables, this is not a hard and fast rule.

Differences in Signal Level

The differences in signal levels carried by microphone and line level cables can be quite dramatic. Nominal microphone level is commonly given as -60 dBV, but can range much higher depending on the microphone. Nominal line level for consumer products is typically -10 dBV and for professional products it is stated as +4 dBu. If we convert these dB values to actual voltages, you can see the differences in the signal levels on each cable. Microphone Level: -60 dBV = 0.001 Vrms Consumer Line Level: -10 dBV = 0.316 Vrms Professional Line Level: +4 dBu = 1.228 Vrms due to the difference in voltage levels of these signals, these cables should be kept separated to avoid crosstalk. A minimum of 50.5 mm (2 in) of separation should be allowed when bundling these cables along a common path. Also, because of the low signal levels on the microphone and line level cables, they should also be kept well away from speaker lines and AC power lines. Separation of 305 mm (12 in) or more is recommended.

VIDEO CABLING

Because video can be distributed in a number of different formats, the cables used will vary as well. We will first look at traditional analog video cabling. It should be noted that analog video distribution is seeing far fewer applications as digital video becomes the standard. However, each of these analog examples are still seen occasionally, and in existing homes with systems already installed.

Composite Video

The composite video signal is a baseband signal that incorporates all of the video, color and sync information into one signal. That signal is then transported over a coaxial cable. The most common coaxial cable used for composite video is RG-59 (Series 59) cable with a solid copper center conductor and a braided copper shield. The cable is most commonly used with RCA style connectors, but may also use BNC type connectors.

The composite video cable is often combined with stereo left and right line level audio cables for a complete A/V interconnection solution. In this combination, the video cable is normally color-coded yellow to indicate it is transporting video.

S-Video

The S-Video signal is nearly gone from the industry, but may be seen from time to time. It has two signal paths, one with video and sync, and one carrying the color information. It is typically terminated with a factory-installed 4-pin DIN style connector.

Television Component Video

Television Component Video utilizes three coaxial cables, with the green carrying the complete black and white image including horizontal and vertical sync. The red and blue cables carry red, blue, and green color information.

RGBhv

In this analog signal configuration, all 5 elements of the image are carried on separate coaxial cables. Red, blue, green, horizontal and vertical sync remain separate from the source to the destination. This is often seen in the form of a VGA connector on a computer being terminated as RGBhv at a projector, using either RCA or BNC connectors.

Digital Audio, Video, and Data

There are a number of cable types used for interconnecting audio, video and data signals using specific interfaces. In most cases, these cables may be purchased pre-terminated from the cable manufacturer. In some cases, more generic cable like UTP, coaxial and fiber may be used to transport these signals if appropriate adapters are used.

Digital Audio

A SPDIF (Sony Philips Digital Interface) signal is carried by a single coaxial cable. In a permanent installation, this would typically be RG59 with RCA connectors.

DVI

The Digital Visual Interface (DVI) is a video interface standard designed to support the transmission of video between computer and a display device. It was designed to replace the VGA interface and to provide connection of digital video directly to a display device. One version also allows analog video to be connected.

DVI cable consists of a multi-conductor cable that terminates on a custom connector using 24 pins for the digital interface and an additional 5 pins for backward analog compatibility. The DVI standard does not set the maximum cable length, but performance considerations place it between 4.5 (15 ft.) and 15 meters (50 ft) depending on cable design and resolution required. Adapters are available to interface DVI to VGA and HDMI.

HDMI

The High-Definition Multimedia Interface (HDMI) is an A/V interface designed to transmit uncompressed digital data, with its main application being the transmission of high definition video and multi-channel digital audio signals between media sources and display devices. The most current version of the HDMI standard is HDMI 2.0. released in the fall of 2014. There are four types of HDMI cables in this specification:

- HDMI Standard
- HDMI Standard with Ethernet
- HDMI High Speed
- HDMI High Speed with Ethernet

Standard HDMI cable is a custom 19-conductor cable with a 29-conductor variant that allows double the current video bandwidth. Standard connectors are the full size Type A, the Type C mini-connector and the Type D micro- connector, which is similar in appearance to the micro-USB connector. The Type B connector is a full size connector with 29-pins for the expanded bandwidth applications.

HDMI cables are rated as "Standard" or "High-Speed" per HDMI licensing, LLC. Standard HDMI cables (Category 1) deliver minimum speeds of 2.25Mbs, at 74Mhz, which is the equivalent of a 720p/1080i signal. High Speed (Category 2) cables have been tested to perform at 340 Mhz, or 10.2 Gbs, which successfully handles 1080p signals. High Speed (or "category 2") HDMI cables have been tested to perform at speeds of 340 MHz or up to 10.2Gbps, which is the highest bandwidth currently available over an HDMI cable and can successfully handle 1080p signals including those at increased color depths and/or increased refresh rates from the source.

The HDMI standard does not specify the maximum length of an HDMI cable since signal attenuation is determined by cable materials and construction quality. Cables must be certified by their manufacturer for use at the given length. HDMI cables are easily constructed for distances of about 5 meters (16 ft) and with higher quality materials and larger conductors can be provided in lengths of about 15 meters (50 ft). Many manufacturers offer amplifiers, equalizers or repeaters to allow standard HDMI cables to be strung together for longer distances.

Various types of protocols and transmit/receive (Tx/Rx) devices are available to transport HDMI signals over twisted pair or fiber optic cable. Some deliver a pure, unaltered HDMI signal while others may compromise the signal quality.

Serial Digital Interface

Serial Digital Interface (SDI) is a family of video interfaces standardized by the Society of Motion Picture and Television Engineers (SMPTE). A related interface is the dual link HD-SDI that is used to provide uncompressed, unencrypted transmission of digital video signals for digital cinema and HDTV 1080P at greater fidelity and resolution than standard HDTV can provide.

Using two Series 6 low-loss 75 ohm coaxial cables terminated with BNC connectors, it is possible to send HD-SDI signals over 100 meters (328 ft) and much farther using optical fiber cable.

DisplayPort

DisplayPort, produced by the Video Electronics Standards Association (VESA), is a digital display interface standard that defines a royalty-free digital interconnection for audio and video. The primary use will be to replace VGA and DVI as the connection of choice between PC and monitor, but may also be included on television sets. The current DisplayPort standard is version 1.2.

DisplayPort uses a custom designed 20 conductor cable terminating on a 20-pin DisplayPort connector. There is also a mini-connector version used with some laptop computers. Maximum cable length is approximately 2 meters (6.5 ft.).

IEEE 1394

The IEEE 1394 standard, also known as FireWire, i-LINK and Lynx, is a communication standard for a high speed serial link used with personal computers, digital audio, digital video, automotive and aeronautic applications with the dominant applications being video transfer and data storage links. The current version of the standard is IEEE 1394c-2006 (FireWire S800T).

There have been 4-wire, 6-wire and 9-wire cable implementations using alpha and beta style connectors, with cable length limited to about 4.5 meters (14.8 ft). The latest release also allows connections using cat-5e cable, coax and single-mode optical fiber cable.

STRUCTURED CABLING

A residential structured cabling system is made up of the following components:

- Network Interface Device (NID)
- Auxiliary Disconnect Outlet (ADO)
- Distribution Enclosure and Devices
- Outlets

The Network Interface Device (NID) marks the point where the external service meets the internal wiring of the home. It is the service provider's responsibility to provide a valid connection from the utility service to the NID, at which point the residential electronics systems integrator provides connectivity to the rest of the home.

The NID is connected to the Auxiliary Disconnect Outlet (ADO), which provides a place for the incoming services to be disconnected for testing purposes. There is usually one cable for each incoming service.

NIDs are installed and grounded by the local access provider or telephone company.

- For houses, NIDs usually are near the electrical service entry/main power panel in a gray or black box, but can be inside the residence.
- For apartments and condominiums, the demarcation is inside the suite, behind a blank outlet cover plate or in a closet or utility room.
- Sometimes, the NID can be a simple jack.

Table 2-11. *TIA 570-C Outlet Grades*

Grade	4-pair UTP Category 5e or Greater	75 Ω Coaxial Cable	Fiber Optic
1	1 cable	1 cable	n/z
2	2 cable	2 cable	2 cables (optional)

The ADO connects to the Distribution Device (DD) via a quick disconnect cable known as the DD cable. The Distribution Device serves as the consolidation point for services coming into the home, and is sometimes referred to as the residential gateway, residential service center, or structured wiring panel. This device directs the various services to the rest of the home via the home's cabling system. It is advantageous to locate this device in a central, easily accessible location to minimize cable lengths and provide ease of maintenance.

A variety of service modules can be installed into the Distribution Enclosure to provide flexibility and expandability. For example, video modules can split the incoming video signal, telephone modules can segregate and run multiple phone lines to various locations, and so on. This modularity is an excellent way to provide a multitude of service options for their customers to choose to purchase for their homes. The distribution location should be installed in a central location, and not in attics, garages or areas subject to extreme temperatures or excessive humidity.

Outlets connect to the central distribution location with different types of cabling (UTP, coaxial, and fiber optic). These outlets are the interface from the cabling system to the actual consumer equipment, such as televisions, telephones, and computers.

Grades of Outlet Locations

The TIA 570-C Standard specifies two levels of cabling for each location, as shown in Table 2-12. A location can consist of a single outlet, or a single room. It is permissible to break apart the cabling within a room or space to provide separate outlets. For example, the 4-pair UTP cable can be separated from the 75 ohm coaxial cable to create separate television and telephone outlets.

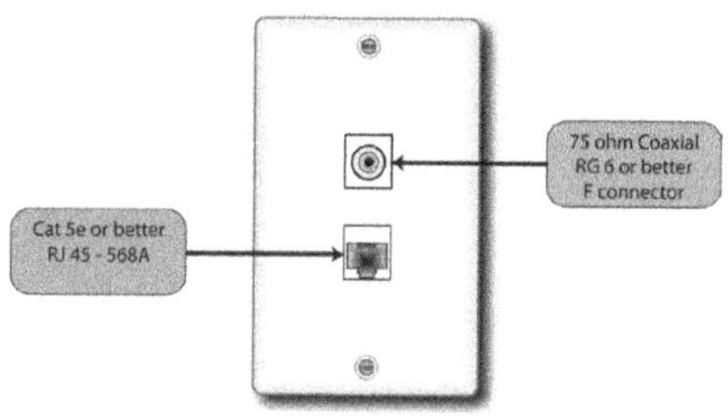

Figure 2-9. *Grade 1 Cabling Requirements*

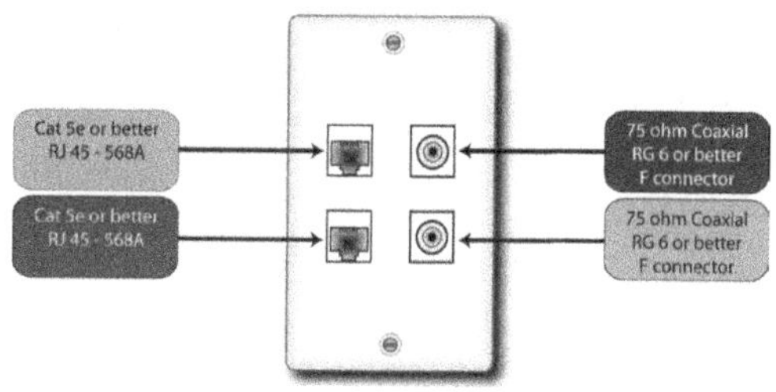

Figure 2-10. *Grade 2 Cabling Requirements*

The two grades are:

Grade 1 — Grade 1 cable, as shown in Figure 2-9, provides a generic cabling system that meets the minimum requirements for basic telecommunications services such as telephone, satellite, community antenna television (CATV), and data services.

Grade 2 — Grade 2 cable, as shown in Figure 2-10, provides a generic cabling system that meets the minimum requirements for basic and advanced telecommunications services such as high-speed Internet and in-home generated video. This grade provides for both current and developing telecommunications services.

These two grades are minimum requirements. Some outlets require even more cables — such as the media room AV cabinet.

UTP

TIA 570-C specifies a minimum of Cat5e for residential communications outlets. Cat6 is recommended, and Cat6A should be considered for applications which may require even higher performance, especially in the future. The following Category cables are currently recognized by the EIA/TIA 568-C and 570-C standards:

Category 3, Cat-3, used for voice telecom applications and data bandwidth up to 16 MHz

Category 5e, Cat-5e, used for voice and data applications with bandwidth up to 100 MHz

Category 6, Cat-6, used for voice and data applications with bandwidth up to 250 MHz

Category 6a, Cat-6a, used for voice and data applications with bandwidth up to 500 MHz

Even though Category 5e cable meets the minimum requirements for the telecommunication cable in both Grade 1 and 2, the 570-B standard recommends the use of Category 6 cable whenever possible rather than Category 5e.

Coax

The 570-C standard recognizes that Series 59 cable can be used for baseband CCTV (Closed Circuit TV) video applications, however, for all RF applications (Cable, Satellite, and Antenna) the standard is 75 ohm RG6 (Series 6) dual or quad-shielded coaxial cable.

Optical Fiber

To take full advantage of the advanced capabilities of the Grade 2 service, optional optical fiber cables may be included as well. Recognized optical capabilities of optical fiber include 50 or 62.5μm multi-mode, or single-mode fiber cable.

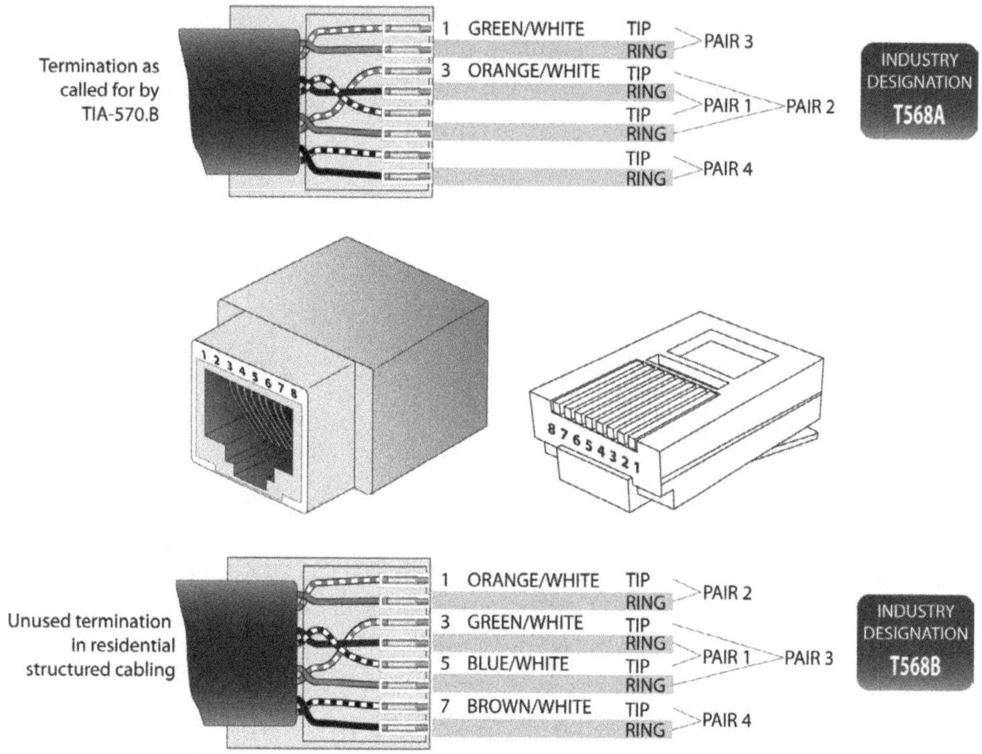

Figure 2-11. *Pinout for 4-Pair UTP Connections*

Hybrid Cables

Hybrid cables have been created for Grade 1 and 2 cabling installations. These cables bundle UTP, coax and even optical fiber conductors under a common jacket to reduce cable installation time when cabling homes for either Grade 1 or 2 structured wiring. Many different types of conductor assemblies are created using cat-5e or cat-6 UTP components.

Distance Limits

Structured cabling systems are designed for easy installation. All cabling is designed around a star topology where a central head end with a distribution device is the origination point for all cabling. Very large buildings may have more than one hub, but most residential installations will only require one central location.

The horizontal cables that run from the distribution device to the telecommunication outlets are limited to a length of 90 meters (295 ft). This leaves 10 meters (33 ft) for equipment connection cables at each end of the link for a total link limit of 100 meters (328 ft). This distance limitation applies to all UTP, coax and fiber optic cables being installed.

Distance limitations are not given in the standard for security, fire alarm and whole house audio systems. Refer to system installation guidelines for the system being installed.

Table 2-12. *Coaxial Cable Types and Termination*

Cable Type	Backbone Cable	Outlet Cable	Connector Type	Patch/Equip-ment Cord
Series 59	No	No	F	Yes
Series 6	Yes	Yes	F	Yes
Series 11	Yes	Yes	F	No
Hard-line	Yes	No	F or N	No

Cable Terminations

4-pair UTP Terminations Figure 2-11 shows the pinout for both UTP jack connections. T568A is the designation for termination of new residential installations as set by the TIA 570-C Standard. Before the TIA/EIA Standard, AT&T developed networks utilizing existing telecommunications infrastructure, and used USOC as its termination method.

To provide backward compatibility for single-line phones, AT&T created its own way of terminating cables for UTP networks, this specification was named 258A. In 1991, the existing AT&T 258A was included in TIA/ EIA 568A and referred to as TIA/EIA T568B termination. Although this standard is not used in current residential networks, it is provided in Figure 2-11 for reference purposes. The T568B termination is often used in commercial networks mainly due to the influence that AT&T has had in this market. Either termination standard is acceptable as long as a particular project maintains the same standard throughout. However, due to its compatibility with Lines 1 and 2 of standard telephone systems, T568A is the preferred protocol for residential projects in new construction.

In larger installation, it is often advisable to use patch panels to manage the network cabling. Most of them allow for runs to be terminated to a 110-type punch block, then all runs appear on RJ-45 jacks on the front to allow for easy reconfiguration.

Coaxial Cable

Coaxial cables installed between the distribution device and the outlet shall be terminated at both ends using an F-type connector. Table 2-13 gives the use of each coaxial cable type recognized by the standard, the connector type to use for termination and whether the cable type can be used for patch or equipment cords.

Table 2-13. *Pull Tension for Coaxial Cable*

Center Conductor	RG 6 Newtons (foot-pounds)	RG 11 Newtons (foot-pounds)
Copper Coated Steel	334 N (75 lbf)	667 N (150 lbf)
Copper	178 N (40 lbf)	356 N (80 lbf)

Optical Fiber

The TIA/EIA 568-C.3 standard allows for many different connectors for fiber optic cable. All small form factor connectors with a FOCIS document (Fiber Optic Connector Intermateability Standard) are acceptable. Termination type is usually determined by the equipment to be connected. Multi-mode fiber connectors and outlets shall be beige for 62.5/125 fiber and black for 50/125 fiber, while single-mode connectors and outlets are blue.

Duplex connectors are keyed and have a crossover configuration, in that port A connects to port B on the other end. Outlet boxes shall provide termination for at least 2 fibers — one for transmit and one for receive.

Cable Installation

There are many factors to take into consideration as you prepare to install wire and cable at a worksite. Good preparation will make the installation process much easier and faster. Preparation starts with planning and for cabling, planning is all about cable administration.

Cable Administration

Many companies have their own methods for preparing wire schedules or cable lists, but for commercial structured cabling, ANSI/TIA/EIA 606-B is the standard that should be applied. The methodology provided in the standard can be applied to all types of cabling.

The ANSI/TIA/EIA 606-B standard lays out a method of marking cables based on four classes of installation. The basic Class 1 format identifies the floor number of the telecom space, an alpha identifier for the space on that floor, a one or two character alpha identifier for the patch panel or IDC block, and finally a two to four character numeric identifier for the patch panel port or IDC block section. This class is easily adapted for use with residential installations, where the telecom space is the location of the distribution device.

This methodology creates a 5 to 8 character ID label for each end of the cable. Plates and panels can be marked with similar tags.

Example: 1A-V08 telecommunications space "A" on the first floor, "V " voice patch block, "08" port eight.

Per the 606-B standard, cables shall be labeled within 12 inches (300mm) of each end of the cable at all locations. The labels shall be machine generated and shall be resistant to moisture, heat and ultra-violet light. They shall have a design life equal to, or greater than, the cable being installed. Outlet labeling is desired but, in residential installations, it is not a requirement due to aesthetic considerations of the living space. All terminations at the distribution device shall be labeled denoting each run and the inclusion of a simple floor plan showing outlet labeling should be a consideration.

Multi-dwelling residences shall be administered in the same manner as commercial building by referring to TIA/EIA-606-B. Not all residential cabling systems are notated according to this standard. However, in all cases, there should be a clear, organized system using alpha-numeric designations and a comprehensive cable schedule.

Path Preparation

Cabling infrastructure planning requires an understanding of the owner's needs and desires. Structured cabling is all about providing sufficient infrastructure to meet both present and future needs. The cabling design starts with the selection of the service grade, 1 or 2, and should also include planning for additional systems including security, control and whole-home audio.

A location should be chosen for the distribution device. Ideally, the location should be centrally located in the residence and be provided with adequate power, lighting, and ventilation. Path preparation may include installing conduit in concrete slab floors, block walls and other spaces that will be inaccessible during normal construction. Use of conduit will also facilitate the replacement of cables if that becomes necessary in the future, but the added cost must be weighed against the future benefit.

Local code requirements should be considered when planning cable pathways. In addition, cable performance must also be considered. Pathways with excessive bending and pathways subject to temperature extremes should be avoided, since they impede cable performance. Also, coordinate with other trades to insure cabling is not damaged by later installations. Planning should place all outlets within the 90 meter (295 ft) limitation for the horizontal cable run from the distribution device.

Outlet Boxes

Various guidelines are observed regarding the infrastructure in the home. Higher end systems will require more extensive cabling schemes. A minimum standard for all homes can be found in EIA/TIA-570-C, which provides for telecommunication outlet locations in each of these rooms:

- Kitchen (minimum 1)
- Bedrooms (minimum 1)
- Master bedroom (2 recommended)
- Family/great room (2 recommended)
- Den/study (2 recommended)

A minimum of one outlet shall be provided in each room and extra outlets should be provided within unbroken wall spaces of 3.7 m (12 ft) or less. Additional outlets should be provided so that no point along the floor line, measured horizontally, is more the 7.6 m (25 ft) from an outlet in that space. The outlets should be planned to eliminate the need for extension cords.

Standard nail-on outlet boxes of sufficient depth can be used in stud wall construction. Nail-on mud rings are also a good choice where it is acceptable to store extra cable within the wall cavity.

Mounting heights should be in compliance with the Americans with Disabilities Act (ADA). Normally, telecommunication outlet heights should be no less than 38 cm (15 in) above the floor, with operating controls placed at a maximum height between 122 to 137 cm (48 to 54 in) above the floor. Check local codes for any additional height restrictions.

Conduit

Some jurisdictions require conduit for low voltage cabling. Even when not required, it is often a good idea to install conduit between key locations to enable future cabling to be pulled. Examples: main equipment rack to theater rack, theater rack to projector location. To ease the installation of pull strings or cable when conduit is used, pull boxes should be installed every 100 feet along the conduit path and when bends in the conduit total to 180 degrees along any one section. Pull boxes should be placed in a straight section of conduit and not used in lieu of a bend. Conduit fittings shall not be used in place of pull boxes.

Distribution Enclosure

The distribution enclosure houses the equipment used for the termination and connection of outlet cables. These devices may be active or passive, or both. Where practical, the enclosure should be centrally located within the building to allow for minimum cabling distances to all outlets. The box equipment may be recessed mounted in between wall studs, or surface mounted on a backboard. It must be accessible to facilitate moves, adds, and changes of the residential premise cabling.

Space allocated for the distribution panel is estimated based on the grade of service and the number of telecommunications outlet/connectors to be provided in the residence. Table 1 in the TIA/ EIA-570-C standard provides a means of estimating the space required.

When electrical power is required at the panel, a minimum of one 15 amp, 120 VAC nominal, non-switched duplex electrical outlet should be provided. The electrical outlet should be placed at a height appropriate for the DD and associated equipment. Metallic enclosures must be grounded per local code.

Pull Tension

Pull tension is the maximum pulling force that can be safely applied to a cable without causing damage. When pulling cable, tension must be applied evenly to all elements of the cable without exceeding the cable's maximum pull tension. If the pull tension is exceeded by pulling on the jacket too rigorously, it might tear and separate from the core. If the core is pulled with too much force, it might be pulled out from the sheath or the conductor might stretch and reduce the gauge of the wire.

When pulling a 4-pair 24-AWG UTP cable, the maximum pulling tension should not exceed 110 N (25 LbF). For a bundle of UTP cables in which the pulling force is spread across all conductors, the maximum pulling tension of 110 N is multiplied by the number of cables to calculate the bundle's maximum pulling tension.

For coaxial cable, the maximum pulling tension is dependent upon the size and materials on the center conductor. Coaxial cables using copper-coated steel (CCS) center conductors are stronger than those made of bare copper.

The maximum pulling tensions for CCA and copper Series 6 and 11 cables is shown in Table 2-14.

When pulling a combination of different types of cable, limit the pulling tension to that of the minimum strength cable.

For all other copper cables, you can use the TANK formula to calculate the maximum allowable pulling tension. The TANK formula calculates T, (the maximum allowable pulling tension in pounds), by multiplying A, (the cross-sectional area of the conductor in circular mils), times N, (the number of conductors sharing the tensile load), times K, (the constant of 0.008 pounds per circular mil for copper.)

The TANK formula, $T = A \times N \times K$

T = Maximum allowable pulling Tension in pounds

A = Cross-sectional Area of the conductor in circular mils

N = Number of conductors sharing the tensile load

K = Constant (K) = 0.008 pounds/circular mil for copper

As an example, if you were pulling in a 25 pair telephone cable, you could calculate the allowable pulling tension using the TANK formula. A 24 AWG copper wire has an area of 404 circular mils.

$T = 404 \times (25 \times 2) \times 0.008 = 162$ lbs. Using the formula, T equals 404 times the quantity of 25 times 2, since there are 25 pairs or 50 wires, times 0.008, for a total allowable pulling force of 162 pounds. Although it is unlikely that you will be called upon to do this calculation, it is nice to know you could, and it shows you the science behind the numbers. The following situations can also cause problems when pulling cable:

- Over or around obstacles
- Around corners
- Too long of a run
- Through a conduit too small for the amount of cable

Wire Lubricant

A way to reduce cable strain during installation in conduit is the use of cable lubricant, or wire lube. Lubricants work by reducing the friction between the cable and the conduit. Dish soap used to be a popular lubricant, but would cause cables to be glued in place when it dried. Many companies now produce commercial cable lubricants with a wide variety of formulas for different needs.

Selecting the correct lubricant for your pull entails knowing the type of jacket materials on the cables, the type of conduit you are pulling into, the ambient temperature at the time of the pull, the estimated time it will take to complete the pull, and whether the pull will be horizontal or vertical. Each of these characteristics has a bearing of the type of wire lube to be selected for best performance.

How much lube you will need for a pull can be calculated using the formula:

$$Q = K \times L \times D$$

Where Q is the quantity of lubricant in gallons (liters), K is the constant of 0.0015 English or 0.00073 for metric measurements, L is the length of the conduit in feet (meters) and D is the inside diameter of the conduit in inches (millimeters).

Large conduits can be pre-lubricated by using a conduit swab to spread a gel type lubricant throughout the conduit, ahead of the cable. Or, by using gel-packs that are attached to the pull rope ahead of the cables and ooze lubricant while the cable is being pulled. Lubricant is especially warranted when pulling cable in PVC conduits as they have a much higher friction co-efficient than metal conduits.

Bend Radius

Bend radius is the minimum radius to which a cable can be bent, without affecting its rated performance. The smaller the bend radius, the greater the material flexibility (as the radius of curvature decreases, the curvature increases). Bend radius is measured on the inside curvature of the cable. A minimum bend radius is the radius below which a cable should not be bent. Larger radii bends are easier to pull and put less strain on the cable being pulled. The minimum bend radius is of particular importance in the handling of UTP,

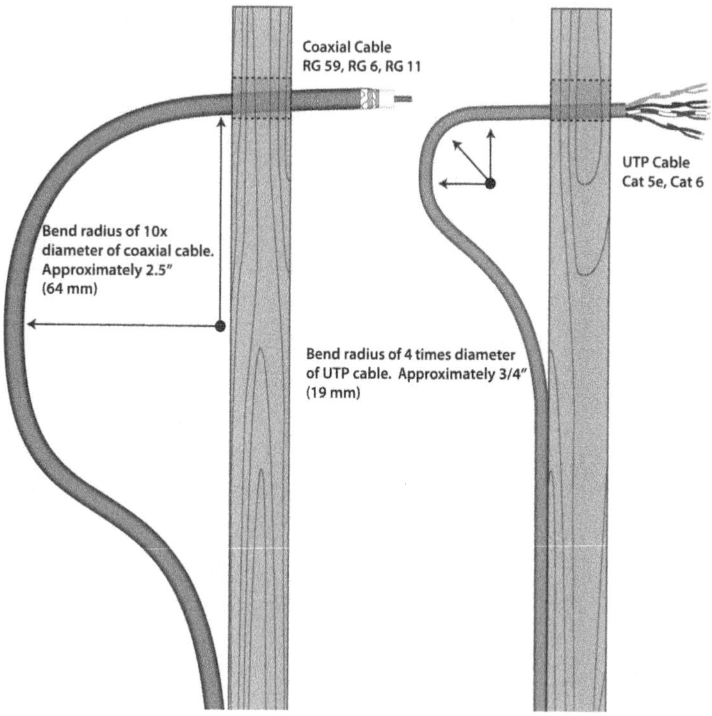

Figure 2-12. *Bend Radius for Coaxial and UTP Cables*

coaxial, and fiber optic cables, and varies with different cable designs. Figure 2-12 shows how bend radius is implemented when cabling with coaxial and UTP cables. After installation and under no-load conditions, bend radius for UTP cable is 4 times the cable's diameter and 10 times the cable's diameter for coaxial cable.

Manufacturer recommendations for maximum pulling tension and minimum bend radius should always be followed when installing optical fiber cable.

Routing Cables

Follow these general cabling recommendations to produce trouble-free installations when routing cables:

Splice — Do not splice cables on the outlet runs if the cable is damaged or too short. Pull a new cable if necessary.

Bend — Do not bend cable sharply or nick the protective sheath covering the insulated wires.

Staples — Use plastic non-metallic-type staples then attach cables to them using nylon ties. Do not overtighten. Do not use staple directly on a cable unless it is designed for low-voltage cables and will not change the shape of the cable (and thus, impair its ability to carry voice/data). An improperly stapled cable might pass a test using a cable mapping device, yet will fail when a keypad or other device is attached.

Conduit — If conduit is installed, always leave a pull cord to facilitate the running of new cable. When pulling cables through conduit, be sure to use a lubricant to reduce pull force on the cable and prevent friction from damaging the jacket. Never run power in the same conduit with telecommunications cable. Only low-voltage monitor and control lines may share conduit with telecommunications cabling.

Carpet — If cables must be installed under carpeting, follow the manufacturer's directions carefully and remember that only one transition from one type of cabling to another is standard in a single room. Avoid installing under carpet runs in damp areas. Note that under-carpet power cables are not permitted.

Fire-Breaks — Where possible, use inner walls for runs to avoid conflict with fire-breaks and insulation. Inner-wall cabling also makes it easier to replace cables when necessary or to add cables in the future. Nonetheless, cabling through external walls is not always avoidable, so installation handling should be the same as for electrical wire.

Power Cable — Do not run signal cabling parallel to power cabling without adequate separation. Instead, cross them at 90° angles, and do not share bore holes with power wires.

Heat — Keep cable away from sources of heat (such as hot water pipes and heater ducts) and glass walls subject to direct sunlight.

Outside — Cables should not be run on the outside the building for both appearance and safety reasons. Cables on the outside of an addition to a building may be allowed under local code regulations, but should be avoided for initial installations. Cables installed outdoors should be rated for Direct Burial.

Spare Length — Leave a half a meter (18") of spare cable at outlets and connection points for future connections and changes.

For structured wiring panels, it is a good idea to allow enough cable to touch the floor, because it will ensure that there is enough slack to route cables neatly on the panel no matter where each device goes. The minimum excess recommended is 18" (.5m) beyond the bottom of the enclosure.

Cable Separation

There are a number of different reasons for providing separation between cables. Electrical codes require separation between cables for safety reasons, while other standards recommend separation to reduce or eliminate crosstalk and other noise issues that might occur.

In the U.S., the NEC requires that Class 1 and other power conductors be separated from low-voltage cables, like Class 2, 3 and communication cables, by a minimum distance of 50 mm (2 in).

TIA/EIA-570-C standard also provides separation guidance for electrical power and low-voltage cabling, but the emphasis is on preventing electrical interference instead of safety. It recommends a separation of at least 305 mm (12 in) between electrical power cables and telecommunication cables, 150 mm (6in) between security and telecommunication cables, and 305 mm (12 in) between electrical power and audio cables. It also recommends at least 305 mm (12 in) between speaker-level audio cables and telecommunication cables. If these cables need to be crossed, do so at right angle for minimal inductive coupling.

Pathways

If these cables need to be crossed, do so at a right angle, for minimal inductive coupling. In most cases, residential cable pathways are created inside walls, ceilings and floors as the building is constructed. Planning is used to create the most direct route to outlets while allowing cables to be enclosed within finished surfaces. Prepping the pathway is a matter of drilling holes, setting boxes or rings, and installing cable support structures where needed.

Conduit

Use of conduit with low-voltage systems in a residence is uncommon, unless the location is hard to reach through normal cabling practices, or if the project calls for future cable upgrading. Where conduit is used, it is most often Electrical Non-metallic Tubing (ENT) or Electrical Metallic Tubing (EMT).

ENT is commonly used in residential and light commercial construction. The corrugated polyvinyl chloride tubing ranges in size from 16 (1/2") to 53 (2") and comes in coils from 30 meters (100 ft) to 450 meters (1,500 ft) in length. ENT is produced in a number of colors suitable for use in plenum and non-plenum spaces. Blue ENT, often called smurf tube, is commonly used for power circuits, while yellow ENT is used for communications and signal circuits and red ENT is used for fire alarm circuits.

Easily the most popular conduit used, electrical metallic tubing is the conduit of choice for light duty applications. EMT, also known as thinwall conduit, is widely used because it is lightweight and easy to bend and cut. EMT is hot-dipped galvanized to prevent rusting when subjected to moisture.

EMT is made from steel and is a good conductor, which is why it is often used as the equipment grounding conductor in electrical systems. EMT couplers and box connectors must be tight and secure in order for it to serve as a proper equipment grounding conductor. EMT is delivered in 3 meter (10 ft) sections for ease of handling. EMT should be stored on racks in dry environments prior to installation. EMT ranges in size from trade size 16 (1/2") to size 103 (4").

Cable Tray

The use of cable tray has become increasing popular due to the demand to rearrange offices, and cable tray's ability to support a large number of cables. Cable tray comes in three common varieties.

Ladder tray consists of two parallel channels connected by rungs (the actual cable supports) in a manner similar in appearance to an extension ladder. Ladder tray is a very common tray for use with larger cables and in locations where appearance is not critical.

Trough type cable tray has similar parallel channels as ladder tray, but has a solid or ventilated bottom instead of rungs. Trough tray supplies a lot more support to cables and has a more finished appearance.

Ventilated trough tray is good for cables that may get warm and need air flow around them. A lightweight tray, known as basket tray, seems to be the tray of choice for communication cables that require additional support, but don't need to be completely hidden. Basket tray can be easily attached to side walls or hung by single or dual mounting rods.

Metal trays of any type that are used to support power conductors must be grounded per the NEC, just like conduit. Tray used just to support low-voltage cables is not required to be grounded per the electrical code, however, it is highly recommended by the Cable Tray Institute and NEMA to ground the tray to provide protection against noise, lightening and EMI.

As you have your cables enter or leave a tray, the cables should be supported so they are not stressed. The use of tray drop-outs can provide additional support for cables entering or leaving a tray.

Cable tray can contain both power and low-voltage cables if a barrier is used to separate the cables. Watch out for EMI when sharing a tray with power conductors. Communication cables of different types should be bundled by use and/ or signal level and routed separately in the tray whenever possible.

Notching and Drilling Studs and Joists

While local codes may vary, the following represents the accepted practices when drilling and notching. Local code must be checked before starting any new project. When drilling a hole through a stud, the edge of the hole cannot be closer than 5/8 inch from the edge of the stud. A nail plate should be used if the hole edge is within 1-1/4 inch from the edge of the stud.

In a non-load bearing wall, a hole cannot exceed 60% of the depth of the stud, and a load bearing wall cannot have a hole that exceeds 40% of the depth of the stud, as shown in Figure 2-13 and Figure 2-14.

A load bearing stud can be notched to a depth of 25% of the stud's width and anywhere along the length of the stud, except when back-to-back to a drilled hole or notch, as shown in Figure 2-15. A non-load bearing stud can be notched to a depth of 40% of the stud's width, as shown in Figure 2-16.

Procedures for drilling joists and rafters are covered by IRC R502.8.1 and R802.7.1. Holes are not permitted within 2 inches (50 mm) of the edges of the joists and rafters, and a hole cannot be larger than one third (1/3) of the depth of the joist or rafter. Holes can be drilled anywhere along the length of the joist or rafter. Drilling can be seen in Figure 2-17.

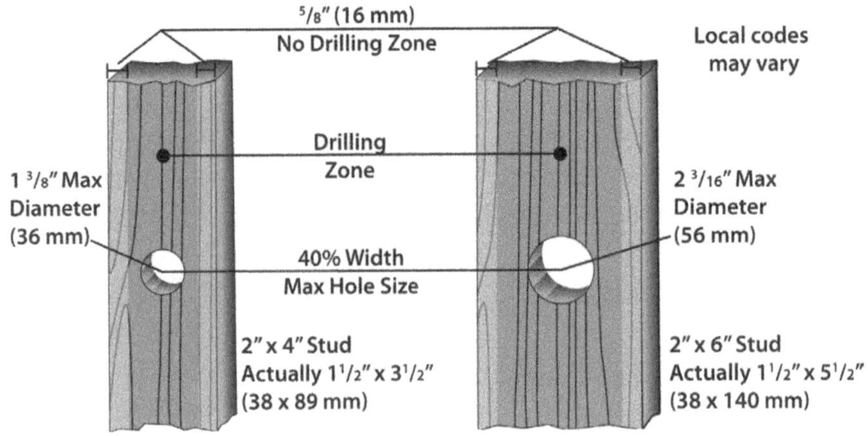

Figure 2-13. *Drilling Load Bearing Studs*

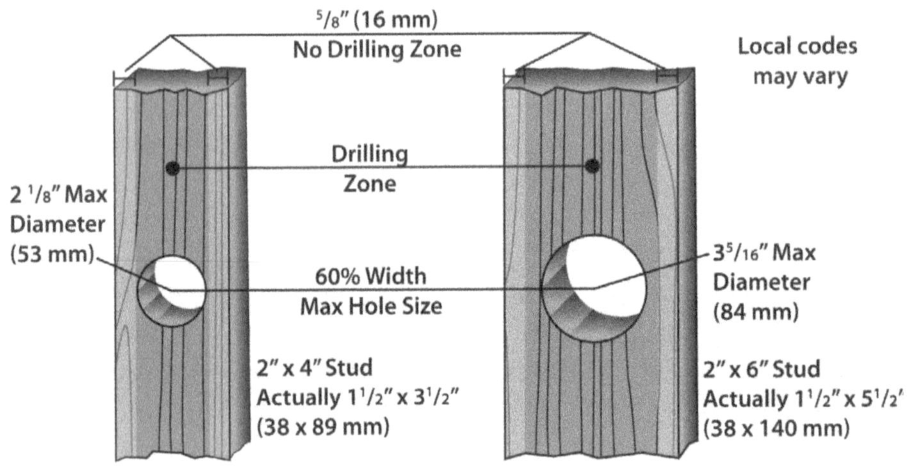

Figure 2-14. *Drilling Non-Load Bearing Studs*

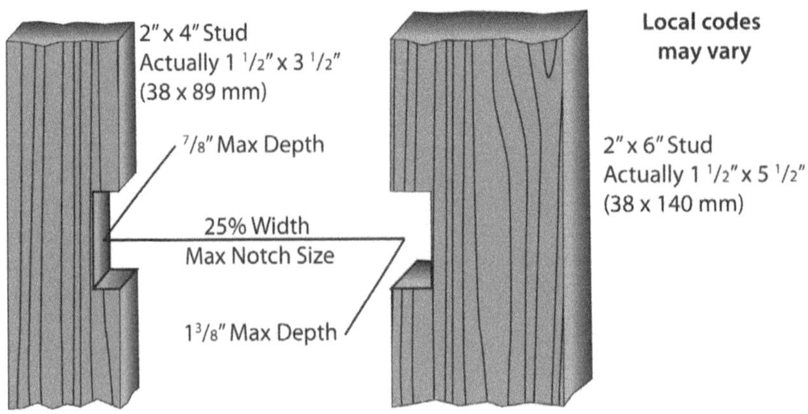

Figure 2-15. *Notching Load Bearing Studs*

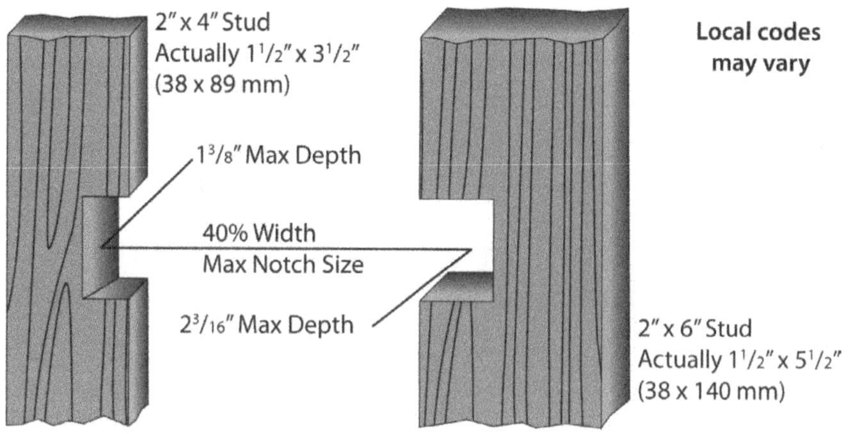

Figure 2-16. *Notching Non-Load Bearing Studs*

Notching joists and rafters is covered by International Residential Code (IRC) section R502.8.1 and R8027.1. The size (depth) of the notch varies with the span of the joist or rafter. Notches along the edge of the joist or rafter cannot exceed one sixth (1/6) of its depth, and cannot be located in the middle third of the joist or rafter. Notching requirements are shown in Figure 2-18. Despite the allowance to notch joists, it is a good policy to avoid notching joists unless absolutely necessary.

Nail plates, also known as notch plates, are installed over a notch or hole where the cable is within 1 1/4 inch of the face of the stud. The plate must be at least 1/16 inch (1.6 mm) thick and cover the entire cable as it passes through the stud. This is covered by NEC 300.4. As a result of the plate, a nail or screw will not be able to penetrate the cable, as shown in Figure 2-19.

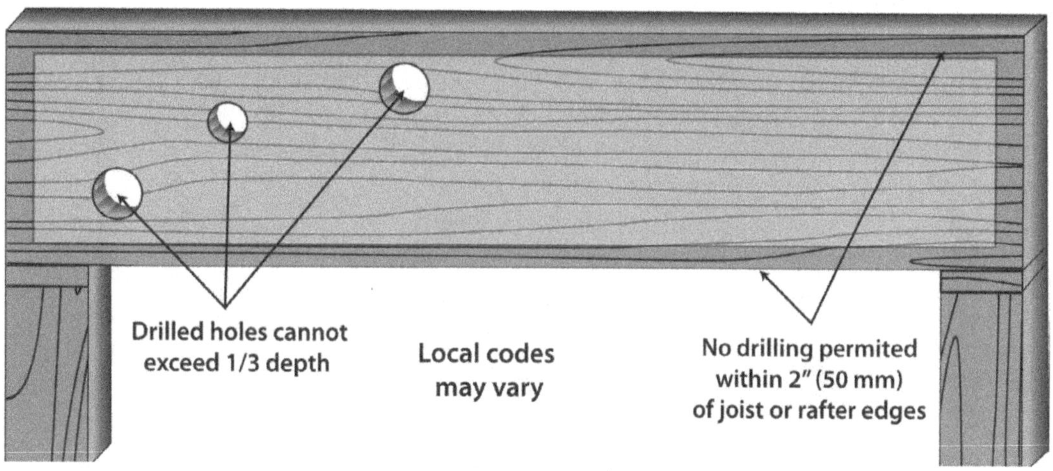

Figure 2-17. *Drilling Joists and Rafters*

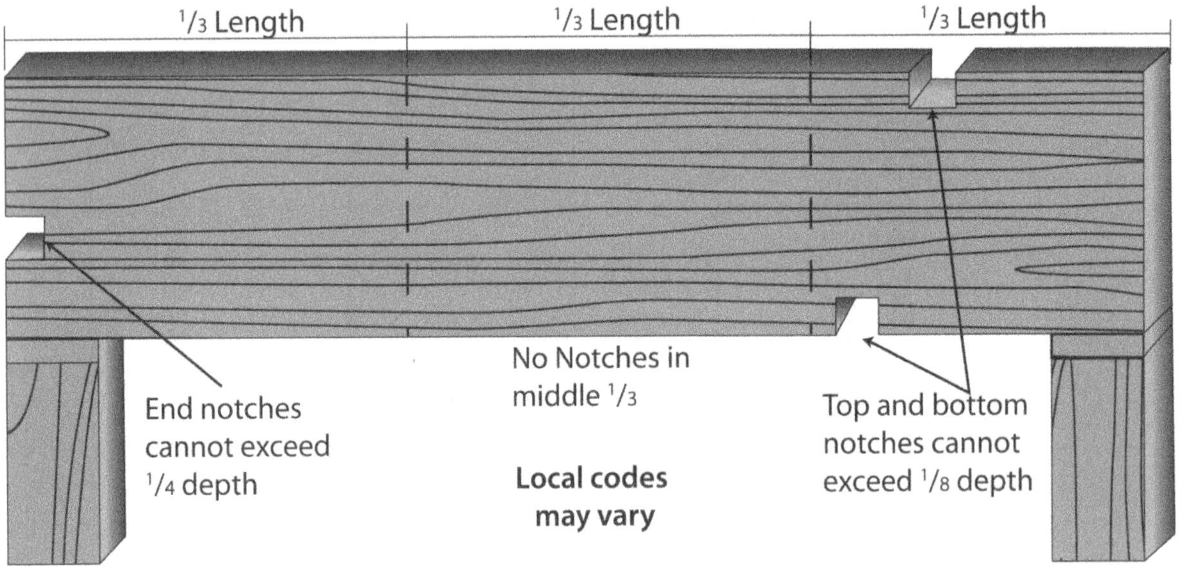

Figure 2-18. *Notching Joists and Rafters*

Supporting Cables

As stated, excessive force that exceeds a cable's pull tension can cause damage to the cable's sheath and core, but this excessive force can also diminish the cable's capacity to carry a signal. Bending, twisting, or other physical changes to the cable will cause it to carry less bandwidth than if it remained in a perfectly straight line. For this reason, care must be taken when securing cables to ensure they can handle the highest quality signal without any signal degradation.

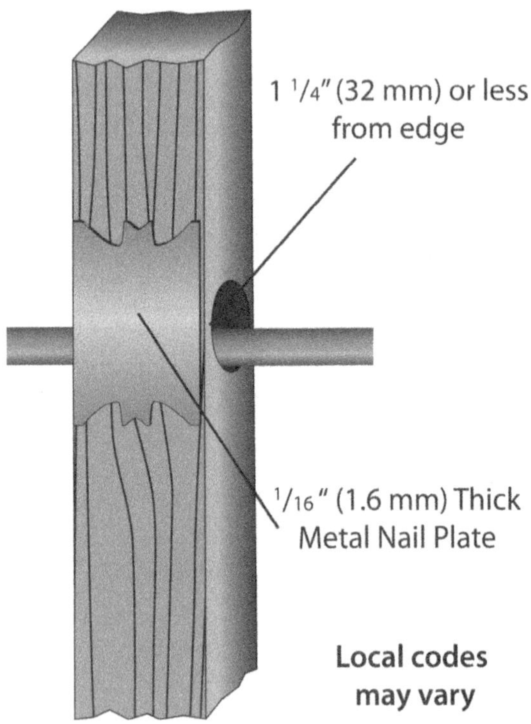

Figure 2-19. *Nail Plate*

Anchors

When running cable in the open spaces above ceilings, you must install your own methods for supporting the cables. Greater care must be taken when installing open cabling to ensure you don't damage cable jackets when pulling cables over previously installed cables. How often you must support a cable will change based on cable construction; however it is a good "rule of thumb" to support cables at least every 3 meters (10 ft).

Category UTP and ScTP cable that is run with non-continuous support is required by standard to be supported every 1.5 meters (5 ft). Also, the support structure should be broad enough so as not to indent cables on the bottom of a bundle. That is why wide J-hooks are specified instead of bridle-rings for Category cable support.

Good cabling practices should be followed when fastening cables for support, as shown in Figure 2-20. Vertical cables must be able to support their own weight. To accomplish this, they must be secured at irregular intervals. Securing them at regular intervals can cause a reflection problem at specific frequencies and should be avoided. Securing at sufficient intervals ensures that no one segment of cable will bear too much of the cable's overall bulk.

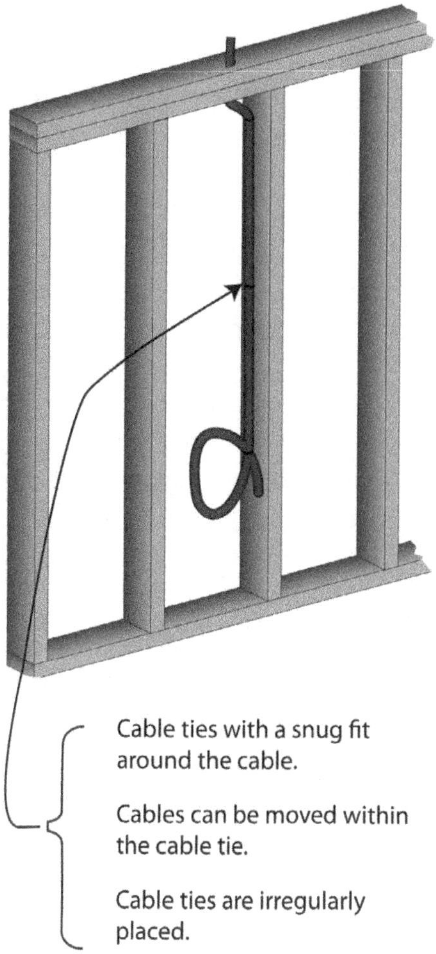

Figure 2-20. *Cable Securing*

Wire Ties

Cable ties, straps, clamps, and other devices should be installed so the cable is supported, yet is able to move within the fastening hardware. If the tie or clamp is making an indentation on the cable, it is too tight and might negatively affect the cable's performance. Cables should not be misshapen or bent by the fastening hardware.

Tightly bundled cables are to be avoided as well, because they will severely impact the ability to carry high-frequency information. Cables should be loosely held together, allowing for some movement of the cables, but tight enough to support their weight.

Firewalls

Firewalls are walls constructed of fireproof material to stop the spread of a fire. During an installation, cable must often be run through these types of walls. It is important to know that puncturing or penetrating these walls must be approved by the general contractor, architect, and fire marshal because it can affect the life safety issues of the building. When puncturing a firewall cannot be avoided, the holes must be backfilled with fire-stopping materials to restore the firewall's integrity. It is also important to be aware of local municipality fire codes for the type of fire-resistant material being used, such as 2-hour or 4-hour caulk or mechanical firestopping devices.

Fire Blocking

During a fire, flame and heated products of combustion can spread via paths of least resistance. Certain assemblies, particularly wood frame assemblies, result in concealed voids or cavities within walls, ceilings, and attics, which not only affect the spread of fire, but also make suppression more difficult.

Fireblocking involves the use of field-installed building materials to prevent the movement of undetected flames and gases to other areas through such concealed spaces.

Although such materials are not required to be tested for fire resistance, they are to be installed to slow a fire's migration and to contain a fire until it can be suppressed. Fireblocks are required at the following locations:

- Between floors
- Between a top story and a roof or attic space
- In furred spaces or the cavities between studs in wall assemblies
- At connections between horizontal and vertical spaces created in floor joists or trusses
- In soffits, and drop or cove ceilings
- In combustible exterior wall finishes and architectural elements
- At openings for pipes, vents, ducts, chimneys, and fireplaces

Fireblocks conform to innumerable configurations, depending on the dimensions and location of the concealed space.

Fireblocks can be constructed of materials such as:

- 2 inches nominal lumber
- Structural wood panels
- Gypsum board
- Cement fiber board
- Smaller fireblocks can be constructed from: Batts or blankets of mineral wool or glass fiber
- Loose fill insulation
- Caulks, sealants, or putties

Service Loops

It is recommended to leave 250 mm (8 in) of cable stubbed into outlet boxes and 1 meter (3ft) at the distribution device. This amount is used as a cushion against miscalculations or bad terminations. Cable should be coiled and stored in the outlet box to prevent damage to cable by other contractors. Service loops should be left at all termination locations. The service loop should allow clearance for movement of mechanical parts, provide enough slack to allow plugs and terminal board to be serviced, and provide sufficient slack to permit one repair, such as cutting off a connector and re-terminating.

System Cabling Verification

Today's residential cabling systems are as complex as those seen in a medium-sized business just a few years ago. These more intricate systems require special testing to validate that they have been wired properly and will function as intended. Improperly wired systems can cause countless troubleshooting hours and result in multiple service calls, thus negatively impacting profit margins and tarnishing a company's reputation.

Cable Testing

Cable testing is a multi-step process, although all steps are not used for all types of cable. Cables used for data transmission have more rigorous testing procedures than most audio, video, and control cables.

The types of cable testing include:

- Visual Inspection
- Continuity Testing
- Verification Testing
- Qualification Testing
- Certification Testing

Visual Inspection

Almost all cable testing starts with a simple visual inspection of the cable when it is on the spool, as it is being installed, and after installation. Check to see that the cable jacket is intact and not damaged, also look out for kinks or tight bends that may create performance issues. Visual inspection after termination will include looking to see terminations are clean and tight; and that proper wire termination lengths have not been exceeded.

Continuity Testing

For most types of cable, testing comes in the form of continuity testing. This test is accomplished using a device called an ohmmeter to test that each wire in the cable is continuous from end to end. This test is usually accomplished by shorting cable conductors together at the far end and then reading the resistance between each conductor. This simple test can also determine if a conductor is shorted or open by the resistance reading displayed between conductors. A short, as shown in Figure 2-21, occurs when two conductors are connected. An open, also shown in Figure 2-21, occurs when one or more of the wires does not attach to its connector. Opens and shorts are most common at the connectors; however, they can exist along the cable run as well. Shorting connectors can be used to test terminated cables.

Verification Testing

Category cable testing requirements include verification (a basic test, required after pre-wire and after trim-out). Verification testing typically uses a wire-mapping tester that verifies continuity of each wire in the cable and also verifies that each wire is terminated in the proper position of each connector.

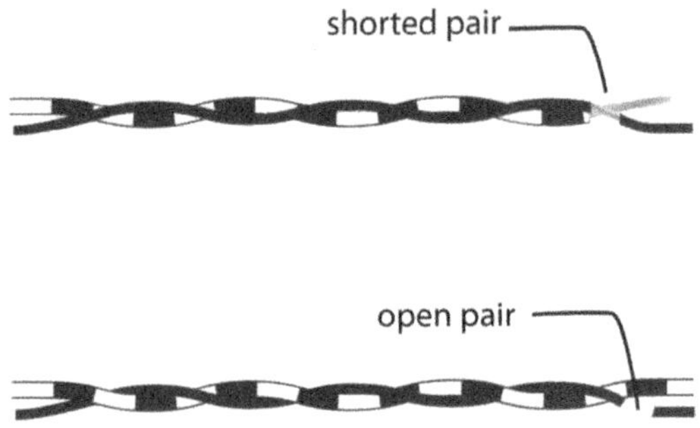

Figure 2-21.
UTP with a Short and Open

Reversed pair occur when the conductors (tip and ring) are reversed along a single pair, as shown in Figure 2-22. Crossed pairs occur when both conductors of one pair are crossed with both conductors of another pair, as shown in Figure 2-23. This happens commonly when one side of the cable is terminated to T568A standard, and the other end with T568B standard, thus crossing pairs 2 and 3. These types of errors are easily found by using a wire mapping tester.

This test does not tell anything about the cables suitability for use with the proposed application.

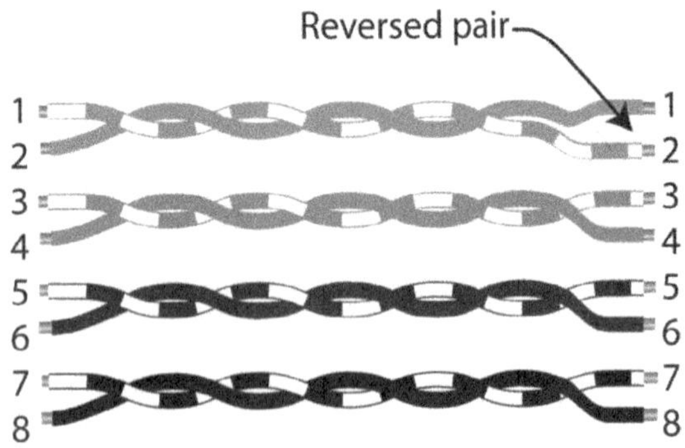

Figure 2-22. *UTP with a Reversed Pair*

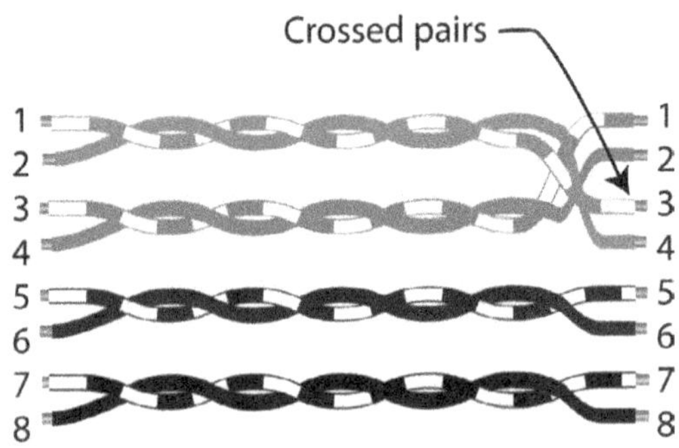

Figure 2-23. *UTP with a Crossed Pair*

Qualification Testing

The next level of testing for Category cable is known as qualification testing. Qualification testing is preferred over verification testing during the "trim-out" phase of the cabling project. This level of testing must be done with a high quality qualification type tester, which is capable of testing for various network technologies, including 100BaseTX and 1000Base-T.

Certification Testing

Another Category cable test, also performed at "trim-out", is certification testing that requires specialized cable testing equipment. The certification tester runs a series of test and compares the results to the cable parameters established in the TIA/EIA-568-C standards, based on the Category of the cable under test.

The tester typically displays a "PASS" or "FAIL" result for the cable, and allows the testing data to be downloaded for review and archiving.

Cable Analysis

The following are some of the tests used by the certification tester to verify compliance with the EIA/TIA-568-C cabling standard:

Wire-map — tests each wire in the cable to assure it is terminated in the proper order

Propagation Delay — the time it takes the signal to travel the cable from end-to-end

Delay Skew — the difference in propagation time for each pair in the cable

Cable Length — overall length of each pair in the cable in meters or feet

Insertion Loss (IL) — the overall end-to-end attenuation of the cable in decibels.

Return Loss (RL) — measurement of signal reflected back up the cable

Near-end Crosstalk (NEXT) — measured crosstalk between cable pairs at transmitting end.

Power-sum NEXT (PSNEXT) — measured sum of NEXT coupled to a pair from all adjacent pairs

Equal-Level Far-End Crosstalk (ELFEXT) - measured crosstalk at receiving end

Power Sum ELFEXT (PSELFEXT) — measured sum of ELFEXT coupled to a pair from all adjacent pairs

Troubleshooting Tips

Troubleshooting starts with having the right tools for the job. There are a number of tools an installer should be familiar with and have on hand to test cabling.

Tools

Common testing tools used by technicians include:

Continuity Tester — is a very basic device that indicates continuity of wires, but does not give an actual resistance reading. Continuity may be indicated by a lit light or an audible tone

Multi-Meter — The proverbial Swiss army knife of the installer's toolbox, the multi-meter can perform many test functions including, measuring resistance, checking continuity, measuring AC and DC voltages, measuring AC and DC currents, and with some models they can also measure audio levels in decibels and test diode and transistor junctions. This essential tool comes in both analog and digital models. They are fairly inexpensive, so every installer can afford one.

Wire-Mapper — If the job entails installing Category UTP cable, a wire-mapping cable tester is an essential tool also. In its simplest form, the wire mapping tester will check for continuity on each conductor of the four-pair cable and also show if the pairs are terminated correctly. This tester requires that the cable already be terminated prior to testing. The tester is connected to one end of the cable via a modular plug, while a sending unit is attached to the other end the same way. The tester will indicate if pairs are open, shorted, reversed and crossed, usually by means of lights or LCD display. The wire-mapping function is also incorporated in more advanced cable qualification and certification testers.

Amplifier Tone and Probe Kit — identifies and helps trace individual cables within a group without damaging the insulation and can also be used to verify cable continuity. The tone generator creates a distinctive audio signal that attaches to conductors in a cable or between a conductor and ground. The probe is a small, portable amplifier with an inductive pickup that will sense and amplify the tone generator's signal when it comes in close proximity to the signal conductor. The probe allows the signal conductor to be tracked and picked out of a bundle of cable if needed.

Impedance Meter — is a special tool used most often with audio system calibration and troubleshooting. It is usually used to check speaker lines for proper loads. An impedance meter normally incorporates an internal oscillator to generate a test tone at various frequencies. The test signal is applied to the device under test and the impedance of the device is shown on the meter. The impedance is measured in ohms and should be noted with the frequency used, as the frequency will change the measured impedance.

Field Strength Meter — is used to measure modulated RF signals commonly found on TV antennas and in cable distribution system. The meter is actually a simple receiver that detects and measures the RF signal present on a cable. The meter is tuned to a channel under test and reads the signal level present in dBm, dBmV or dBμV. The meter is used to measure signal levels from antennas and to adjust and calibrate RF levels present in a RF distribution system.

Optical Power Meter — is a device used to measure the loss in optical signal level as the light passes down an optical fiber. This is usually a two part tool consisting of a light source and the power meter/detector. A known amount of light is inserted into one end of an optical fiber and the meter is attached to the other end. The meter detects and displays the light level present at the far end in dBm and when subtracted from the known injection level, give the amount of signal loss present across the fiber path. Many meters allow testing at multiple light wavelengths to allow a more accurate representation of the fiber's loss.

Lineman's Test Set (aka: Butt Set) — an essential tool for working on voice systems. It is used to monitor a line for dial tone, check for proper polarity, line voltage, and Caller ID information. The special alligator clips, equipped with a bed of nails, allows tapping into a line (aka Butt in) to monitor and test a live circuit.

PROCEDURES FOR TROUBLESHOOTING

Network Cabling

The following are some steps to help troubleshoot and correct network wiring issues:

Documentation — proper documentation of the cabling infrastructure is vital. Knowing where each end of the cable is located will save valuable time and resources. Be sure that no active equipment is attached to cabling system before proceeding.

Test equipment — prior to starting, assure the test equipment is in proper working order, correct test are selected, and the unit is calibrated properly. Test equipment adapters and patch cables do wear out and should be checked often for proper functionality.

Visual verification — all cable runs and terminations should have been visually verified at pre-wire and trim-out. It is much easier to correct an issue prior to the walls being closed up.

Verification testing — verification will prove that the cabling and terminations have been correctly installed. If a cable/termination proves to be faulty, it must be corrected before further testing can be done. Opens, shorts, crossed pairs, mixed pairs, damaged cables or outlets will cause this test to fail.

Qualification/Certification testing - This comprehensive level of testing provides detailed confirmation of the cable run's actual performance, across several parameters, not just that is it properly installed and connected.

A number of different issues can cause a fail or low quality pass. NEXT and all its variants. Most often, this test fails due to poor quality termination, too much wire untwisted, and defective outlets. Crushing or kinking of the cable can also be at blame. Re-termination or replacement of the outlet will normally correct this issue. In some circumstances, removing the wire ties and allowing the cable to lie normally may also help.

Distance. The twist in the wire pairs will actually make the transmission path longer than the actual horizontal wire run. Removing service loops and using shorter patch cables might help. Also confirm that the NVP settings are correct for the cable under test. If the test shows a really short link, confirm the tester patch cable is performing correctly and that the outlet is terminated correctly. Worst case scenario. In some situations, the link will just not pass, and the cable may need to be replaced.

Once the system has been commissioned and is actively being used — special network test equipment can be utilized to aid in trouble shooting. Port and link discovery, hub flash, and PoE are some of the tests available.

Some problems might be a result of intermittent electrical noise, changes in ambient temperature, improper system ground, or problems with the active equipment connected to the cable. In rare cases, the link light may be on, but the circuit is still not functioning properly; perhaps the patch cable is too short, which can cause the signal on the transmitting pair to overpower the receiver. Use of a longer patch cable can be of assistance with this issue.

Many of these same procedures and tests apply to the installation of coaxial and fiber based networks as well, although different tools and test equipment may be needed for these tests.

CHAPTER 3

RETROFIT INSTALLATION

INTRODUCTION

When cabling or equipment is installed in an existing home, this is known as retrofit installation. Although many construction methods are not conducive to this type of work, homes built with dimensional lumber framing in North America and some other areas allow for retrofitting, and in 2009 the industry in the U.S. reported that over half of their projects were retrofit projects.

A retrofit is fundamentally different from new construction. Instead of sharing a jobsite with other trades, a contractor is essentially invading someone's home. Never forget that this is exactly the perception that some family members will have when a technician is in their house.

THE "RETROCRATIC OATH"

The most effective way to overcome this perception is the behavior of the installer in the home.

- Have a drop cloth and a vacuum when arriving to start work. Put on shoe covers to avoid tracking anything into the house.
- Put down a drop cloth in the main work area first, and put all tools and materials on it as they are brought into the house. Use a hallway drop cloth when using an attic stair; the attic is the dirtiest area in the house.
- Use a placemat to protect counter and floor surfaces in work areas.
- Always clean up as work progresses. Don't let a local mess spread through the house.

- Be considerate of the family as well - avoid loud or crude language and treat them with consideration. An installer is not a guest but a professional chosen to provide a specialized service.

The main benefit of retrofit etiquette is to establish the trust and respect of the homeowner. This will result in enthusiastic referrals to their friends and compliments about the business owner. It will make them more relaxed when working in their home.

RETROFIT ETIQUETTE

Keep these points in mind when working on a project in a client's home:

- If the client can see an effort is being made to protect their home and keep it clean, they will be much more likely to be forgiving if there is an accident or mistake.
- A good way to put this in perspective is to remember that many things in a high end home cost more than the average car.
- Protect them all.
- The best case is to avoid making a mess in the first place.
- Use trash bags looped over a glow rod, or a dust collection hole cutter, to catch most of the dust and debris when installing ceiling speakers
- Use paper, plastic or a placemat to catch dust and debris when making and trimming out wall outlets. Always vacuum up sawdust and chips immediately after drilling.

PLANNING THE RETROFIT PROJECT

Completing a successful and profitable retrofit project requires three P's:

- Planning
- Practice
- Patience

Planning

The initial impulse might be to jump right into a project and begin working. However, the carpenter's motto "measure twice before cutting once" should guide how the work is planned. Careful planning before drilling, cutting, or punching holes into walls and ceilings is the best practice. Such forethought requires additional time and patience. However, three hours of planning might save six hours of re-work.

- Plan Ahead. Prepare floor plans; determine equipment and material needs; diagram the wiring layout; strategize with staff and coworkers.

- Plan on Surprises. Each project presents its own unique challenges. Count on the need to fashion some innovative procedures for completing the job. Allow time for these unexpected possibilities.

Practice

Retrofitting is an art that requires practice. When working behind walls, ceilings, and floors, practice using the appropriate tools, pulling and pushing wire and grabbing cable without being able to actually see it. With experience and practice a technician will improve at these tasks.

The technician should practice using all retrofitting tools and techniques at their office (on a practice wall) before trying them at a customer's job site. Do not use tools you are not familiar with.

Another good "Test Bench" for retro is a new construction change order. The contractor is expecting to patch after the work is done, so he will be grateful And if a mistake is made, a wall patch is expected anyway.

Patience

The good retrofitter knows the value of patience on the job. Retrofitting can be a frustrating experience and rushing the work can lead to ill-advised and costly mistakes. In the long run, patience pays off.

RETROFIT TOOLS

A set of tools that covers the major types of operations encountered during a retrofit is crucial to a successful project which is completed on time with minimal complications. In this chapter, the following are discussed:

- Exploratory tools
- Tools that make wall openings
- Pushing and pulling tools
- Tools for making holes

Tool Starter Checklist

While there are specialized tools for many projects, it is important that you have a few basics when working at any site:

- Stud sensor
- Sheetrock saw
- Electrical tape
- Small flashlight
- Knife
- Two-way radios
- Wire/cable cutter
- Electric drill (for concrete/brick construction)

When working, always remember to keep inventory of your tools to prevent potential issues with losses. Use of a retrofitting tool pouch will help maintain tool management. There may also be a requirement for safety equipment, especially if the site is a construction site.

Stud Sensor

Mirror

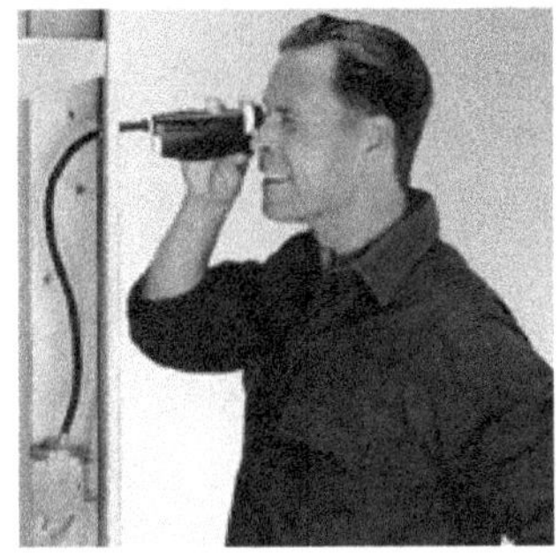

Fiber Optic Scope

Video In-Wall Scope

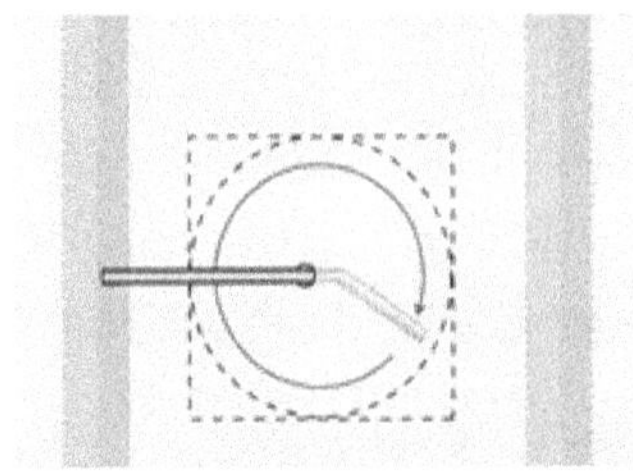

Exploratory Hole

Figure 3-1. *Exploratory Tools*

Exploratory Tools

Exploratory tools help locate openings and spaces where wires can be run. They can also help locate cable that has already been pushed or pulled.

Stud Sensor

Stud sensors are "must-have" tools. With them, spaces between studs or joists can be located so an opening can be safely used to run a cable. Stud sensors operate by detecting changes in density behind walls.

In addition to locating clear, open spots, stud sensors can also locate fire-stops and cross braces. However, stud sensors can give false readings when there are pipes and insulation in the wall. Recalibrate a stud sensor at different locations to get more accurate readings. Always make several passes over an area to re-check findings

Mirrors

A mirror attached to the end of a rod can help in seeing what is in a wall cavity or to find a fish tape or cable behind a wall. In conjunction with a bright flashlight, a technician will be able to see all the way up and down a wall or in a ceiling space.

The mirror device shown in Figure 3-1 works like a periscope and has a built-in light.

Scopes

A fiber-optic scope is very handy for seeing into hard-to-reach places. Light is transmitted down a set of fibers in the flexible shaft and the image is sent back another set of fibers for viewing through the lens. With a focusable lens, distances from one inch to two feet can be seen.

Video In-Wall Scope

A video wall scope can provide a B&W or color image on its built-in screen or even to an external video monitor, which is a nice step up from the other devices.

Making a Small Exploratory Hole

Making a small exploratory hole in a wall or ceiling helps uncover any obstacles. Use a stiff wire to feel for any "surprises" if there is any doubt as to what is behind a surface. A periscope-type device, or fiber-optic scope, can also be used to inspect the space inside the wall.

Wire Bits

Spring steel wire bits are primarily used to create reference points when running cable between floors or rooms.

For example, imagine that a retrofit project requires drilling into a wall cavity from the attic. Normally, this would be done by measuring over from the wall and then making the same measurement in the attic. However, this is difficult to do in an attic. Using a wire bit as a long, tiny drill bit, a hole can be drilled through the ceiling into the attic. The wire can then be located in the attic, followed by measuring over into the wall cavity top plate and drilling down.

If a mistake is made, the resulting hole is unnoticeable and can be tried again.

Tools to Make Wall Openings

In order to create openings for outlets, speakers or distribution panels, holes will be cut in various types of materials. The best tool to use depends on the type of wall or ceiling material.

Templates

Always use a cut-in template when making an opening.

A template will:

- Prevent damage to the wall surface
- Ensure that the opening is level
- Make sure the opening is the right size

Sheetrock Saws

Sheetrock saws are used on drywall and sheetrock material (predominantly newer houses). Their sharp tip makes starting the cut easier. Place the tip against the drywall and wiggle the handle to drive the tip through the drywall. Then begin cutting.

Rotary Tools

Rotary tools are used on walls made of a lath/plaster combination. This is harder than sheetrock and sawing through it with a regular drywall saw creates strong vibrations that can crack the adjoining plaster. The best way to make cuts in lath and similar plaster material is to use an electric router.

Make a pilot hole in the wall or work the bit in from an angle to get started. Hold the tool firmly to guide the bit inside the template. Routers are also good for cutouts in bath and kitchen ceramic tile walls. They create a lot of dust, so use drop cloths and have a good vacuum cleaner for cleanup.

Oscillating Tools

The oscillating tool may be used as an alternative to the rotary tool in situations where cutting tile, wood, or lathe and plaster is necessary.

Wire Bits

Cut-in Template

Rotary Tool

Sheetrock Saw

Oscillating Tool

Figure 3-2. *Tools for Making Wall Openings*

Tools for Pushing or Pulling Wire

There are various tools for pushing or pulling wire through holes that are already drilled, or across attics and other crawl spaces that cannot be seen or reached. Fish tapes, fiberglass rods, push rods, and pull sleeves are commonly used tools for this type of work.

Ball Chain (Wet Noodle)

A ball chain is ideal when something extremely flexible for retrieving wire or cable is needed. The ball chain can easily be dropped down through multiple predrilled holes from an attic or upper floor through uninsulated walls. However, pulling a ball chain around sharp corners could break it. Instead, use a fiberglass tape or rod.

The ball chain usually comes with a flexible shaft which has a built-in magnet, for retrieving the ball chain from a wall cavity.

Larger sizes of ball chain are very effective for vertical wire fishing. It is extremely flexible, so it goes around and through obstructions such as electrical wire and plumbing. Choose a size that has a 30-50 lb. pulling strength, or use a pull cord.

Metal Fish Tape

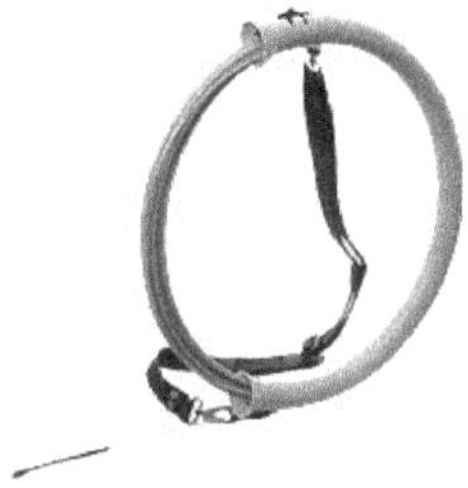

Fiberglass Fish Tape

Pull Sleave

Fiberglass Rod

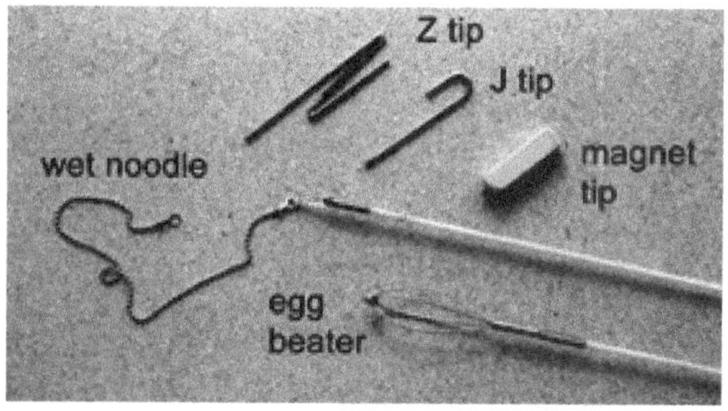

Rod Tips

Figure 3-3. *Tools for Pushing and Pulling Cable*

Metal Fish Tape

Fish tapes serve as the primary tool for pulling wire through conduit or other enclosures. They can also be used to pull wire through walls and attics. They come in a wide variety of sizes, metal or fiberglass and in lengths from 10 feet to over 200 hundred feet.

Fiberglass Fish Tapes

Fiberglass fish tapes (small-diameter rods) come coiled in a tube and can make 90-degree bends without deforming. They come with bull-nose ends to attach a cable or pull cord. Colored bright yellow, they are easier to see in attics and crawl spaces. (Regular metal tapes are nearly invisible in dark spaces). This type of tape is especially useful where there are live circuits!

Extremely flexible fiberglass tapes (like metal tapes) are also packaged in coil dispensers. When several bends are required they work very well for conduit or in other places.

Fiberglass Rods

Fiberglass rods are a popular alternative to fish tapes. They come in different lengths, (up to 6 feet) and are fitted with a threaded coupling that allows them to be screwed together to make longer lengths. Glow-in-the-dark colors are also available for easier visibility.

Fiberglass rods are lightweight, fairly stiff and are easier to control than tapes. In many situations, holes can be located and fished with a fiberglass rod more easily than using a tape.

Fiberglass Rod Tips

In addition to the bull-nose tip, there is a wide assortment of other tips that can be used with fiberglass and other rods:

- The J tip is used to grab cable, fish tapes or pull cords.
- The Z tip has two grooves that snag a wire or pull cord and hold it firmly. The cable can be retrieved, or pushed across a crawl space to another installer.
- A ceramic magnetic retriever is used to grab and carry a short ball chain (wet noodle) for long distances, making it easier to maneuver the rod out of a wall opening.
- The egg beater attachment lets the installer work the rod over joists, insulation and ductwork without hanging up. It allows the rod to flip and twist over obstructions.

Push Rods

Fiberglass push rods, "glow rods" as they are often called, have a metal bull-nose end to attach a wire in order to push it through holes and wall cavities.

Fiberglass Poles

Fiberglass poles come in a variety of sizes and lengths (from 8 to 20 feet) and work well for pushing and pulling cables through open spaces such as attics or crawl spaces.

Jet Line

Jet line is the most common and least expensive wire-pulling device. Any of the rods mentioned can easily feed a jet line cord. Make the cord a few inches longer than twice the length of the wire run. Pull it into place with wires and leave for adding future wires, making sure that it slides freely.

Pull Sleeves

Pull sleeves eliminate the need for taping wires together to pull; a big time saver that leaves no residue on the wire. Remember to tape the sleeve to the wire bundle to prevent it from pulling off the wire if the bundle has to be pulled back.

The pull cord works well with a pull sleeve when pulling large cable or multiple cables with a connector attached. Pull sleeves come in several sizes, but the small size usually accommodates two RG-6 cables and two Cat5 cables.

Tools for Making Holes

There are several types of tools that can be used to make clean, precise holes in most materials with the minimum of mess.

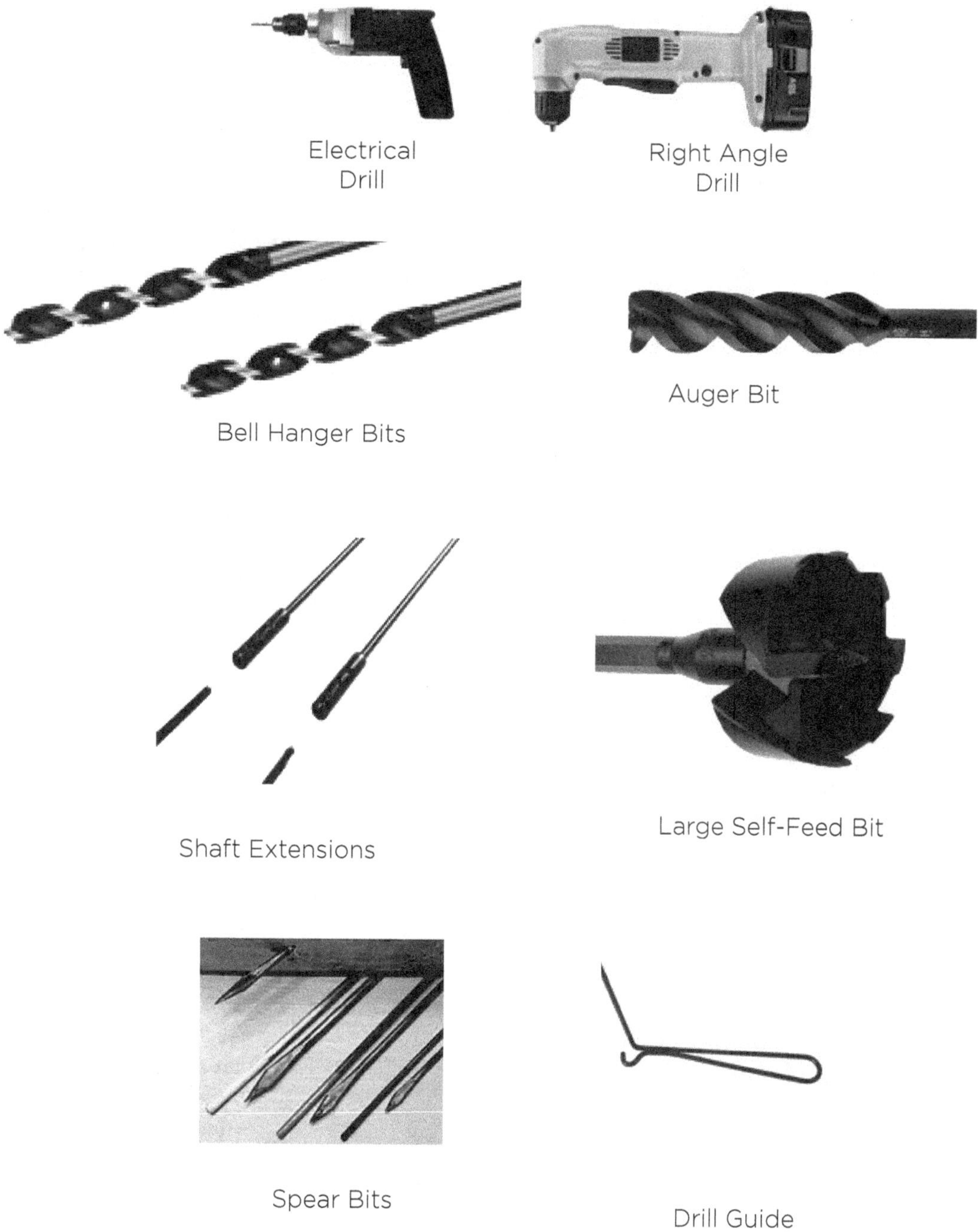

Figure 3-4. *Tools for Making Holes*

Standard Drills

Retrofitting often requires drilling at a long distance from the drill, through several boards at a time, and in tight closed settings.

Cordless Right Angle Drill

The right angle drill is a retrofit technician's best friend. This tool will allow the installer to drill holes in extremely tight spaces without the need to hack apart a client's drywall.

With this drill and an assortment of 4" to 6" drill bits, the installer can drill sideways through studs using holes that would need to be cut anyway, such as speaker cutouts for in-wall speakers and double-gang wall plate cutouts for wiring bundles.

The right angle drill can also be used to drill through the top plate of a wall in order to run wiring to in-ceiling speakers or the top and bottom plates to run wiring from one level to the next. This is typically accomplished by cutting a hole in the ceiling near the wall to be drilled and inserting the entire drill into the floor cavity. (Remember, in projects using in-ceiling speakers, the center channel speaker hole can be used to access the wall's top plate). The entire drill can usually fit as long as the hole is big enough to accommodate the drill battery.

Drill Bits

The following drill bits are commonly used depending upon hole-size and depth:

- Bell hanger: A standard twist bit on a long shaft which can be used for wood or metal. Sometimes has a hole to allow a pull string to be pulled back through the drilled hole
- Auger: Has a self-threading tip, and should be used a lower speeds, and only in wood.
- Spear: Best used for drilling wood, especially at a sharp angle.
- Specialty: Includes bits made to make larger holes.
- Masonry bits (concrete/brick/stone)

Bell Hanger Bits

Bell hanger bits are used for holes from ¼" to ½" in diameter. Bell hanger bits come with tapered and non-tapered shafts in lengths of 2, 4, and 6 feet. The taper allows the bit to be easily removed from the drilled hole.

These bits are excellent for drilling through nails with minimum damage to the bit. They are also well suited for drilling through metal framing and walking up wall cavities.

The non-tapered bell hanger bit is also useful for keeping the drill straight through the multiple wood members. When the drill is removed, the two (or more) holes line up, which allows for easier feeding of push rods back through the holes. (A tapered twist bit has a tendency to deflect and shift the second hole off center, making it difficult to find the second hole after the bit is extracted).

Auger Bits

Auger bits drill holes from ½" to 1", and they come on 4 - 6 foot shafts, for feeding up or down wall cavities. Auger bits have a self-threading tip to grab the wood and help pull the bit, thus reducing the pressure to force the bit through the wood.

Auger bits are intended for slow-speed use on wood. If a nail is hit, back the bit out and make the hole in another location.

Many of the auger and bell hanger bits have a small hole drilled through the tip of the bit hat can be used as a pull rod. Attach a pull wire through the hole of the bit (after the hole is drilled) so that when the drill bit is pulled back through the hole, the pull wire can be gripped.

Spear Bits

Spear bits have sharp points making them easy to start into wood and for drilling at an angle. They are available in sizes from 3/8 to 1/2 inch with a rigid shaft in lengths of 2 to 4 feet. Spear bits may have holes in the tip for attaching wires or pull strings. Another advantage of spear bits is that they can drill easily through insulation material. The spear bit can also make holes in wood at a sharp angle, without "walking" away from the desired starting point.

Another advantage of spear bits is that they can drill easily through any insulation material. The spear bit can also make several holes in a row without walking (moving away from a straight line).

Specialty Bits for Larger Holes

The spear and twist bits discussed previously work best for drilling holes up to ½" diameter. Drilling holes 1 inch or larger for multiple cables, especially using a long shaft, requires specialty bits. The larger the hole, the longer it takes to drill the hole. When the feed screw on the bit goes through the other side, the drill needs to be pushed to break through the last 1/8 inch of wood.

These bits are designed to make larger holes with minimum shaft pressure, therefore allowing the bits to be used on a long shaft. Large "self-feed" bits are designed to make larger holes with a minimum of shaft pressure, allowing them to be used with very long shafts. Waste wood chips are pushed down the gap in the side of the bit and then behind the bit, preventing binding. Standard Forster bits need to be backed out and waste cleared during drilling. Both are effective if there are knots or voids in the wood.

Shaft Extensions

Specialty bits can be expensive. An alternative method is to use short versions and then use extensions to reduce bit replacement costs.

Shaft extensions come in 2, 4 and 6 foot lengths. Drilling up or down through a top or bottom plate will require at least 8 feet of shaft. A good combination is a 4 foot drill shaft with a 4 foot extension.

Secure the extensions to the drill shaft with set screws. For example, if it is required to drill from the attic to the basement in a two-story house, longer lengths can be created by adding extensions.

Drill Guides

Drill guides are used to guide a flexible drill bit shaft in the wall. The guide can be used to easily direct the bit to the location to be drilled. They are also very effective for guiding glow rods past obstructions like braces and furring strips inside a wall cavity.

CONSTRUCTION TYPES

This section reviews the basic concepts of frame-built residential construction and examines the two standard framing techniques used over the past century of house building. Understanding these framing layouts will assist in the practice of successfully planning and carrying out the retrofitting process.

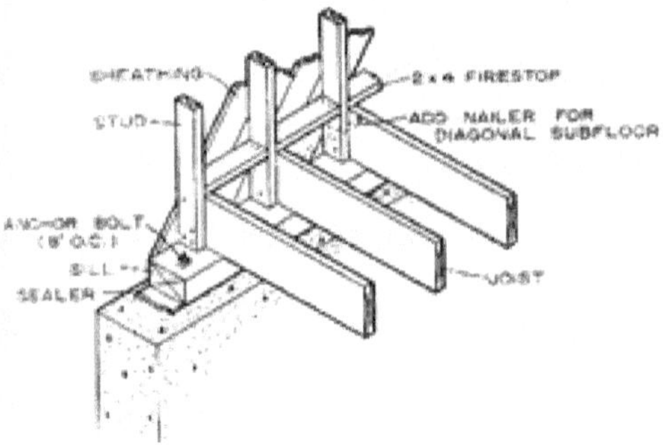

Figure 3-5. Balloon Framing

House Framing

Two basic types of house framing have dominated the last century's residential construction:

- Balloon Framing
- Platform Framing

Balloon Construction

Builders used balloon framing in home construction from the late 1800s until roughly the beginning of World War II (1939-1945). In balloon construction, a board called a sill plate is attached to the top of the foundation wall (lies flat on that wall). Floor joists (timbers arranged parallel from wall to wall to support the floor) are laid on top of the sill plate and the exterior wall studs are nailed to the joists to create the first floor. These wall studs may extend up as exterior studs for a second story.

The joists for both floors are nailed directly to the exterior wall frame. Interior wall studs are also nailed directly to the floor joists. The whole frame is tied together as it is built. Cross bracing between joists and studs provides necessary strength.

Platform Construction

Platform framing gets its name because each floor is built on a platform or deck. The sill plate is laid on the foundation wall and a platform is built on top with joists covered by a plywood floor material. Exterior walls are then fabricated as a unit with studs attached to a base plate and top plate.

The completed wall section is tilted into place and the base plate is nailed to the deck.

The second story of a platform house is simply a repetition of the first floor nailed on top. Strength in a platform house comes primarily from the exterior wall covering. Knowing the differences between these two house-framing techniques helps plan a retrofit strategy for where to drill holes, how to draw wire and what to expect behind walls and under floors.

Knowing the differences between these two house-framing techniques helps plan a retrofit strategy for where to drill holes, how to draw wire and what to expect behind walls and under floors.

Impact on Retrofit

Balloon framing makes it easy to get wires up the wall from the basement or crawl space because of its open construction. (However, if there is a fire-block, it will be necessary to drill through it to run wire up the walls).

In platform construction, the deck is built on the foundation and the wall is nailed to the deck. Running wire up the wall is more challenging in platform construction because drilling up through the flooring material and the wall bottom plate is required. The plate is always on top of the flooring so it is difficult to see exactly where to aim. Drill as close as possible to the rim joist (the outer joist to which exterior siding is attached). This will get the hole close to the center of the plate.

What has been said about the first floor construction also applies to the second floor. In some houses, it will be necessary to drill through a fire-block in the wall, and the second floor flooring board may extend into the wall space. However, in general it is very easy to get between floors in balloon construction.

In platform framing, the second floor platform is built on top of the first floor walls. The top of all load-bearing walls has a double 2 x 4 plate. To run wires between floors requires drilling a hole in the bottom and top plates away from the outside rim joist. Once a hole has been drilled up or down to get into this floor space, there will be a clear shot to get across to the first floor ceiling. This is beneficial when installing ceiling speakers.

Foundations

House foundations are one of three types depending on when and where the house was built:

- Basement
- Raised foundation (about 24 inches off the ground creating a crawl space)
- Slab on grade
- In balloon framing, the wall studs and floors joists are tied together directly on the foundation wall. Wood floor planks are nailed onto the floor joists and usually extend to the outside wall surface.

Attic Framing

Where the exterior walls meet the roof is similar in both the balloon and platform framing. There will always be a double top plate where the exterior wall joins with the ceiling joists and rafters.

There are basically two general exterior wall-to-attic framing situations:

Roof rafters resting on the wall

- Where the rafters rest directly on the wall top plate, there are tighter quarters and it is more difficult to drill down from above. Drilling up from below is possible but be careful not to drill through the roof after going through the top plate.

Roof rafters parallel to the end wall

- Where the wall is parallel to the rafters on the end of the building, there is usually space to stand up. It is easy to drill up into the attic or down from the attic into the wall.

RETROFIT TECHNIQUES

There are a variety of different techniques that can be used in retrofitting. We will discuss three of these techniques to demonstrate how to use the tools properly.

Note: the techniques given for each example are only one of several ways to complete these installations. We will also point out alternate techniques.

These retrofitting techniques assume three things about how to run retrofit cables:

- Running cables from basement to first-floor outlet in an insulated wall
- Running cables from the attic down to the second floor's outlets and devices
- Running cables for in-wall speakers around a flat panel

Scenario A: First Floor to Basement

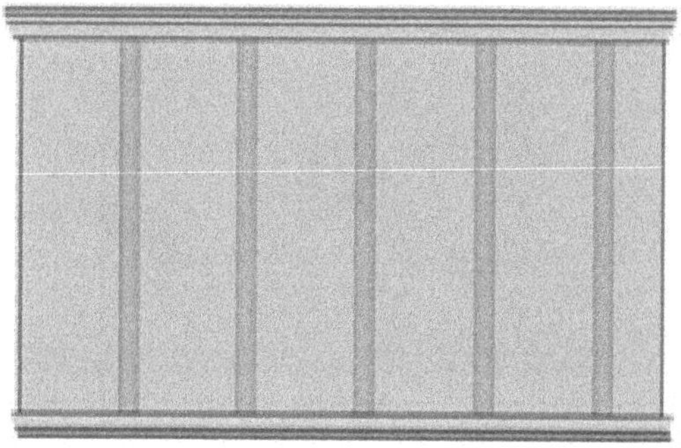

Front View

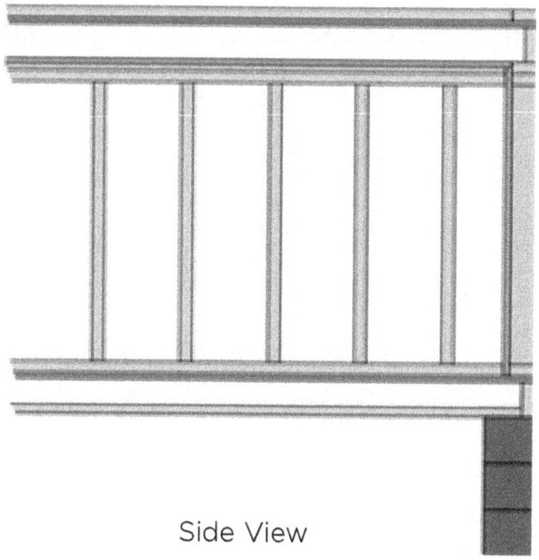

Side View

STEP 1

Locate and mark studs

Note: If possible, use an interior wall for the cable run

Advantages:

- No insulation
- Wall is away from rim joist

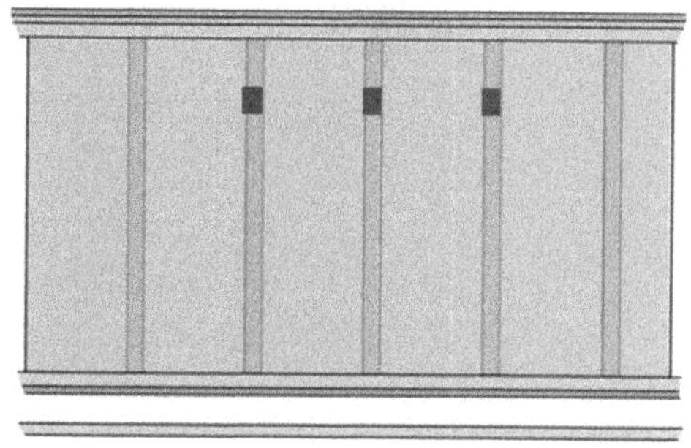

Step 2

Cut in outlet location

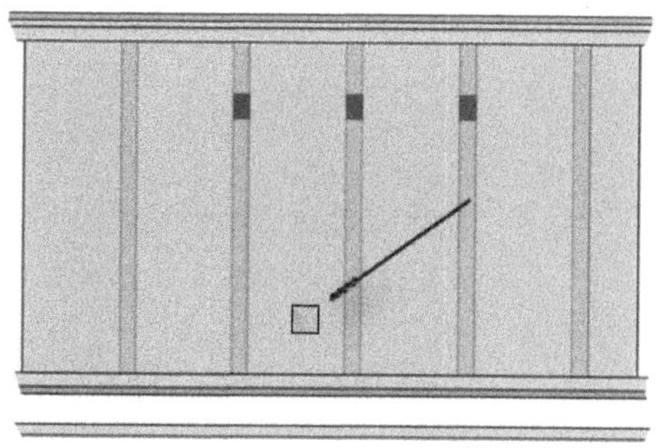

Step 3

Guide drill bit to inside corner of wall cavity

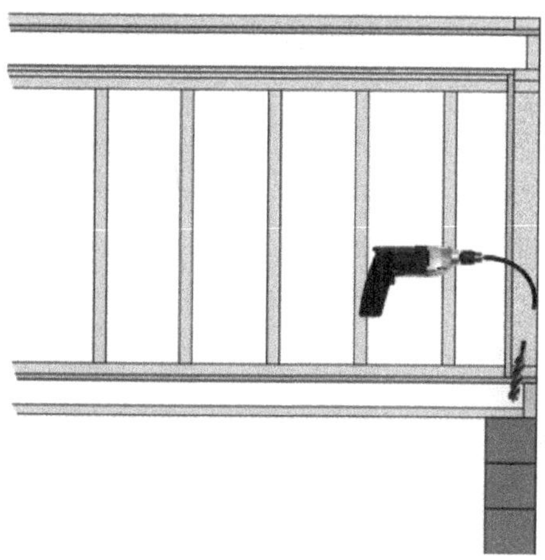

Step3 (Side View)
Guiding to the inside corner (closest to drywall) will help to avoid the Rim Joist

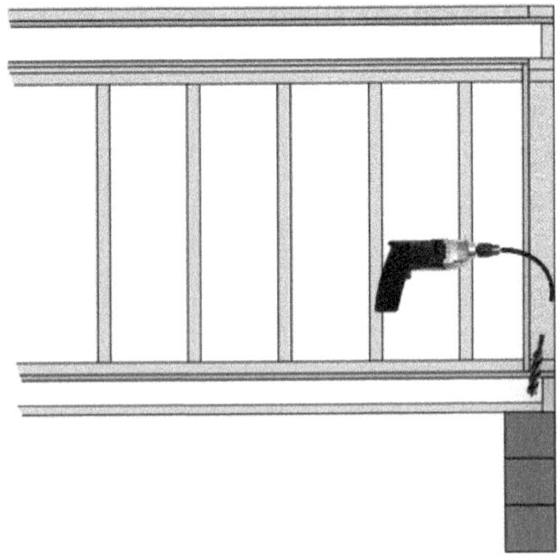

Step 4
Drill through the bottom plate into the basement

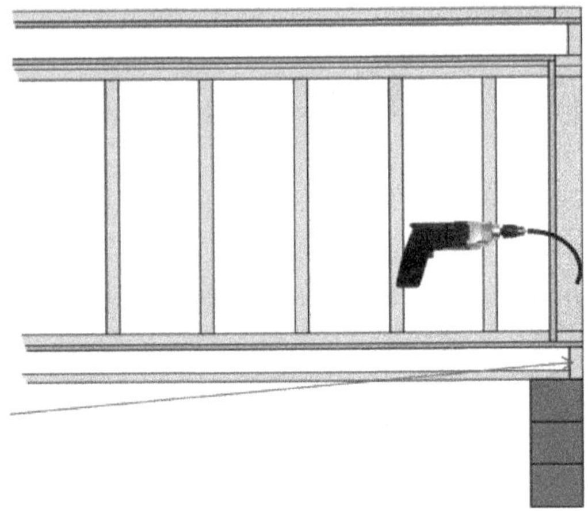

Step 5
Feed a pushrod with ball chain attached up the wall from the basement

Note: Marking the rod with a piece of tape can help to let you know when you've fed the correct length to the cut-in hole

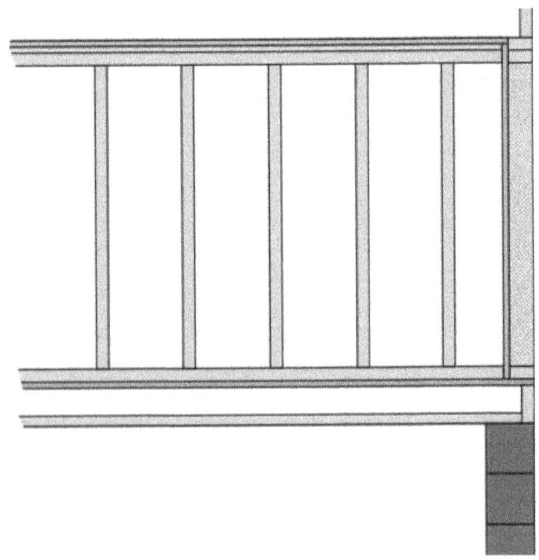

Step 6
Use the bendable rod with magnet attachment to carefully fish out the ball chain

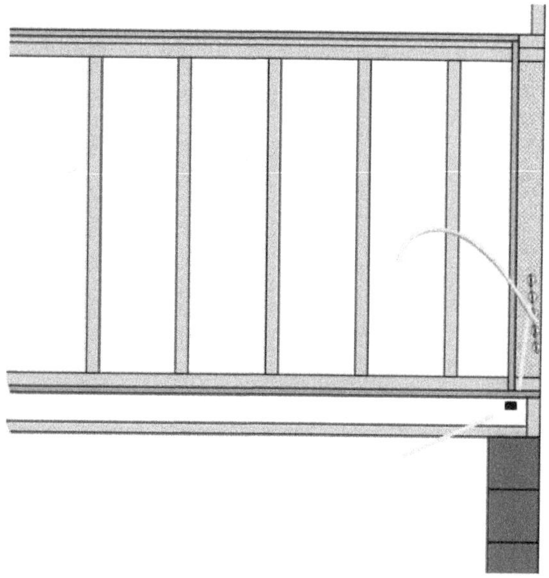

Step 7
Attach a pull cord to the ball chain and feed down to the basement

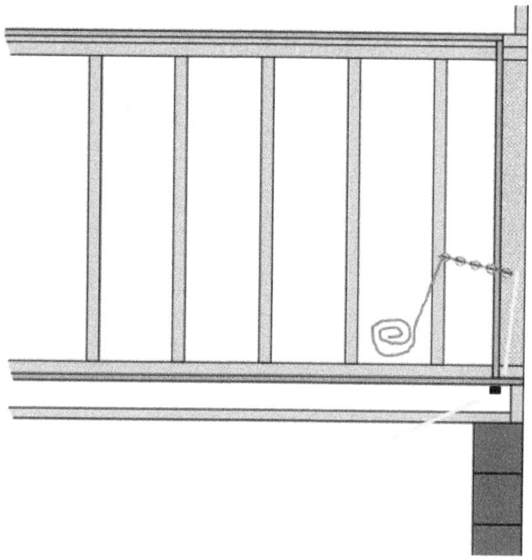

Step 8
Attach a pull cord to the ball chain and feed down to the basement

Step 9
Attach the cable to the pull cord and complete the cabling run

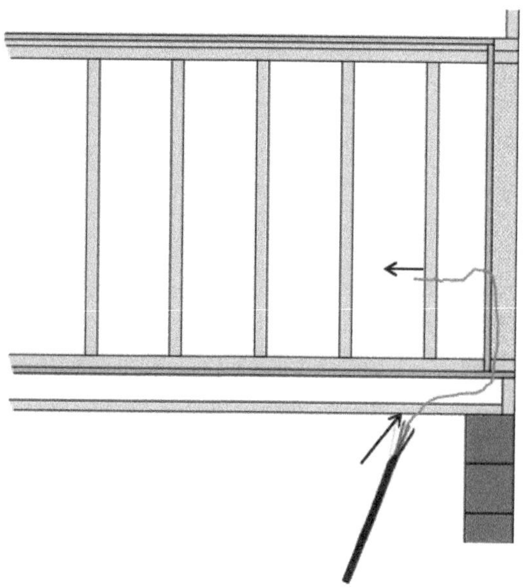

Step 10

Attach the cable to the pull cord and complete the cabling run

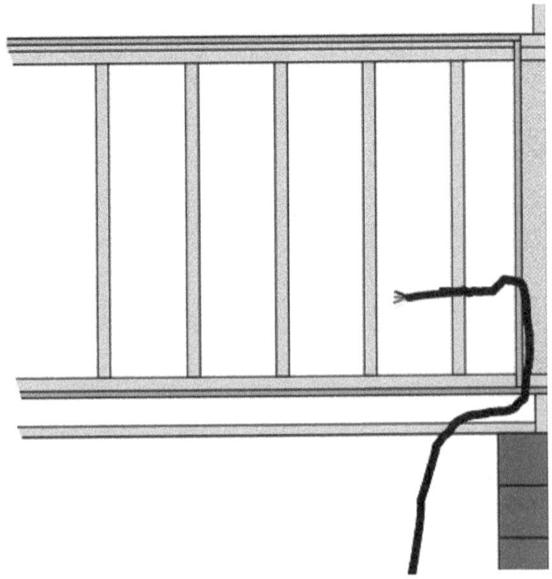

Scenario B: Outside Wall to Attic

Front View

Side View

In houses constructed with the roof joists resting on the top of the wall, there will be little or no room to get to the top plate from the attic. It is easier to drill up into the attic from the second floor.

Step 1
Locate and mark studs

Note: If possible, use an interior wall for cable run

- No insulation
- Wall is away from roof edge

Step 2
Cut in outlet location

Step 3
Measure and mark bit to prevent drilling the roof

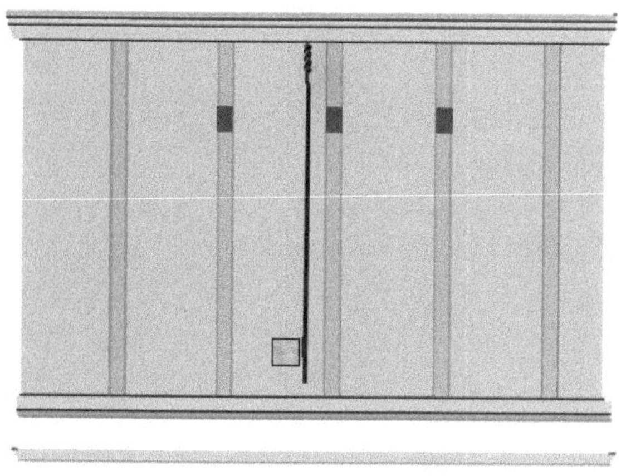

Step 4
Guide the bit up the back corner of the wall cavity

Tip: Put drill in reverse, and use short bursts, to help the bit "walk" up the wall cavity

Note:
Using the back corner helps to avoid insulation and provides a reference path for the push rod when fishing the wires

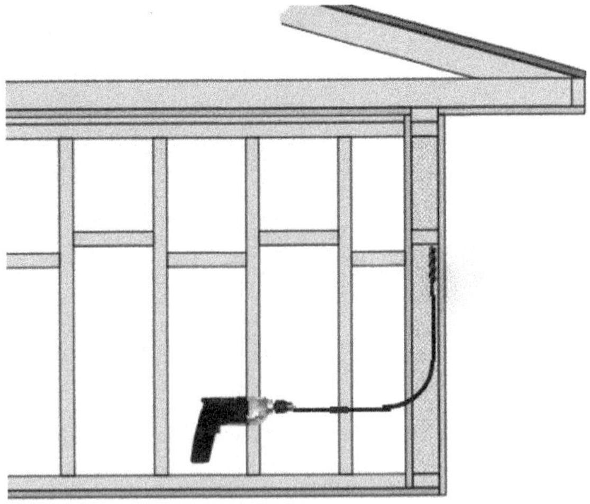

Step 5
Drill through the fire block and top plate

IMPORTANT:
If you lose sight of the tape in the wall

STOP DRILLING!

You do not want to drill through the roof

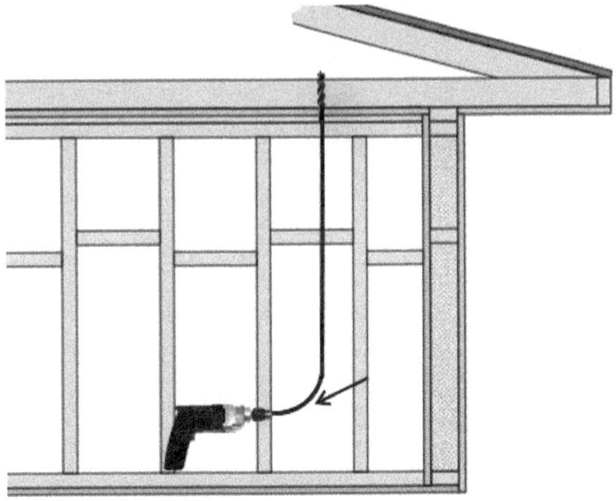

Step 6
Feed the pushrod with the pull cord attached up into the attic

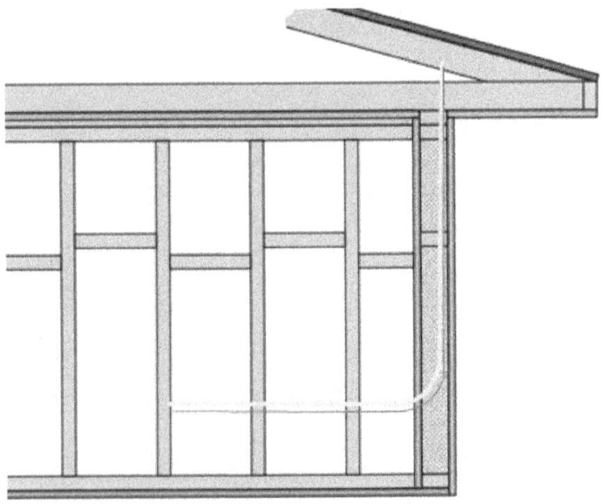

Step 7
Continue to push the rod until it flexes against the roof, making it easier to grab the pull cord

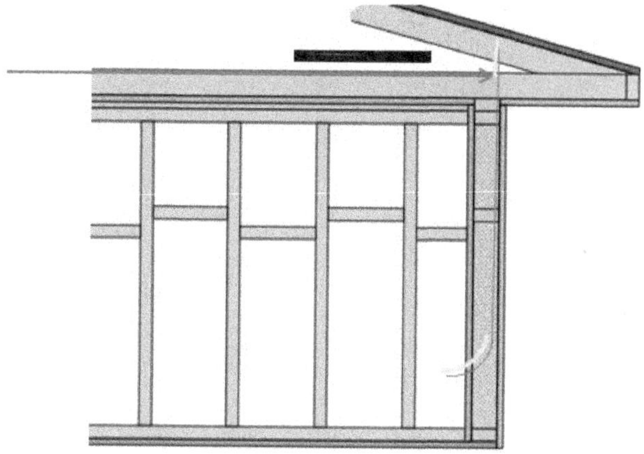

Step 8
Use a telescoping pole with Z-Tip to fish the pull cord out of the corner

Scenario C: Speakers around Flat Panel TV

Step 1
Locate and mark studs

Step 2
Map out TV mounting and speaker locations

Step 3
Cut in outlet and speaker locations

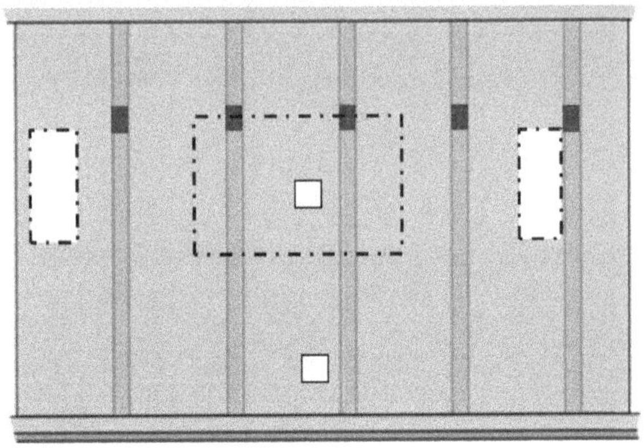

Step 4
Drill through all studs on both sides to reach the speaker locations

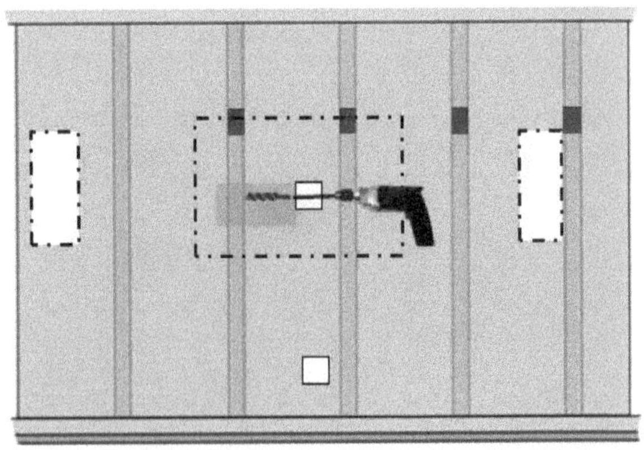

Step 5
Feed pushrod with ball chain attachment into wall cavity

Step 6
Use magnetic retriever to fish out ball chain

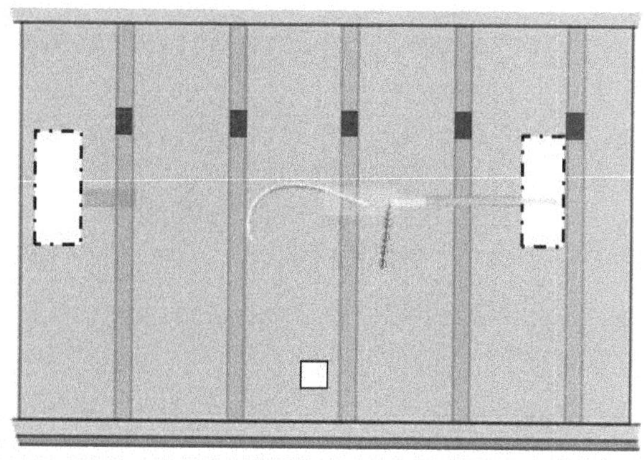

Step 7
Use ball chain to fish pull cord and use pull cord to fish cables

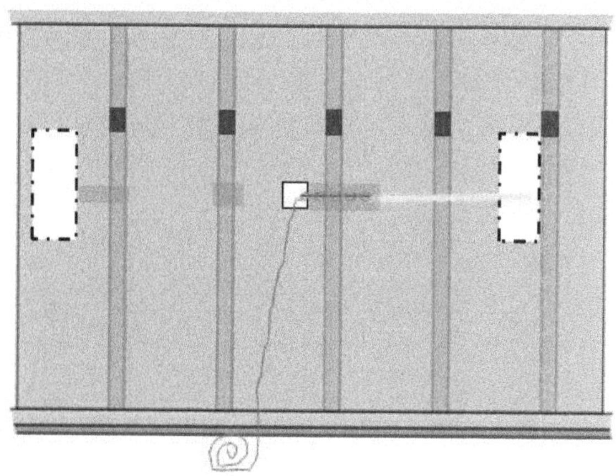

Step 8
Repeat: Steps 5 / 6 / 7 for remaining speaker location

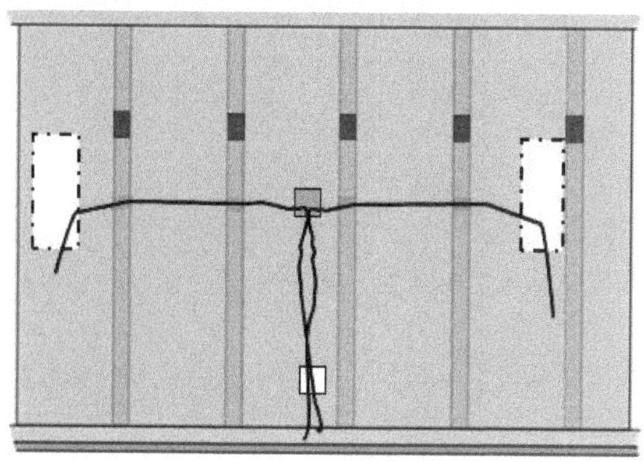

Step 9
Install speakers, mount flat panel TV

Note:
The spacing may appear uneven between the speakers, but when you remove the background...they are clearly equidistant

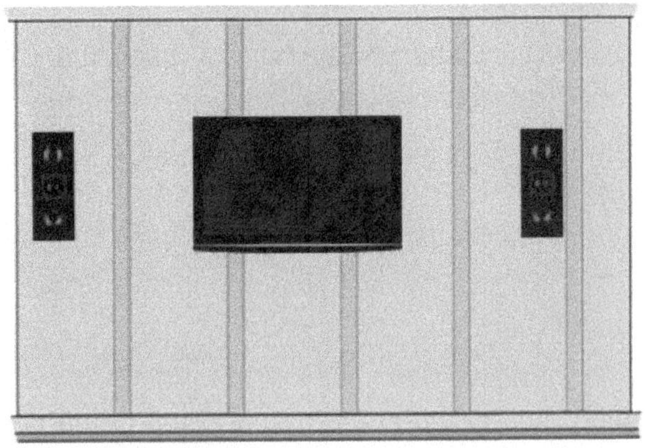

CHAPTER 4

AUDIO SYSTEMS

In this chapter, we will discuss audio systems that are found in the home. The first section deals with the surround systems in media rooms and home theaters. Several topics will be covered, including system designs, new developments in immersive surround sound, and system calibration. Also covered is distributed audio, how these systems have evolved in recent years, and an overview of the renewed interest in high resolution music and vinyl. In all cases, the reader is assumed to have solid knowledge of the fundamentals covered in Fundamentals of Residential Electronic Systems. The content here builds on that foundation.

AUDIO SYSTEMS IN THEATERS AND MEDIA ROOMS

Home theaters and media rooms provide customers with the ability to enjoy virtually any form of musical, film, television or game entertainment, and to hear it in the audio format in which it was created. Movies in a truly good home theater are spectacular events, with large high-resolution images and audio that can surpass that which can be heard in commercial cinemas. Legacy two-channel stereo is available and so is up to 7 channels of uncompressed high-resolution audio. It is an extensive palate of enjoyable experiences.

Consumer Education

Technically, we understand how to deliver good sounds to our customers' ears. The essential guidelines can be found in CEDIA courseware, recommended practices, and other resources. However, many customers may have picked up ideas of their own, some correct, and others misguided. It's important to consider the value of CEDIA technical references beyond their obvious utility. These standards and recommendations can be used to reinforce the CEDIA integrator's argument for design improvements. The typical home theater consumer has numerous preconceptions about sound and video technology, some of which are erroneous. The priorities of most consumers revolve around interior design features which, while beautiful, sometimes run contrary to proper technical practice. In addition, interior designers and architects play a pivotal design role for many consumers, and many are not trained on A/V design principles. The CEDIA designer should use the chapter and verse of this book and other proven resources as a reference for proper design to inform the client. The final result will be a successful project or at the very least an informed consumer more properly equipped to prioritize design decisions.

Surround sound, or multichannel audio as it exists now, places the listener in the midst of an array of loudspeakers, three across the front, two or more at the sides, perhaps two more at the rear of the room and perhaps others at elevated locations to provide a sense of height. Movie makers started it all with a desire to put viewers in the acoustical space that was seen on the screen, to make them feel more involved. The word to describe the sense of being in a realistic acoustical space is "envelopment". If the action was taking place in a cave, the surround sound system provided the right kind of acoustical ambiance-highly reflective and reverberant. You were there. If it was in a small room, the ambient sounds would be appropriately more intimate, and so on. As the multichannel technology developed, sound designers were able to send specific sound effects, gunshots, ricochets, door slams, etc. to different loudspeakers located around the cinema and to create motion effects: aircraft flyovers, cars whizzing by, and so on. All of this makes dramas, adventure films, and games more involving. In music, multichannel audio allows both you and the performers to share an acoustical setting like a concert hall or jazz club, perhaps surrounding you with other audience members, cheering and clapping. On the other hand, the sound designer may decide to put you in the middle of the band. Anything is possible. You can be part of the audience at a sporting event, or in some totally imaginary world in a game. It is quality entertainment.

Multichannel and Immersive Audio

Over the years, the channel count in audio has increased from 1 to 7.1 in the horizontal plane, and now, with the new immersive or 3D configurations, to additional channels in elevated locations. In the beginning, it was necessary to compress the digital files using lossy perceptual codecs, but with time these became less lossy, and then lossless (what comes out is what went in, but we use less storage space). Now, we can even expand the bandwidth beyond that which humans can normally hear, and the dynamic range from inaudible to intolerable, so nothing need be lost.

In the beginning, the height channels were upmixed from the base 5.1

channels, able to create an effect, but not one intended by the originators of the program. Now there Dolby ATMOS, Auro-3D, DTS:X and possibly others to come, all of which can deliver height information through discrete channels that was created in the original mix. Different formats have different preferred locations for the loudspeakers which creates a problem because not all movies are likely to be available in all formats. The compatibility of different loudspeaker arrangements with programs created in the different formats is an important matter yet to be settled. The problem exists in cinemas as well as home theaters, the latter requiring a significant reduction in channel count as well. Serious minds are at work on the problem.

Whatever the final channel count, the first requirement is to set up a front soundstage that, in all movies and television, accompanies a picture. It consists of left, center and right (L, C and R) loudspeakers. The center channel does most of the important work, delivering dialogue and most of the on-screen sound effects. Only in higher budget movies are sounds steered among the front speakers to follow the action, and even then, not all the time. The "ventriloquism" effect takes care of localization; the brain wants to believe that sounds come from lips if someone is speaking, a gun if there is a gunshot, and so on. To provide a persuasive sense of envelopment, and on occasion to deliver directed sound effects, there are left and right side surround loudspeakers. In a five-channel system these would be located beside and slightly behind the prime listening location; behind, so that it is possible to create something of a back-to-front (or the reverse) flyover illusion. In a seven-channel surround system, there are two loudspeakers behind the listener to provide convincing rearward localizations and motion effects, so that the side loudspeakers can be more flexibly located (slightly to the front is advantageous for envelopment). More channels and loudspeakers can lead to more convincing spatial illusions, even if they are in the same horizontal plane as the other loudspeakers.

Horizontal Loudspeaker Layout

The horizontal loudspeaker layout is defined from the perspective of the prime listening location. In the example shown in Figure 4-1a, the prime listening location is in the center of the seating area; this is obviously not a requirement. If there is to be only one pair of surround loudspeakers, as in a 5.1-channel system, they should be placed within the angular range ±100º to ±120º. If there are four surround loudspeakers, as in a 7.1-channel system shown in Figure 4.1b, the side loudspeakers can be placed symmetrically within the angular range spanning ±60º to about ±100º, and the rear loudspeakers within the angular range spanning approximately ±135º to ±150º. A 6.1-channel system could obviously have a single center-rear loudspeaker, but it is recommended that the signal be split between two rear loudspeakers. Note that, in some rooms, the rear loudspeakers cannot be, or need not be, on the rear wall since is the angles that really matter. Given the flexibility in surround speaker placement, in a small room with two rows there is a benefit to placing monopole or bipole side loudspeakers in positions that are equidistant from each row. This yields a simplified sound level calibration which does not bias one row over another.

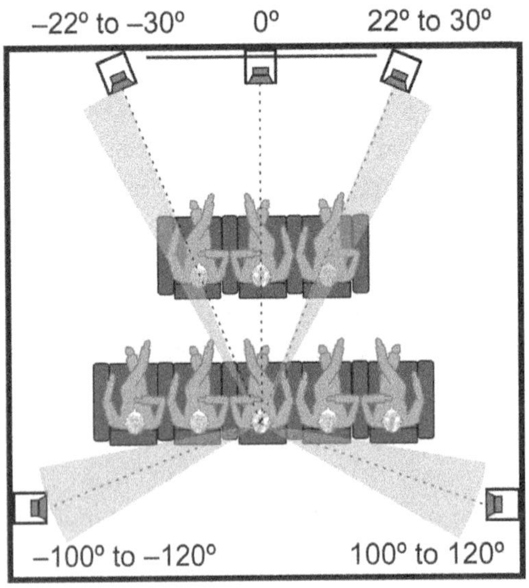

Figure 4-1(a). *Five Channel*

If it is necessary to use additional surround loudspeakers for large audience areas and/or in large rooms, those added loudspeakers should be spaced by equal angles within the angular range shown in Figure 4-1(b).

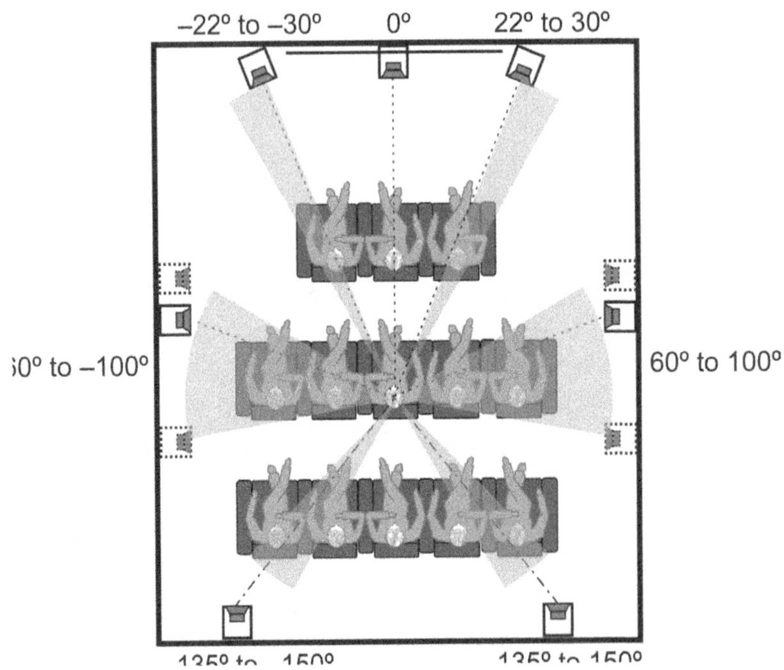

Figure 4-1(b). *Seven Channel*

Finally, the prime listening location, and as many other listeners as possible, should be placed on the center line of the seating array, preferably half way between the side surround loudspeakers. From the perspective of perceived envelopment, these are the best seats in the house. They are also the best seats in the house to avoid hearing steering artifacts in upmix algorithms, whichare the unintended momentary bursts of sound in surround loudspeakers. In the past, some designers have avoided this location because they believed that there were low-frequency acoustic nulls at that location. This is true if only a single subwoofer is used. However, if two or more are used in the manners prescribed in the Subwoofer section later in this chapter, these nulls are eliminated, and several listeners are exposed to better and more uniform bass.

Loudspeaker Elevations

The front three loudspeakers should be mounted with tweeters at, or close to, ear level. A vertical discrepancy between center and side channels of about 2 ft (60 cm) is acceptable across the width of a large screen. The ventriloquism effect often deals with even greater directional errors than this when all of the on-screen sounds emanate from the center channel. Surround loudspeakers should be elevated about 2 ft (60 cm) above ear level, this being a compromise between the requirements for multichannel music (all loudspeakers at ear level) and movies (surround loudspeakers elevated). Be careful to ensure that listeners have line-of-sight contact with the tweeters of the three front loudspeakers. This may require staged multilevel seating, which has the additional advantage of allowing one listener in each row to be on the center line of the room – staggered seating is not required. Elevating the surround loudspeakers allows them to be heard by all listeners in each row. In very narrow rooms, high wall locations will help avoid localization of the side loudspeakers by those listeners on the edges of the audience area.

Height Channels/Immersive-3D Audio

There are a few algorithms that upmix 5.1-channel programs, to simulate signals for height channels. They do not all agree on where the loudspeakers should be placed. If you wish to incorporate one of these proprietary technologies, please follow the provider's guidance. In general, though, when adding more channels it is probably a good idea to place them at horizontal angles different from those already occupied by the L, C and R loudspeakers, simply to gain "free" benefits of enhanced envelopment, while introducing a sense of elevation.

The new discrete immersive 3D formats share the problem of not agreeing on where the loudspeakers should be located. It may matter a lot, it may matter a little, that remains to be discovered as the hardware and software rolls out and program material becomes available. Human listeners seem always to hear planes and helicopters overhead, even when there are no loudspeakers in those locations. If they are located overhead, the sense of height is more persuasive, and other sounds can be directed to those new locations to create directional excitement.

The option of reflecting sound off the ceiling from ear-level upward-firing loudspeakers also exists. This is a much more uncertain method of generating height illusions because loudspeakers of practical size are directional only at very high frequencies. The result is that some high-frequency transient sounds can generate the impression of height, but lower frequency sounds from those loudspeakers cannot. There is an effect, but it cannot be as persuasive as sounds originating from loudspeakers in or on the ceiling, especially if multiple listeners are to be entertained.

A Perspective of Seating

Figure 4-2 illustrates the concept of a "sweet triangle", showing which listeners get a good perspective on the front soundstage. Obviously, as listeners are seated farther from the center line and closer to the front, the front soundstage becomes more distorted and unbalanced. Those on the center line also are treated to the best sense of envelopment from the surround channels.

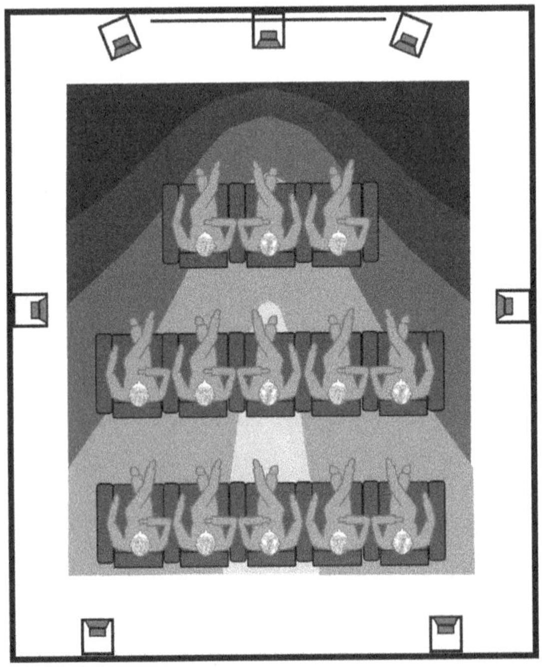

Figure 4-2. *Sweet Triangle*

Signal Processing in Program Recording and Reproduction

Central to the functioning of a home theater audio system are four processes:

- Downmixing
- Upmixing
- Digital codecs
- Bass management

The first three exist because, until quite recently, the "information space" allocated to audio was limited. In the days of analogue film, it was extremely restricted, with two noisy optical sound tracks of limited bandwidth being normal. In the early days of surround sound, a few films had multichannel magnetic stripes added, but for general distribution it was two channels. Dolby adapted the basic technology of the failed Quadraphonics audio encode/decode process into Dolby Stereo, also known as Dolby Surround, to address the limitation. In this scheme, four audio channels (left, center and right front, and a single surround channel) were matrix encoded (downmixed) to two, and then, on playback, matrix decoded (upmixed) to four again. However, the resulting four channels were compromised, mainly by crosstalk (leakage of sounds from one channel into another). Listeners were surrounded by sound even when it was not appropriate. This was particularly annoying when portions of dialogue, mainly sibilant "splashes", were heard coming out of the surround channels. Noisy, distorting, optical sound tracks simply made it worse. The solution at the time was to low-pass filter the surround channel. Another basic fault was that there was only a single surround channel, which, even when sent to two loudspeakers, is clearly not adequate to generate much in the way of spatial or directional complexity in small rooms. Bidirectional out-of-phase surround loudspeakers (incorrectly called "dipoles") were proposed by THX as a solution. In small, acoustically "dead", rooms it was an inadequate solution; what was needed was uncorrelated information radiating from discrete side surround channels.

However, it was not long before clever engineers found ways to improve the quality of the two-channel audio on films, and to provide some separation between the left and right surround channels. With this increased decorrelation, including some that could be electronically added if none was in the program, the result was much more satisfying envelopment, immersion, and opportunities for occasional directed sound effects. It was a huge advance. Fosgate, Shure HTS, THX, Lexicon Logic7 and Dolby all made useful contributions to the evolution of upmixers. Fast acting steering algorithms and clever signal processing to fooled the ears into thinking that we were listening to five discrete channels–at least some of the time. The best ones were entertaining, but not faultless. "Pumping" and momentarily misdirected sounds were common. At this point, all of the channels became full bandwidth and we were on our way to better things.

Digital Discrete Audio and Audio Codecs

Those better things happened in the digital domain, when Dolby was able to store five discrete channels and a Low-Frequency Effects (LFE) channel in blocks of digital data stored between the sprocket holes in films. The problem was that this is very tiny area in which to store so much digital information; too small to store five full bandwidth uncompressed audio signals. The enabling innovation was AC-3 (Audio Codec 3) in which a perceptual encode/decode algorithm tried to anticipate the portions of the audio signal that would be masked (not heard) and would either encode it more simply, using less data, or eliminate it entirely. In this manner, the size of the data storage file became scalable. With increasing "compression", more audio information would be lost, hence the name lossy codecs. The trick was to find a way to lose information while retaining the highest possible perceived sound quality. It is an exercise in compromise. The data rate for Dolby Digital on film is 320 kbit/s, on DVD it could expand to 448 kbit/s and on Blu-ray it can go to 640 kbit/s. There were several competing lossy codecs at the time, and it was a great challenge to evaluate them because most of the time they were essentially transparent, only occasionally revealing to listeners that they had manipulated the sound. All lossy codecs can be tripped up by certain sounds, but listeners sometimes had to be trained to hear the problems in the best ones. Looking back, Dolby AC-3, now the basis of Dolby Digital, was a well-optimized algorithm, as was the competing DTS Surround codec that operated at a higher data rate. Dolby Digital Plus has an even higher data rate. Now, we have reached the stage where, at least for home theater, we have lossless codecs that save substantial data storage space but reconstruct the sound tracks exactly, with no loss whatsoever.

Adding interest and complexity is the fact that several of these formats support multiple sampling frequencies from 48 kHz, through 96 kHz to 192 kHz, with choices of 16, 20 or 24 bits per sample. Different combinations of these will necessitate adjustments to the channel count.

Downmixing

Downmixing is the process of combining several channels into a smaller number of channels, usually by means of an analog matrix encoder. Dolby Stereo/Dolby Surround, the original surround format, was a 4/2 downmixer: four channels in, two channels out. The encoded channels are identified as Lt and Rt, for Left total and Right total. This distinguishes them from simple L and R labels which are for unencoded stereo channels. Now there are several downmixers in the marketplace (e.g. Dolby, DaySequerra, DTS/Neural, SRS Circle Surround) used in the film and gaming industries as well as in the satellite and terrestrial radio and television broadcast industries, including sports events where crowd sounds and arena ambience add to the excitement.

Obviously this downmix encoding anticipates that consumers will be upmixing their playback, which happens increasingly in home entertainment, home theater, and premium car audio systems.

Upmixing

Upmixing is the processing of an audio signal so that it can be reproduced through a higher number of channels. For example, a two-channel signal can be "upmixed" to 5, 7 or more channels, most commonly using a form of active matrix decoding. If the input signal was deliberately encoded (e.g. 5.1 channels "downmixed" to two channels), the upmixing on playback is attempting to restore the original number of discrete channels. This it can do only imperfectly, although the best upmixers are quite impressive. However, it is possible to go farther, and upmix to more channels than were in the original, including height channels, if desired.

If the two channel input signal was not deliberately encoded (downmixed), as in the case of conventional stereo program, the upmix process is "blind", and what is heard is significantly left to chance. Nevertheless, conventions of stereo recording are sufficiently uniform that much of the blind-upmixed result is predictable. For example, the featured artist is most likely to appear in the center channel, the rest of the band will be in the left and right front channels, and ambient reflected sounds and reverberation are likely to appear in the surround channels. A lot of stereo music sounds good through an upmixer, and some upmixers have "music" settings that are optimized to increase the chance of a pleasant result.

If the input signal is already a digital discrete 5.1 channels, an upmixer variant will derive signals suitable for reproduction from the 6.1 single rear channel or the 7.1 pair of rear channels. Nowadays, some upmixer algorithms have been extended to include two or more height channels. It is important to remember that it is highly unlikely that stereo recordings were ever monitored on a multichannel upmixer, so what is heard could not have been anticipated by the recording engineers; occasionally "strange" sounds are the result. It is this unpredictable nature of upmixing that has led to numerous variations, some well-known (Dolby and DTS are widely available) and some proprietary to specific brands of hardware (e.g. Harman Logic7 and QLS, SRS Circle Surround), each one having distinctive audible properties. Playing back Dolby encoded sound tracks on a Dolby upmixer ought to sound good, but feel free to try others. Television audio may be simple stereo, not encoded at all, or it may be encoded in any of several downmixers. Sporting events are often surround encoded. For consumers, it is a good idea to listen to the upmix options available in their surround processor or receivers to find their favorite, and especially to know where the "bypass" switch is located for those occasional (mostly music) programs that, because of how they were recorded, are incompatible with spatial enhancement. It is entirely possible to have a favored upmixer for two-channel television programming, another for sports, one for movies, and another for music–perhaps even more than one for different kinds of music. It sounds complicated, but that is the way it is. Up-to-date information on the growing collection of signal processes can be found at the manufacturers' websites.

Bass Management

Bass management is a process in which the low bass frequencies from the 2, 5 or 7 discrete channels are stripped away, combined and sent to a common subwoofer channel. To this is added, with appropriate gain adjustment, sounds that were placed in the Low-Frequency Effects (LFE) channel. A common recommended crossover frequency is 80 Hz, although others are possible–lower, not higher, would be preferred in order to avoid localizing the subwoofers.

The obvious advantage of this is that the 5, 7 or more channel loudspeakers can be smaller, with all of the low bass being reproduced by one or more subwoofers that were designed for the purpose. Relieved of the task of trying to reproduce low bass, the satellite loudspeakers can now play louder. Another advantage is that subwoofers are very often self-powered, meaning that the power amplifiers in a receiver are liberated to play the satellite loudspeakers at a higher level. A less obvious advantage is that multiple subwoofers can be employed in specific arrangements that exercise control over room resonances, making available floor areas within which several listeners can hear more similar and better bass. The use of subwoofers assigned to individual channels, commonly referred to as stereo subwoofers, do not share the advantages of bass management and are discouraged. See Subwoofers, later in this chapter.

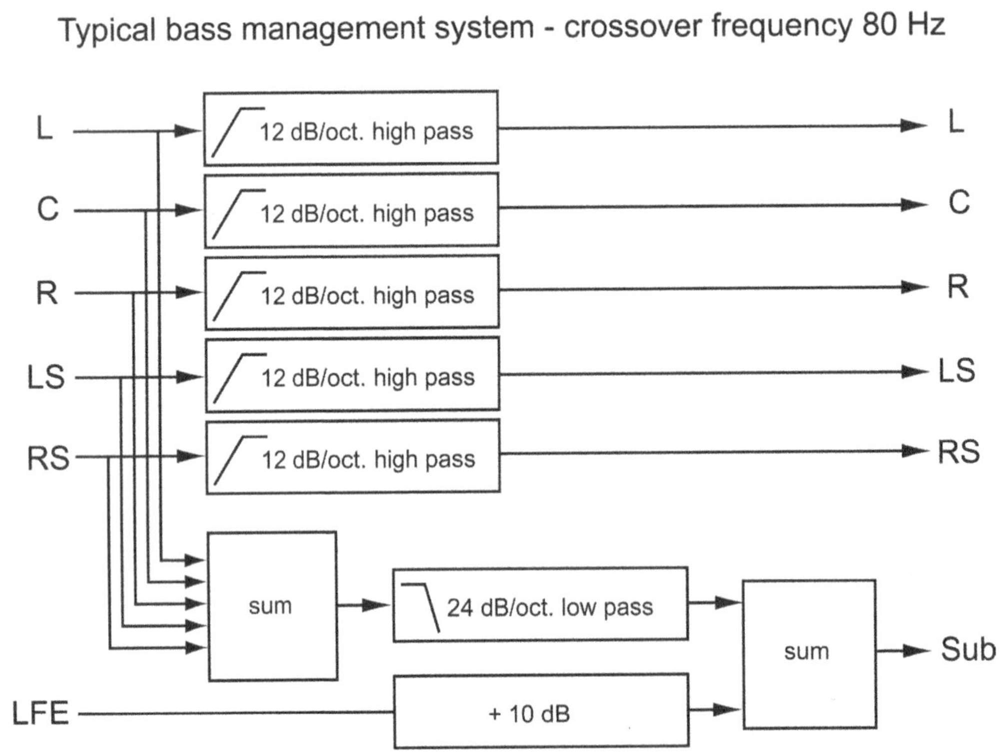

Figure 4-3. *Bass Management*

Crossover Mismanagement

Crossover mismanagement is what happens when the low-and high-pass filters built into the electronics are incompatible with the frequency responses of the loudspeakers delivering the sound to our ears. In Figure 4-3, the signal being supplied to the subwoofer(s) is low-pass filtered at 24 dB/octave, while that being sent to the satellite loudspeakers is high-pass filtered at 12 dB/octave – there is a mismatch. If the satellite loudspeakers had a built-in rolloff of 12 dB/octave at 80 Hz, an argument could be made that, in the combination, there would be a resulting 24 dB/octave high-pass characteristic, and all would be well. However, this is the real world, and no such assurances can be made. In fact, many satellite loudspeakers in use, even those claiming an 80 Hz rolloff, radiate substantial amounts of energy below the intended 80 Hz crossover frequency, even after the signal is high-pass filtered at 12 dB/octave. The result is that there is overlap between the subwoofer output and the satellite output and what is heard in a room is quite unpredictable. For a single listener, equalization can yield a satisfactory result, but if the intent is to use multiple subwoofer arrays to generate a more uniform bass sound field, then the result will be diminished by the unwanted acoustical output from the satellites. To complete the picture, other satellite loudspeakers exhibit output that falls off before reaching down to 80 Hz so that there is a gap in the frequency response in the crossover region.

Next, consider the effects of room resonances/standing waves, which are abundant and energetic in this frequency range. These greatly distort any simplistic thoughts of tidy high-pass/low-pass transitions from subwoofers to satellites. There are solutions, imperfect but worth doing, but they all include making acoustical measurements at the key listening locations from each of the satellite loudspeakers and the subwoofer (or subwoofer array). Then, using parametric equalizers, the high-pass and low-pass characteristics need to be tailored to match the target curves, say 24 dB/octave, so that overlap and gaps are avoided for those listening locations. This is an area of the setup that is not well handled at the moment, and it requires a level of competence with acoustical measurements and filter design that is daunting to most installers.

The Electronics

A/V Receiver

Although it is still possible to purchase separate components for every function, it is now increasingly common for home theaters to have a multichannel A/V receiver at their core. All of the necessary functions are combined in one large chassis. Problems with ground loops are minimized, and many compatibility and setup issues are simplified. It seems like a good idea.

If there is a topic to ponder, it is amplifier power. With 5, 7 or possibly more power amplifiers combined in a single chassis there are issues of heat dissipation and power supply capability. As a result, manufacturers face some serious issues, and have engaged in a specifications gamesmanship that requires vigilance on the part of the consumer and installer. With finite capacity from the power supply, it is possible to drive two channels to a higher output level than all 7, for example. So, some manufacturers state power ratings in stereo, not all channels operating. Some do both. Some will specify a power rating for a broadband signal, covering most or all audible frequencies, while others will specify it for a single frequency, such as 1 kHz.

The latter is obviously of little use, but it leads to larger numbers. It is also possible to specify a power output that is sustained for a brief interval - a kind of peak power statement. Also, distortion specifications at rated power are inconsistent. There are many variables, and not all manufacturers have chosen the same set, so comparisons between models and brands are difficult. See "Power Ratings of Power Amplifiers" below.

Unfortunately there is no perfect solution. Even if the manufacturer is very detailed and totally candid in the spec sheet, it is hard to know how the device will perform in the real world. Typically, not all channels are driven to full capacity at the same time. If they are, it would likely be for a short interval, during a dramatic sound effect sequence in a movie. In the end, there is no substitute for real world use, but change the loudspeakers, and the results may change.

The availability of automated delay, level, and equalization functions in receivers are attractive, but the installer should have the capability of measuring system performance using "outboard" instrumentation. Only then will there be an assurance that it was done correctly, and that what was done was the right thing, and not something misguided. Unfortunately this still happens. See the following section on equalization.

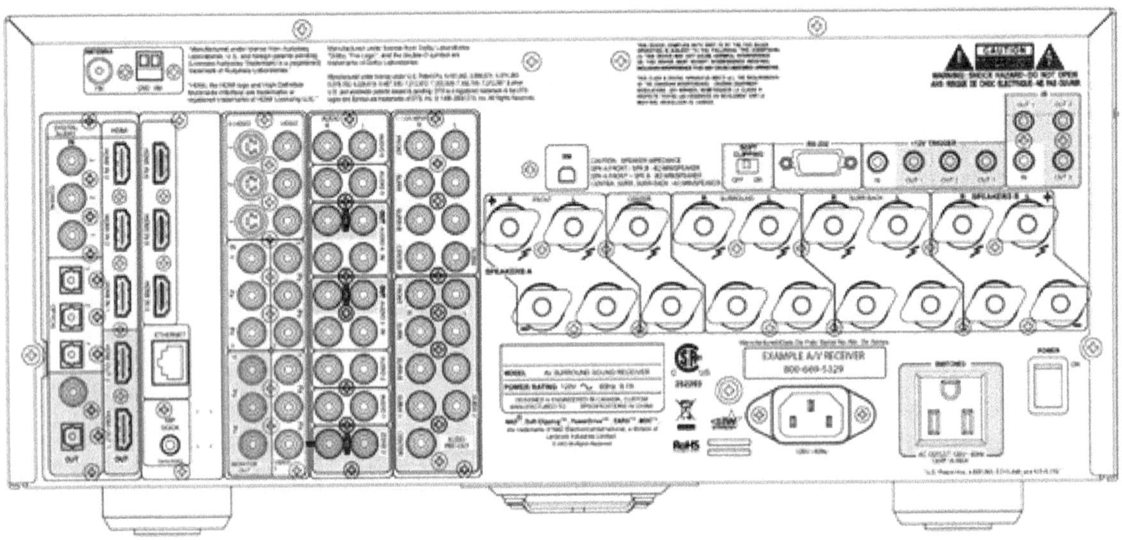

Figure 4-4. *Surround Sound Receiver*

Surround Processor

A separate multichannel processor outputting line level signals for power amplifiers is clearly the most flexible route. There is little reason to keep things simple, so such devices are often more flexible in setup options than receivers, and some offer a greater variety of processing alternatives. Some incorporate elaborate setup aids, including measurement and equalization. The latter must be treated with caution, as will be discussed later.

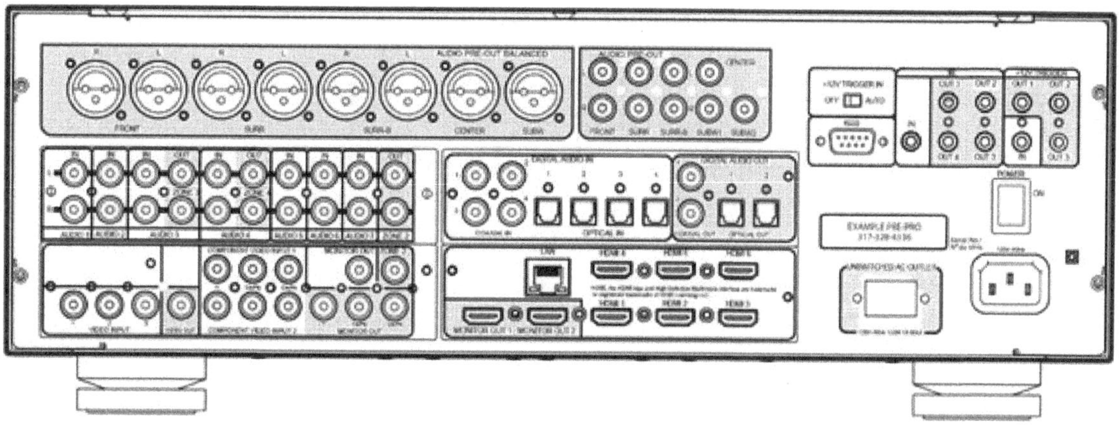

Figure 4-5 *Surround Sound Preamp-Processor*

Power Amplifiers

The best news about stand-alone power amplifiers is that they are likely to sound good. Audibly inferior power amplifiers are uncommon, although claims of superior sound abound. However, there are differences and functional quirks worth noting.

There are several types of power amplifiers, in both analogue and digital forms, and then there are tube/valve, amplifiers. Traditional analogue amplifiers are described as:

- Class A, in which the output devices (transistors or tubes) operate continuously over the entire audio waveform. Best used in low-power applications because they are very inefficient, dissipating much of their consumed power as heat and therefore needing massive heat sinks for a given audio power output capacity.
- Class B, in which separate output devices are used for each polarity, positive and negative, of the audio waveform. Very efficient, but susceptible to crossover distortion in the zero crossing region. Not a serious contender in audio.
- Class AB, is a Class B design in which some overlap is allowed so that the positive-to-negative transition is smoothed. Power output capability is very high, efficiency is much higher than pure Class A, and distortion can be very low. A justifiably popular design.

Tube or valve amplifiers are common in high-end audio, where certain listeners believe they have distinctive advantages. When used in low-signal-level electronics, there are no real concerns, except the need for maintenance – like light bulbs, their performance changes with time, and replacement is eventually necessary. When tubes are used as output devices in power amplifiers, another issue comes to the fore; output impedance. In the signal path to a loudspeaker, it is essential to minimize the signal losses, otherwise the sound from the loudspeaker is changed. Consequently, large wire (small gauge numbers) is used to minimize resistance. It is also necessary to minimize the output impedance of the power amplifiers. In technical terms, this is specified as the damping factor of a power amplifier, defined as 8 ohms divided by the output impedance–the larger the number, the lower the output impedance. Solid-state amplifiers typically have output impedances in the range 0.01 to 0.04 ohms. Tube amplifiers typically range from 0.7 to 3.3 ohms, and occasionally even more. These large losses, placed in series with the frequency- dependent impedances of loudspeakers, cause audible changes in spectrum; the loudspeakers have essentially been "revoiced" by the power amplifier. Such products should be avoided in home theaters.

Switching (Class D) amplifiers, are those that rapidly/ultrasonically switch between two voltage levels to generate a square wave having a variable mark-to-space ratio or a variable pulse density, either of which tracks the audio waveform. The output devices are either fully on or fully off, meaning that heat dissipation is very small and large heat sinks are not necessary. However, switching ideally should be instantaneous, and the time of switching needs to be extremely well defined or distortion results. The result is that, over the years, there have been Class D amplifiers of differing sound quality. Obviously, the output waveform needs to be low-pass filtered to eliminate the high-frequency switching information, leaving only the audio-frequency signal. This is accomplished with a passive network that contributes output impedance, which, if not compensated for, can change the frequency response of loudspeakers. With their minimal heat sinks, these devices are very compact, and simple versions can be quite inexpensive. Class D amplifiers are widely used in subwoofers, and compact audio systems, and highly evolved versions of them are now able to compete in sound quality with good conventional analogue designs.

Bridging Amplifiers

Some stereo and multichannel power amplifiers are designed to allow the combination of two amplifiers to drive a single loudspeaker. When this is done, the available power goes up, but the permissible minimum impedance the bridged amplifier can drive also goes up. Read the amplifier specifications carefully and know the minimum impedance of the loudspeaker being driven.

Power Ratings

Power ratings of power amplifiers should be simple to understand, but they are not. The main reason is that the power rating depends on what the amplifier is driving. As a standard convention, amplifiers are rated according to how much power they can drive into a resistive 8-ohm load. But, the real world the load for amplifiers is loudspeakers, which are not pure resistors, and they exhibit both inductive and capacitive reactance. In addition, the impedance is not constant at all frequencies; a nominal 8-ohm loudspeaker system might vary from a low of 3 ohms to a high of 20 ohms or more at different frequencies. The higher numbers are not problem, but the lower ones may be. So, from the outset there are significant complications, and it is important to understand that some of the numbers shown in spec sheets are, at best, crude approximations to reality. It is done to keep things simple, but in doing so, important truths are hidden from us. Given these observations, a prudent person would choose power amplifiers using a very conservative interpretation of the specifications: in other words try to give yourself some "headroom".

Modern power amplifiers are well described as "constant-voltage sources". They attempt to maintain a specific voltage across the output terminals even when the load impedance varies, as it does with frequency, and when using loudspeakers having different nominal impedance ratings: 8, 6 and 4 ohms are common. Thinking simplistically, if one is listening to an 8-ohm loudspeaker and replaces it with a 4-ohm loudspeaker without changing the volume setting (the same voltage signal is appearing at the output terminals of the power amplifier), then the 4-ohm loudspeaker will draw twice the current from the amplifier, and therefore will dissipate twice the power (power = voltage × current). Suddenly, a 100 watt (rated at 8 ohms) amplifier is required to deliver 200 watts into a 4 ohm load. The question is "Can it succeed?" The answer is "perhaps", because it depends on how the amplifier has been designed.

Several factors conspire to define how much power an amplifier can deliver into a load: voltage swing, current delivery capability, heat sink dissipation capacity among them. The performance of the power supply is a major factor when high powers and high currents are being delivered. Because loudspeakers are such complicated loads, almost certainly dropping well below 8 ohms even if rated as 8 ohms, and each one exhibiting different forms of reactive (capacitive or inductive) phase shifts, amplifiers are designed to deliver their rated power into 8 resistive ohms, but also to be able to deliver more power into lower and reactive impedances because it will be needed. The question is: how much more? With some loudspeaker loads it is possible that, at some volume setting less than maximum, the safe power delivery capacity will be exceeded, in which case the amplifier will exhibit increased distortion. Ultimately a protective circuit will be activated, limiting the output or shutting down the amplifier. Reactive loads can cause increased power dissipation in the output devices, in which case the protective circuit measures instantaneous current and voltage, detecting dangerous phase angles and protectively clipping the output. Here, another set of design variables determine how an amplifier sounds because, at clipping, the beneficial effects of feedback are substantially lost. Clean clipping up to about 6 dB is difficult to hear, but many designs misbehave when they clip, generating spurious signals during even moderate clipping that have detrimental audible effects. There are no specifications for such things. Different designers choose different solutions, from "beefing up" the amplifier so that it does not need so much protection, to designing ever more elaborate protection circuits that avoid false triggering on high-frequency transients.

Consequently, one is left to examining specifications for information. There it will be found that some power amplifiers have enough current capacity to be able to double their output power into half the load impedance. This would be specified as, for example: 150 watts @ 8 ohms, 300 watts @ 4 ohms, 600 watts @ 2 ohms. Such products are relatively rare, and probably expensive, large, and heavy. But they do offer assurance that even poorly designed loudspeakers, with extremely low and/or reactive impedances, can be driven. Most power amplifiers will deliver less than double power, such as: 200 watts @ 8 ohms, 350 watts @ 4 ohms. And then there are specifications that mention only 8 ohm loads, which are simply not very helpful.

Ultimately, one wants to confirm that the amplifier can deliver sufficient power to the loudspeaker being used that the required sound level can be created. To be able to estimate whether that is likely to occur, one needs data from the loudspeaker manufacturer on the true impedance characteristics (notably the minimum impedance) of the load, and data from the amplifier manufacturer explaining how the amplifier performs into different load impedances. Because the reactance of loudspeakers is not specified, and the tolerance to load reactance in power amplifiers is not specified, it may be wise to allow some headroom.

Some other factors of importance in reading specification sheets are:

- There are power ratings (e.g. FTC) that describe the long-term output capabilities. The long-term ratings are quite well standardized benchmarks, but are far removed from typical use in homes. They underestimate the power available with program material having varying sound levels.
- Short term, transient, "dynamic" or peak-power ratings are less well regulated and in general may overestimate the real output capabilities.
- Real needs are likely to lie between these two extreme values, but the transient demands may well be tested by games and movie sound effects.
- Power ratings that test the device over the entire audio frequency range 20 Hz–20 kHz are more meaningful than those that test at a single frequency, say 1 kHz.
- In multichannel units, a per-channel rating based on all channels operating (say 5, 7 or 9) seems honest, but is unrealistic in cinema and music sound tracks. Expect the numbers to be on the low side. A rating with the two stereo channels operating is certainly realistic for stereo listening, but misses the all-important center channel for home theater applications. At present, there seems to be no definitive single number rating scheme for power output per channel of a multichannel home theater power amplifier or receiver.

How Much Amplifier Power Do We Need?

Understanding Sound Fields in Rooms

The optimum sound level for sound reproduction is a topic of great interest in the audio industry at the moment – often called the "loudness wars", in which dynamic range in music is reduced, compressed into only the high sound level regions, in an attempt to be louder, more "attractive" than the competition. It is happening in movies too, to such an extent that cinema owners, responding to complaints from customers, often turn the volume down. What happens then is that the dialog, which is sometimes not always intelligible at the best of times, becomes even less intelligible. This happens in home theaters as well, where, because everything is scaled down, sound levels that might have been acceptable in a large cinema are not comfortable at home. So, just as cinema owners turn the volume down, so do home theater owners – it is not at all common for movies to be played at the calibrated 0 dB volume setting; often it is 10 dB or more lower.

A popular target for high-end home theaters has been 105 dB SPL at the prime listening location. Assuming that this is for a single loudspeaker, and we have three across the front and a surround channel contributing a similar amount, the combined maximum sound pressure level can reach 111 dB. These are rock concert sound levels, and some serious electro-acoustic work is needed to reach them where we are seated. As impressive as these sound levels are for momentary dramatic sound effects, they are simply too loud for sustained exposure from the point of view of enjoyment or, more importantly, from the perspective of hearing conservation. So, keep this in mind when advising customers on the capabilities of the system.

There is, unfortunately, no clear statement of the duration over which this high sound level must be sustained, nor the frequency range over which the requirement applies. This is understandable, in the sense that there are no standards for dramatic sound effects in movie sound tracks, nor for crescendos in music. Neither is what one would call "steady state" or "continuous", but there are many times when neither would be correctly described as "transient, peak or instantaneous". Hence, from the outset there is uncertainty about the requirement, and users are forced to decide how conservatively they wish to apply the requirement in selecting power amplifiers for the intended task.

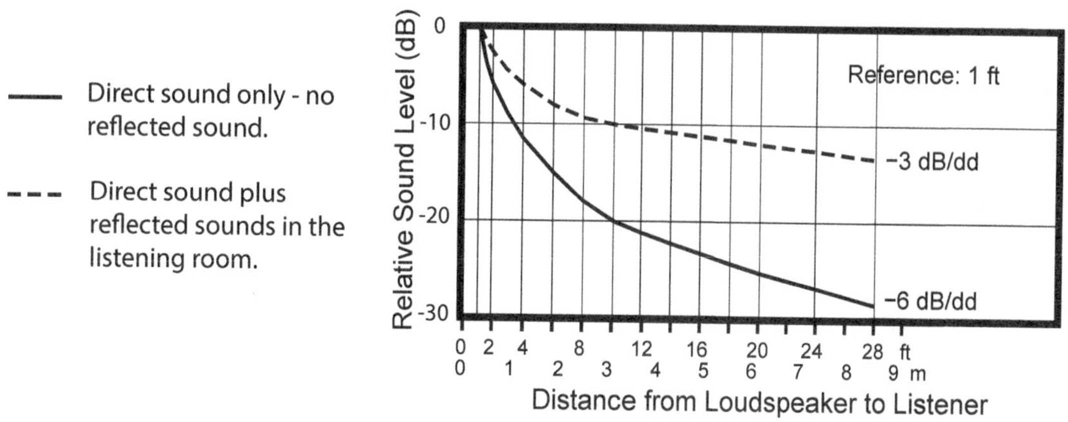

Figure 4-6. *Levels as a Function of Distance*

Consequently, at the end of this exercise, when power requirement numbers are created, users must decide what amount of "headroom" is either incorporated into the manufacturer's specification, or how much headroom must be added to it, in order to prevent audible overload in the home theater installation.

So, first, let us understand how sound propagates in rooms. Common loudspeakers are small compared to the distances at which we listen to them, so it is reasonable to think that they behave as "point sources" radiating an approximately spherical wave front, the sound level of which decreases at a rate of about 6 dB for each doubling of distance (−6 dB/dd).This is illustrated in Figure 4-6, where it is seen that, close to the loudspeaker, the sound level falls away very rapidly and as distance increases, the decline is less rapid.

What we have just examined is the direct sound, the first sound to arrive at a listener's ears. This is perceptually the dominant factor for sound localization, but, in rooms, reflected sounds contribute most of the sound energy that we hear, and in small home theater rooms the strong reflections occur sufficiently quickly that they are seamlessly integrated into our overall perceptions of most common sounds, including speech. So we also need to examine how the sound field, including reflections, changes with distance from the loudspeaker. In Figure 4-6, this is shown as the −3 dB/dd curve (see Toole, 2008, Figure 4.13). In terms of perceived loudness of sounds, this is the curve we are most interested in, which is fortunate because it falls away much less rapidly.

Thinking in terms of what we hear in rooms, if we wish several listeners to hear similar sound levels, the farther we can get them from the loudspeakers the better things will be. Obviously, small rooms will present the greatest difficulties to satisfying several listeners.

The power amplifier needs are not difficult to estimate because the behavior of loudspeakers in small rooms is well understood. It has been common to estimate these needs based on the "inverse-square-law" (−6 dB/dd) data, but with what we now know it is better to use the −3 dB/dd data, which include room reflections. Obviously, the amount of reflected sound depends on both loudspeaker directivity and room acoustical treatment, so it is prudent to compute both, and to assume that real needs lie somewhere between the two values. In typically-furnished domestic listening rooms and properly designed home theaters (mid- frequency reverberation time of about 0.4 s), the real value is likely to be closer to the-3 dB/dd estimated power needs. In acoustically overdamped, "dead", rooms, something closer to the -6 dB/dd curve may be more representative. The difference in power requirements is good incentive not to be excessive in the use of acoustical materials - the numbers quickly reach impractical levels. Overly damped rooms simply do not sound pleasant, even to converse in, which is another reason to be cautious.

Determining the Amplifier Power Requirements

Step 1: Determine the sound level at 1 m from the loudspeaker that results in 105 dB at the listening location. Measure the distance from the loudspeaker in question (probably the front-center loudspeaker) to the head location for the prime listener. Using the graph in Figure 4-7, find the sound levels that are required at 1 m for the two curves: direct sound only and direct sound plus reflected sounds at a distance similar to the one you measured (small differences will not matter, or you can interpolate). If there is no good match, use the equations provided in the Figure to calculate a more exact pair of numbers. This is done by first calculating the "dB decrease" in sound level from the loudspeaker to the listening location for the two types of sound field, and then adding these numbers to 105 dB to obtain the sound level required at 1 m. Remember to use the reference distance (d1) in the units in which the distance was measured. The result of Step 1 is two numbers: one for the direct sound only and one for the direct sound plus reflections.

A summary of the process to determine amplifier power needs for a given home theater installation. The graph in this Figure differs from Figure 4-6 in two respects: the distance axis is logarithmic, not linear, and the reference distance is 1 m, which is the standard for loudspeaker sensitivity ratings.

Step 2: Loudspeaker sensitivity. Loudspeaker manufacturers should state this as a sound pressure level (dB SPL) at 1 m distance with a drive signal of 2.83 volts, measured in an anechoic space (e.g. 90 dB/1 m/ 2.83 volts, or something very similar). The obsolete way of specifying sensitivity was to use 1 watt input. This was impractical because loudspeaker impedances can vary substantially with frequency making an overall specification impractical. Because contemporary power amplifiers are essentially constant voltage sources, a voltage input specification is more rational, and 2.83 volts was chosen because this is 1 watt into 8-ohms, and a resistive 8-ohm load is most commonly used to determine power amplifier output ratings. A quick search of loudspeaker manufacturers will reveal several that have not kept up, and a few that seem to be evading efforts to determine how they arrived at the published number. A few use "in room" measurements, which is a totally non-standard specification, but it leads to a higher number for the spec sheet. Some manufacturers still use the old "xx dB/1W/1m". If this is encountered ask the manufacturer to explain what is meant because if the nominal impedance is, for example, 4 ohms, the standard 2.83 volts drives 2 watts into the loudspeaker, not 1 watt, and the sensitivity rating is incorrectly high by 3 dB (flattering the product). If this is not the case, the drive voltage had to be changed to a non-standard 2 volts (P = V2/R = 22/4 = 1 watt). On the other hand, if the sensitivity was measured using 2.83 volts, then the input signal statement on the spec sheet is incorrect (it is not 1 watt), and users will have to compensate for the fact that the impedance is 4 ohms. This will be done in Step 5.

How much amplifier power do we need?

The objective is to be able to deliver 105 dB SPL at the listening location. For this we need some facts:

- The distance from the loudspeaker to the prime listening location (in meters, feet or inches).
- The sensitivity of the loudspeaker: X dB SPL @ 1 m @ 2.83 volts input.
- The nominal impedance of the loudspeaker being used.

Step 1. Determine the sound level at 1 m needed to produce 105 dB at the listening location. For this use the values stated in the Figure below, or use the equations in the Figure to calculate the value for any specific distance. That value will be the calculated "dB decrease" added to 105 dB SPL.

Step 2. From manufacturer's specifications, determine the sensitivity of the loudspeaker, a statement of the sound level it creates at 1 m for an input of 2.83 volts (2.83 volts delivers 1 watt into 8 ohms).

Step 3. Subtract the loudspeaker sensitivity from the sound levels required at 1 m (Step 1) to determine the "dB difference", the amount the sound level at 1 m must be increased in order to produce 105 dB at the listening location. You will end up with two numbers, one for the direct sound only, and one that includes reflected sounds.

Step 4. Calculate the amount of amplifier power needed to generate 105 dB at the listening location using the following equation:

Amplifier power (watts into 8 ohms) $= 10^{(\text{dB difference}/10)}$

This will be done for each of the "dB difference" numbers determined in Step 3. An 8-ohm loudspeaker is assumed.

Step 5. If the nominal impedance of the loudspeaker being used is less than 8 ohms, calculate how much power is needed for this loudspeaker using the following equation:

(8 ÷ nominal impedance of loudspeaker) × 8 ohm amplifier power = amplifier power required for the nominal impedance

For example, if an 8 ohm loudspeaker requires 100 watts (determined in Step 4), and the loudspeaker we intend to use has a nominal impedance of 4 ohms the calculation is: (8/4)×100=200 watts. Look for a power amplifier that is specified to be able to drive 200 watts into a 4 ohm load.

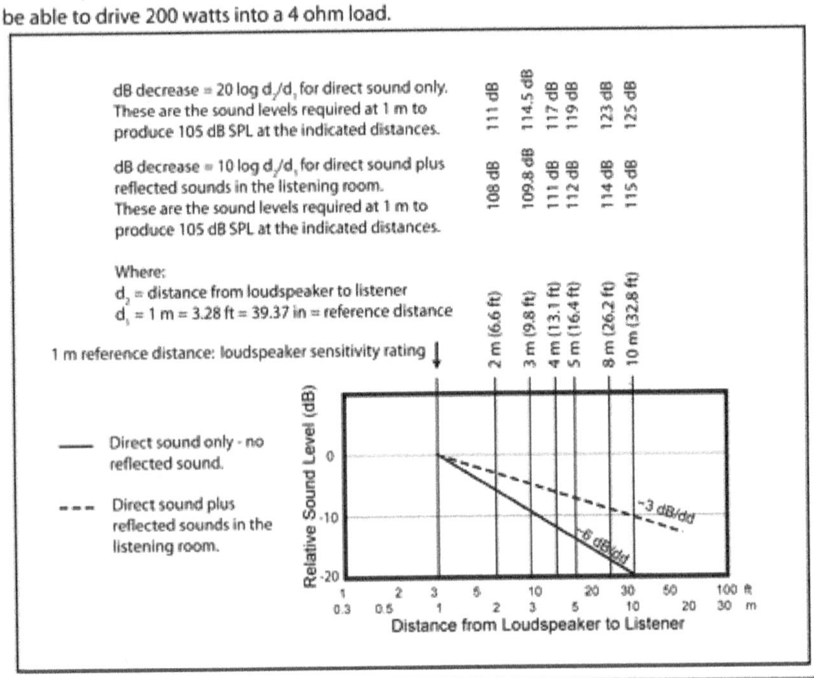

Figure 4-7. *How Much Amplifier Power Do We Need?*

Step 3: Now, assuming that a realistic sensitivity rating has been found (say 90 dB at 1 m, 2.83 volts input), subtract it from the two numbers determined in Step 1, giving the dB increase in sound level at 1 m that is required to generate 105 dB SPL at the prime listening location.

Example: Suppose the prime listener is 3 m (9.8 ft) away from the loudspeaker. Figure 4-7 indicates that 114.5 dB is needed at one meter from the loudspeaker to produce 105 dB at the listening position when reflected sounds are ignored, and 109.8 dB to produce 105 dB when reflected sounds are included. The chosen loudspeakers have stated sensitivities of 90 dB at

1 m with 2.83 volts driving them. Stated differently, 2.83 volts into an 8 ohm loudspeaker (1 watt) produces 90 dB SPL at 1 m. How much more power do we need to produce the required sound levels? Subtract 90 from 114.5 and 109.8 giving us 24.5 dB and 19.8 dB respectively.

Step 4: Use the following equation to calculate the amplifier power needed to drive an 8-ohm loudspeaker:

- Amplifier power (reflections ignored) = 10(dB difference/10) = 10(24.5/10) = 282 watts (into 8 ohms)
- Amplifier power (reflections included) = 10(dB difference/10) = 10(19.8/10) = 96 watts (into 8 ohms)

This is a highly informative exercise. The dB difference between the two conditions- reflections (109.8 dB) vs. no reflections (114.5 dB)–is 4.7 dB, a factor of 2.95 in power. 2.95 x 96 watts = 283 watts; a significant increase. Looking at Figure 4-7, one can see that the dB difference increases with distance, making the discrepancy more profound at large listening distances. Relevant to this discussion is the fact that any steady-state measurement in an acoustically "normal" listening room, and any level calibration done using broadband or filtered noise, operates on the-3dB/dd curve.

Step 5: So far, we have simplistically assumed that the loudspeakers have 8 ohm impedances. If that is the reality, no more needs to be done. However, if the average impedance is lower, and a more realistic impedance rating is, say, 6 ohms, or even 4 ohms, the numbers we have just generated need to be adjusted. The loudspeaker sensitivity rating used 2.83 volts as an input. If the loudspeaker had an impedance of 8 ohms, the input power would be 1 watt (V2/R = 2.832/8 = 8/8 = 1 watt). If the loudspeaker impedance were 6 ohms, the power input would be 8/6 = 1.33 watts, and at 4 ohms the power input would be 8/4 = 2 watts. If the minimum impedance dips to 3 ohms, as some do, the input power would be 8/3 = 2.7 watts, and so on. Putting this into the present context, if the chosen loudspeaker in the example shown above had an average impedance of 4 ohms, we would need a power amplifier that was capable of delivering 2 x 96 = 192 watts into 4 ohms when reflections are included, or 2 x 282 = 564 watts into 4 ohms when reflections are ignored. Suddenly, the numbers can become very large, and many of the amplifiers available for use begin to look very small.

If the prime listening location were at 4 m (13.1 ft) the corresponding numbers would be:

- Amplifier power (reflections ignored) = 500 watts (8 ohms), 1000 watts (4 ohms)
- Amplifier power (reflections included) = 125 watts (8 ohms), 250 watts (4 ohms)

Note that the 6 dB difference in sound levels at this distance results in a factor of 4 difference in power requirements in the two conditions. How is it that we seem to be making do with much less power than this? There may not be a single definitive answer, but the following factors may be relevant:

- Amplifier power ratings tend to be steady-state ratings, and depending on the design of the power supply, they may be capable of substantially higher output for short durations–transients such as musical crescendos, gunshots, explosions, etc.
- Most customers do not play at "reference" level in a domestic environment. Even a 3 dB reduction in volume–just nicely noticeable–cuts power demand in half. Reports of even greater reductions are common. Playback at-10 dB (roughly half the perceived loudness) uses 1/10 the power that would be used at a volume setting of 0 dB.
- We are talking about a single channel and the others contribute to the overall sound level. In addition, there is evidence that a multidirectional sound field can be perceived to be louder than that provided by a single loudspeaker.
- If the power amplifier clips cleanly, without artifacts, evidence exists that listeners can tolerate, and even may not be aware of, up to 6 dB of hard clipping. This is equivalent to a factor of 4 in power headroom.

The lesson here is to pay close attention to the real sensitivities and the real impedances of the loudspeakers being used, and, if possible, avoid those that exhibit unreasonably low impedances if the cost of power amplifiers is a concern. At longer listening distances the power-handling capacities of the loudspeakers must also be carefully considered.

Equalizers and Equalization

An equalizer is an electronic filter that changes the frequency response of a signal. The classic device is a graphic equalizer, a set of 1/3-octave or octave wide filters, each with a slider to adjust how much the signal would be boosted or cut within that frequency band. Newer versions may offer other filter resolutions. One can "draw" a frequency response with the sliders, making it very intuitive. More precise, and ultimately more accurate in its ability to address specific problems, is the parametric equalizer consisting of a smaller number of filters, but each one is more elaborately adjustable. Instead of boosting or cutting over a set of fixed frequency bands, parametric equalizer filters each can be adjusted to a center frequency of choice, then adjusted in bandwidth to cover a large portion of the audible spectrum or to address a specific narrow band, and finally each filter is adjustable in gain or loss. So, parametric filters have three adjustable parameters: frequency, bandwidth (or Q) and gain/loss. Such filters are less intuitive and really need to be used in conjunction with a measurement system capable of showing what the problem is, so that appropriate filter settings can be made to address it. In truth, apart from tone control compensations to alter tonal balance to suit a customer's taste, any equalization should be done using measurements. Nowadays, it is common for all filter functions to be implemented digitally, and fully-or semi-automatic digital algorithms exist that can take a measurement, process it and create an optimized set of parametric filters that will allow the final overall performance of the system to match a predetermined target curve.

At this point, it is important to know what needs to be measured, and in that regard it is fundamental to understand that the loudspeakers and the room function as a system – they cannot be separated. Most of the sound we hear in a room, or measure with a microphone, is reflected sound. This complex sound field includes characteristics of both the on and off- axis sounds radiated by the loudspeakers, and how those sounds have been modified by acoustical (reflecting, absorbing, scattering) characteristics of the walls, floor and ceiling, as well as furnishings. At low frequencies, below about 300 Hz in typical home theaters, the dominant factor is room resonances and the associated standing waves. In this frequency range, there is a good relationship between what is measured and what is heard. Above that frequency, however, two ears and a brain react to reflected sounds arriving from different directions at different times quite differently than an omnidirectional microphone and an analyzer. What we measure does not perfectly correlate with what we hear. Also, and this gets to an important issue, not all problems that may be revealed in a room curve measurement are correctable by equalization, and worse, not everything that may look like a problem actually is an audible problem.

The basic idea of "room" equalization is a gross oversimplification and if not done correctly good sound is not the result. A full discussion of this topic is beyond the scope of this document, but a few simple guidelines may be of assistance:

- Below about 300 Hz in home theaters, and certainly in the subwoofer frequency range, acoustical measurements are useful if they have resolutions greater than about 1/10-octave. Similarly, equalization is useful, and parametric equalizers can be used to attenuate prominent peaks in the bass. Ignore narrow dips, and be cautious about amplifying broad dips more than a few dB. In this manner, it is usually possible to deliver good bass to the prime listening location, but listeners in other locations will hear something different. Using multiple microphone locations and combining the data according to a routine (of which there are a few) yields a compromise in which several listeners may hear improved bass, but nobody may receive fully optimized bass. As discussed in Subwoofers below, and in CEA/CEDIA-CEB22, there are ways to use multiple subwoofers to reduce seat-to-seat variations so that global equalization will have a more widespread beneficial effect.

- Above about 300 Hz in home theaters the rules change. Here, the evidence is that if one begins with loudspeakers having smooth and flat on-axis frequency response, and relatively uniform directivity as a function of frequency, then what is heard in the room is likely to be satisfactory if the acoustical treatment in the room is not overly frequency selective. The most common failing is to use absorbers and scattering devices that are too thin, thereby absorbing only the high frequencies and degrading the sound from the loudspeakers. A measurement made in such a room would indicate insufficient high frequencies, and that indeed is the case. The spectrum of reflected sounds is excessively different from that of the direct sounds. However, the remedy is not equalization, which would modify the performance of the loudspeakers in an unfortunate direction. Instead, the acoustical treatments should be altered to be more wideband, the ultimate goal being that absorbers should be not less than about 3" (76 mm) thick, and diffusers and scattering surfaces should aim to be about 8" (200 mm) deep. These are challenging dimensions in many installations, but try to get as close as possible.
- In general, difficulties arise because a room curve (a frequency response measured with a mic in a room) cannot discriminate the way two ears and a brain can do. Everything is lumped together, and if there appears to be a problem in the form of a non-flat, non-smooth curve the question is what to do about it. There is no way to separate the performance of the loudspeaker from that of the room. There is no way to know, if the problem is the loudspeaker, whether the fault is frequency response, which equalization can fix, or non-uniform directivity, which equalization cannot fix (the solution is a better loudspeaker). As for the room, more useful information can be gleaned from a visual inspection of the acoustical treatment of room boundaries than from a room curve. In fact, without comprehensive measurements on the loudspeakers, it is almost impossible to draw useful conclusions from room curves. It is not a simple process, which means that a lot of typical "room EQ" procedures and processors will make mistakes.

Loudspeakers

It is no exaggeration to say that the quality of sound heard in home theaters is primarily determined by the loudspeakers. As discussed above, the room is a dominant factor at low frequencies, but the loudspeakers progressively become the principal factors at frequencies above about 300 Hz. The challenge is to anticipate how a loudspeaker might sound in a room before it is installed. Unfortunately, at the present time, few manufacturers make available sufficient performance specifications for this to be possible. Ideally, what is needed is high-resolution (1/20-octave) on and off-axis anechoic frequency responses covering at least the front hemisphere, and an estimate of total sound power output. In this data one would look for smooth and flat on-axis behavior, with similar performance maintained in off-axis data to angles that embrace the first reflections in small rooms (about 40° to 80° horizontally and 20° to 60° vertically [Devantier, 2002; Toole, 2008]). The latter requirement translates into a constant, or smoothly changing, directivity index as a function of frequency. All of this is in ANSI/CEA -2034 "Standard Method of Measurement for In-Home Loudspeakers" (2013).

Unfortunately, this kind of information is not normally in loudspeaker specification sheets, so the first task is to ask the manufacturer if it can be provided. If not, the recommended practice for an integrator is to perform some tests of their own. Lacking acoustical facilities, it is fortunate that there are several FF T-based measurement systems that can acquire useful quasi-anechoic (time-windowed) data. These are made at a distance of 1 m or more, with the loudspeaker placed as far away from room boundaries as possible (a very large room is extremely beneficial, or, weather permitting, the outdoors is nature's own anechoic space). Try to find a situation that allows at least a 10 ms reflection-free time window, which yields useful data at frequencies from about 200-300 Hz and upwards. Make measurements directly on-axis, and at angular intervals off axis up to 60° to 80° horizontally, and with the loudspeaker on its side, "vertically", all at a constant distance. While not as rigorous as a true anechoic measurement, the practice serves to inform the integrator as to the speaker's suitability and verify its proper operation. In fact, measurements of this kind are used by numerous small loudspeaker companies to design their products. Once the performance of a "mystery" loudspeaker has been determined, and there is confidence to use it, it only remains to ensure that all samples of the product are similar. This can be done by checking just the on-axis frequency response in the field. Given that large measurement space is not likely to be available at a work site, decide on a practical, relatively short, distance as a "field-test" reference (2-3 ft. would work). Make a measurement at this distance in the original setup, noting precisely where the mic is positioned relative to the tweeter (on axis is preferable) so that the setup can be replicated in the field. This is the field-test reference curve. Then, on site, make a similar measurement on each of the loudspeakers to be installed, again staying as far from room boundaries as possible. First compare the results to the "field- test reference" from the original tests, and then compare the samples with each other. It is sometimes revealing to find out how similar, and how different, some products are.

A contemporary home theater or media room should be capable of all forms of audio entertainment: movies, television, stereo and multichannel music, and games. All of these should sound similarly good. If good loudspeakers have been selected, the really difficult work has been done. If not, there may be no remedy. The remaining tasks include acoustical treatment to control reverberation time to below 0.5 s (for good speech intelligibility) and to attenuate flutter echoes and late discrete reflections (for the same reason, and to avoid their distracting effects). It is not an automatic requirement to arbitrarily absorb early lateral reflections as has been the practice over the years. While this has the effect of increasing front soundstage focus, it can adversely affect desirable spatial effects, resulting in a less open, spacious, sound quality. Some customers, especially fans of stereo music listening, may have a strong opinion one way or the other. After discussion, the customer is, of course, right.

Placement of acoustical absorbers should be primarily directed in the front half and lower areas of the room so as not to reduce envelopment. Placement of any absorption or scattering on lateral surfaces should be evaluated for their effect on soundstage width and overall spaciousness. Finally, with or without multiple subwoofers to reduce seat-to-seat variations in bass, measurement and equalization of low frequencies – up to 300 to 500 Hz, say – rounds out the installation.

The front left, center, and right loudspeakers ideally should be identical, or as least as similar as possible, so that the front soundstage is perceived as a seamless continuum. Under no circumstances should the center channel be compromised because it is the workhorse of the system, providing not only dialogue, but many/most of the on-screen sounds and sound effects heard in films and television. The center channel also provides a positional anchor for important sounds because everyone in the room can reliably localize to its position. The sound quality of a center loudspeaker is superior to that of a phantom "stereo" center image, and is a perfect timbral match for the left and right images. It is the way movies are made. One of the principle advantages of the center channel is its function to widen the listening area (sweet triangle) for front soundstage focus. For these reasons, eliminating the center channel is something to be avoided - only to be done if there is no alternative.

While there is an allowable tolerance for displacing the center channel from exact height alignment with the left and right front speakers, perfect alignment will yield an audible improvement of focus and is recommended. This can be accomplished with the use of an acoustically transparent screen. Further, if the misalignment of center height exceeds two feet due to the use of a flat panel TV or non-acoustically transparent screen, it is recommended that the center be placed above the screen and the right and left be directed higher to maintain best alignment. Placing the center below the screen is a problem in theaters if the direct sound from the center loudspeaker is obstructed by listeners in the forward rows of a multi-row layout, or by furniture, such as a coffee table.

Continuing to the surround loudspeakers, one can easily understand that in an ideal situation, all loudspeakers in the system should be identical, especially because in some films, games and multichannel music mixes, sounds are directed to discrete surround loudspeakers in the expectation that they will exhibit the same timbral characteristics as the front channels. This is especially true of games and "middle of the band" music mixes, but it also applies to some sound effects in movies. Because power demands of surround loudspeakers are commonly less than those for the front channels, it common to reduce the scale of the side and rear surround loudspeakers, but there should not be a degradation of the timbral accuracy.

So, why are surround loudspeakers sometimes differently designed? First of all, there is a desire to make them unobtrusive, if not invisible, because they are located on walls well away from the picture and they visually stand out. This normally is interpreted as a need for in-or on-wall/ceiling units. Acoustically, there is a need for wide dispersion in many installations, because there may be multiple rows of listeners and the side walls may be quite close. It is important that all listeners receive strong and high-quality direct sounds from the loudspeakers so that the localization of sound effects and recorded enveloping sounds are well heard and timbrally accurate. This requirement is easily met by conventional wide-dispersion designs, either forward firing or bi-polar (bidirectional in-phase).

A common problem faced by designers is that in smaller, narrow rooms, the side walls are so close to the audience area that those who are seated close to those walls can localize the side loudspeakers, which is a distraction. The cause of the problem is the inverse-square law, illustrated for a single loudspeaker in Figure AA, where the direct sound (which determines localization) falls away at–6 dB/double distance. If left and right side loudspeakers are equidistant, as they would be in the prime listening location in the center of the room, everything is fine–the left and right ears receive equal levels of sound, and a nice sense of envelopment prevails. However, even a one-seat movement away from center is enough to upset the balance, and envelopment deteriorates. More movement to the side and the imbalance increases to the point where listeners will start to localize the side loudspeaker nearest to them. There also is no envelopment, and the essential purpose of surround sound is corrupted.

How can this be avoided? Unfortunately, there is no perfect, or easy, solution. To create a sense of envelopment, it is important that the sounds arrive at our ears from the sides, not from the front or back of the rooms – that is why side loudspeakers were located there in the first place. Envelopment is a perception requiring long delays, much longer than can be created by reflections in small rooms – the enveloping sounds are in the multichannel program mix. The basic problem is physics (propagation loss and the inverse-square law) – the sound level decreases too rapidly with distance from the typical side loudspeakers. One possible solution is to use loudspeakers having a reduced propagation loss, like true floor-to-ceiling line sources that exhibit direct sounds diminishing at-3 dB/dd and total sound fields diminishing at about-1 dB/dd (compare to Figure AA). Constant-beamwidth transducer (CBT) designs offer another option (see Toole, 2008, section 18.4.4). In both cases, it is possible to move across a room, up to the loudspeakers themselves, and the sound level changes little.

Failing these options, it is possible to reduce the attraction of the side loudspeakers by rolling off the high frequencies (as was done in the original four-channel Dolby Surround decoders). Some surround processors permit tonal adjustments in side channels, or a resistor can be inserted in series with the tweeter, both of which "turn down" the treble. The bidirectional out-of-phase (commonly known as "dipole") configuration achieves this by creating an imperfect null 90° to the wall at frequencies above about 500 Hz. This works only for a single row of listeners, though, and their heads should be on the null axis, perpendicular to the wall. All of these options move us away from the original goal of high quality timbre-matched loudspeakers, and essentially degrades the overall fidelity of the system. The remaining option is to elevate the side loudspeakers, letting the more directional high frequencies propagate over the heads of the audience. Finally, it may be necessary to admit to your customer that some seats are simply not as good as others, as in fact they are in the cinemas we are attempting to emulate. Obviously, if there is an opportunity to make the room wider, moving all listeners farther from the side loudspeakers, take it.

Requirements for rear-channel and height-channel loudspeakers are likely to be met by conventional wide-dispersion forward firing units strategically placed to allow an even sound coverage over the widest group of listeners.

Subwoofers

It could be argued that bass management and subwoofers, together, are one of the greatest advances in audio. First, it is possible to reproduce very low, even subsonic, frequencies at very high sound levels. That alone is impressive, but then we notice that not all frequencies are equally well reproduced, some notes "boom" and other notes are missing, and the effects are different in different parts of the room. Welcome to the world of acoustical standing waves in small rooms. Equalization could improve the bass for the prime listening location, but other seats were different, some of them very different.

This remained one of the persistent problems in sound reproduction, generating elaborate schemes to optimize room dimensions, cautions to avoid sitting in the center of rooms, further cautions to avoid placing subwoofers in corners, and so on. And then, suddenly, the rules change. Scientific research led to an understanding of how to use multiple subwoofers to control which of the room resonances would be allowed, and which would not, simplifying the sound field in rectangular rooms. With this, it became clear where to sit and where not to sit in order to hear more consistent bass seat-to-seat variations were substantially reduced so that equalization had a similar beneficial effect at several seats, not just one.

Benefiting from bass management and the rules to be discussed depends on the use of a rectangular room. A rectangular room is highly predictable from an acoustical perspective and is the preferred shape for a high performance theater. The rules for rectangular rooms are quite simple. First all subwoofers must be identical, set to the same gain and polarity, and driven by the same "sub output" signal. Other than that:

- Two subwoofers at the mid points of the two side walls, or
- Two subwoofers at the mid points of the two end walls, or

· Four subwoofers in the corners, or
· Four subwoofers at the mid points of all four walls,

All result in a similar pattern of standing waves in the room. The last arrangement works well to minimize seat-to-seat variations, but because it is very inefficient, making the subwoofers work unnecessarily hard, its use is discouraged.

If you are able to follow the rules, the acoustical result is the reduction in stimulation of numerous standing waves or resonances in the room. The remaining resonances form significant peaks and nulls in the room but these are in predictable locations. Knowing this allows us to locate listeners so that their heads avoid significant nulls in the standing wave pattern. These nulls are at lines drawn 25% of the way across the width and length of the room, as shown in Figure YY.

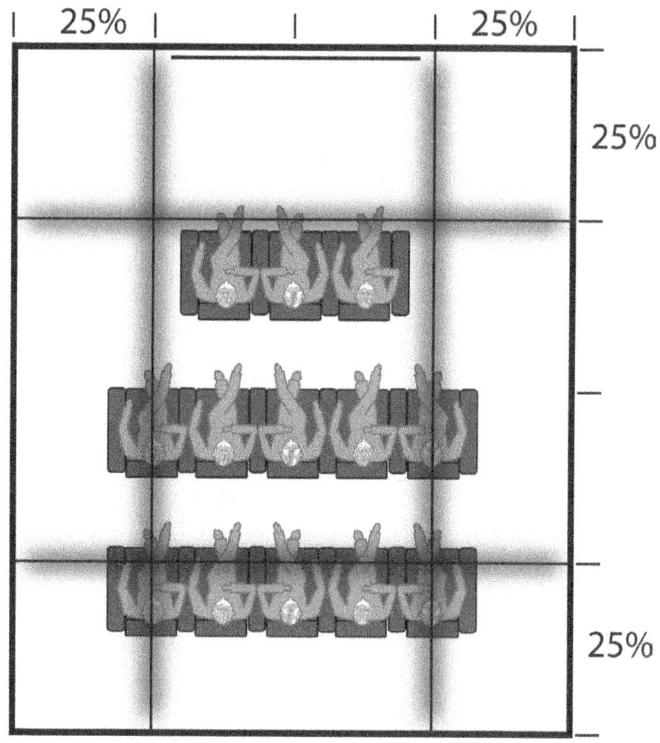

Figure 4-8. *Sub-Woofer Nulls*

Non-rectangular rooms or rectangular rooms that are not acoustically symmetrical must be handled quite differently. For these spaces, proprietary algorithms exist that digitally process the signals supplied to four subwoofers that need not be identical. Likewise, listeners can be located with greater freedom. Whatever arrangement is chosen, the optimizer will do the best it can. Several arrangements can be experimented with.

Structural Details

In custom home theaters, it is common to mount loudspeakers in custom cabinetry, ornamental, if it is visible, or functional, if it is hidden behind the screen or a stretched fabric wall covering. In all cases:

- The structure must not rattle or buzz.
- The front baffles of the loudspeakers must align smoothly with the neighboring surfaces, if possible with the gap closed using a rigid material.
- The space around the loudspeaker and the cabinet should be filled with compressed glass or cellulose fiber. The side and rear surfaces of the loudspeaker cavity may, if it is practical, be perforated with slots or holes.
- If the loudspeaker being mounted in this fashion was designed for free-standing operation, as essentially all bookshelf and tower loudspeakers are, then equalization will be necessary to reduce the excessive bass caused by the 2ϖ (half-space) mounting. If the loudspeakers were designed for in-wall mounting, no such equalization should be necessary.
- Vibration isolation is a frequent concern about loudspeakers in cabinetry. There are two differing perspectives on the topic:
  - Let the loudspeaker vibrate, but isolate the vibrations from the structure, or
  - Couple it to the structure so that the added mass prevents vibration.

If isolation is attempted, it must be effective down to the lowest frequency radiated by the loudspeaker, meaning that the suspension system must have a resonance frequency that is even lower. The compliance of the suspension must be appropriate for the mass being supported-an arbitrarily selected spring, pad or puck of neoprene will not suffice. Also, the loudspeaker must not contact any part of the structure. This makes it difficult to deal with some of the acoustical issues discussed above. On the other hand, a custom cabinet or a wall structure are substantial masses, and the alternative perspective on the topic is to add that mass to the loudspeaker making it difficult for it to move. Perhaps additional masses can be attached to the loudspeaker if there are concerns. Drywall is an inexpensive and effective damped mass. Of the two options, the latter seems more attractive. Subwoofers are especially problematic whichever option is chosen.

SURROUND SOUND SYSTEM SETUP AND CALIBRATION

Audio Verification

Audio verification ensures that a home theater system is functioning properly and within published specifications. The importance of this step cannot be over emphasized. A system that is broken or operating below specifications cannot be properly calibrated. It is the obligation of a professional A/V contractor to perform due diligence on the system. The process of verification is a prime selling-point for hiring a CEDIA company that greatly differentiates it from lesser contractors. The cost of verification should be included in the proposal and heralded as a necessary and high-value service. Verified components are worth more to the consumer. Further, it is a timesaver, as malfunctioning equipment is often the true source of sonic problems which confound listening tests and extend calibration time. Troubleshooting a system after the fact is costly, and too often these unseen defects are left uncorrected with unsuspecting customers who assumed they had purchased top quality components. Ultimately, the system falls short sonically. If caught in time, the solution to errant components is easily corrected by warranty replacement or a simple repair.

Improperly operating or connected equipment can produce dialog that is difficult to understand, vague sonic focus (imaging), poor envelopment, uneven frequency response and other audio anomalies. To avoid these scenarios and achieve the highest-quality results, each component and aspect of the equipment must be verified in a logical and systematic way via various testing procedures. These system verification tests examine the electronic components to ensure each one will work flawlessly in the home theater environment. The electronic systems technician who performs the majority of the tests prior to installation saves valuable installer time and presents the highest level of professionalism. In-shop testing where testing tools are easily accessible and components can be quickly setup is more efficient and much less stressful than working in the customer's home. Of course, not all testing can be accomplished in advance.

Some imperfections can actually be a result of the installation process and must be verified once the system is installed. Most problems are highly audible and their discovery after-the-fact by a calibrator hired by the client can be highly embarrassing. This is especially true when the fix dramatically improves system sound quality. This scenario plays out every day in the market where customers bring in a new contractor to solve mysteriously poor sound quality that has been nagging them since their purchase. Don't assume all components are perfect out of the box or that the installation was perfect; even the best manufacturer or installer can make mistakes. Moreover, it is not a particularly uncommon occurrence.

In-shop verification tests include:

- Speaker Impedance Test
- Signal Presence and Power Test
- Speaker Rub and Buzz Test
- Driver Polarity Test
- Lemon Test
- Speaker Near-field and Bass Management Test

On-site verification tests include:

- Hum Test
- Speaker Cable Continuity Test
- Speaker Room Measurement Test

Speaker Impedance Test

The load impedance test measures the impedance (opposition that a circuit offers to a flow of current) of each speaker in the home theater system. Audio amplifiers produce voltage and current. The voltage and current are AC (alternating current), meaning the current flows in both directions and the load is both resistive and reactive. Resistance is a material's opposition to the flow of electric current, which is measured in ohms. Reactance is the frequency-dependent opposition to the flow of current, which is also measured in ohms. In a DC (direct current) circuit, the current flows in a single direction; the load is purely resistive and has no reactive component. Since in audio we are dealing with musical signals which are composed of various frequencies of alternating current, we need to evaluate the impedance of a speaker versus its DC resistance. Simply measuring the resistance of the speaker offers no value in understanding the load it places on the amplifier.

An impedance meter measures both the resistive and reactive nature of the load by generating an alternating current (AC), which is fed to the device-under-test (DUT). Do not use an ohmmeter. An ohmmeter is typically part of a DMM (digital multi-meter) or volt-ohm meter and measures only the resistive nature of a load and not impedance.

Test Setup — The speaker load is measured at the speaker's terminals using a short length of speaker wire, as shown in Figure 4-9. This requires the use of an impedance meter, because the load is not purely resistive, but also contains inductance and capacitance. To allow measuring the speaker impedance across the audio bandwidth, the impedance meter used in this example measures impedance at 100 Hz, 330 Hz, 1 kHz, and 10 kHz.

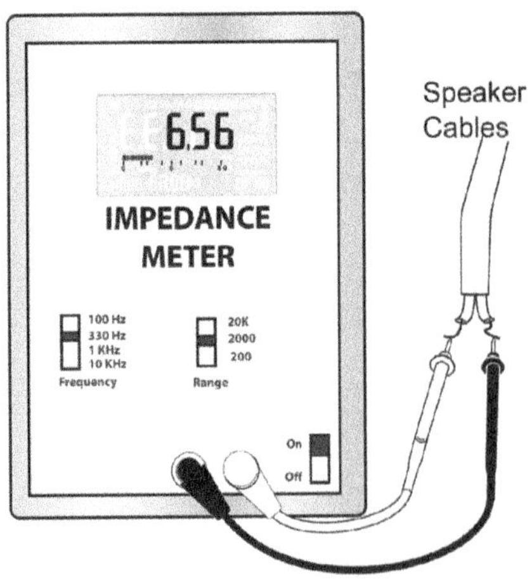

Figure 4-9. *Load Impedance Test Setup*

Testing Procedure — This procedure is repeated for each speaker in the system, except the subwoofer (unless it is a passive speaker with a remote amplifier).

1. Attach a short run of speaker cable to the speaker's input terminals and connect it to the impedance meter.
2. Measure the impedance using each frequency range provided on the impedance meter. The impedance will change over the frequency range of 20 Hz to 20 kHz. The measurements are taken by selecting each frequency, one at a time and writing the measurements in a chart like the one shown in Table 4-1.
3. Verify the impedance measured against the speaker's specification. The resistive nature of the load should be consistent with the manufacturer's specifications, and no lower than 3 ohms.

The impedances should be nearly identical from speaker to speaker assuming each speaker in the system is the same make and model. There is no better way to reproduce sound faithfully than to have identical speakers throughout the system.

Table 4-1. *Impedance Measurements*

Frequency	Impedance (Ohms)
100 Hz	?
330 Hz	?
1 KHz	?
10 KHz	?

Failed Test — If the impedance curve varies from a particular speaker compared to the others yet the speakers are identical models, then investigate the speakers to ensure the cabling and crossovers within the speakers have been assembled correctly. Try switching out the speaker leads to eliminate them as a cause. Cables (both speaker leads and internal speaker wiring) may pass a continuity test yet have a problem with higher frequency signals.

Significant variations (> 2 ohms) in impedance from speaker to speaker can reduce sonic focus and make matching sound levels more difficult. Exceptionally low impedances (below 3 ohms at any frequency) can place undo strain on the amplifier and cause excessive distortion. Unusually high impedances compared to "like" speakers can mean an output mismatch and a loss of linearity at various frequencies. Solving the problem may require repair of the speaker so it's best to test this in advance and ask for assistance from the manufacturer. Speaker leads with coils/transformers or with any electronic circuitry may also be a source for trouble.

Signal Presence and Power Test

The Signal Presence and Power Test measures the output power of the amplifier and confirms signal presence. This test can be accomplished both in-shop or on-site. Besides confirming the proper operation of the amplifier, it confirms the correct and matched output of each amplifier channel.

Test Setup — This test requires a test DVD with a 1KHz tone (or signal generator), a power meter, and an oscilloscope with true RMS voltage capability (the AudioTools Audio Scope works well for this by incorporating a power meter function on the scope view). The best procedure is to substitute the speaker with a high-power, non-inductive, load resistor (matching the speaker's impedance). This test should be completed after the impedance check to properly determine the correct load at the chosen frequency to set for the power meter.

1KHz is the standard frequency most amp manufacturers use for published specifications and thus is appropriate for verification purposes. A more insightful test would be done using lower frequencies (30 Hz to 150 Hz) with all channels driven. This tests the amplifier in a more realistic fashion but the setup requires a power resistor for each channel. Use high power resistors which can dissipate 100 to 200 watts. These are not your run-of-the-mill ¼ watt resistor but they are readily available at a variety of sources. Make sure each channel's level is zeroed out in the preamplifier speaker level menu prior to testing.

Testing Procedure — This procedure is repeated for each speaker/channel in the system, except the subwoofer (unless it is a passive speaker with a remote amplifier). Begin setup with the receiver/amplifier off.

1. Attach two short runs of speaker cable to the load resistor's terminals. Choose a load which matches the speaker's impedance at that frequency. Connect one set of the remaining leads to the oscilloscope's inputs and the other to the power meter's inputs.
2. Set the oscilloscope to measure RMS voltage at its maximum range and the power meter to read maximum wattage. The power meter load setting should be set to match the impedance of the power resistor.
3. Adjust the amplifier volume control to minimum and turn it on. Turn on the 1 kHz tone.
4. Slowly turn the amplifier volume up while monitoring the oscilloscope; stop once you see the sine waveform on the oscilloscope begin to flatten. You may have to reduce the scale on the oscilloscope to see the waveform.
5. Back off on the volume setting until you see a perfect sine wave on the scope. Note the power level at this point. This is the true RMS maximum output of the amplifier channel just prior to clipping.

Note: As an alternative to using a power meter you can use the indicated RMS voltage and load impedance with this formula to calculate the power.

Power = (Voltage * Voltage)/Impedance

6. Repeat the test for each speaker channel.

Failed Test — A failed test is indicated by any channel not meeting published specifications for the amplifier or one channel showing anomalous output compared to the other channels. Consult the manufacture for failed units and replace. Be sure that you've properly measured and set the correct loading on the power meter.

Note: Most amplifiers have different power output specifications for different loads. Consult the amplifier manual or contact the manufacturer for guidance. Speakers with unusual impedances (> 8 ohms or < 4 ohms at 1kHz) may produce anomalous results and may not indicate a problem with the amplifier.

Speaker Rub and Buzz Test

Speaker buzz is an unwanted "edgy" tone, usually of a low-frequency nature, that can be present in an audio signal. The room might rattle at various frequencies, and this can be easily confused with buzzing so it's a good idea to evaluate the speaker in a controlled setting like your shop. Rattles are created from loose materials in the room; where buzzing is created within the loudspeaker itself. Buzz is also different from hum, which may be a result of poor grounding. Once the system is on site, it can be tested for hum and rattles within the home theater system. For this test, each speaker is tested using a single tone stepped sine wave sweep from a test DVD (or signal generator). Be sure to use a sine wave as a square or triangular wave can sound like a buzz itself.

Test Setup — Use the 20 Hz to 20 kHz single tone stepped sweep from a test DVD (or signal generator), as shown in Figure 4-10. An audio signal generator is preferred since it allows the technician to more easily identify the frequency at which the speaker fails.
Testing Procedure — Listen to the speakers up close; the audio emanating from the speaker should sound clear without any buzzing artifacts. Try increasing the gain incrementally; some problems only occur at higher output levels.

Failed Test — You should be listening for mechanical rubbing as evidence of a defective driver. All speakers will have a tendency to resonate at certain frequencies and this may not be evidence of a problem. Be aware that some ported speakers can generate a chortling sound at certain frequencies below the operating range of the speaker which may not be a malfunction. It's also important not to dwell on frequencies causing a resonance at high sound levels. This may not be a malfunction, but rather a characteristic of the design. Such loud resonances can damage speakers. Keep in mind the speaker was designed for music not pure sine waves. If there is a problem with the speaker, contact the speaker manufacturer for further assistance. The solution will likely be replacement of the offending driver.

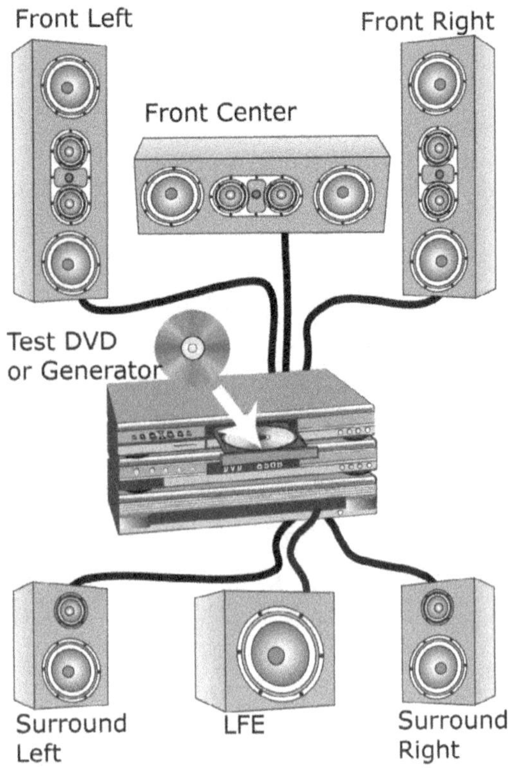

Figure 4-10. *Speaker Buzz Test Setup*

Driver Polarity Test

In the manufacturing process, speakers can sometimes be inadvertently wired with the positive and negative internal driver terminals reversed. While this mistake is not common, it is not an exceptionally rare occurrence. The driver polarity test is designed to ensure each speaker in the home theater system has correct polarity. This test is to be repeated on-site after installation to ensure all cabling maintains the acoustic polarity to each speaker. An incorrectly wired speaker can destroy proper sonic focus and envelopment yet it is an easy item to detect and correct.

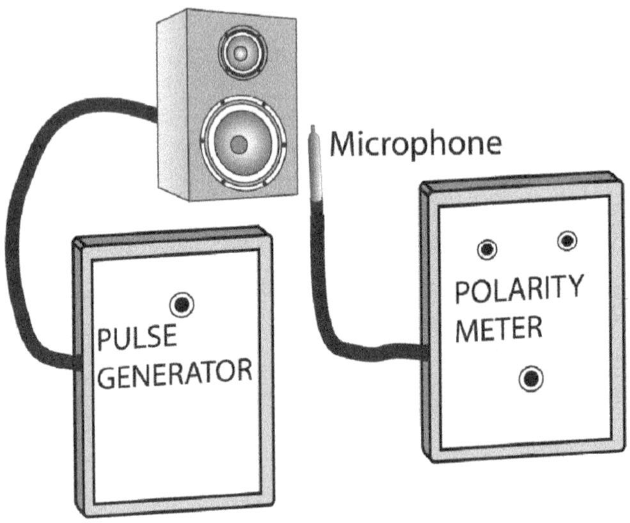

Figure 4-11. *Acoustic Polarity Test Setup*

Test Setup — Driver polarity verification is performed by placing a polarity tester in front of each of the speaker's drivers with a polarity signal pulse applied to the speaker, as shown in Figure 4-11.
Testing Procedure — Complete this test with all speakers in the system noting that like speakers should test the same.

1. Input the line level polarity test signal into the pre-amplifier of the system or connect the polarity pulse generator directly to the speaker depending on the device you use.

Note: If you use a line level signal generator, take care to observe the absolute polarity of the pre-amp and amplifier used. Some pre-amps and amplifiers actually reverse the polarity of signals passing through them. You can establish the nature of your amplifier by testing a raw speaker driver with clearly marked positive and negative input leads. A negative polarity indication shows that the signal was reversed by the amplification. Now you'll have a standard to allow correct evaluation of all other speakers.

2. Turn on the pulse generator for one speaker. Using a line level signal generator it is possible to fire multiple speakers in a system simultaneously but this creates the possibility of false reading from other speakers output in the room. You can only test one driver at a time so it's best to minimize the number of pulses your meter might detect by firing only a single speaker.
3. Hold the analyzer microphone in front of the speaker, preferably centered and very near the driver (<6"). Your chosen polarity checker should indicate that all drivers in all speakers are identical in polarity. By performing the test on each driver you can isolate the offending driver. Be aware that we are not necessarily concerned that the polarity be positive, but rather that they are the same. If desired, absolute polarity of positive is easily achieved by reversing the speaker cable leads to the speakers. Such an outcome is possible if your customer's amplifier is phase reversing but is not considered an audible issue to most technicians. A customer discovering that the leads are all backwards may be a bigger sin. Our concern is that the internal wiring of the speaker is correct.
4. Dipole surround speakers usually have a single woofer and nearly side firing tweeters. The woofer and the forward firing tweeter should have the same polarity and the rearward firing tweeter should be opposite in polarity.

Failed Test — Check to ensure the speaker cables have been connected correctly to the back of the speaker. If they are indeed connected correctly, contact the manufacturer. One of the drivers inside the speaker might not be wired properly, and the speaker might need to be replaced.
Note: In some loudspeakers, it is also possible that the midrange or tweeter

is intentionally wired with a reversed polarity by the manufacturer. You can verify this with the manufacturer to ensure the speaker has been wired correctly. If all "like" speakers have this apparent anomaly, it is likely correct. In some cases, it may be possible to repair the incorrectly wired driver to solve the problem. Make sure you contact the speaker manufacturer to confirm that there actually is a mistake.

Lemon Test

Performing a complete diagnostic on each component is a valuable tool, however some problems do not manifest themselves immediately. Time, use, and heat can change the picture. Luckily, most defective components fail within the first 48 hours of use which allows the contractor an opportunity to protect themselves from lost time replacing defective components onsite and the customer from the frustration of a temporary blackout.

Test Setup — Connect all components for proper operation in a convenient place in the shop. A seldom used area is best since a proper test should run undisturbed for 48 hours. It's also useful for the equipment to be behind a closed door to limit disturbing noise levels. While it's not advisable to over-stress products in non-ventilated areas or beyond recommended operating levels, it's a good idea to try to duplicate the conditions of the final installation. This is especially useful for hard-to-test components like amplifiers, DVD players, and video projectors. Be sure to confirm that each product is designed for this type of continuous test. Some components may have manufacturer imposed limits on continuous use and you should be aware of these.

Testing Procedure — Find a way to allow each component to operate continuously over the test period. Blue-ray players in repeat mode test themselves and provide a source for the other components. Speakers should be included in the test for the sake of the amplifier as well as their own sake. Some speaker and projector manufacturers recommend a break-in period for their products and this testing will help settle in components for a more complete final calibration. A useful trick is to place speakers face-to-face with their connections out of polarity. This will help to reduce the noise level somewhat. It's advisable to look in on the testing periodically to discover any failed products. It doesn't do much good to test a system for 48 hours if the DVD player failed after just two hours.

Failed Test — The merits of this test will become very clear after just one failure. The precaution of pre-testing will allow you the time to procure a replacement product and complete a successful project on time.

Speaker Near-Field and Bass Management Test

The Speaker Near-field Test is designed to verify the proper operation of speakers and system crossovers. A real time analyzer (RTA) capable of high resolution measurements greater than or equal to 1/10th octave is used to generate a plot of the speaker's near-field frequency response. It can be accomplished as either an in-shop or on-site test. On-site is the most common method given that you are also verifying the proper setup of the system crossovers. In- shop testing allows you the time to correct manufacturers defects in speaker crossovers and drivers but these problems tend to be rare. A near-field measurement is designed to minimize the effect of room resonances and echo, by placing the microphone very near the driver being tested. Of course, a customer's home theater is not anechoic so reflections and resonances can distort the measurement particularly in the low frequencies. Very near the speaker the direct sound will have the dominant effect on the response over room effects. This region close to the speaker is referred to as the near-field by acousticians. To further reduce the room's effect, a speaker can be moved to the center of the room, or if you are extremely (overly) committed, outside in nature's anechoic chamber.

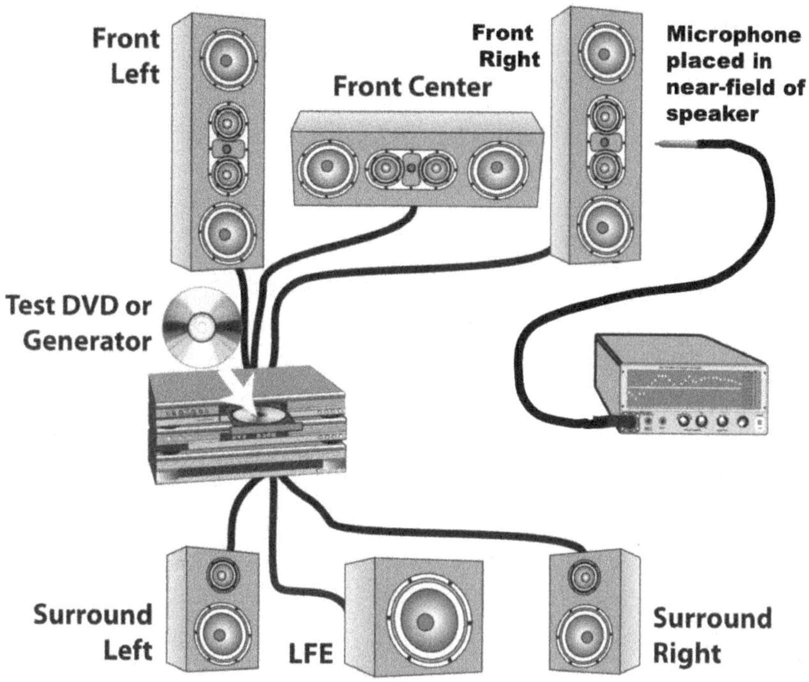

Figure 4-12. *Speaker Near-Field and Bass Management Test Setup*

Placing the measurement microphone on axis with and within an inch of the driver is the most reliable way to avoid room effects, but this means that each driver is measured individually. For two-way and three-way speakers, this complicates the process since you will have limited time onsite and you should be more interested in the composite response of all the drivers in the speaker. A common rule-of- thumb is to place the microphone a distance equal to twice the distance between the centers of the topmost and bottommost drivers and at a central height. It is not recommended to go beyond a one meter distance, as a tall floor-standing speaker might require, since the microphone will likely then be beyond the near field.

Given that the higher frequencies (typically above 300 Hz) are least affected by room effects, the resulting measurement is quite accurate there. It is in the lower frequencies, as from a woofer or subwoofer, where the most anomalies will occur prompting a very close measurement as outlined above. An additional benefit of the test is possible by comparing your on-axis measurement of the speaker with measurements at various off-axis angles. A well designed speaker should produce a very similar response at all angles beside, above, and below the primary axis of the speaker. An acceptable and commonly observed difference is that the high frequencies of the off-axis measurement will begin to slope downward as the measurement angle increases off-axis. A good off-axis response plot will show this sloping while retaining the basic shape of the on-axis measurement. A poor off-axis measurement will have obvious differences and significant deviations from smoothness.

Test Setup — Use the 20 Hz to 20 kHz pink noise tone from a test DVD (or signal generator), as shown in Figure 4-12 as well as a high resolution RTA sound analyzer. Use a microphone stand to position the RTA microphone the prescribed distance (see above discussion) directly on-axis and facing the speaker. Some microphones are designed to produce their most accurate measurement when pointed upward and perpendicular to the sound source; consult the recommendation of the microphone maker.

Testing Procedure — This procedure is repeated for each speaker one at a time being careful to match microphone position and distance. Be sure to zero out all tone and equalizer controls in the pre-amplifier and set all speaker controls (boundary gain or screen compensation) to the same setting. Variations in speaker room placement can also affect the results.

1. Position the microphone in front of the first speaker and note the exact distance between the microphone tip and the speaker. This must remain constant from speaker to speaker.
2. Before engaging the pink noise tone, set the RTA scale to 1/3 octave and review the RTA plot noting the loudest 1/3 octave bands ambient noise level.
3. Engage the pink noise test tone for this channel and adjust the amplifier gain to cause the pink noise level to exceed the ambient noise by at least 20 to 25 dB per 1/3 octave band. Generally, an average 1/3 octave level of 70 to 75 dB is sufficient unless the room is excessively noisy. Note the sound level of the 1/3 octave band at 80 Hz. This band's level should be the same for all speakers including the subwoofer. Use the amplifier gain control to compensate.

Note: Use of a higher RTA resolution beyond 1/3 octave will yield valuable added data, but such plots are often very confusing to any consumer who might review it. The 1/3 octave plot may hide some problems so it's a good idea for you to begin each test at the higher resolution but display the data in 1/3 octave mode for the customer.

4. Once the plot is stabilized, save it for comparison.

Note: A common artifact of a near-field measurement is the exaggeration of the dip seen at the crossover frequency for the tweeter. If there is a pronounced "V " in this region (~2000–2500 Hz) try a few minor adjustments of the microphone height and/or distance to minimize the effect. You may not be able to eliminate it totally.

5. Repeat the procedure for each speaker.
6. For the subwoofer, place the microphone within 1 inch of the driver or output port. You'll need to adjust the gain downward to match its level at the 80 Hz 1/3 octave band.
7. Use the RTA's plotting function (often in a separate PC application) to overlay all the plots noting any anomalies. Save this plot to include in a final calibration report.
8. Time permitting, repeat the procedure for one of the speakers, this time, repositioning the microphone to several horizontal off-axis points at 15°, 30°, 45°, 60°, and finally 90°. Overlay these plots to judge off-axis performance. The angle can also be varied vertically for a complete analysis.

Failed Test — A detailed review of carefully level matched plots should show no more than a 1 to 2 dB variation. Make sure you have zeroed out any tone or equalizer controls on the preamplifier and speakers. Speakers in very different room locations and mounting techniques will display larger variations, so be prudent. Obvious anomalies may reveal a defective driver or at least a poorly matched set of speakers. If you are concerned, repeat the test, this time placing the microphone within an inch of the driver in question. Compare it to one of the presumably correct drivers tested the same way. This more rigorous test should reveal the truth. Defective drivers should be replaced or the speaker as a whole should be replaced.

To confirm bass management settings, check the roll-off of the response to confirm it is consistent with the preamplifiers crossover setting. For example, an 80 Hz crossover should show a roughly 3 to 6 dB drop at 80 Hz. Given the room's impact on the lower frequencies, you may not see a perfectly smooth roll off on the main speakers. If you are concerned, again move the microphone within an inch of the main speaker's woofer to get a clearer view of its actual bass response and crossover slope. For obvious errors, double check the preamplifier's crossover setting and confer with the manufacturer if the problem persists. If you matched all speakers' response at 80 Hz, overlaying all plots should reveal a well behaved transition from the subwoofer to the main speakers with a clear crossover near 80 Hz (plus or minus 5 Hz due to room effects).

Note: Dipole speakers present a special problem for near-field measurements. The true response of the speaker is heavily dependent on room interaction via reflections. The most accurate way to determine its response is to measure at the listening position. Of course, you can revert to the very close measurement technique as done with the subwoofer to evaluate proper crossover operation and speaker response.

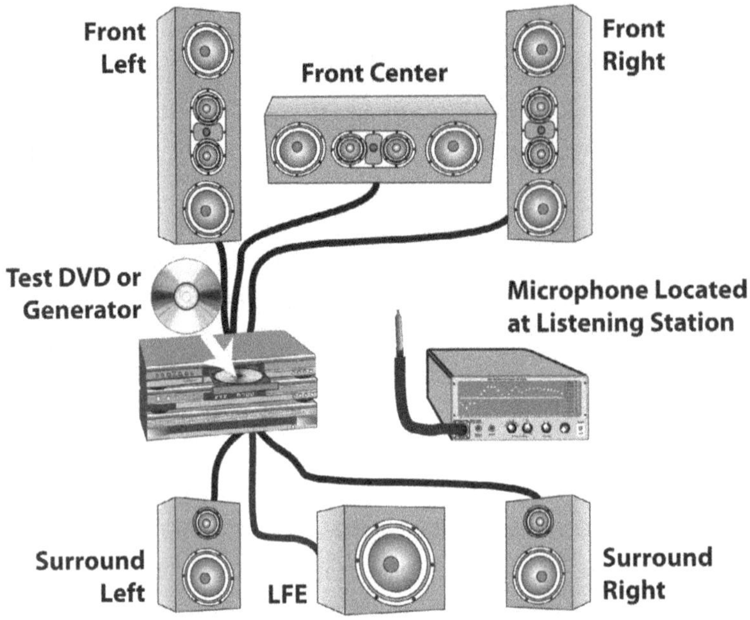

Figure 4-13. *Hum Test Setup*

Hum Test

Hum is a continuous, undesired sound at the frequency of the incoming AC power line (60 Hz in the U.S., 50 Hz in much of the rest of the world), or a harmonic of the AC power (120/100 Hz). It might be caused by improperly shielded or improperly grounded audio cables or electronic components. The difference in electrical potential at various grounding points in a home theater system will often cause a ground loop. Each electronic component's ground should ideally be at zero volts. A ground loop commonly creates a low-frequency hum or buzz heard in the speakers, with the loudness of the hum directly related to the difference in potential among the component grounds. This happens as soon as one of the electronic components is plugged in, such as the subwoofer, cable-TV decoder, satellite-TV decoder, video display, amplifier, processor, or DVD player. The hum test verifies hum is not present in the home theater system.

Test Setup — The test setup is shown in Figure 4-13. With the equipment on and the processor set to the DVD input, set the loudness to 0. Play a test disc with a digital zero signal, also known as digital black.

Testing Procedure — Listen to each speaker up close and measure the sound with a spectrum analyzer. The sound output should be inaudible to the ear and measure less than-60 dB SPL.

Failed Test — The following are some methods to help eliminate ground loops. The first offender to look at is the powered subwoofer and the cable-

TV or satellite-TV decoders at the entry point to the system. Use a ground isolating adaptor (a simple "ground lifter" found at hardware stores) on each component power cord, one at a time, to see if the hum disappears. If that eliminates the hum, do not leave the grounding adaptor in the system, but instead ensure that good grounding techniques are followed throughout the system to eliminate the hum.

Only as a last resort, use an isolation transformer on the cable TV feed line. These transformer-based ground isolators will work fine with analog cable-TV, but depending on the design, it might interfere with or block reception of HDTV signals via a digital cable or satellite dish feed. In all cases, if the subwoofer has a ground-lift screw, try first removing or replacing the screw to see if it increases or eliminates the hum. The following are a few more tips: Try plugging the subwoofer into a different AC outlet in the room. For safety, never permanently install a "cheater plug" or "ground adapter" to bypass the 3-wire grounding AC plug on the subwoofer. A ground adapter to test can be used temporarily to see if the subwoofer AC connection is a part of the ground loop problem. With the power OFF, reverse the AC plugs, one at a time, of any other components that have a standard 2-prong AC plug that isn't polarized. Each time a plug is reversed, turn on the system with the attached component and the subwoofer to see if the hum disappears.

Speaker Cable Continuity Test

The speaker wire loop resistance test verifies the installation of the cables from the amplifier to each speaker by checking for shorts and opens on the cables.

Test Setup — This test requires the use of a digital multi-meter (DMM) set to measure resistance, as shown in Figure 4-14 (analog multi-meter will also work).

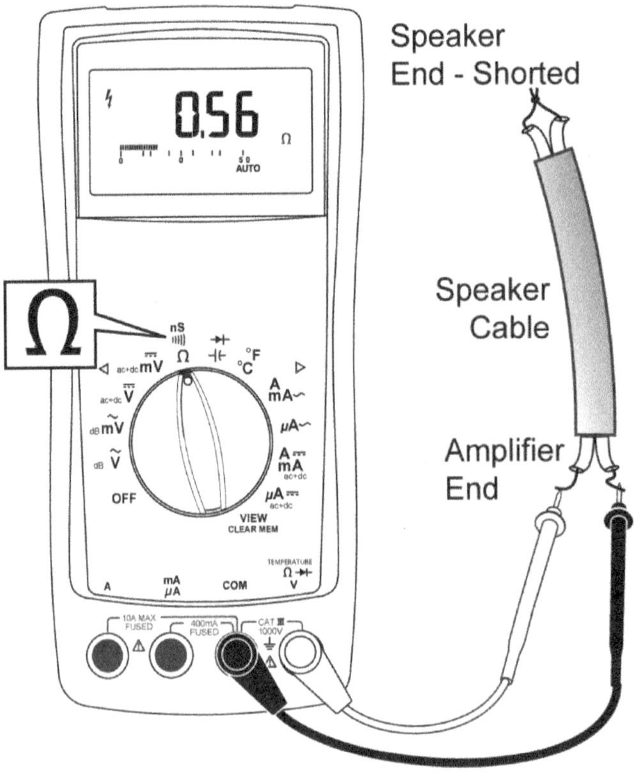

Figure 4-14. *Speaker Loop Resistance*

Testing Procedure — This procedure is repeated for each speaker channel connected to the power amplifiers. This test should be accomplished prior to any other testing, including the polarity test and before powering up the amplifiers.

1. Short Test: Remove the speaker leads from both the amplifier and the speaker.
2. Measure the resistance between the two leads using your DMM. There should be maximum resistance showing no continuity. A continuity tester can also be used for this.
3. Continuity Test: Short circuit one end of the wire by twisting the ends together or coupling them using a shorted terminal connector or other convenient method.
4. Using the other non-shorted end of the cable, measure the resistance using your DMM. Verify that the speaker cable measures less than 0.2 ohms.
5. 5. Reconnect the speaker cables to the amplifier and the speakers.

Failed Test — Be sure to double check your setup and repeat the test if you see a malfunction. It's best to replace the defective cable discarding it immediately to avoid reuse. When using in-wall speakers, it's always important to complete testing at the last minute before installing the actual speaker. For pre-wires, be careful locating leads to avoid encounters with HVAC, electrical, and drywall installation using CEDIA guidelines. It's also a good practice to inspect your cables periodically during construction but especially just prior to drywall installation. An excellent precaution is to use conduit or wire chases to allow cable replacement and upgrade after-the-fact.

Speaker Room Measurement Test

The Speaker Room Measurement Test is designed to verify the proper operation of speakers and system crossovers as does the Near-Field Test but with an additional consideration. For this test, we'll also be reviewing the way speakers interact with the room. A real time analyzer (RTA) capable of high resolution measurements greater than or equal to 1/10th octave is used to generate a plot of each speaker's frequency response as measured at the listening position. You can review the same basic functional requirements as the near-field test but the plots will be more heavily affected by room interaction. This test is also used during the calibration process to facilitate the proper setup of speaker crossover controls (boundary gain and screen compensation) as well as any equalization that is available. The goal of the test is to correct any response variations caused by speaker position differences and room interaction.

Test Setup — Use the 20 Hz to 20 kHz pink noise tone from a test DVD (or signal generator), as shown in Figure 4-15 as well as a high resolution RTA sound analyzer. Use a microphone stand to position the RTA microphone at the prime or central listening position. An alternate more accurate approach is to use a group of 4 or more microphones placed within the listening area and connected to the RTA via a microphone multiplexer. This technique captures a statistically more relevant room response. Techniques vary as to the proper way to position multiple microphones. One is to place a microphone in each seat at ear level. The other is to attempt to randomize the microphone positions by height, length and width position relative to the room.

Testing Procedure — This procedure is repeated for each speaker one at a time, being careful to not to change microphone positions once the test has begun. Be sure to zero out all tone and equalizer controls in the preamplifier and set all speaker controls (boundary gain or screen compensation) to the same setting prior to beginning. Also double-check that the bass management settings are set properly.

1. Before engaging the pink noise tone, set the RTA scale to 1/3 octave and review the RTA plot noting the loudest 1/3 octave bands ambient noise level.
2. Engage the pink noise test tone for this channel and adjust the amplifier gain to cause the pink noise level to exceed the ambient

noise by at least 20 to 25 dB per 1/3 octave band. Generally, an average 1/3 octave level of 70 to 75 dB is sufficient unless the room is excessively noisy. Note the sound level of the 1/3 octave band at 80 Hz. This bands level should be the same for all speakers including the subwoofer. Use the amplifier gain to compensate.

Note: Use of a higher RTA resolution equal to or greater than 1/10 octave is recommended but such plots are often very confusing to any consumer who might review it. The 1/3 octave plot is more appropriate for display to your customer but may hide some problems so it's a good idea for you to complete each test at the higher resolution but display the data in 1/3 octave mode for the customer.

3. Once the plot is stabilized, switch to a high resolution RTA setting of 1/10 octave or higher. Note any response anomalies and save it for comparison. A useful approach is to compare the speaker's room response with the near-field response. Differences between the two plots can usually be blamed on room interaction and are good prospects for correction by equalization or adjustment of the speaker's crossover controls.

Note: Speakers measured beyond the near-field will display a marked sloping of the high frequencies as compared to their near-field plot. This is normal and it is not recommended that the sloping be totally removed, but rather adjusted via tone control or EQ to taste. In rooms where there is excessive absorption in place, the sloping may be absent. This is a possible sign that some treatment should be removed. Speakers which have poor off-axis response can show a markedly different response than the original near-field response. Most room effects (besides high frequency sloping) occur in the low frequency region below 1000 Hz and usually below 300 Hz. Therefore, these speakers may be distorting themselves without the room's help.

4. Repeat the procedure for each speaker including the subwoofers as a whole.

Note: If bass management is used, multiple subwoofers should be measured and equalized simultaneously. This is because their sum response is the true response and can be quite different from each subwoofers individual response.

5. 5. Use the available equalization or speaker settings to attempt to match the response of all speakers.
6. 6. Use the RTA's plotting function (often in a separate PC application) to overlay all the plots noting any anomalies. Save this plot in 1/3 octave mode to include in a final calibration report.

Failed Test — A detailed review of carefully level matched plots should show no more than a 1 to 2 dB variation. Make sure you have properly adjusted any tone or equalizer controls on the preamplifier and speakers. If any speakers demonstrate exceptional anomalies, it may be prudent to perform a near-field test to confirm the speaker is working properly.

Audio Calibration

Calibration is the process of evaluating, verifying, and tuning an audio system to optimize performance according to established sound quality goals. It is one part of the larger process of sound quality management performed by a trained CEDIA professional. Sound quality management or SQM encompasses all phases of system planning, design, project management, verification, and calibration. The calibration of a home theater sound system is its critical final phase and an important opportunity for an overall SQM review.

For passionate audiophiles, calibration is an art form of listening and making mechanical adjustments usually strictly by ear and, too often, without measurements. For the pure technician, calibration may only involve the adjustment of equalization, time delays, and speaker levels potentially ignoring mechanical adjustments that would solve acoustical problems. Still others leave it to an automated tool in the preamp/processor to complete. In a perfectly designed room, purely electronic adjustments work well. Unfortunately, in the real world, the calibrator often faces a room that was designed by amateurs.

The acoustical framework is defined as the physical layout of key acoustical elements including speakers, subwoofers, and listening positions. While a scientifically correct acoustical framework should be laid out during the design phase, there may be opportunities for fine tuning or correction of unanticipated on-site problems. The need to make final mechanical adjustments may be required for a quality result.

Calibration is the validation and adjustment of anything that affects sonic performance. A systematic combination of electronic tuning and mechanical adjustment makes for the best results. Therefore, the calibration process must proceed step-by-step, always aware that electronic adjustments may be changed by mechanical changes and vice-versa. The iterative process is one of evaluate, adjust, then evaluate again.

One calibrates a system by adjusting various parameters and design elements to produce a specific and quantifiable outcome. We attempt to quantify results based upon the sound quality goals. Obviously, sound quality can be a highly subjective thing to evaluate. Therefore, the sound quality goals must by specific enough to identify technical requirements yet stopping short of dictating qualitative preferences.

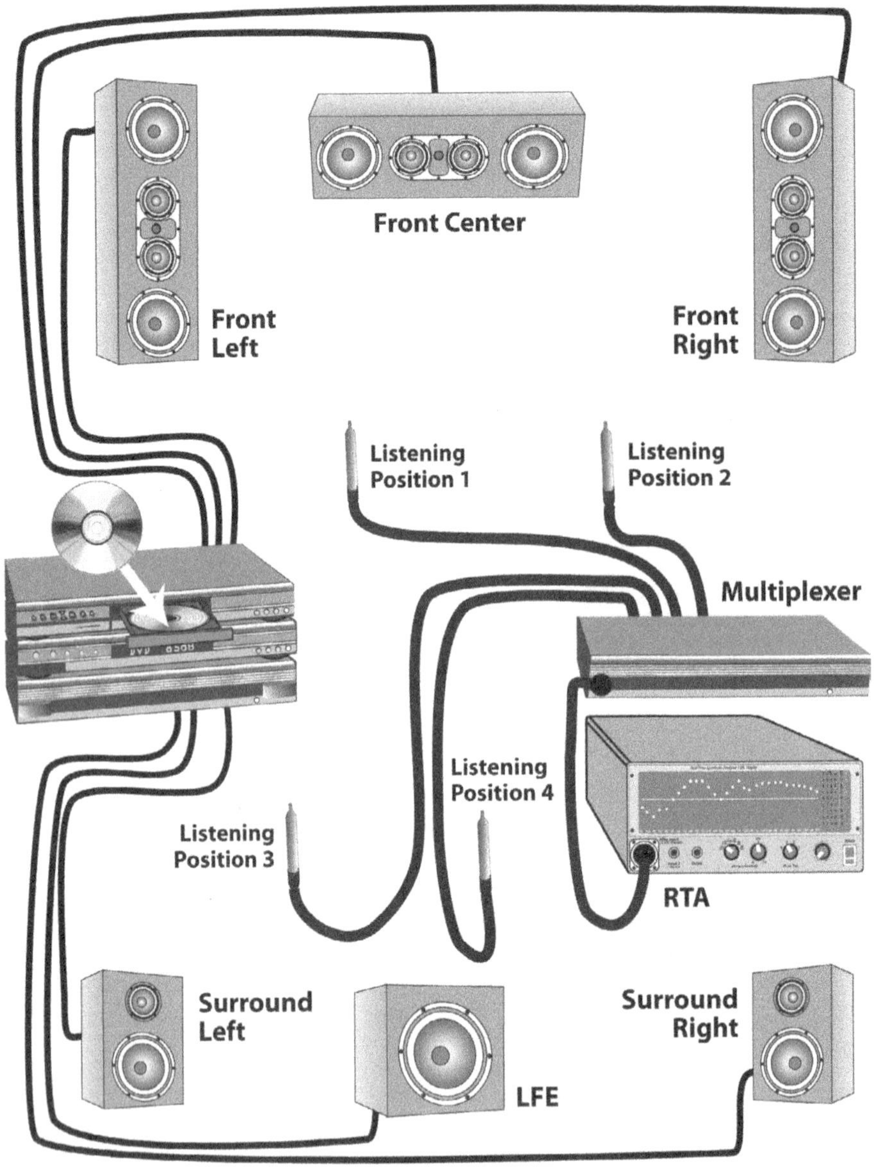

Figure 4-15. *Speaker Room Measurement Test Setup*

Sound Quality Goals

- *Clarity* - Clarity is the prime acoustical goal because its perfection depends on the successful attainment of all other goals. Of paramount importance is dialogue intelligibility in movies, but one must be able to understand musical lyrics, detect quiet background details, and sense realism for acoustical sounds.
- *Focus* - The ability to precisely locate each reproduced sonic cue or stereo image in a three-dimensional space is defined as acoustical focus. Recordings contain many such images superimposed side-to-side and front-to-back in every direction for 360 degrees around the listener. A system is said to have pin-point focus if, from the perspective of the listener, each of these images is properly sized, precisely located, and not wandering. Good focus also provides that

individual images be easily distinguishable from amongst others within the limits of the recordings quality.

- *Envelopment* - An audio system should reproduce virtual images of each recorded sound presenting the listener with its apparent source location in a three-dimensional space. Each sonic image relates apart of the recorded event and together these sounds compose a wrap-around soundstage that envelopes the listener. Proper envelopment requires that the soundstage be seamless for 360 degrees without interruption by holes or hot spots caused by speaker level imbalance or poor placement. While envelopment requires three-dimensional imaging of all sonic cues, of pivotal importance is the realistic recreation of the ambient sound field of the recorded venue. Focused sounds become more realistic as they move side to side and front to back with the backdrop of the ambient sounds of the intended venue.
- *Dynamics* - Dynamics is simply defined as the difference between the softest and loudest sounds reproducible by a sound system. While much emphasis is placed on the loudness side, it can be shown that the audibility of the softest sounds is an equal measure of system performance. Among the acoustical requirements for proper envelopment, focus and clarity is the necessity of hearing the sonic cues relating these qualities. If they are overwhelmed by excessive ambient noise or reverberation in a room, they are not properly audible. At a minimum, a system must be capable of reproducing loud passages with ease and without excess while soft sounds remain easily audible.
- *Response* - The frequency response of a system is a measurement of the relative levels of all reproduced audio frequencies. The smoothness of response can be observed in a variety of ways; as improper tonal balance including boomy bass, excessive treble, improper musical timbre, or a general lack of realism. Factors of importance include selection of high quality components and proper system set-up, including (in a small room) proper listener position, speaker position, and correct use of equalization. At a minimum, the system must be non-fatiguing at all sound levels, articulate, and faithful to the original signal.
- *Seat-to-Seat Consistency* - From seat to seat and row to row, the experience should be satisfying. Care should be taken to avoid placing listeners too close to walls and speakers, noting that centrally located seats are generally the best (there will always be a best sweet spot). The largest limiting factor here is the inclusion of too many seats. Acceptable seating locations are arranged within a triangular shaped area (sweet triangle) creating a single acceptable seat near the main speakers and gradually widening towards the rear (see Figure 4-2).

Final Calibration

The final calibration is the culmination of the sound quality management process. It represents an opportunity to validate that all aspects of SQM have been accomplished for a professionally designed system and to make design adjustments in non-engineered systems. The procedures can be defined as an iterative process using the following model:

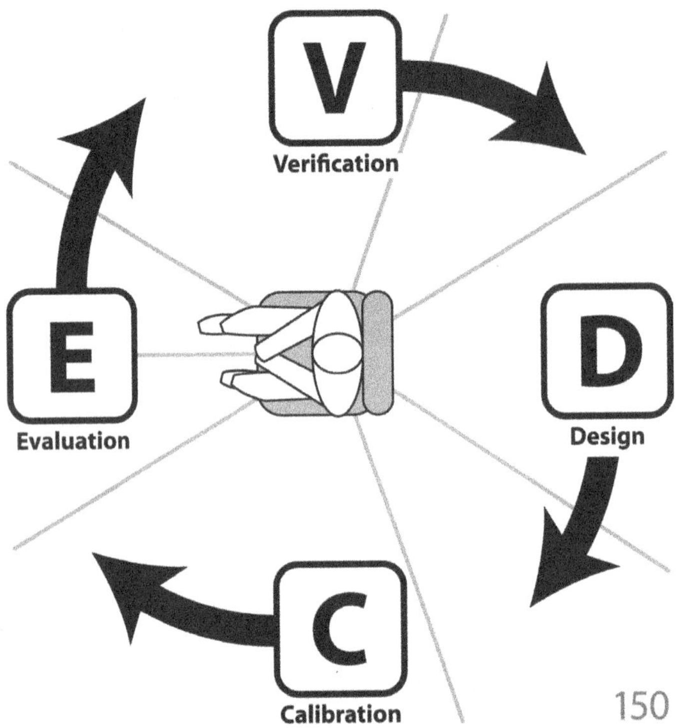

Figure 4-16. *Calibration Process Model*

Always begin with evaluation. Steps involved with the equipment calibration are:

Evaluation

- Initial test of system prior to calibration setup; don't waste time setting up to calibrate a non-working system
- Completion of a critical listening review of sonic goals
- Listening area response measurement (spatially averaged)

On-site Verification

- Calibrate bass management settings on pre-amp or processor; set small/large settings, select crossover frequency (80 Hz recommended)
- Check pre-amp/processor sub-functions
  - Input level or attenuation; try to make various sources similar in sound level
  - Set Dolby Pro-Logic settings (Panorama, Dimension, Center width)
  - Tone controls should be neutralized

  - Equalization should be turned off or neutralized (if present)
  - Check digital audio input mapping
  - Check audio/video mapping

- Source component check
  - All source components are working and set for best audio
  - Check Blu-Ray output settings (DTS HD, Dolby TrueHD, Multichannel output)
- Speaker near-field measurement; check that all speaker response plots are similar and crossover slope is correct
- Speaker response measurement at Listening Position; review that all speaker response plots are similar, note corrections to be enacted during calibration phase
- Complete speaker polarity check
- Complete resonance sweep; discover any vibrations caused by room furnishings by playing a sine wave sweep from 30 Hz to 300 Hz at a high level and then identify and eliminate the vibrations

Design Review

- Review seating positions; seats should be away from walls, and avoiding room's quarter length and width positions
- Review subwoofer placement; if necessary, reposition subwoofer(s) to counteract strongest length and width modes based upon initial listening position RTA plot
- Review front speaker placement; if necessary, reposition to achieve 45° to 60° separation from primary listening seat and make sure there is clear line-of-site to all listeners.
- Review left and right front speaker toe-in alignment; adjust to optimize focus by listening to reference recordings
- Review center speaker placement; position center speaker within 2' of LR height, make sure there is clear line-of-site to all listeners
- Review side speaker placement; position side speakers to symmetrical positions slightly behind primary (100° to 120° off center axis) or position side speakers to symmetrical positions equidistant from both rows of listeners, elevate side speaker positions to 18" above listener's heads
- Review rear surround speaker placement; position rear speakers to symmetrical positions equidistant from all listeners, elevate side speaker positions to 18" above listener's head
- Review side wall acoustical treatment; reposition treatment to balance soundstage focus vs. envelopment (remove treatment at front speaker reflection points to enhance envelopment or add to enhance focus), 25% absorption coverage is maximum recommended
- Review surround field treatment; reposition rear wall absorption to absorb front speaker reflections (center of wall), reposition diffusion

to diffuse surround speaker reflections, minimize absorption in upper rear half of room
- Review front wall acoustical treatment; reposition treatment to absorb front speaker low frequency reflections, add treatment behind projection screen
- Review ceiling acoustical treatment; add treatment for rooms without carpeting or larger rooms (25% maximum absorption coverage)

Electronic Calibration
- Equalize individual speakers based upon initial speaker response check by adjusting speaker crossover controls and individual speaker equalization (subwoofers should be adjusted simultaneously not individually).
- Equalize combined speaker response using global equalization settings.
- Set reference level according to pre-amp/processor manufacturer procedures.
- Set speaker levels in preamp/processor menu to match reference sound level, follow-up by fine tuning surround and center speaker levels by ear to accommodate all seats.
- Set speaker phase by calibration of time delay settings according to preamp/processor manufacturer procedures.
- Set subwoofer sound level; calibrate subwoofer sound level using RTA response plot until there is a smooth transition at the crossover frequency.
- Set subwoofer phase by changing time delay until crossover 1/3 octave band is at maximum level and there is a smooth transition at the crossover for combined speaker response.

Evaluation
- Re-evaluate acoustical goals; begin process again to revisit mechanical changes and recalibrate electronic settings to compensate

Immersive Technologies Update:
Recent developments in sound production technology have enhanced but also complicated the audio calibration process. As of this writing, Dolby has introduced Atmos, DTS is set to introduce its DTS:X technology, and Aura 3D is already well established as another option. The differences between these technologies are significant, but the common thread is the inclusion of additional speakers to enhance spatial envelopment and the creation of focused imaging in all directions. There are three keys to the successful calibration of systems employing these technologies:

1. Speaker placement for newly employed side and ceiling speakers

is dictated by guidelines provided by the individual companies. Correct recreation of the immersive effects is dependent on the correct placement of all speakers. (With the exception of DTS:X, whose "remapping" technology is designed to compensate for speaker position).

2. The inclusion of additional speakers, especially those near the listening positions, can introduce the possibility of speaker localization. Localization is the effect of creating a "hot spot" which can dilute and even collapse the envelopment of the overall sound or surround stage. It is prudent to take steps such as using bi-polar surround speakers and even repositioning to keep all speakers at least 5 to 8 feet from any listener. Manufacturer guidelines show acceptable variations for speaker position and the calibrator should take the maximum license to avoid localization.
3. The core framework for multi-channel reproduction remains stereo, 5.1 and 7.1 soundtracks and is likely to remain the mainstay for years to come. Any system design must be consistent with the established guidelines and sonic goals previously dictated. At the core of all immersive technologies is a fundamentally unchanged reliance on the proper placement of the basic 5.1 or 7.1 framework. New calibration techniques and tools are soon to be development to simplify calibration of additional speakers. In particular, test tones which allow each speaker to be evaluated (full range pink noise, polarity, ETC, etc.) must be created to allow a complete analysis. Equalization must be possible for all channels in AVR menus or as an independent device inserted in front of the power amplification.

As a final note, Dolby has developed the Atmos Enabled speaker design. This design employs a ceiling aimed speaker; be aware that the actual time delay measurement for these speakers must include the path of the reflection.

DISTRIBUTED AUDIO SYSTEM ENGINEERING

Distributed audio, or multi-room audio, was one of the disciplines which served as a foundation for the custom electronics industry as we know it today. Before home theater, the early pioneers of integration were finding ways to distribute music throughout the home and control that system from several different locations. The way this is accomplished today is often quite different than just a few years ago, due to a number of new technologies, network enabled components, and entirely new categories of audio sources. But the fundamentals of delivering background music to various sized spaces remain the same. For a detailed overview of traditional distributed audio systems, see Fundamentals of Residential Electronic Systems, Chapter 10. This section provides more advanced technical knowledge which builds on the content of that chapter.

Although many new methods of distributing audio signals are now available, there will always be the need for proper wiring, and an understanding of how to get proper coverage and background music levels in a variety of room types.

In-Ceiling Speaker Guidelines

Ceiling speaker placement can have a significant impact on the listener's experience. Since most distributed audio in the home is in stereo, this must be taken into consideration when selecting speaker locations. The goal is for most listeners to hear a stereo image if possible. In order to accomplish this, the designer must determine how the room will be used and where people will most likely be congregating. The Left and Right speakers then need to be placed so that all listeners can hear both sides of the stereo content. In a large room, such as a game room, this might mean having two pairs of speakers with opposite L/R configurations.

Some spaces, such as bathroom and kitchens, are best covered by using dual voice coil (stereo) speakers which reproduce both Left and Right channels. Placing a single point stereo speaker over a bathtub allows for an acceptable stereo image in that area, and another stereo speaker over the sink provides music for the person brushing their teeth. If a pair of mono speakers was used, the person at the sink would hear one channel of stereo, while the person in the tub heard just the other channel. It is important to note that one must always check to see that the product used in a high humidity environment such as a bathroom, shower, high heat steam, or sauna application has been designed for use in this type of specialty application.

In applications like medium or larger kitchen layouts, people tend to move about while preparing food. Again, the single point stereo speaker will provide the needed dispersion and evenly placed stereo imagining. Odd numbers of this type of speaker can be used to accommodate the unique shapes and traffic patterns of designer kitchens.

Some general guidelines for distributed audio include:

- Avoid placing speakers directly over areas which are likely to be used heavily for conversation
- Avoid speaker placement over doorways or heavily traveled pathways where a noticeable shift in SPL can be detected
- Design for typical operation at an SPL level 12 to 15 dB above the ambient background noise. In some cases, this background noise may be very minimal, but in an entertainment area where many people will be talking, that noise floor will be much higher.
- The variation in SPL from one area of the room to another should be minimal. A 3 dB variation would be ideal; 6 dB is acceptable.
- Use backboxes to ensure consistent performance of all speakers.
- Sweep the system with a sine wave from 20 Hz to 20 kHz to identify and eliminate buzzes and rattles.

Listing Plane Coverage

The primary goal of a high-quality sound system is to provide the listeners with an acoustic level higher than that of any background noise. The system must also ensure a wide frequency range, guarantee a smooth frequency response, and a uniform sound pressure level to provide optimum listening pleasure.

Speaker directivity (or dispersion) indicates how effective a speaker is at sending sound in a particular direction. Because each sound frequency has a different wavelength, it is not likely for a speaker to have the same directivity at all frequencies. As seen in Figure 4-17, different frequencies generally produce different dispersion patterns. Shown in Figure 4-18 are the relative amplitudes of various frequencies across the listening plane.

The goal of placing in-ceiling speakers is to provide a uniform level for listeners as they move about the room. This is accomplished by separating the speakers such that they fall within the 6 dB threshold, as shown in Figure 4-18. The 6 dB threshold is the coverage angle of the speaker where the sound drops off by 6 dB. The listening plane is often set for 5 feet (1.5 m) above the floor, to be close to the ear height of a standing person. A lower listening plane, about 3 feet (1 m), is used for a room that is primarily occupied by seated people. The height of the ceiling, which contains the speaker, also affects uniformity of coverage because of the coverage angle of the speaker. The distance between speakers should be adjusted so that the speaker coverage pattern overlaps at the 6 dB threshold of the speakers being installed. Many standard ceiling speakers have a 90 degree coverage pattern which allows the speaker spacing to be twice the distance from the listening plane to the ceiling and provides an overlap at the 6 dB threshold. For even more uniform coverage, speakers can be arranged to overlap at the 3 dB threshold, but this will entail more speakers to cover the same space. Careful review of the speaker's specification should indicate the directivity angle to be used in establishing uniform coverage.

Higher ceilings allow for increased spacing between speakers, but will require more amplifier power to generate the same level as a speaker in a lower ceiling. If we double the distance from the listening plane to the speaker, we reduce the provided SPL by up to 6 dB. To get that 6 dB of level back, we would need to quadruple amplifier power output.

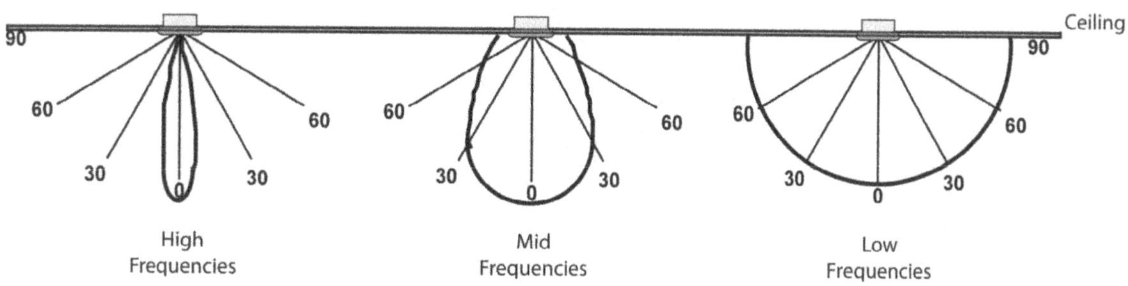

Figure 4-17. *Speaker Directivity*

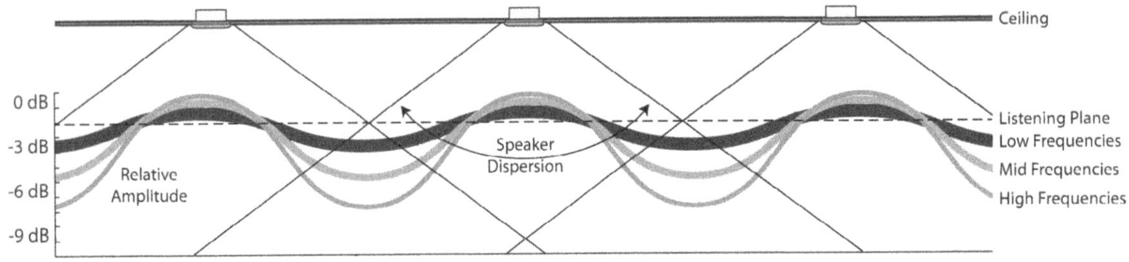

Figure 4-18. *Relative Amplitude of Three Ceiling Speakers*

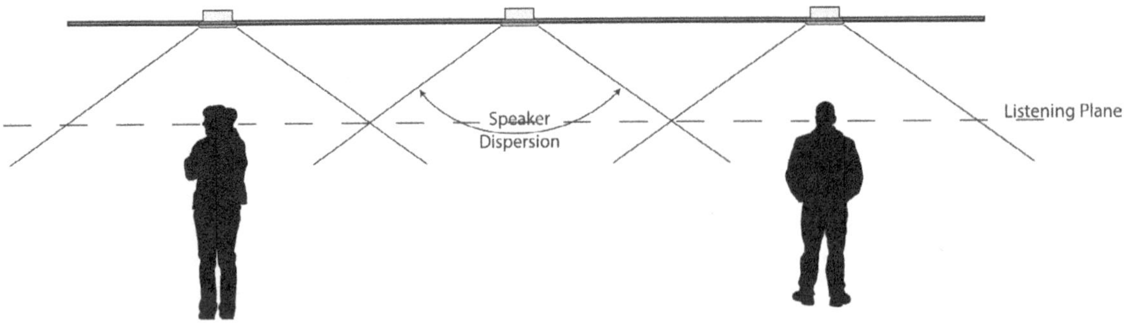

Figure 4-19. *Listening Plane When Placing Ceiling Speakers*

In-Wall Speakers

In-wall speakers provide a more traditional stereo field in situations where the listeners are seated and stationary, such as a den or office. They integrate well into the décor and can be painted to match the walls.

- Place in-walls at ear level in a standard two-channel angular configuration (45-60° between them at the listening position). Make sure you know the room and furniture layout.
- Use backboxes or sealed speakers to reduce sound transmission to adjacent rooms.
- If speakers are placed above ear level, specify a model which is amiable, so that the listener is on axis to at least the tweeter.
- Take care not to conflict with in-wall wiring, plumbing, or HVAC.

Outdoor Speakers

In most residential systems, there are outdoor spaces which are used regularly for relaxing and entertaining. Adding audio to these areas really enhances them and allows family and friends to enjoy music or the play-by-play of their favorite sporting event.

But the speakers, cabling and control considerations outdoors are very different from indoor applications. All components must be designed to withstand the elements; cold, heat, moisture, and dust. The designer needs to be aware of these requirements and select products carefully.

Cable and Control

Whether buried or not, all cabling outside of the home should be rated for direct burial. It will have an extremely durable jacket, and will ensure dependable performance. Any control devices intended to be used outside should be able to resist the elements, or be properly protected from them.

Speaker Types

Outdoor speakers come in a wide variety of styles. Most manufacturers offer bookshelf type full range speakers which are specially designed for outdoor use. These are often installed under the eave and aimed into the area to be covered. Also very popular are speakers which blend into the landscape, such as "rock" speakers. In recent years, many types of outdoor subwoofers have also become available, which greatly enhance the overall accuracy of outdoor systems.

Design Considerations

Transducers made to withstand harsh conditions are usually quite rugged, and heavier than their indoor counterparts. This usually results in lower efficiency. In addition, the outdoor acoustical space does not benefit from the reflections found in a room, so much of the sound is "wasted" rather than being enjoyed by the listener. These two issues mean that a great deal more power will be required to achieve performance similar to what the client is accustomed to indoors. Outdoors, the SPL will drop 6dB for every doubling of distance from the speaker to the listener. So when calculating the power needed, take into consideration the added power requirements based on the speaker sensitivity and the increased loss over distance. It is always a good idea to specify a separate amplifier for an outdoor zone, one that is capable of delivering high current. Outdoor speaker configurations often involve parallel or series/parallel wiring, so attention must be paid to the total impedance load presented to the amplifier. In general, keeping the speakers closer to the listeners will not only deliver more sound with less power, but minimize the amount of sound affecting the neighbors.

Invisible Speakers

"Invisible" speakers visually become part of the wall by being mounted flush with the wall's surface. A face panel makes up the active surface of the speaker, and is mounted into a frame and positioned in the wall with drywall screws attaching the frame to the studs.
Invisible speakers require some careful design and installation considerations:

- Be sure to specify good equalization capabilities, to achieve smooth response
- Add subwoofers in spaces where low frequency performance is desired
- Avoid locations where damage to the speaker is likely
- Record the paint specifications in case replacement is necessary

Subwoofers

Although subwoofers are not commonly seen as part of a distributed audio system, their addition can enhance the overall bass response in spaces where higher SPL and full-range performance is desired.

A variety of subwoofer types are available:

- Flush-mount
- In-wall
- In-ceiling
- Free standing
- In-floor (some models are installed in the floor with a grate to cover them)

Make sure the overall system is calibrated for balanced response, and consider allowing the subwoofer to be turned off when quieter background music is desired.

Constant Voltage Systems

A Constant Voltage speaker distribution system (also called a high impedance or 70-volt system) is typically seen in commercial rather than residential applications, where audio must be distributed over a large area. In some designs, the amplifier uses a step-up transformer or autoformer at the output of an audio amplifier and a step-down transformer at each speaker to provide a constant voltage output that can be used by multiple speakers (in this case, 70 volts), as shown in Figure 4-20.

Speaker cabling can be run over relatively long distances with less loss, due to the higher voltage and lower current, and can support many speakers as compared to typical high-current speaker wiring. An advantage of this system is that decreased wire size can be used to connect amplifiers and speakers, with less power lost to the resistance of the wire. Disadvantages include the additional cost of the transformer, reduced frequency response, and possible distortion if transformers are overdriven.

The most popular 70-volt system is the direct-drive system, offering lower cost, less weight, and less bulk than other systems. These systems also allow maximum volume levels to be set at each speaker. However, shorted or grounded speaker lines may cause significant damage to amplifiers. Amplifiers with transformer coupled outputs are less likely to be damaged. Although 70-volt systems tend to be the most common application for constant voltage systems in the North American market, it should be noted that 100-volt systems are very popular throughout the rest of the world.

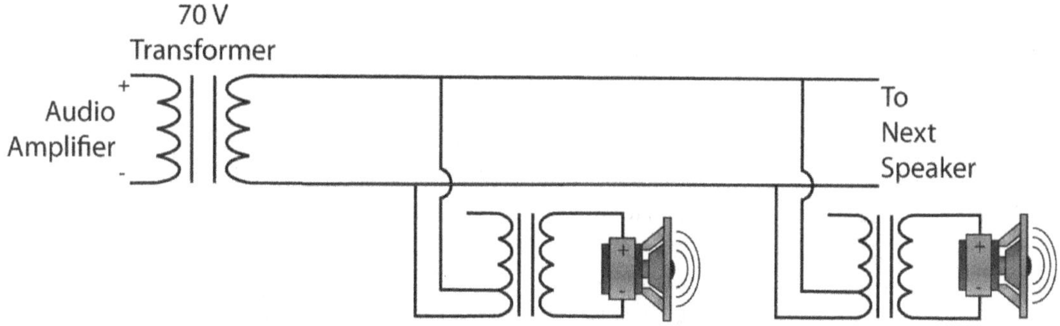

Figure 4-20. *70 Volt Distribution System*

MULTI-ROOM AUDIO IN THE 21ST CENTURY

The advances in wired and wireless networking over the past decade have led to many new possibilities in the field of multi-room audio, as well as heightened consumer awareness and expectations. Gone are the days when the only way to accomplish multi-room audio was through a centralized distribution system, requiring large power amplifiers and dedicated wiring runs to each room of the home. The advancement in wired and Wi-Fi network devices that allow components to be placed easily around the home opened the doors to the new paradigm of decentralized systems, allowing not only for the ease of adding the latest digital streaming services, but also for decentralized audio solutions to be seamlessly added to a modern audio system.

Centralized systems have been an industry standard for years. In the past, all multi-room systems were centralized with sources and amplifiers located in one location and all speakers and control keypads wired back to that location, requiring the use of "home-runs" of cable. Such a system guaranteed reliable performance and provided shared or independent access to source component and zone control options as well as other features to be made available across the entire home. While those systems still remain a viable option, networking technology has allowed for the decentralization of many of these systems with a local area network handling the distribution of both audio content and the signaling that allows users to easily control their audio from multiple locations in the home, eliminating the need for "home-runs."

The other major change to multi-room audio that has come about in the past few years is the transition from having audio content being entirely stored at home to having a large percentage of many users' audio content being provided via a network connection or, even more importantly, from an Internet-based source.

Another key change that must be taken into consideration is the impact of the smartphone on a user's expectations for their home audio. Modern multi-room audio systems must be able to adapt to having users demand access to the same audio content the users have on their phones or tablets.

Phones or tablets must be able to be used as an audio source in most systems. In the past, this was normally done with physical cable connections or docking devices, but modern systems must allow for users to be able to make these connections wirelessly from anywhere in the home. Phones and tablets are now key audio sources in a multi-room audio system. In addition to acting as source devices, these same phones and tablets are also now an important control interface option that users expect to be able to use at any time as a convenient way to control their home's audio.

Because of the wide variety of content now available via the Internet, there has been a simultaneous decline in the need for large audio matrix devices capable of switching multiple analog or digital sources in a home. Only a few years ago, an installation might have included multiple CD changers, iPod docks, etc. In a modern system, a single streaming audio source may be sufficient to meet a user's needs. There are two primary ways to add streaming audio as a source to a multi-room audio system. The first involves using a hardware device as a dedicated source that is always available, and the second involves providing a way of accessing audio content on demand from a mobile device like a phone or tablet.

Streaming Audio from a Dedicated Streaming Source

There are many options in the marketplace for an integrator to choose from when selecting a dedicated streaming audio source. The typical CEDIA member company has the choice of using standalone dedicated streaming products (offered by several well-known manufacturers), or using integrated solutions where a streaming source is built-in as a source option on a smart TV, game console, AVR, Blu-ray player, or multi-room controller/amplifier.

Advantages of a Dedicated Streaming Source

Always available: The dedicated source is always present in the system and can be accessed by anyone in the home at any time.

Easy to integrate: A dedicated source is easy to integrate into a larger home automation system or to use for programming scenes and favorites that a user can conveniently access.

Higher Audio Quality: Many streaming audio devices offer support for audio quality exceeding CD-quality and even allowing playback of High-Res Audio (24-bit/192kHz) as an option.

Reliability: By using a dedicated source, audio installers are free to use dedicated, wired connections when needed, eliminating the risk of signal loss or connection issues that can come from a wireless connection.

Easy access to local audio files: For users with their own audio collections stored on a computer, USB, or NAS drive, having a dedicated source provides an easy way to connect with and access those collections.

Disadvantages of a Dedicated Streaming Source

Limited streaming content: Many streaming devices are limited to a fixed number of content providers. While this can be expanded by software/firmware updates, most of these systems are always playing catch-up, trying to add the newest streaming services to their product offerings. If a new service starts operating that offers enticing content to its users, there is typically a delay before the service can be accessed by a dedicated device. Options like Bluetooth®, AirPlay®, and GoogleCast® can provide an alternative that allows a user to access new audio services as soon as they become available. See below for further discussion of these options.

Location: When installing a dedicated streaming source, installation location becomes a consideration, with some systems limited to a centralized structure where all devices must be grouped together in one area of the home. This location might impact accessibility via wireless connections such as Wi-Fi and Bluetooth. For example, an equipment rack located in a basement at one end of a home will have limited Bluetooth access and be more difficult to get to if a user wants to insert a USB flash drive with music files.

Updateability: Depending on the device, updateability can become a consideration. Some devices can offer easier updates to provide new service offerings and feature updates for users than others. For users who express an interest in keeping up-to-date with the latest streaming sources, the ease and frequency of updates can become an important consideration.

Limited Control Options: Most dedicated streaming sources offer a variety of control options when integrated into a 3rd party control system, but only offer app control for normal operation. If a user is interested in a dedicated keypad or touchscreen for control without using a 3rd party control system, the options available become more limited.

Streaming Audio from Mobile Devices

The proliferation of smartphones and tablets in the marketplace combined with the popularity of digital audio content has led to the situation where many people carry their favorite music and audio content with them at all times. When combined with the capability of streaming additional audio from their home network or from the Internet, the result is that most users can have complete access to their favorite music at all times, and are now demanding the ability to enjoy that content anywhere in their home. While music is likely the most important audio content for many people, keep in mind that the actual content can be quite diverse, including such additional items as audiobooks, podcasts, etc.

When using a mobile device as an audio source there are several considerations:

Type of Content

Locally Stored Audio - When using a mobile device as a storage device for audio, the same considerations that affect all digital audio file storage still apply. Audio content can be stored in multiple file formats including but not limited to MP3, M4A, WAV, FLAC, etc. Within those formats, there are multiple possibilities for encoding the content at different bit rates and with different audio sampling size options. This is in addition to the possible limitations imposed by Digital Rights Management (DRM) that can limit playback of certain audio to a limited number of devices only. In other words, there are many items that must be taken into consideration in order to ensure that the audio can be played properly in the way that the user intends. When creating any of these files, proper consideration must be taken for naming the files and for creating the appropriate tags for systems to index and access the files properly (song/track names, album names, artist names, genre, etc.). All of these items are outside the scope of this section.

For the purposes of this section and distributing the content in a multi-room environment, the main considerations for an audio installation profession is whether the content stored on a mobile device is capable of being properly accessed and played. The assumption for the remainder of this section will be that all audio content is properly encoded/formatted/stored for the desired access and playback.

Streaming Audio from a Network/Internet - Streaming audio from a local network or, more importantly, from an Internet source has become one of the most popular methods for accessing audio in the 21st century. A user's mobile device becomes the key access point for the content and is often also used as the primary control device for that content. In this regard, the mobile device is used as an audio source in a multi-room system and the primary considerations for the installer is how the audio output will be delivered from the mobile device to the home's multi-room system. The type of streamed content available to users via the Internet grows almost daily and includes internet radio and services such as Pandora, Spotify, Deezer, Tidal, Apple Music, Rhapsody, Slacker, TuneIn, vTuner, etc.

Audio Delivery Method

Physical connections

Analog Connection - Most mobile devices include an analog audio output that allows a physical cable connection from the device to an input jack of an audio system. This method allows an easy connection to traditional audio systems, but suffers the limitation of any physical connection: the mobile device becomes tethered to a particular location and must remain in place whenever it is being used for audio playback. The key advantage of this type of connection is that the analog output from a mobile device is now free of any formatting/encoding/DRM limitations and can be easily distributed around a home using any conventional method.

Digital Connection (File storage device) - Most mobile devices include a USB-type connection that allows them to be used as a file storage device to provide audio content to a separate playback device. As with the analog connection, the biggest limitation of this type of connection is that the device is tethered and must remain in place while it is being used as an audio source.

Figure 4-21. *Wireless Distributed Audio System Topology*

Wireless Connections

Local connection (e.g. Bluetooth) - Bluetooth has become one of the most popular ways for users to connect their mobile devices to an external audio system. The audio systems range from standalone amplified speakers to dedicated Bluetooth receivers that connect to larger audio systems, including multi-room systems. Almost all mobile devices on the market today offer a Bluetooth audio connection of some type. While an in-depth discussion of Bluetooth is outside the scope of this section, the key considerations for audio installation professionals are:

Range: Bluetooth is typically limited to a range of about 10m (33 feet) or less.

Audio Quality: Bluetooth offers an audio encoding method that is less than CD-quality, but there are additional encoding systems that some Bluetooth products offer such as aptX® that improve the quality to "CD-like" levels. Keep in mind that for encoding systems like aptX, both the mobile device and the Bluetooth receiver must be capable of handling the encoding method.

Single Connection Point: A mobile device can only connect to only one

Bluetooth playback device at a time. This is acceptable when connecting to something like a single amplified speaker but complicates the issue using Bluetooth audio as a source in a multi-room audio system.

Location of the Receiver: While there are many Bluetooth capable devices/systems that can be used to distribute Bluetooth audio around a home, most of these use an internal Bluetooth receiver that limits the range to the areas near the receiver. Flexible systems exist that allow the separation of the Bluetooth receiver and its associated audio output, allowing the receiver to be placed in a more ideal location within the home and the audio signal to be distributed from a separate location elsewhere.

Control and Metadata: With Bluetooth, protocols for handling bi-directional control of the audio and for transmitting metadata are not always available in a playback device, so that while audio can be transmitted and played, the only control options remain at the mobile device itself. If users require the ability to pause, skip tracks, and view the metadata information of their audio from a remote area of their home, the Bluetooth receiving device must be capable of handling this requirement.

Expandability of Content: The Bluetooth connection allows almost infinite expandability of content. Whatever audio source is available to the mobile device can be outputted to the Bluetooth connection. Any new apps, streaming services, or internet sources that come to the market and are accessible by a mobile device will be able to use the Bluetooth connection.

Wi-Fi Network Connection (e.g. AirPlay®, GoogleCast®, Spotify® Connect) - There are now several options for users to make a wireless connection to their audio system that overcomes many of the limitations of Bluetooth.

Range: Because these types of connections use Wi-Fi, their range is not only greater, but also expandable as needed. By using Wi-Fi range extenders or additional Wi-Fi access points, range is no longer an insurmountable issue and can far surpass that available via Bluetooth or similar connections. Audio Quality: This depends on the service being used, but is generally better than Bluetooth can offer due to the use of a wider-bandwidth Wi-Fi connection.

Multiple Connections: Many of these types of connections allow streaming to more than one device simultaneously. Additionally, like Bluetooth, it is possible to use the output from AirPlay or GoogleCast to use as a source input into a larger multi-room distributed audio system that can be routed anywhere in the home.

Control and Metadata: Many of these types of connections allow bi-directional control and metadata. This allows keypads/touchscreens or 3rd party apps to control the audio content being provided by the mobile device. Expandability of Content: As with Bluetooth, there is an almost infinite expandability of content. Whatever audio source is available to the mobile device can be sent to an AirPlay or GoogleCast type of connection. Any new apps, streaming services, or internet sources that come to the market and are accessible by a mobile device will be able to be used easily in the multi-room system.

Wireless Distribution, Network Based Distribution

One of the key reasons that streaming audio systems have been able to proliferate so quickly in the marketplace is their capability to be connected easily through wireless connections, requiring no new wires or cables from their users. For a DIY consumer, this is a key selling point and for many installations done by a professional audio installer, it can be a key consideration as well.

Wi-Fi Connections - Devices that connect via Wi-Fi follow the same constraints as any other Wi-Fi device. They must remain within range of their access point and communicate only with that same access point. When the range of a Wi-Fi system needs to be expanded, this can be done with additional Wi-Fi access points or range extenders. Expanding a Wi-Fi network allows for any Wi-Fi device to connect from more locations and often provides the benefit of adding increased range for App control of devices within the home.

Mesh-type Connections - Some devices operate in a mesh type of network that lets a device connect to another device within range rather than requiring a Wi-Fi access point. In this type of system, the range can be expanded by adding more devices to the system, each within range of another device. These devices can typically connect both to a Wi-Fi or wired Ethernet connection as well as establishing their mesh connection to each other. Control is usually accomplished via an App from a smartphone or tablet that is connected via Wi-Fi to the home network.

Integrating These Technologies into Legacy Systems

Most streaming audio devices provide either analog audio outputs or digital audio outputs that can be easily integrated into legacy systems. The issue that arises is control of the overall system. Legacy systems are often controlled by dedicated keypads or custom control interfaces that cannot support controlling a new streaming source that has been added to the system.

This often leads to a "2-control" solution where a user is required to turn on their legacy system and select the new streaming device as the source. After that, the user can control their audio content and volume level via their streaming device's App. This is not an ideal situation for a user and removes many of the aspects of intuitiveness and ease-of-use that they liked in their multi-room audio system.

One way to avoid this is to do a larger project that replaces the key source components and user interfaces of a system so that a single control can be used for the entire system. Depending on the scope of the project, the user's requirements, and the project budget, another alternative is to remove all existing user interfaces and let users use their native streaming device apps to control their entire system, turning rooms on and off, adjusting volume, and selecting content.

If the budget allows for it, some of the problems with mixing new streaming devices into a legacy audio distribution system can be overcome by adding a 3rd party control system or home automation system.

One advantage of a legacy system is that an audio installer can often utilize existing wiring and gear. Updating the source equipment can often be done without replacing speaker wiring or existing speaker installations when the budget or customer requirements don't require new speakers.

How this New Paradigm Fits into the Business Plan

The success of streaming audio in the marketplace brings a lot of new opportunities to CEDIA channel integrator. Most consumers are now very familiar with streaming audio, and are expecting it as part of their home's audio/video system. Understanding the customers' needs and their expected uses of their home audio system will go a long way toward specifying the proper system to meet these needs. There are revenue opportunities that can come from any of the following:

Recurring Monthly Revenue - As networked audio becomes more important, there are many opportunities for audio installers to "own" the network for their customers, configuring and maintaining the home network or even just the audio portion and charging a monthly fee to their customers for doing so.

Wiring and Speaker Installation - While there are many consumer wireless systems on the marketplace, many consumers desire the look of a professionally installed audio system where loudspeakers are hidden in the ceilings or walls rather than by using amplified speakers around the home.

Updating Legacy Systems - Finding new customers can often be a difficult business proposition. By being able to update legacy systems, audio installers can reach out to customers they already know and add new revenue opportunities for their business.

HIGH RESOLUTION AUDIO

For decades the public lived with, and enjoyed, the sound of AM/FM radio and vinyl records. In the early 1980s, these formats were joined by the compact disc (CD) and for a time the CD format threatened to completely extinguish the vinyl format. By the late 1990s however, digital music files burst upon the scene and by the mid 2000's Apple with its iTunes software, Apple Music Store and iPod products turned the tables on the CD format by leading the charge for downloads becoming the format of choice for consumers. Now just a decade later, both downloads and physical media sales (CD) sales are slumping, and today's new way to consume music—streaming—has become, by far, the overwhelming method to enable the public to listen to music.

The one caveat with the migration over to streaming audio has been vinyl. The once dismissed format is enjoying an unforeseen renaissance in popularity that in many respects has overshadowed the music industry's next-generation high-resolution audio format that is slowly gaining acceptance.

Streaming Media Trending

Each year, the research company Nielsen releases its annual year-end music report, and the 2014 numbers told an interesting story. According to the company's research, physical media sales, which include the upward trending vinyl LP format declined, while on-demand streaming content consumption rose 54 percent to reach the 164 billion stream figure.

Given the continuing emphasis on streaming media and services such as Pandora, Spotify, Rhapsody, and newer services such as TIDAL and Apple Music, the public, which includes custom electronics professionals, should expect this category to continue to thrive. Looking at how streaming services have grown over the past few years, the Recording Industry of America Association (RIAA) reports that since 2011 paid subscriptions for on-demand music services have more than tripled. In 2014, those numbers grew 26 percent over the prior year to 7.7 million subscribers.

How this affects the systems integrator is hard to say. Likely what installers may prefer to look at beyond the actual content libraries of these services is the quality of these streams. Currently, TIDAL is the only service that offers "CD-quality" streams without having to buy specific hardware. Deezer, like TIDAL, is another European streaming service, which has come over to America with "CD-quality" streams. Unlike TIDAL, Deezer's Elite service is available exclusively through Sonos.

What is High Res Audio?

There is a debate among marketing executives that would like to interchange the specifications of the CD format (16-bit/44kHz) with the term high-resolution audio, and those who contend that high-resolution audio offers a superior listening experience to "CD quality." While not finalized, the RIAA, The Recording Academy Producers & Engineers Wing, the organization that produces The Grammys, the Digital Entertainment Group (DEG) and the Consumer Electronics Association (CEA) have begun work on specific definitions for high-res audio. The RIAA is focusing more on branding and consumer identification. Recently, the record industry body announced a new logo to allow consumers to identify high-res music more easily. Using the term "High Resolution Music," which was agreed to jointly between the various parties, the RIAA states the label is now defined as, "recordings which have been mastered from better than CD-quality [48kHz/20-bit or higher] music sources, which represent what the artists, producers and engineers originally intended." Simplifying the RIAA's statement, dealers should look for files and content labeled 24-bit/44kHz, 24-bit/48kHz, 24-bit/96kHz and 24-bit/192kHz. Moreover, the audiophile DSD format offers files usually labeled as 2.8MHz and 5.6MHz, or DSD64 and DSD128. The newly created logo is designed to identify recordings made available in the U.S., Canada and Europe for commercial downloads and streaming.

Assembling a High Res System

In the early days of digital audio, computers provided the most convenient method to play back high res audio files. While still the case today, a number of companies have developed products that play a variety of digital formats, including high resolution.

For users that are employing either an Apple or PC computer, there are a number of software solutions that facilitate the playback of high-resolution such as Amarra, JRiver Media Center and Pure Music. Using computers in the vast majority of cases means the audio will need to be converted to analog at some point to facilitate the connection to a preamplifier, integrated amplifier or A/V receiver. To accomplish this task, dealers will need to utilize a digital-to-analog converter (DAC). These external boxes were once a niche audiophile product back in the 1990s, but recently the popularity of DACs has exploded because of the public's consumption of streaming media and high-resolution audio.

A modern DAC usually features a choice of a USB (for computer connections) as well as coax and optical inputs. Outputs normally include RCA, but high-performance models will sometimes offer XLR (balanced) output options. These products are designed to maintain signal quality—and in a growing amount of cases through the asynchronous USB technology—which was developed by the audiophile company Wavelength Audio to allow the DAC to control the clocking functions of the computer to minimize distortion due to digital jitter to best ensure the best possible signal. Depending on the system, that converted analog signal can be sent to active (amplified) speaker in a smaller, desktop type of system or as previously mentioned, sent to a receiver or preamplifier as part of a larger system.

Digital Audio Comes in Many Forms

Lossy formats such as AAC and MP3 currently dominate the market. However, with storage becoming more affordable, consumers are increasingly using formats such as Apple Lossless and FLAC, which offer a higher quality audio and still provide some reduction in needed storage space.

Digital files can be confusing in that AAC, MP3, Apple Lossless, WAV and AIFF all employ different methods to meet their respective goals. The one common element of these file formats is they all employ Pulse Code Modulation (PCM) technologies.

As for Direct Stream Digital (DSD), this is a format that audiophiles will often say sounds better than PCM. DSD utilizes a completely different method to sample and store its data, and for the most part it's been a niche technology that's never been used outside of the audiophile community. DSD is the format behind the Super Audio CD format (SACD) that reached its height of popularity around the turn of the millennium. Currently most, if not all DACs that are available in the consumer market will play the PCM-based files. A small, but slowly increasing number of DACs are adding DSD file playback compatibility to their respective feature sets.

A note on data rates: CD quality equates to approximately 1,400kbps and high-resolution audio files reach as high as 4,400kbps. For comparison purposes, streaming media can be as low as 92kbps, and as already noted, up to "CD quality levels." Most music downloads offer 128kbps or 256kbps of quality.

The Return of an Old Friend

Earlier, it was pointed out that Nielsen's year-end numbers had one bright spot in the category of physical media sales: the vinyl LP. In 2014, vinyl sales increased 52 percent over the previous year, and vinyl sales represent 6 percent of total sales. Vinyl sales have been trending upwards for several years, and the interesting part of the vinyl format's revival is the fact that much of the format's sales are "off the books" as used record sales.

Enthusiasts would argue that vinyl has always sounded better than digital audio, particularly CDs. In addition, there are some audiophiles that point out the reason why vinyl sounds better is that despite its inferior signal-to-noise ratio, the mastering engineers of yesteryear produced more dynamic recordings than what today's mastering engineers are allowed to produce. This is an ongoing argument that relates to the topic of the "loudness wars" and how music is made, but even discounting the mastering argument, vinyl sales are legitimately growing.

These days, turntables costs range from as little as $300, to as much as $120,000. Phono preamplifiers, which are a necessary component to amplify the low-level signals produced by a phono cartridge, range in cost from $100 to thousands of dollars. There are also turntables on the market the ship as "turnkey" solutions with cartridges preinstalled and even built-in phono and USB preamps that eliminate the need for other components. One quick note on these USB-equipped models: USB turntables are popular for consumers that want to convert their analog LPs into digital files for storage on their networks and iTunes folders. It's also proof that turntable manufacturers are adapting to today's market.

References

F.E. Toole, "Sound Reproduction", Focal Press 2008.

Devantier, A. (2002). "Characterizing the Amplitude Response of Loudspeaker Systems", 113th Convention, Audio Eng. Soc., Preprint 5638.

CHAPTER 5

VIDEO SYSTEMS

Since the early 1900's when the idea of sending images through the air became a reality, an entire industry has grown up around the television set. The progression from black and white to color was followed by massive movie screens and higher quality audio and visual effects. Even now, with digital technology becoming the norm, we must remember that this too will evolve into the next technology age. As a result, the goal for most homeowners is an integrated audio visual system that showcases today's technology, but that will constantly evolve as technology makes new advances.

In an ideal television system, program material would be produced, distributed, and reproduced in such a way that the audience could view the final product exactly as it is intended to be seen. That is the essence of a functional communications system. The goal of the systems integrator is to produce images that accurately reproduce the incoming electronic signal. Systems integrators must strive to reproduce quality levels seen in the motion picture theatre industry. In an effort to improve that industry's image, the quality of projected film has improved under close scrutiny from several independent organizations. In our current television system, the HDTV in our home is the weak link in properly presenting program information. You must never lose sight of the fact that system integrators are an offshoot of the entertainment industry.

From conception of the color system in 1953, it has taken the program production community endless years to achieve fairly consistent quality in source materials. These efforts can be seen in both NTSC and ATSC materials. As a systems integrator, you must reproduce this material accurately.

A PRIMER ON IMAGE QUALITY

To work with video signals and video displays, it is important to know the basics of image quality. Understanding how the eye and the brain "see" images provides greater insight as to how different metrics will affect the perceived image quality.

Human Eyesight

The human eye has two different types of receptors, rods and cones, which are unevenly distributed across the retina. The eye contains approximately 100 million rods and only 7million cones.

Rods—translate light into monochrome (from black to white):

- More sensitive and are used in dim lighting and at night
- Prevail in the periphery of the retina
- Have lower visual acuity than cones

Cones—convert image to color, separate cones for red, green, and blue:

- Less sensitive than rods and are used in daylight
- Predominately in the center of the retina
- Three kinds of color sensitive pigments (red, green and blue), which allow each type to respond to a different range of the visible wavelength (If one or two of the pigments are missing, a form of color blindness results.)
- Sensitive to color wavelengths that are very similar to the RGB wavelengths of the video signal
- Receives a binary signal that is either on or off
- Color is specified by which cone is excited and how often it sends a signal
- Have high visual acuity

The brain takes all these signals from the rods and cones and processes them in order to create a visual image.

Perception of Color

Light, as humans experience it, is a narrow range of electromagnetic radiation that is visible to the human eye, and is responsible for the sense of sight. Visible light consists of wavelengths that range from approximately 380 nanometers to approximately 740 nanometers. The eye perceives these different wavelengths as different colors. The cones in the eye each contain one of three types of chemical pigments that are sensitive to red, green, or blue. When all three colors are mixed together the result is what is considered white and the absence of all colors yields black. A video imaging system has the ability to show virtually all visible colors depending on the ratio of these three colors.

Visual Acuity

Visual acuity is the human eye's capacity to distinguish details and shapes. This acuity is measured in the eye's ability to resolve fine details at a standardized distance. The generally accepted benchmark for good visual acuity is the Snellen fraction 20/20. This fraction denotes that an observer standing 20 feet away can discern letter down to the 20/20 line of an eye chart.

These letters are sized to occupy a small fraction of one degree of visual viewing angle. One degree of viewing angle is equal to sixty subdivisions called arcminutes. The strokes and voids that form the letters of the 20/20 line of the eye chart are one arcminute thick. This means that for a person with 20/20 vision, the smallest observable detail is one arcminute. In the world of video, this translates to having the ability to discern 60 pixels per degree of viewing angle.

Human visual acuity is at its highest in the center of the field of vision, and is surprisingly low in the periphery field. For this reason, it is critical to maintain adequate vertical resolution.

THE METRICS OF VIDEO QUALITY

When evaluating the performance of a display device there are generally four major metrics to consider:

- Dynamic Range
- Color Saturation
- Color Accuracy
- Resolution

Dynamic Range

Dynamic range (commonly called contrast ratio) is the difference in light output of the brightest value (white) to that of the darkest value (black) and is typically stated as the ratio between maximum and the minimum brightness values (e.g. 100:1).

Dynamic range is the metric of a picture on a display that most notably drives the perception of image quality. This is because the rods of the human eye are responsible for processing light intensity (black and white) and are more sensitive and numerous than the cones which process color. In other words, humans perceive detail in black and white and the color enhances that detail. Wide dynamic range gives the "effect" of higher resolution by revealing detail and provides added depth of field. Without good dynamic range, the video image will begin to lose detail in the very dark or very bright portions of the picture.

High Dynamic Range

At the time of writing this book, there is a movement for a significant increase in dynamic range, called High Dynamic Range (HDR), or in some instances Enhanced Dynamic Range (EDR). The general purpose of HDR is to create significantly greater peak white levels to better represent bright scenes in real life. In today's flat panel displays and projectors, white levels are typically under 100 nits. As standards move forward, the goal is to hit up to 5,000 - 10,000 nits for very brief periods of time. An example of HDR would be watching a video of an aluminum airplane flying on a sunny day. As the plane tips its wings and the sun reflects back towards the viewer's eyes, there would be a brief, intense white level that mimics a real life experience. HDR in consumer displays is nascent but will make a large impact moving forward.

Color Saturation

Color saturation is the amount of color in the picture. Having too much or too little color will distort the image. This is especially important when considering human skin tones. An under-saturated image will make people look pale, while an over-saturated image will make them look sunburned.

Color Accuracy

Color accuracy is a measure of how faithfully the display produces each of the primary colors (red, green, and blue) in its pure form. Because these colors are not produced by mixing, they must be accurate so that a red Ferrari on the TV looks like the one in the customer's garage. If the colors are weak, the picture will look lifeless; if they are too strong, everything will look like a cartoon.

Color Gamut and Color Space

As most have experienced, the amount and quality of color on displays vary greatly. This is in part due to the quality of the display, but not completely. There are two factors regarding which colors can or cannot be reproduced by a display: gamut and color space.

Technicolor defines gamut as "a range of colors that a particular device can capture or show" and color space as "a predefined specification that delineates a particular group of colors. A color space is mapped into a device's gamut so the device's colors correspond to real-world colors." What this means is that there are significantly more colors of the visible spectrum that displays cannot reproduce. However, increases in technology and new color space standards that are increasing display gamut. Currently, the International Telecommunications Union Recommendation (ITU) BT.709 is the standard color space for HDTV. The industry is moving towards ITU BT.2020 which has approximately 50% more colors than BT.709. However, the transition to Rec. 2020 will take multiple years to implement. The standard color space for digital movie theaters is DCI-P3 (Digital Cinema Initiative) which falls roughly in-between BT.709 and BT.2020.

Resolution

Video resolution is defined as the number of picture elements (pixels) from side to side (horizontal resolution) and/or top to bottom (vertical resolution) of a display device. Resolution is commonly expressed as either the product of the horizontal and vertical resolution (i.e. 1920x1080) or the vertical resolution and scanning format (i.e. 1080p). As the number of pixels increases (assuming the size of the display stays the same) the size of the pixels gets smaller and smaller, allowing for finer detail. However, for an average viewer (20/20 vision), increasing the number of pixels above 60 per degree of viewing angle (meaning the pixels become smaller than one arcminute) will have no effect on image detail as the viewer's visual acuity is not high enough to discern the difference.

It is important to note that both the display device and the source material have a native resolution and it is very common for these to be different. Even if both the source and display claim to be "1080p," there are often slight differences. For example, it is common for content providers to reduce horizontal resolution (remember that human visual acuity is best in the center of the field of view, and it gets lower in the periphery) if compression is necessary when sending video information. This reduction in horizontal resolution results in differences between the native resolution of the display (1920x1080) and the resolution of the source material received from the broadcast company. If a difference in resolution occurs, somewhere along the line, pixels must be added, deleted, cropped, or shifted via processing. This processing is typically done by the display device itself, but can be affected by settings in the source device, or even done by an outboard video scalar, or more commonly "scaler".

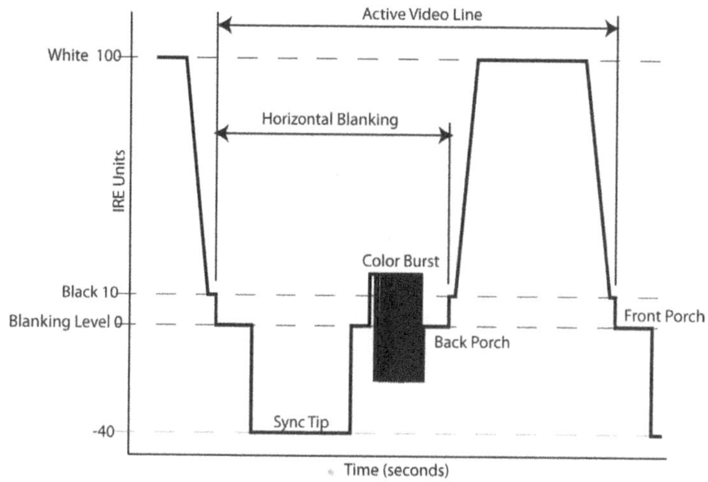

Figure 5-1. *NTSC Signal*

NATIONAL TELEVISION SYSTEMS COMMITTEE (NTSC)

In 1940, the Federal Communications Commission (FCC) established the NTSC to create standards for analog video distribution. In 1953, this organization set the color television standard that was implemented in the United States, and eventually in Mexico, Canada, and other countries.

The NTSC standard for television defines a composite analog video signal with a fixed vertical resolution of 486 of the total 525 horizontal lines stacked on top of each other. The remaining 39 lines are known as the vertical blanking interval (VBI). They are used for sync and vertical retrace, and can also carry closed captioning and vertical interval timecode information. Like the image itself, these lines are interlaced and split into two halves as well.

The NTSC waveform is shown in Figure 5-1. The following are the components of an NTSC signal:

- Active Video Line — represents a single horizontal video line
- Color Burst — a signal used to keep the chrominance subcarrier synchronized in a color television signal
- Front Porch — a brief (about 1.5 μs) period inserted between the end of each active video line and the leading edge of the next line sync pulse
- Back Porch — the portion in each scan line between the end (rising edge) of the horizontal sync pulse and the start of active video

ADVANCED TELEVISION SYSTEMS COMMITTEE (ATSC)

The Advanced Television Systems Committee (ATSC) developed the ATSC standards for digital terrestrial, cable and satellite television broadcasts; including the High Definition standards, among others. Analog terrestrial (off- air) NTSC broadcasts in the U.S. were shut off in 2009 and all full-power broadcasters in the United States were required to transmit in the ATSC format. Conversion in Canada was completed in 2011 and is scheduled in Mexico for the end of 2015. In Europe, The Netherlands was the first country to convert (2006), and others have followed. This means that all full-power broadcasts from those stations must be digital, but does not guarantee high definition broadcasts because one option for broadcasters is simply a standard definition digital transmission (lower horizontal and vertical resolution). As most of the existing content remains SDTV, this will remain in effect for years to come and must be dealt with by systems integrators.

The ATSC was formed in 1982 by the following member organizations:

- Joint Committee on Inter Society Coordination (JCIC)
- Electronic Industries Association (EIA)
- Institute of Electrical and Electronic Engineers (IEEE)
- National Association of Broadcasters (NAB)
- The National Cable Television Association (NCTA)
- Society of Motion Picture and Television Engineers (SMPTE)

The ATSC works to coordinate television standards among different communications media, focusing on digital televisions, interactive systems, and broadband multimedia communications. The organization also develops digital television implementation strategies and presents educational seminars on the standards. The digital standards being created by the ATSC include High Definition Digital Television (HDTV), Standard Definition Digital Television (SDTV), data broadcasting and multi-channel surround-sound audio, and Direct Broadcast Satellite (DBS).

VIDEO DISPLAY RESOLUTION

Resolution is the amount of detail that can be seen on the screen and is typically referred to by its vertical resolution (480, 720, 1080 and 2160) and scanning method (i-interlaced or p-progressive). But that only tells part of the picture. Video detail is also measured in pixels (picture element). Pixels are single points of color and light on the monitor. In video systems, the pixels are measured vertically by the number of scan lines that move across the screen that are stacked on top of each other and horizontally by the number of pixels in each scan line.

Typical numbers for video resolutions are 640× 480, 1280 × 720, 1920 × 1080, and 2160 x 3840 which are accompanied by a suffix of "i" or "p" to denote whether they are interlaced (i) or progressively scanned (p). So 480p would be understood to be 480 lines, each containing 640 pixels and progressively scanned. To confuse things, since moving to Ultra High definition (UHD), the marketing references are now based on horizontal resolution i.e. UHD/4K is 2160 x 3840 and UHD/8K is3840 x 7680. It should be noted that 3,840 is not truly 4K or 4,000, as 4K is a DCI standard and uses a slightly wider aspect ratio of 1.89:1 (2160 x 4096) as opposed to ATSC's 1.78:1 aspect ratio. The frame rate is always assumed to be 60 frames per second (FPS) unless it is otherwise noted, such as 1080p24 or 1080/24p, which would denote the film-based rate of 24 frames per second. Table 5-1 shows 9 of the more popular ATSC formats of the 18 formats specified in the ATSC standard.

Common Advanced Television Systems Committee standards include:

- Standard Definition Television (SDTV); 480i
- Enhanced Definition Television (EDTV); 480p
- High Definition Television (HDTV); 720p, 1080i, 1080p
- Ultra HD/4K

Table 5-1. *Popular ATSC Video Display Formats*

Name	Resolution			Pixel Count	Frames Per Second
480p30	480	Progressive	640 × 480	307,200	30 (29.97)
480p60	480	Progressive	640 × 480	307,200	60 (59.94)
720I	720	Interlace	1280 × 720	921,600	30 frames (60 fields)
720p30	720	Progressive	1280 × 720	921,600	30 (29.97)
720p60	720	Progressive	1280 × 720	921,600	60 (59.94)
1080i	1080	Interlace	1920 × 1080	2,073,600	30 frames (60 fields
1080p24	1080	Progressive	1920 × 1080	2,073,600	24 (23.976)
1080p30	1080	Progressive	1920 × 1080	2,073,600	30
1080p60	1080	Progressive	1920 × 1080	2,073,600	60

Video Scanning

The video scanning process is how pictures are drawn on a TV screen. It was originally accomplished by scanning an electron beam back and forth as in Cathode Ray Tube (CRT) technology, and is now accomplished by addressing digital pixels in a matrixed grid in digital type displays such as LCD or Plasma displays. A complete image on the screen is called a frame and the rate at which the frames are displayed is called the refresh rate. This is expressed in hertz and is the number of frames per second that the television displays. This is not always the same as the rate at which frames are transmitted, which is the frame rate and is expressed in frames per second.

With CRT displays, the image is created by means of an electron beam moving back and forth to excite colored phosphors on the back side of a fluorescent screen. The colors used for the phosphors are red, green, and blue because these three colors can be mixed to create any color in the visible spectrum, including white (RGB equal energy all on) and black (RGB off).

On a digital fixed pixel displays (LCD, PDP, DLP, DILA, etc.), the image is made up of a fixed number of pixels in a grid pattern. Each pixel on a digital display can be individually addressed and controlled by the processor; however, for efficiency this is not practical.

A more practical approach is to address the pixels in rows and columns. The number of connections is equal to the number of rows plus the number of columns, which results in thousands of connections (e.g., 1920+1080=3000 connections per color). This method is preferred over the alternative where the number of rows is multiplied by the number of columns because the results would exceed the millions mark (1920 × 1080 = 2,073,600 connections per color). This works because if one row is given a positive voltage (+5V), one column is given a negative voltage (-5V), then the single pixel at the intersection has double the voltage (10V) of any other pixel and is switched on.

Progressive Scanning

Progressive scanning or sequential scanning was first popularized on personal computer displays, but was in fact the original method used in the first CRT television sets. Progressive scanning displays each horizontal line of a frame consecutively in order from top to bottom, as shown in Figure 5-2.

After each line is completed, the next consecutive line beneath it is addressed, again from left to right. This process is repeated until the entire frame is completed, which typically takes about 1/60th of a second, or about 17 milliseconds.

With computer signals, there is a complete new frame of information every time the screen refreshes, so the refresh rate and the frame rate are typically the same, and often at 60 HZ (though it is not uncommon for computer displays to refresh at higher rates). However, for television broadcasts, the frame rate is typically 30fps. This is due to the bandwidth limitations of television broadcast systems, which is also why interlaced scanning is preferred.

Interlaced Scanning

Interlaced scanning is the method used by most broadcasters for all NTSC signals at 480i, in addition to the most common ATSC transmission format of 1080i. It was the very first form of video compression technology. With interlaced scanning, it is possible to reduce the broadcast video bandwidth requirement by a factor of two when compared to progressive scanning, without reducing the displayed resolution.

In the standard two-to-one method of interlacing, the odd numbered horizontal lines are displayed in the first picture frame, called the first field. The even numbered lines are displayed next in the picture frame, called the second field, 1/60th of a second later.

The completed frame in the interlacing system is "constructed" by two sequential fields, each carrying a set of alternating lines. The two fields appear so soon after each other that our eyes can't tell that the image wasn't displayed all at once. Because of this system, the television refreshes at 60 HZ, but we are only seeing 30fps (frames per second).

There are artifacts associated with interlacing. The first is combing, or offset vertical lines resulting from a moving edge displayed at two different points of time, as shown in Figure 5-3. An example of this would be the edge of a ball moving from left to right at high speed.

Another is jitter or interline twitter, which is caused by thin horizontal edges that seem to jump up and down because they are being displayed on only one line at a time. This could happen if a news reporter were to wear a shirt with thin horizontal stripes, which is why they never do. Current "de-interlacing" technology is capable of effectively limiting these artifacts while giving TV broadcast interlace systems a two-to-one bandwidth advantage because only half of the image is being transmitted at any given time.

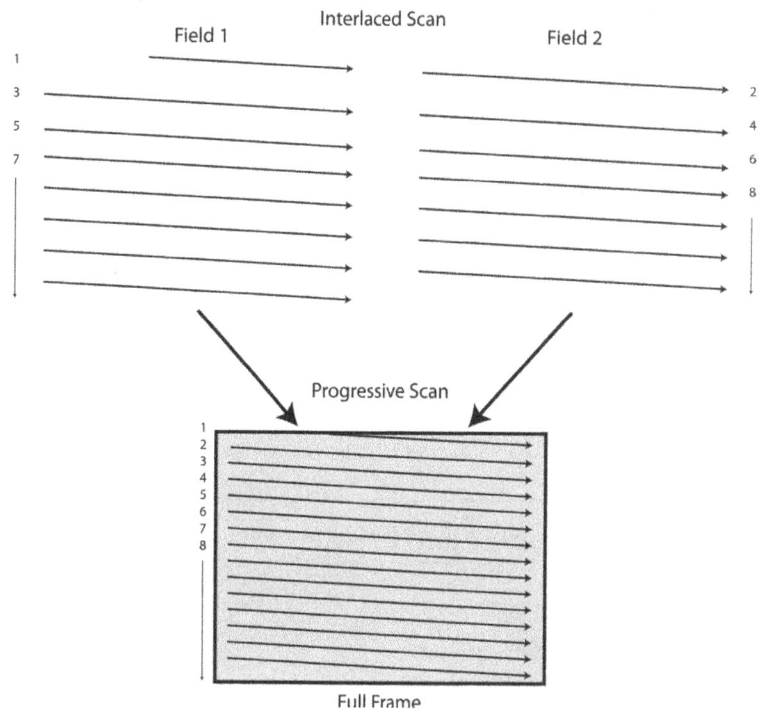

Figure 5-2 *Interlaced to Progressive Scan*

DIGITAL VISUAL INTERFACE (DVI)

In the 1990s, the demand for digital devices began to increase exponentially. Devices such as DVD players and Direct Broadcast Satellite (DBS) systems were being developed that began their signal in the digital domain, but converted it to analog before sending it to the display device. Then, if the display device was digital, it converted the signal back into a digital format for display. After digital displays became common, the need for a digital connection became more important.

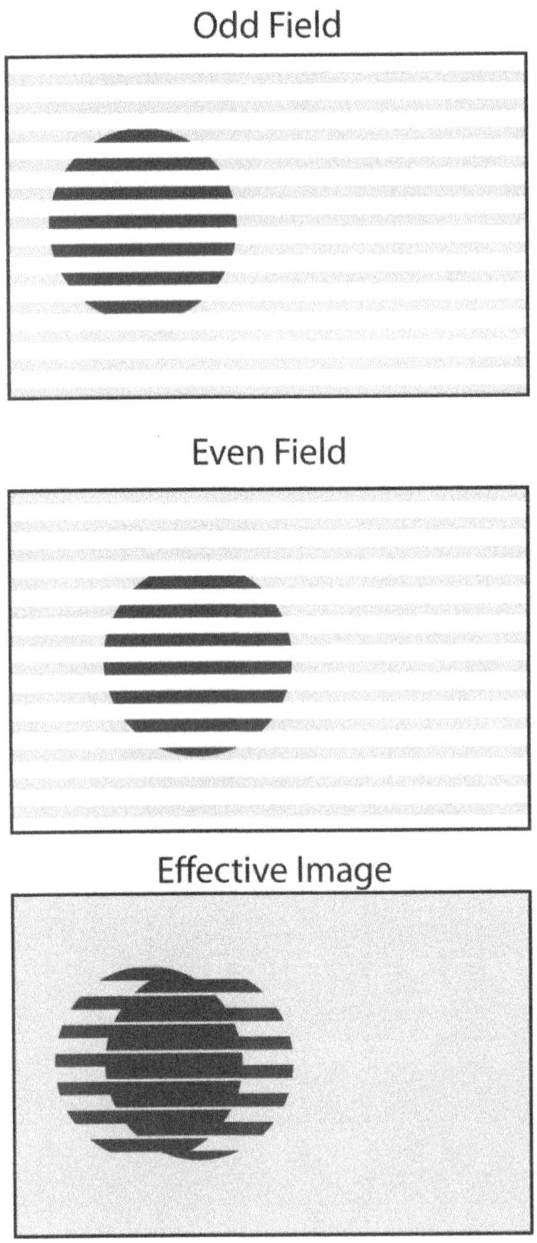

Figure 5-3. *Combing Artifacts*

Digital Visual Interface (DVI) was the first digital connection standard for consumer devices. It was launched in 1999 to connect LCD monitors to personal computers. DVI is able to replace the VGA connector that has been used with monitors since the introduction of personal computers. It enables PCs and monitors to maintain an uncompressed, all-digital signal path and removes any artifacts that might have otherwise been introduced as part of the analog signal process. As a transition for analog to digital signals, the DVI connector was designed with the ability to handle both types of signals.

It briefly caught on in consumer electronics before being replaced by the digital-only High Definition Multimedia Interface (HDMI), which will be covered shortly. DVI is still used in some commercial applications today due to the stronger connector. Figure 5-2 shows the specifications for an integrated DVI connector.

DVI Connections

There are three types of DVI connection pin outs. DVI-A is for analog-only connections, DVI-D for digital to digital connections, and DVI-I that integrates both analog and digital signals in a single connector so that either an analog or digital display device can be connected. In the two digital-capable versions of the connector, there are "single link" and "dual-link" options. The single link DVI has a single set of red, green, and blue digital video connections for a maximum resolution of 1920 × 1080 @ 60 HZ with 24 bits of color information (8 bits each for red, green, and blue).

The dual link variant has two sets of digital video connections for a maximum resolution of 2560 × 1600 @ 60 Hz with 24-bit color or optionally to maintain the 1920 × 1080 @ 60 Hz resolution limit of single link, but with 30, 36 or even 48 bits of color information. 1920x1200 is technically the maximum resolution of DVI, but that is primarily a computer resolution, so we will ignore it and instead concentrate on the more common 1920 × 1080 resolution used in consumer electronics. Figure 5-4 shows DVI male and female connectors. DVI and HDMI are electrically compatible so adapters are available to convert between the two connector formats.

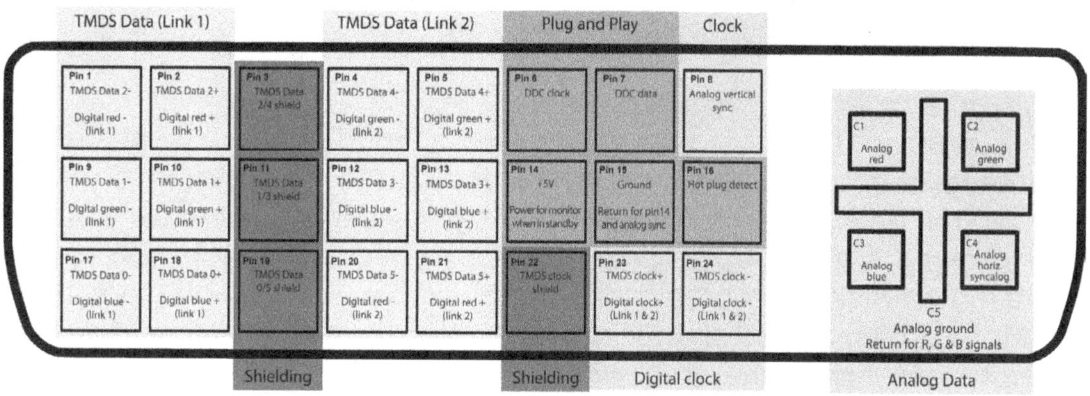

Figure 5-4 *DVI Connector*

1 TMDS Data 2- [Digital red — (Link 1)]
2 TMDS Data 2+ [Digital red + (Link 1)]
3 TMDS Data 2/4 shield
4 TMDS Data 4- [Digital green — (Link 2)]
5 TMDS Data 4+ [Digital green + (Link 2)]
6 DDC clock
7 DDC data
8 Analog vertical sync
9 TMDS Data 1- [Digital green — (Link 1)]
10 TMDS Data 1+ [Digital green + (Link 1)]
11 TMDS Data 1/3 shield
12 TMDS Data 3- [Digital blue — (Link 2)]
C1 Analog red
C2 Analog green
C3 Analog blue
C4 Analog horizontal sync
C5 Analog ground [Return for R, G, and B signals]

13 TMDS Data 3+ [Digital blue + (Link 2)]
14 +5 V [Power for monitor when in standby]
15 Ground [Return for pin 14 and analog sync]
16 Hot plug detect
17 TMDS data 0- [Digital blue — (Link 1) and digital sync]
18 TMDS data 0+ [Digital blue + (Link 1) and digital sync]
19 TMDS data 0/5 shield
20 TMDS data 5- [Digital red — (Link 2)]
21 TMDS data 5+ [Digital red + (Link 2)]
22 TMDS clock shield
23 TMDS clock+ [Digital clock + (Links 1 and 2)]
24 TMDS clock- [Digital clock — (Links 1 and 2)]

HIGH DEFINITION MULTIMEDIA INTERFACE (HDMI)

The High Definition Multimedia Interface (HDMI), shown in Figure 5-X, is an implementation of the DVI technology, which abandoned the analog capabilities but added audio and control information so that every device in an audio/video system could be connected with the same type of cable.

HDMI uses a new, smaller connector to provide a one-cable connection solution to the consumer.

A single cable connects each HDMI device to each other. This was designed to make installations friendlier and save equipment panel space. HDMI is electrically compatible with DVI so that a DVI device can connect to an HDMI device, but only digital video will be transmitted due to the limits of DVI.

HDMI Video Resolution

To make the transition from DVI easy for consumers, HDMI version 1.0 was originally designed with the same video bandwidth limits as single-link DVI, so the maximum resolution was limited to the same 1920 × 1080p @ 60 Hz with 24-bit color. It has since been upgraded in version 1.4 to allow higher resolutions and more color depth. The maximum resolution of HDMI 1.4 is 4K × 2K, i.e. 3840 × 2160p at 60 Hz 48 bit color, or 4096 × 2160p 60 Hz.

HDMI Video Color Depth

HDMI version 1.0 provided for 24-bit color (8 bit RGB). While this was adequate for the typical consumer and was also the limit of most display devices at the time of its introduction, display devices are now able to support more color information. Consumers are also becoming more discerning as more high definition content becomes available. With 24-bit color, there is a limit of 8 bits, or 256 shades of each color for red, green, and blue that when mixed, can create up to 16.7 million colors. That sounds like a lot of colors, but the 256-shade limit causes visible "steps" or contouring in areas where there is supposed to be a smooth transition from brighter to darker areas of the same color.

With 30-bit color (10 bit RGB), there are 1024 shades of each color for much smoother transitions and just over 1 billion colors. This is the actual limit of most current consumer displays. 36-bit color provides 12 bits per color and allows for 4096 shades of each and almost 69 billion colors, while 48-bit color provides 16 bits per color allowing for 65,536 shades of each and over 280 trillion colors. The 30-bit, 36-bit and 48-bit color depths are often referred to as deep color. Figure 5-5 shows the color depths for various versions of HDMI.

HDMI Audio

The HDMI connection standard provides for up to 32 separate channels of uncompressed high-definition digital audio up to 1536 KHz in addition to video. It can also carry new forms of extremely high resolution compressed audio in true 7.1 channel formats with bit rates up to 28 Mb/second. The two most popular ones are Dolby True HD and DTS HD Master Audio. New immersive audio formats, such as Dolby Atmos® and DTS-X™ will also fit within the HDMI 2.0 specification.

Both use theoretically lossless compression and are capable of delivering audio quality far beyond the level of any digital recording previously available in consumer electronics.

v1,0 – v1.2

Color Depth (RGB)	Possible Colors
24 Bit	17 Million
30 Bit	1 Billion
36 Bit	69 Billion
48 Bit	280 Trillion

V1.3 – v1.4a

Figure 5-5 *HDMI Color Depth*

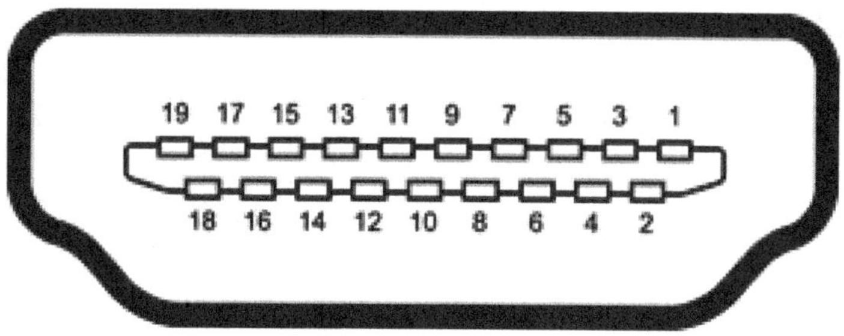

Figure 5-6. *HDMI Connector*

Pin 1	TMDS Data2+	Pin 11	TMDS Clock Shield
Pin 2	TMDS Data2 Shield	Pin 12	TMDS Clock-
Pin 3	TMDS Data2-	Pin 13	CEC
Pin 4	TMDS Data1+	Pin 14	Reserved (N.C. on device)
Pin 5	TMDS Data1 Shield	Pin 15	SCL
Pin 6	TMDS Data1-	Pin 16	SDA
Pin 7	TMDS Data0+	Pin 17	DDC/CEC Ground
Pin 8	TMDS Data0 Shield	Pin 18	+5 V Power
Pin 9	TMDS Data0-	Pin 19	Hot Plug Detect
Pin 10	TMDS Clock+		

HDMI Control

The CEC (Consumer Electronic Control) function is a feature specific to HDMI-enabled equipment. It is intended to allow communication between HDMI-connected devices so that simple commands (like "play") on a DVD player will control other devices downstream such as setting the A/V receiver and TV to the proper input, all without any special programming. This will enhance the end-user experience by reducing the number of button presses for each desired action and minimizing the required knowledge for control of each device in a media system. This has not been implemented well at this point across different brands, which means systems integrators must ensure that all devices are controlled and work properly in completely digital systems.

HDMI Versions

Typically, HDMI releases a new specification every 3 years. At the time of writing, the most recent version is HDMI 2.0. However, to remove confusion in the consumer market, HDMI LLC requires that its manufacturers not reference standard numbers, instead providing supported features. There are four types of HDMI cables regardless of supported features: standard, standard with Ethernet, high-speed and high-speed, with Ethernet. For any cable that is going behind a wall, it is good practice to install high-speed cables, as resolutions and bit-rates will only increase as time goes on. For more detailed information on HDMI see the Appendix.

High-Bandwidth Digital Content Protection (HDCP)

One aspect of a digital delivery system is the ability to protect content by performing Digital Rights Management (DRM). In DVI and HDMI, this takes the form of High-bandwidth Digital Content Protection (HDCP) which is a form of DRM developed by Intel Corporation. It uses a very advanced key exchange system which is very secure and unfortunately very difficult to distribute among multiple displays throughout a home.

If a source is protected with HDCP, then any display device connected to it must also support it, or the source will turn off its output and nothing will be displayed. Furthermore, HDCP licensees agree to limit the capabilities of their products. For example, high-definition digital video and audio content is often restricted to lower quality on non-HDCP compliant analog video outputs such as component video connections. Today's new digital source devices (players, STBs, etc.) do not even have non-HDCP outputs.

ASPECT RATIO

Aspect ratio is the relationship of screen width to the screen height. Traditional NTSC/PAL-based televisions use a 4:3 aspect ratio. This means that for every four inches of screen width, there are three inches of screen height. For example, if a screen is sixteen inches wide, it will be twelve inches high. Another form of "shorthand" that describes the aspect ratio is the simple division of the two numbers in the ratio such that the ratio is normalized to one screen height. For example, 4:3 becomes four divided by three, or 1.33:1. This is a more consistent way to describe aspect ratios because there are so many of them. It is also easier to remember that a higher number relates to a wider screen. Here are some of the most common aspect ratios:

1.33:1 — (4:3) — the native format of NTSC- based television, VHS, and DVD.
1.66:1 — the European widescreen standard.
1.78:1 — (16:9) — the native format of ATSC- based high definition television, Blu-ray Disc, and many film-based movies.

1.85:1 — a film-based movie format often used as a cost-saving measure for the studio.
2.35:1 and 2.39:1 — used for anamorphic film-based movies, often called Panavision, CinemaScope, or just "scope". Was 2.35:1 on movies before 1970 and 2.39:1 on movies after that. Sometimes rounded to 2.40:1.

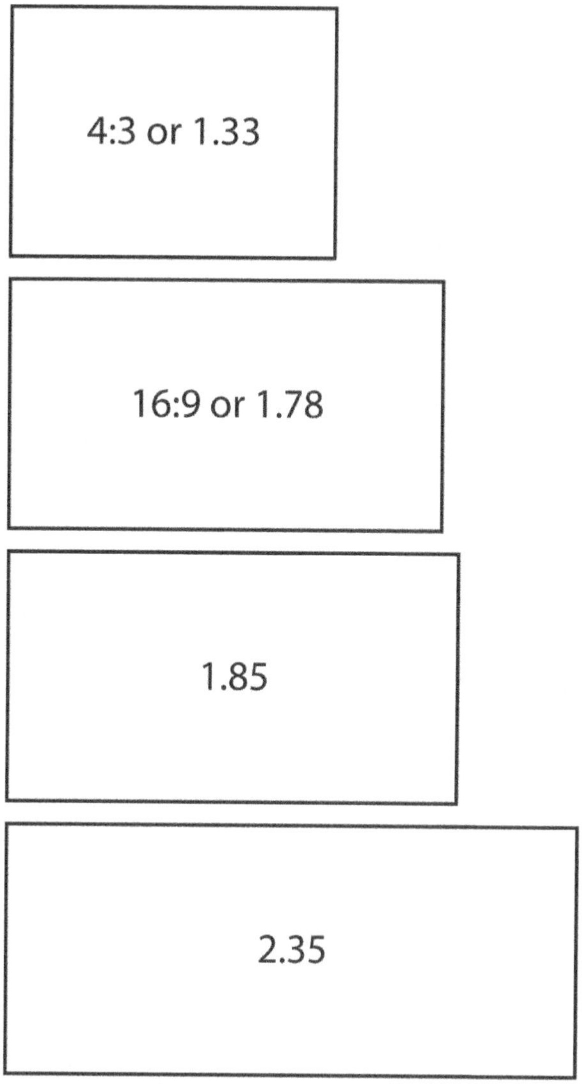

Figure 5-7 *Common Aspect Ratios*

Most ATSC-based HDTV displays have an aspect ratio of 1.78:1, which allows for a wider screen. Since most movies are created in a widescreen format (with an aspect ratio of 1.78:1 or higher), HDTV displays allow movies to be played back in their native widescreen format often without the black letterbox bars on the top and bottom of the screen.

For movie aspect ratios that exceed 1.78:1 such as 1.85:1 and 2.35:1, some letterboxing will occur, though it will be much less pronounced than on a display with a 1.33:1 aspect ratio. Figure 5-7 shows the differences between common aspect ratios.

Calculating Screen Dimensions from Aspect Ratios

The following are some handy formulas to calculate screen dimensions for different aspect ratios. This can be helpful when determining the largest possible screen:

For 1.33:1 screens:

- Width = 1.33 × Height = 0.80 × Diagonal
- Diagonal = 1.66 × Height = 1.25 × Width
- Height = 0.75 × Width = 0.60 × Diagonal

For 1.78:1 screens:

- Width = 1.78 × Height = 0.87 × Diagonal
- Diagonal = 2.04 × Height = 1.15 × Width
- Height = 0.56 × Width = 0.49 × Diagonal

For 2.39:1 screens:

- Width = 2.39 × Height = 0.92 × Diagonal
- Diagonal = 2.59 × Height = 1.08 × Width
- Height = 0.42 × Width = 0.39 × Diagonal

Figure 5-8 1.33:1 Aspect Ratio Screen with Constant Width Masking

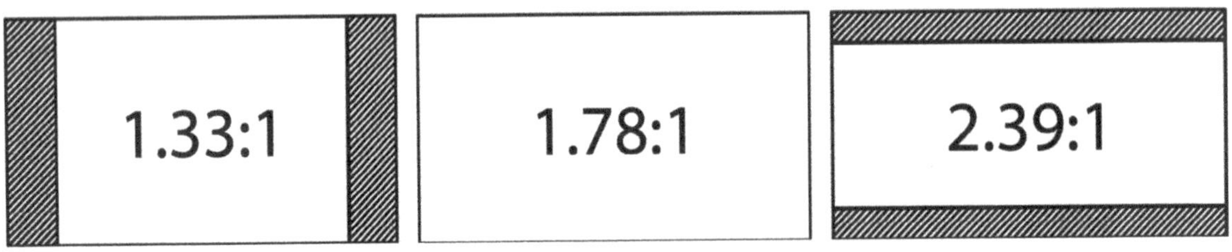

Figure 5-9 *1.78:1 Aspect Ratio Screen with 4-Way Masking*

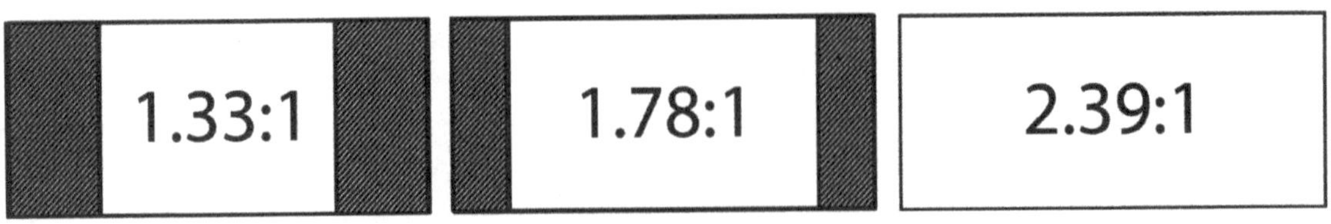

Figure 5-10 2.39:1 *Aspect Ratio Screen with Constant Height Masking*

NTSC Video and Cinemascope

The original movie films were close to the 4:3 aspect ratio of standard definition television. As television developed and began to compete with movie theaters, the film industry had to find ways to be more competitive at attracting an audience. The biggest development was the invention of widescreen cinema. The television industry could not compete with the magnitude of movies on the wide screen.

Among filmmakers, changing the aspect ratio of film capture at the camera became the unique signature of the producer, director, or movie studio. In addition, film camera manufacturers assisted the development of this niche by becoming involved in the creative process. Filmmakers with a new vision could enlist the design ideas of the camera maker. Thus, new camera and sound systems were developed to further the art, widen the technical offerings, and attract and keep the movie-going community.

As a result, over the years, a large database of movie materials using a wide range of visual aspect ratios and sound system requirements has been generated. To address this, projection screen manufacturers have developed multi-aspect screens with motorized masking to change the shape of the screen to match the content being watched. This technique is also common in higher end home theaters.

Figure 5-8 shows the impact of starting with a 1.33:1 aspect ratio screen and maintaining a constant width using masking. Figure 5-9 shows the impact of starting with a 1.78:1 screen and using 4-way masking, while Figure 5-10 shows a 2.39:1 screen with a constant height masking system.

Also, lens manufacturers have designed movable anamorphic lenses to stretch the image to fill the screen and allow electronic system contractors to utilize all of the light output and resolution of their customers' projectors.

Anamorphic Processing

Since filmmakers and theaters wanted to differentiate themselves in the market by making widescreen movies, but their film and cameras were designed for an aspect ratio of 1.33:1, the easiest way to accomplish this with the most resolution possible was with an anamorphic lens.

When the movie is filmed, a special lens is put on the camera that records a very wide image, but stretches it vertically to utilize as much of the space on the film as possible. This not only captures more light, but it also preserves as much vertical resolution as possible. Then, when the movie is mastered, all of the extra light and resolution provides for a better quality recording.

3D VIDEO TECHNOLOGIES

Another technology that is becoming more common in the commercial market as well as the home cinema is 3D. As of the publication of this document, 3D display technologies have seen slower than expected adoption among consumers, however, with new technology developments, and the continued support of manufacturers as well as content providers, 3D probably here to stay although not at the level originally anticipated.

Therefore, with the multitude of 3D formats and technologies currently on the market, it is important to be able to assist clients interested in 3D by designing a system that will fit their needs as well as offer the best possible performance for the application.

3D video technology is derived from the way the human brain and eyes work. The pupils of a person's eye are about 2.5" apart. Each eye views a scene from a different angle and generates a unique image. The brain then merges the images (this is called 3D image fusion) to create a single picture. The slight difference between the image from the right eye and the image from the left eye allows the brain to judge depth, and thus, 3D vision is attained.

In order for the human brain to interpret depth into a two dimensional picture, the video display system must recreate the effect of each eye receiving a different angle of the picture. Although there are a number of different ways to accomplish this, for the purposes of this document, the discussion will focus on the three most popular methods: active shuttering, polarization, and autostereoscopic.

Active Shutter 3D

Active shutter systems rely on a single high frame rate-capable display. In the case of a projector, it is important to note that no special screen materials are necessary as the projected image can be properly reproduced on just about any front or rear projection screen surface, including matte white surfaces. "Active" shutter glasses are used to create a 3-D experience for the viewer. These active 3D systems work by presenting the left and right eye images interleaved in rapid succession. As an example, in a 120 Hz active 3D system, the 60 odd frames (from 1-119) would be intended for the left eye, and the 60 even frames (from 2—120) would be intended for the right eye.

The glasses are actually LCD shutters that allow the user to see only one image at a time, through either their left eye or their right eye. The individual lenses in the glasses actually alternate between being opaque and transparent, operating in sync with the images being displayed from the projector via either an infrared emitter, or through an imperceptible sync "flash" that the projector displays during the blanking between frames. In either case, when a left eye image is being presented by the active 3D display, the left lens of the glasses is transparent while the right eye is opaque, and when a right eye image is being presented by the active 3D display, the glasses' right lens is transparent while the left is opaque.

Active shutter systems have dominated the 3D display market over the past several years, and continue to be a viable format for 3D in the home due to their high resolution capabilities as well as the ability to integrate with multiple screen materials easily. However, there are some potential imaging problems that should be considered when designing an active shutter system, including cross-talk, flicker, and ghosting. Also, the expense of the individual active glasses may be a turn off to some clients, so be sure to discuss their expectations prior to recommending one 3D technology over another.

Polarization 3D Systems

Another method for creating stereo imaging is through the use of polarizing filters. This technology may also be referred to as "passive" 3D. When using this polarizing technique for projector and screen applications, the imagery from two projectors is overlaid onto a single screen, with one projector dedicated to content intended to be viewed by the left eye and the other dedicated to content for the right eye. Opposing polarizing filters are placed in front of the lens of each projector. Next, the projectors display the distinct left and right eye images onto a specially coated screen that maintains the left eye / right eye polarization of the reflected light. The viewer wears "passive" polarized glasses that match the polarizers installed on the projectors. Thus, the viewer's left eye only sees the content rendered by the left eye projector, and the viewer's right eye only sees the content rendered by the right eye projector. Those distinct left and right eye images are interpreted by the human brain as 3D.

In addition to projector and screen polarization systems, there are a few display manufacturers that are currently producing FPR (Film-type Patterned Retarder) flat panel displays for 3D imaging. These displays use the same concept as the projector setup discussed above, however, they are designed with a polarizing filter on every other line of pixel elements (i.e. filter #1 is applied to the odd lines of resolution from 1-1919 and filter #2 is applied to the even lines of resolution from 2-1920) that can be turned on or off depending on whether the viewer is watching 2D or 3D. With the filters turned on, and the viewer wearing a pair of "passive" polarizing glasses, all the odd lines of pixels would be seen by the left eye and all the even lines would be seen by the right eye, thus creating a 3D image.

When considering a polarization type 3D system, it is important to note that standard resolution metrics for evaluating image clarity do not apply. A number of recent studies have indicated that even though the left eye and right eye images are produced as every other line, (which would seem to create an image that had lower horizontal resolution) due to the image fusion process that occurs in the brain, the resulting 3D image is perceived as having the same horizontal resolution as a standard 2D picture of the same size and resolution.

Polarization type 3D systems typically offer a 3D experience that is free of flicker, with low cross-talk, and minimal ghosting. Also, in a projector and screen setup, because each projector is being tasked with displaying a traditional 60 Hz signal, bandwidth requirements are not extraordinary and standard cables and signal distribution can be employed.

There are some potential drawbacks to using passive 3D which should always be taken into consideration. Passive 3D does require a special screen to maintain polarization and the need for independent left eye/ right eye equipment could mean increased costs to the client. Furthermore, vertical viewing angles can be limited and viewing distances must be designed properly to ensure the 3D image is reproduced correctly.

Active/Passive 3D Systems

In active/passive 3D systems, a single, wide bandwidth Active 3D projector is employed along with a rapidly switching LCD polarizing shutter that is installed in front of the lens.

Much like a full active 3D system, an active/passive system operates at 120 Hz, alternating left and right eye content frame by frame. At the same time, the LCD polarizing shutter switches polarization, frame by frame, in sync with the projectors' display of each frame. Since the active polarizing shutter is installed on the projector, the viewer wears passive polarized glasses.

This active/passive system design delivers all of the simplicity and cost of ownership benefits of a single projector in a full active 3D system, while also delivering the reduced cost benefits of passive polarized glasses.

Since it is based on polarization, the active/passive design does demand a specialized screen that preserves the polarization of the projected light, just as is required by a full passive 3D system.

Autostereoscopic 3D (AKA "Glasses Free")

There are two common ways to create a 3D image without using glasses, the first of which is through the use of a parallax barrier. A parallax barrier is a device placed in front of the normal pixel array of a display which consists of a layer of material with a series of precision slits, allowing each eye to see a different set of pixels, creating a sense of depth through parallax. A disadvantage of the technology is that the viewer must be positioned in a well-defined spot to experience the 3D effect.

The second common method of creating an autostereoscopic image is through the use of a lenticular lens system. A lenticular lens is composed of many small, curved magnifying lenses that, when viewed from varying angles, magnify different portions of an image, and create the illusion of depth. In the case of 3D displays, the lenticular lens array is designed such that the lenses are angled to magnify every other line of pixel elements for either the left eye or the right eye (similar to the FPR filters). A lenticular lens system can have similar viewing position limitations to parallax barrier systems, however, as the technology evolves, manufacturers are developing ways to actively adjust the lenses for varying viewing angles through facial recognition and other motion detection technologies.

3D Display Calibration Notes

When designing or calibrating a 3D display that uses polarizing or active shutter glasses, always remember that the glasses will affect the light output experienced by the viewer and this reduction in light output will, in-turn, affect the dynamic range. It is also possible for the polarizing filters to affect the color gamut. For these reasons, it is highly recommended that a separate calibration from the standard 2D calibration be performed to adjust for viewing through the 3D glasses.

VIDEO SOURCES AND TRANSMISSION MEDIUMS

Video signals can originate from or be reproduced by a number of different sources. There are many types of video signal transmission. Signals broadcast over the air from a TV station or from space via a satellite source, transmitted via coaxial or fiber optic cables from a cable TV or streamed from an Internet-based broadcaster, and signals transmitted from some local source (home or commercial property) such as a DVD and Blu-ray players where the video display is located. Broadcast signals can be wired or wireless. In most cases, at least part of the transmission process is wireless.

Broadcast Signals

Broadcast signals used in a home are divided into three types:

- Terrestrial
- Satellite
- Cable

The type of signal used is based on location and availability of the service, cost, and personal preference.

Terrestrial Signals

For many years, analog terrestrial broadcast signals were the only source for home viewing. The NTSC standard used for over-the-air (OTA) broadcast has been unchanged for more than 50 years. Today, digital broadcast signals (the ATSC standard) are also available. In fact, high definition signals were first readily available to consumers over the air and terrestrial broadcasts still produce the least compressed and best picture of all three technologies.

Terrestrial signals are received by an antenna at the user's location and carried through a cable to the RF (radio frequency) receiver or tuner (usually in the HDTV). To get the signal from the local broadcast station to the antenna at the customer's house, it must be sent through a very high powered RF modulator, which converts the high definition video signal to something that can be broadcast over the air from a high-powered antenna tower to antennas on homes over 50 miles away. The terrestrial signal can be broadcast on VHF (very high frequency) or UHF (ultra-high frequency) channels.

- Very High Frequency (VHF) — the radio frequency range from 55 MHz (wavelength ~18 ft.) to 216 MHz (wavelength ~4.5 ft.). This band covers channels 2-13 with a space in the middle from 87.8 MHz to 108.0 MHz allowed for FM radio signal transmissions.
- Ultra-High Frequency (UHF) — the radio frequency range from 470 MHz (wavelength ~2 ft.) to 806 MHz (wavelength ~1.25 ft.). This band covers channels 14-69.
- The 698-806 MHz band (Channel 52-69) has been sold by the

FCC; it will be used for a new open-access cellular communications system.
- ATSC antennas cover both UHF and VHF frequencies.

Factors Affecting Reception

With the old analog TV signals, the distance from the equipment to a broadcast tower directly affected the ability to receive a signal because as analog signals get weaker, they produce a "snowy" picture. Digital broadcast signals, on the other hand, are either received or not received. There is no "snowy" or bad reception. Typically in digital, when a signal is weak, and the receiving tuner stops "seeing" the signal, the image may get choppy (pixelated). If it is lost altogether, the last successful signal might be "frozen" on the video display for a short period of time. Integrators can use a signal level meter to optimize antenna setup for maximum signal strength and reception.

Satellite

The broadcast of satellite video signals started in 1962 with the Telstar satellite. Before the advent of satellite transmission, the only way to view video from Europe was to record it on magnetic tape and send the tape by plane to the United States.

Commercial satellite reception became a reality as hotels, restaurants, bars, and other public venues discovered the marketing value of providing live broadcasts of sporting events that were not available in customers' homes. However, the 12-foot diameter dish used in the 1980s was not consumer friendly and therefore not really considered for residential use due to its size and cost. Eventually, smaller receiving dishes (6-9 ft. diameter) were designed and satellite broadcasts became residentially viable. These smaller dishes, though still large by today's standards, allowed virtually anyone with a line of sight viewing of the satellite, to buy or rent a dish and receiver and have access to a large number of channels from around the world.

Once this happened, satellite broadcasts became a direct competitor for signals sent by cable TV providers. Satellite broadcasts also expanded the reach of signals to those communities not served by cable. This expansion allowed consumers in rural areas access to hundreds of channels.

Today, satellite signals are typically Direct Broadcast Satellite (DBS), and require the use of a dedicated receiver specific to the service provider. All consumer channels broadcast over satellite are digital. Digital channels use MPEG-2 or MPEG-4 compression technology. And, because they are digital, the signals can be received even at reduced power using a small dish (usually under 2 feet in diameter).

The upstream interactivity is limited for DBS and is usually accomplished by telephone line hook up to the DBS set top box (STB). Satellite is available in both standard definition and high definition. In fact, they have so many channels that it is impractical to try to transmit all the channels down the wire at the same time. As a result, DBS satellite distribution systems require specialized distribution systems when there are more than a few satellite receivers in a system.

Cable Television

Today, cable systems not only deliver video programming, but also Internet connectivity, telephone service, and other services where data is received or sent. To get all of this information across the country, most cable providers rely on fiber-optic cabling to bring the signal to the home or to a nearby distribution point. Once inside, cable providers transmit all signals through the home using coaxial cable, and most television sets use internal tuners for choosing stations.

Cable networks offer both digital and analog channels, and all of the channels are present on the wire at the same time. As a result, cable TV distribution systems are much simpler and more flexible in terms of installation options. Just like DBS satellite, cable's digital channels use MPEG-2 or MPEG-4 compression technology.

The analog channels do not use any compression and are subject to snowy or distorted images and sound as if the signal is too weak or too strong. Also, cable set top boxes offer full "upstream" interactive services such as pay-per-view or video-on-demand ordering, without a telephone or any connection other than the cable feed.

Local Source Signals

Local source signals are sent and received by equipment at the same location (for example, a Blu-ray player sending a signal to a television).

Digital Versatile Disc (DVD)

The Digital Versatile Disc (DVD) was originally designed to replace the laser disc format. However, it soon replaced the video cassette recorder (VCR) as the main source for purchased (and rented) movies and concerts in the home. The output of the DVD player can uses a variety of connectors, and the native video format on the disc is 480i resolution. In addition, the output may also be interlaced or progressive. All DVD content is in digital format using MPEG-2 compression technology.

DVD discs are interactive with random access capabilities, which allow selection of any preset portion of the movie as a starting point or to view special features such as deleted scenes, cast and crew commentaries, or other additional information.

Although the video image on a DVD player is either 480i or 480p, most DVD players can "upconvert" the image to 720p, 1080i or even 1080p. The output choices are usually composite and S-video for 480i, and component video for anything up to 1080i. DVI and HDMI can store and output resolutions up to 1080p.

Serial Digital Interface (SDI) output was once available on DVD players, but this is no longer used in consumer products because there is no copy protection is available. As such, most players have this output as a result of a third-party modification. It is a single coaxial cable that carries the uncompressed digital video data exactly as it was recorded onto the disc. This type of interface and HD-SDI is common for passing DTV (Digital Television) signals around broadcast stations, and is not common on consumer devices, but the integrator should be aware that it exists.

Blu-ray Disc

Blu-ray disc is a system that has the capability to store up to six hours of high definition video signals (720p/60, 1080i/60, 1080p/24, or 1080p/60) on a disc the same size and shape as a conventional DVD, but with up to 25 GB of capacity for a single-layer disc. On a dual layer disc, it has almost six times as much storage as a DVD, with 50 GB of capacity. It also has provisions for drastically increased audio resolution compared to DVD, but this format is not without its compromises.

With the new high definition discs, part of the copy protection system requires that the source and display "shake hands" on the signal content via the HDCP encryption method mentioned previously. The final Blu-ray specification calls for three different classes of players:

Profile 1.0 (Initial Standard) — the first and second generation of players from most manufacturers and is not part of the final specification. The only real requirements of this profile are that the player has 64kB of on-board memory and that it is able to play Blu-ray Discs.

Profile 1.1 (Bonus View) — also known as the "Final Standard" profile. In addition to the 1.0 specifications, it adds requirements for 256 MB of local storage memory for special features and also requires secondary audio and video decoders to allow for audio commentaries and "Bonus View" Picture-in-Picture capabilities.

Profile 2.0 (BD Live) — includes all of the requirements of Profile 1.1 and increases the requirements for local storage memory to 1 GB for things like downloadable special features and also requires Internet connection capability to access that downloadable content.

Profile 3.0 — includes an audio-only player specification and does not require any of the stipulations made upon any of the other profiles.

Profile 5.0 (Blu-ray 3D)—has all the features of Profile 2.0 and extends support for 3D video playback.

Computers and Televisions

The line between computers and consumer electronics grows thinner every day. Computers are now commonly being used as a source in home theater applications. To fit into the mix, they have evolved considerably. They are becoming much more intuitive and easier to use and now most include a DVI or HDMI connector with HDCP capabilities and output settings, such as 720p and 1080p that are compatible with high-definition TVs instead of just computer monitors. Microsoft's Windows Media Center Edition is a special version of Windows intended specifically to be used in the home and connected to a consumer HDTV.

Video Game Consoles

The first CRT-based use for interactive gaming was developed in 1946, but, it was not until the early 1970s that the first video game console became readily available. Atari's introduction of the black-and-white game PONG began the trend of including the video game console as an integral part of a video system. Since the 1970s, video game consoles continue to offer higher and higher levels of video performance.

Today, video games are very well developed and the biggest games have production budgets that rival blockbuster Hollywood films. These models and features are constantly changing, and it is important for the integrator to stay current and well-informed on their functionality.

Streaming Media Devices and App-Based Source Material

For over a decade, we have seen a transition away from optical disc video (DVD and Blu-ray) towards internet streaming and cloud video content. This is due to many factors including access to vast amounts of content, ease of use and portability and has become increasingly popular in the residential A/V market. With the rapid increase of broadband speeds (Nielsen's law of bandwidth states broadband speeds have doubled every 12 months) and advanced compression schemes such as HEVC (High Efficiency Video Coding), optical disks will likely decrease in overall demand in the coming years. However, for the video purist and those looking for special releases, Blu-ray will stay an important part of residential AV design.

Streaming Devices

One of the most common ways that clients are accessing these digital files is through the use of streaming media devices, which are basically little black boxes or simple HDMI enabled sticks that act as gateways for the home entertainment system to access content that is available through the network. Many of these devices allow access to files stored on a local computer or hard drive as well as access to content from the internet through built in software and provider apps such as Netflix and Hulu.

Most manufacturers of stand-alone streaming media devices are building them with smaller and smaller form factors so it is not uncommon for them to have a single HDMI output for connection to the A/V system. For this reason, it is critical to verify functionality and HDCP compatibility when integrating this new technology with older displays.

Aside from stand-alone black boxes, many manufacturers integrating network connectivity and streaming services directly into traditional A/V devices such as displays, receivers, Blu-ray players, and game systems. With the potential for multiple points of access, and different levels of network connectivity and feature sets, it is critical to discuss the desired functionality of the system with the client and design the system accordingly. This is just one more reason why proper network design and configuration is critical to the success of the integrated residential system. In order to ensure a robust and reliable client experience when integrating streaming media, it is highly recommended that each device have a robust network with Quality of Service (QoS) to video streaming devices. Technicians responsible for the commissioning of these systems must have a solid understanding of the network and how to properly configure it, whether wired or Wi-Fi.

HEVC and Ultra HD/4K Streaming

It is important to take a moment to understand HEVC as it will play a pivotal role in streaming quality for the foreseeable future. Before HEVC (also known as H.265) was developed, the standard compression algorithm for HDTV was H.264. In 2007, the engineers at the Motion Pictures Experts Group (MPEG) recognized that higher resolutions were coming and with H.264, the bit-rate was far higher than increases in residential bandwidth. Thus, to meet the higher resolutions, MPEG decided to create a new algorithm that would not increase bandwidth requirements (approximately 20Mbps). In order to accomplish this, MPEG decided created a significantly more complex, processor intensive standard that could pack an Ultra HD/4K image into the same bitrate as H.264 and 1080P without noticeable loss of image quality. In order to accomplish this, devices capable of decoding HEVC require much greater processing power than H.264 devices. Thus, when considering upgrading to Ultra HD/4K streaming devices or displays, all devices must be HEVC compliant (based on its internal hardware) to stream Ultra HD/4K content.

Cutting the Cord

There is a saying that everything old is new again. We know this to be true in audio, as there has been a resurgence in vinyl listening over the last few years. The same can be said about video, particularly with off-air antennas. There has been a relatively recent movement of "cutting the cord" where customers get rid of their cable or satellite service and use only an off-air antenna and streaming services. This can be an effective way for consumers to cut costs. Many countries have converted their terrestrial broadcasts from analog to digital and thus picture quality is not an issue. Alongside terrestrial broadcasts, traditional premium subscription channels have now started and internet based subscriptions without a required cable subscription, which removes one barrier to cord cutting. There largest barrier to cutting the cord is live sports, which still have a strong-hold with cable and satellite providers.

Whether clients are cord cutters and binge watch video streaming services, or are still dedicated to optical disks, it is clear that solid residential network design and performance is key. The home of the future includes multiple concurrent HD or Ultra HD/4K streams. These bandwidth intensive habits require carefully planned networks, comprised of both hard-wired and wireless network connections. While hard-wired Ethernet connections are always preferable (as they are full duplex connections as opposed to half-duplex for wireless), it is not always practical to run a cable. There are advantages and disadvantages to both Ethernet and wireless connections which is covered in more detail in Chapters 10 – 12.

Digital Media Servers

A digital media server is any device that stores and organizes digital audio and video files for playback on a traditional entertainment system. Well-designed media server systems offer a compelling user experience through their ease of access to a large database of content. As storage space becomes more readily available and hard drive costs continue to decrease, media servers have seen an increase in consumer adoption during recent years.

There are two approaches to hardware for media servers: general-purpose hardware designed for PCs and purpose-built hardware that was designed for the application of audio/video playback. In general, a purpose-built media server will be quieter, offer superior video quality, and a more user-friendly form factor. General-purpose components are less expensive. Reliability is a paramount concern for the integrator—look for hot-swappable hard drives and products with a reputation for quality. Like hardware, operating systems can also be general purpose or purpose-built. A general-purpose operating system can easily offer additional features like games or web browsing. A purpose-built operating system often provides a more cohesive user experience, faster browsing, and fewer hiccups.

It is important to note that with media servers, as with streaming media devices, an in-depth knowledge of networking is required to successfully integrate these products.

TYPES OF VIDEO DISPLAYS

There are many types of video displays available for home use and display technology is a rapidly developing field. What is cutting edge today is the norm tomorrow and becomes "old news" in a couple of years. Quality and cost points vary drastically, and more money does not always guarantee higher quality. Video display decisions must consider a wide variety of factors, including the home environment and the customer's expectations and budget.

Direct view TV sets are ones in which the image is being emitted directly from the surface of the display. This includes flat panel Plasma, LCD, and OLED displays. They typically are available from 10" to 70" diagonally, with a few recent exceptions such as 103" plasma and 108" LCD displays recently being released. One company has recently displayed a 150" prototype plasma display, but the size, weight, and price of displays limits the market size of this product category.

Front projection is typically a two piece system with a projector mounted at the back of the room and pointed at a screen mounted on the wall in the front of the room, just as seen in a movie theater. The projector is typically a LCD, DLP, or LCOS and the screen is usually a specially coated opaque sheet of flexible vinyl.

This design is used most often when a very large image size is desired and it is common for the screen to be anywhere from 80" to 120" though larger sizes of 150" or more are not unheard of. They are much easier to install than a 150" plasma display because the screen material can be rolled up and carried by a single person.

Rear projection displays are typically one large unit with a screen and projector built into the same chassis, but for screens over 80," it is usually necessary to have a separate screen and an outboard projector. Just like front projection, the image comes from typically DLP or LCD, but it is pointed at the back side of the screen. Because of space concerns, the projectors typically use very wide-angle lenses and the image is reflected off of a mirror to make the set shallower. Aside from the lens, the projector is typically the same design as a front projection unit, but the screen must be translucent because the light passes through it. Rear projection systems are slightly more difficult to install because the best screens are rigid glass or Lexan, so moving a large one through a home can be tricky. Also, a properly designed room containing the projector controls the light and reflective surfaces.

The factors to consider when choosing a display are numerous and each plays a part in making a good picture. TVs that get everything right are typically the most expensive, so unfortunately price can be just as much a factor as anything else.

Video Display Technologies

There are many different ways for a TV to produce a picture, video display technologies currently on the market includes:

- Plasma Displays
- Liquid crystal display (LCD)—LCD Flat Panel Displays, LCD Projectors
- Active Matrix Organic Light Emitting Diode (AMOLED)—OLED Flat Panel Displays
- Liquid Crystal on Silicon (LCoS) Projectors
- Digital Light Processing (DLP) Projectors

LCD (Liquid Crystal Display)

The origin of the liquid crystal display is not as easy to trace as some other displays. The discovery of liquid crystals was first made in 1888, and it took various scientists over 75 years to discover and develop all of their properties. In 1964, George H. Heilmeier created the first functioning monochrome LCD display. In 1970, Wolfgang Helfrich and Martin Schadt patented the twisted nematic field effect LCD that is the basis of what is used in watches and calculators today.

From there, color was added and numerous iterations of the LCD technology have been developed, culminating in what is known as a Thin Film Transistor (TFT) display. There are numerous variants of TFT technology, and each is subtly different with its own benefits and compromises. Historically, larger LCDs were more expensive than comparably sized displays based on other technologies such as CRT or plasma. However, with the increase in production and demand, the price gap is narrowing significantly. LCDs come in three types: rear projection, front projection, and direct view (flat panel).

For LCD projectors, three small TFT-LCD panels are used as a series of "light valves" where incidental light from an illumination source (typically a Metal Halide or UHP lamp) is divided into red, green, and blue using special dichroic mirrors that transmit only light with a certain wavelength. Then, each color of light passes through the LCD and is recombined through a prism from which the picture is projected.

With flat panel LCD displays, there is also an illumination source (typically a tubular fluorescent bulb) that passes through the panel. Instead of three separate panels, each individual pixel is composed of three subpixels, one each of red, green, and blue that gets its color from an additional color filter.

Active-Matrix Organic Light-Emitting Diode (AMOLED or OLED)

The foundational technology, Organic Light-Emitting Diode (OLED), is based on the electroluminescence found in some organic materials. Formerly known as organic electro-luminescent (OEL), an electrical field was applied to the electrodes, producing a self-luminous diode that required backlighting or diffusers. OLED is an emissive technology that does not require backlighting to function, unlike current LCD screens. Small-sized OLEDs can be printed on a flexible substrate that can be bent and shaped. The emissive technology allows OLED display to have blacker blacks and wider viewing angle than LCD flat panel displays. Active Matrix refers to the technology behind the addressing of pixels in the OLED display. The size of AMOLED displays is currently limited by the cost of production technology, but the future is very promising. Two current limiting factors in OLED production is the life of the blue organic compounds, which is about half the life of PDP, LED and LCD technologies, and the adverse reaction OLED technology has to the presence of moisture.

DLP (Digital Light Processing)

Texas Instruments developed a unique chip design in 1987 that uses microscopic mirrors to reflect light towards a projection screen to turn a pixel on, or away from the screen to turn a pixel off. These tiny mirrors are called Digital Micro Mirrors (DMM) and a DLP chip is referred to as a Digital Micro-mirror Device, or DMD.

On the space of two postage stamps, millions of articulating robotic mirrors take one of three positions: off, on, or some mixture of the two. The micro-mirrors are mounted on tiny hinges. These hinges enable the panels to tilt either toward the light source in a DLP projection system (ON) or away from it (OFF).

There are two different ways to use DLP technology into projectors. The first and highest quality version is the 3-chip DLP, which uses three DMD panels in a very similar fashion to LCD projection technology. Each of the three panels is dedicated to a primary color of red, green, or blue. A light source (typically a xenon lamp) is filtered through a prism and directed to each panel, which uses its millions of mirrors to set the intensity of each pixel. The three colors are then combined and sent out through the lens to make the image.

Solid state LED/laser DLP projectors are becoming more common in home theaters. They utilize LED or laser light sources, and offer significant advantages over those using traditional lamps:

- Lower heat generation
- Quieter operation
- More consistent brightness and image color over time
- Up to 20,000 hours of operation (laser)
- Up to 60,000 hours of operation (LED)
- Projector may be tilted and pointed in virtually any direction without affecting the light source

The single-chip DLP is a popular, and less expensive, implementation of the DLP technology. As its name implies, this version uses just one DMD and creates color by using a color wheel. This is the most economical DLP design because it is a very simple layout where the light source (lamp) passes through a spinning color wheel before reaching the DMD. This way the light is colored without being split into three separate paths. So, the DMD only receives one color at a time and redirects the appropriate amounts out through the lens.

The DMD and color wheel change so rapidly (thousands of times per second) that most of the time humans can't tell that there is only one color on the projection screen at any given time. However, in bright scenes with fast horizontal motion, some people can occasionally be distracted by what is called the "rainbow effect." This occurs when our peripheral vision begins to detect individual bands of red, green, or blue colors on the screen (fortunately, it does not affect everyone).

LCoS (Liquid Crystal on Silicon)

LCoS consists of a liquid crystal layer that sits on top of a highly reflective material. Below this material is another layer that contains the electronics used to activate the pixels. LCoS uses a reflective LCD display panel with a high open area ratio. By placing the wiring area and switching elements under the reflective layer, it is possible to achieve an almost seamless image. This technology borrows many of the features of LCD and combines them with the reflective design of DLP. Several companies are producing versions of this technology. Recently, this technology has been further developed by JVC and its D-ILA (Digital Direct Drive Image Light Amplifier) technology as well as Sony with its SXRD (Silicon X-tal Reflective Display) devices and has become increasingly popular in home theater projectors.

Front Projection Screens

The perfect front projection screen would focus 100% of the projector's light back at the audience, reject any light not coming from the projector, and be acoustically transparent, all without compromising color balance, detail, or focus. We will discuss the various approaches to each of these goals. The two most common types of screens used today are flat and curved.

Flat Screens

Flat screens have been available in the residential market for years. The pros of flat screens include:

- Easy to install
- Proven, familiar technology
- Excellent for 16:9 and 4:3 imagery

The cons of flat screens include:

- Pincushioning — when the sides of the image bows outward. It is called barrelling when the image bows inward.
- Non-Uniformity of Brightness — on a flat screen, the distance from the center of the lens to the center of the screen is shorter than the distance from the outside of the lens to the outside of the screen. This causes the center of the screen to be slightly (or even greatly) brighter than the image on the sides.

Curved Screens

Curved screens have existed since the 1950s. However, it has been a relatively recent development to put curved screens into home theaters. The timing of the curved screen revolves around the introduction of anamorphic lenses on front projectors.

There are multiple reasons behind using a curved screen with an anamorphic lens:

- Brightness — a curved screen more closely matches the curvature of the lens making the distance closer to equal. This provides a more even brightness level throughout the screen. The problem is exaggerated with wide aspect ratios.
- Reflective Light — a curved screen is designed to reflect light more uniformly back towards the audience instead of off walls, which can give a better perceived contrast ratio.
- Pincushion — curved screens have no pincushion for anamorphic projection.
- Viewing Angle — a wider perceived viewing angle is created by a curved screen.
- Aesthetics — there are some people who just appreciate a curved screen because it looks cool!
- Black Bars — no horizontal black bars on almost any aspect ratio.

While all but the widest movies will have vertical bars, most curved screens have motorized masking to alleviate this.

The cons of curved screens include:

- Can cause barreling with lower aspect ratio if not designed properly
- High cost due to anamorphic lens requirement and motorized masking

The curved screen is designed specifically for anamorphic lens imagery. If the customer is not using an anamorphic lens, a flat screen is a better choice because using a curved screen with a non-anamorphic lens can cause mild to moderate barreling of the image.

Screen Gain

Quality projection screens are optical devices in every sense of the word. They can be designed with optical elements to focus the light from the projector back towards the audience in a narrower pattern than simply a white painted fabric or wall. When doing this, the perceived brightness goes up because the light is redirected towards the audience instead of bouncing off towards the side walls and ceiling. This creates a narrower range of viewing angles. But because most dedicated rooms have specific seating areas in ideal locations, the viewing angles are well within a reasonable range.

A plain piece of matte white vinyl will typically have a gain of 1.0, meaning the light coming at it is reflected in a natural way rather than being absorbed, diffused, or focused in any way. Common screen gains are between 0.8 and 2.0 though there are models available that are both above and below that. Typically, screens with gain below 1.0 reflect less light than it receives, but has greater contrast, while screen with gains above 1.0 reflect more light than it receives but have a narrower angle of view.

Too much gain can cause hot-spotting, which is what happens when the projection distance is too short for a high-gain screen, and the light on the edges of the screen "bounces off" instead of being reflected back towards the audience. The result is a lot of gain in the center of the screen and no gain on the edges, which makes for a big difference in brightness across the image. This occurs when the screen gain (1.5, 1.8, 2.0, and so on) is greater than the projection distance ratio (projection distance divided by screen width). Gray screens provide improved contrast ratio over a white screen at the expense of high brightness. Many have a gain of 0.6-0.9 meaning that they actually absorb some of the light from the projector). This is so that the darkest areas of the picture will be enhanced to give the image more depth and dimension. For the same reasons, these screens also maintain contrast ratio better in higher ambient light situations.

Masking

Many consumers are disappointed to discover that not all widescreen images are alike. There are multiple aspect ratios that cause black bars to appear even on a widescreen display: 1.85:1, 2.35:1, and 2.40:1 images will cause horizontal bars, while 1.33:1 images will have vertical bars. Understanding aspect ratios is the key to understanding the widescreen display. Masking screens are used to help conceal this phenomenon from the customer. Masking screens have motorized black bars, which move in or out to make the frame appear wider or narrower to remove the black bars on the screen. The masks come in vertical, horizontal, and both vertical and horizontal, all of which lead to a better perceived image quality and a happier customer.

Acoustically Transparent Screens

Acoustically transparent (AT) screens typically are perforated screens with many very small holes to minimize their impact on acoustic quality. There is always some audible and visible distortion on AT screens, but technology has made a significant decrease in the impact over the last few years. Using AT screens allows for the speaker height to be at the center of the screen allowing for better sound imagery particularly for the back rows of seats.

All of these advantages come at a cost of loss of image gain and resolution from the projector. Thus, when designing the system, the loss of lumen output must be calculated by using an AT screen and then increasing the output (upgrading) of the projector accordingly. Another way to make up for the loss of brightness due to an AT screen is to increase to a higher gain material to make up for the loss. For example, the electronic systems technician could use a brighter projector or implement a 1.5 gain screen with perforations instead of a 1.3 gain screen (the 1.5 gain screen with perforations will act approximately like a 1.3 gain screen).

Acoustically Transparent Screens and Masking

As customers move toward wider screens and screen masking, there is a tendency to place the left, center, and right speakers behind the screen (allowing for a wider viewing experience). When masking this type of system, it is possible the masking will move in front of the left and right speakers. Even if the masking is made out of acoustically transparent material, there are some adjustments that must be made.

In this situation, the speaker equalization must have two settings. If the left/right (LR) speakers are behind the masking it may negatively impact the quality of the sound. This way, there must be two presets: one for when LR are open and one for when LR are covered by masking. Technology is continuing to evolve to solve these issues.

Throw Distance

Throw distance refers to the distance that a projector can be from the screen and fill the screen, as shown in Figure 5-11. For example, if a flashlight is shown on a wall in a dark room, it would display a small circle of light close to the wall. As the flashlight is moved farther away from the wall, the circle of light gets bigger. The same thing occurs with a projector. When a projector is moved farther away from the screen, the projected image is larger. To keep the math simple, throw distance is usually expressed as a ratio of screen width. So, for a screen that is 100" wide and a projector with a throw distance ratio of 1.5–2.0, the projector's lens is placed between 150" and 200" away from the screen. Most lower-end projectors have decent zoom ranges to allow for some variation in throw distance in order to ease installation. Higher-end projectors offer interchangeable lenses, which allow for a greater range of throw distance options without compromising performance. Some of the lenses offer the ability to have a throw distance of over seven times the screen width or even as close as 0.6 times the width for use in narrow rear projection applications.

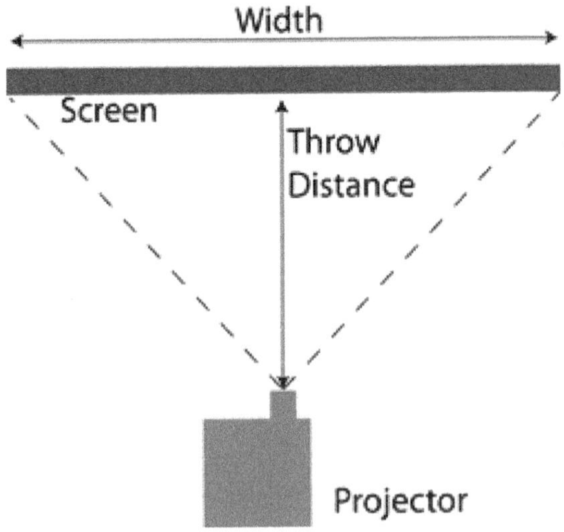

Figure 5-11 *Throw Distance*

VIDEO CALIBRATION

Display calibration is the last step in setting up a video system. It is often the difference between a mediocre "out of the box" image that is designed to "pop" on a showroom floor under fluorescent lights and an excellent image optimized for the home viewing environment. The key goal is to match the creator's intent with regard to image reproduction.

Calibrating the Display System

There are generally nine steps required when performing an advanced calibration:

1. Set the black level (brightness)
2. Set the display gain (contrast or picture)
3. Adjust the light output (luminance)
4. Select appropriate gamma curve
5. Measure colorimetry (white balance) and adjust for correct gray scale
6. Set the color level (color or saturation)
7. Set the tint for flesh tones (tint or hue)
8. Adjust the color gamut (if display is equipped with a color management system)
9. Set sharpness

Required Tools

There are two groups of tools needed to calibrate a video display, light measuring devices and test pattern sources.

Tools to Measure Light

Fundamentally, there are two ways in which to measure light intensity: illuminance and luminance.

Illuminance — the illuminance method measures the light source directly by pointing the light metering device at the source to determine the intensity of the light falling upon objects. This type of measurement yields the luminous power of the source. A front screen projector may be thought of as a white light source having a certain illuminant value. The unit of measure for that value is the 'lux'.

In this measurement mode, the light meter must be designed and calibrated to measure illuminance. One lux is equivalent to ne lumen per square meter. When a projector manufacturer measures the luminous power of the projector product, lux output is measured at the plane of the screen to derive the actual lumens rating of the projector. Because the light measurement is inversely proportional to the square of the distance, the lumens value obtained is independent of screen size. This is known as and seen in specifications as ANSI Lumens and is meaningful for estimating screen size and light output required based on room lighting conditions. A brighter room needs a brighter engine...for home theaters this is not as important as dynamic range (seeing steps in dark black and bright white), and measuring light as the eye sees it (off the screen).

Luminance — the second method of measuring light involves the intensity of light emitted, or reflected, from a surface. The light reflected from a projection screen falls into this category along with rear screen displays and direct view monitors (CRT, plasma, and LCD). Ideally, the light emanating from a surface does so equally in all directions. A surface that disperses light evenly is referred to as a lambertian surface.

There are three types of luminance-style calibration instruments available to the technician when making video calibration adjustments. The first two may be configured, or modified, for illuminance measurement so be sure to select the correct luminance version for the specific application. The three categories of instrumentation available for display calibration are:

- Spectral
- Colorimetric
- Comparative

Each type of instrument has special features and advantages.

Spectral Measurement

The spectroradiometer measures luminous power of a light source at many incremental wavelengths both inside and outside the visible spectrum. It

samples the light at successive wavelengths (like an RTA in audio, but at wavelengths from 380-720 nanometers), measures the power, and then displays the information in a table as a graphic representation.
This device is typically considered a laboratory instrument, although today's versions are quite portable and can operate from batteries.

Colorimeter

The colorimeter provides correlated color temperature, luminance readings, and CIE x,y coordinates. Based upon a tristimulus filter system, the colorimeter will read the average luminous power of a light source. A colorimeter does not have the ability to incrementally measure or represent the luminous power at specific wavelengths, so it may not be suited for accurate measurement of all types of light sources unless the filters are "offset" to measure different spectral footprints like DLP, LCoS, etc. Each of its photodiodes measures the energy passing through its respective color filter. The color filters must be carefully designed and selected to match the human eye response curve.

Comparative

A third type of instrument used in video calibration is the color comparator. This device uses the human eye's ability to tell the difference between two nearby colors. The comparator contains an internal light source calibrated to a known color temperature standard. This light source, positioned directly within the user's field of view, is placed visually side-by-side with the light emitted from the display to be calibrated. This method does not provide measured data, but instead relies on the calibrator's ability to distinguish between subtle differences in color. Every integrator should have one or all of the above tools in the kit.

Test Patterns

A test pattern, sometimes known as a test card, is a television test signal. The pattern usually has a set of line-up patterns, enabling televisions to be adjusted to show the picture correctly. Evaluation and setup of video levels requires the selection of a proper test signal, or pattern, as a system stimulus.

Test pattern software is available on CD, DVD, or Blu-ray formats that operate in a standalone player or from a computer. One caveat of using players and computers is that without evaluation of the levels from the outputs of these devices, the technician is still subject to the production variations in their accuracy. To avoid this, standalone calibrated test pattern generators can be used for the most consistent results.

Common Test Pattern Descriptions:

SMPTE Color Bars — The Society of Motion Picture and Television Engineers created this variation of the traditional color bar test pattern. In this pattern, the top two-thirds of the television picture contains seven vertical bars of 75% intensity. This test pattern is used for visually setting COLOR and TINT. A full color image of the SMPTE bar pattern can be seen on the back cover of this book.

PLUGE — PLUGE is short for Picture Line- Up Generation Equipment. The PLUGE shown in Figure 5-12 is a monochrome test pattern primarily intended for proper calibration of contrast (system gain) and brightness (black level). It comprises three small vertical bars for brightness (black level) control setup and four or more boxes of increasing luminance level for adjustment of contrast (system gain).

Figure 5-12 *PLUGE Pattern*

There are a wide variety of PLUGE patterns available for making the proper brightness and contrast adjustments, but if possible, it is recommended that patterns with "above white" and "below black" be used in order to increase the accuracy of the calibration. Another useful feature found on many PLUGE patterns is slight movement of the boxes, which will reduce the effect of persistence of vision when looking at and calibrating for the pattern.

Grayscale Bars—for a visual check of gamma and dynamic range.

Window — the window pattern is a solid square or rectangle, called a window, positioned at the center of the screen within a fully black surround, as shown in Figure 5-13. The area of the white window is typically 15—20% of the visible picture area. Window size is not critical. Window patterns are used with intensity ranging from a few IRE to 100 IRE (100%). The IRE is a unit of measure used by broadcast engineers to measure composite video. During video setup and display calibration, window patterns may be adjusted to any level in IRE or percent of full output that facilitates the use of test equipment while keeping the display system operating within a linear region. Raster (full screen) can be used on most display types (except plasma and auto-iris projectors) when OSD gets in the way.

Resolution — the resolution (multi-burst) test pattern is a monochrome pattern traditionally used to evaluate television system bandwidth and frequency response, as shown in Figure 5-14. For video calibration, it is a useful tool for the setup of the sharpness control function in the display. The sharpness control should be adjusted until the edges of vertical detail are just crisp, but not overemphasized. Sharpness injects extra gain and some noise, so its use should be exercised sparingly.

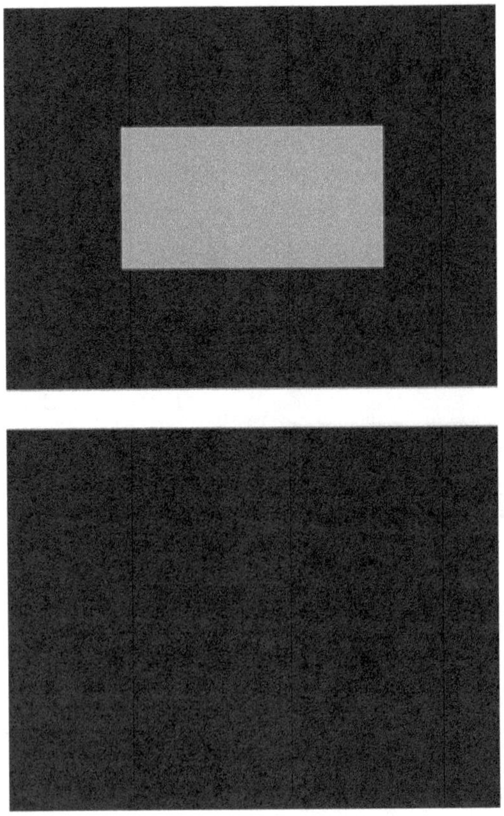

Figure 5-13 *Window Pattern*

Verification and calibration adjustment of basic video level can be done with the simplest of test patterns. Various patterns may be used such as those mentioned previously and PLUGE, 100% window, pulse and bar, and needle pulse. The essential requirement for the test pattern is that it be constructed to possess a defined wlack level and a white level portion that attains 100% output.

The SMPTE color bars, PLUGE, Windows (10%, 20%, 80%, and 100%), and Resolution are the test patterns normally used for calibration. Each test pattern works best for a specific goal:

- Use the PLUGE for steps 1 and 2 of the nine-step process. (Black level and display gain).
- Use the Window patterns for step 3,4, & 5 of the five-step process. (Luminance, Gamma, and Colorimetry/Gray Scale).
- Use the SMPTE color bars for steps 6 and 7 of the five-step process. (Color Saturation and Tint).
- Use color windows for step 8 (Color gamut)
- Use a resolution patter for step 9 (Sharpness)

Note that the hue or tint control is only needed when the source is composite video or S-video.

For component video, color level adjustment is needed, but no hue adjustments are necessary. For R GB connections, no color level or hue (tint) adjustments are necessary.

If only one pattern is available, make it the SMPTE color bar pattern. The color bar test pattern provides the reference color information necessary to use the chroma and luminance channels. The C channel of S-Video and the Pr, Pb channels for component video are easily evaluated with this test

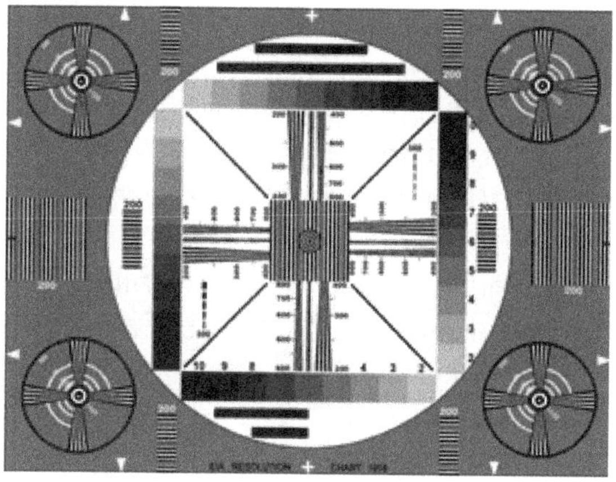

Figure 5-14. *Resolution Chart*

pattern. In fact, the color bar test pattern includes an 80% level white reference, which makes it useful for adjustment of both the Y channel and the color channels.

Use the window test patterns for adjustment of display gray-scale controls. Window pattern levels are recommended as follows:

- For a two point grayscale calibration, use either 20% or 30% window for lowlight (bias) adjustments, and a 70% or 80% window for highlight (gain) adjustments
- For a ten point grayscale calibration; start with a 10% window and calibrate at increasing 10% increments up to the 100% window

Lastly, use the resolution test pattern for final touch-up of any sharpness or detail control.

Other Equipment

Another important item for testing is a good, sturdy camera tripod. The tripod is indispensable for holding the light measurement device in place while evaluating results and making display adjustments. It is actually much more important than just a way to hold the instrument in place, though. One variable characteristic of displays is the quality of their screen uniformity. When projecting a full white screen or using the window pattern, for example, it might be possible to see variation in brightness across the screen's surface.

How to Handle Fixed Systems

Some appliances, such as DVD players, have buried service menus that allow level setup. Wherever possible, these settings should be checked and set to a neutral position so they are not altering the signal from the disc in any way. This is where display or video processor memory setups are important. Most displays and external video processors (and scalers) have the ability to control level adjustments for each input.

Color Space and the "Color of White" Concept

The display calibration process involves adjustment of display control parameters to ensure that the viewer sees images within the proper grayscale tone range as the content creator intended. More fundamentally, display system calibration is the process of faithfully reproducing the original art. To accomplish this requires an understanding of basic colorimetry and the "color of white" concept.

The combination of the three primary colors will produce white light. This is true, but the difficulty arises in balancing the energy of the primaries. A slight dominance of one or two will significantly affect our perception of white. Our perception of white is influenced by the relationship of colors and the ambient illumination regardless whether it is natural or artificial. There is NO one color of white.

For calibration and testing, however, technicians use what is called the "known color of white" to provide a standard illuminant point. For most video calibration applications, D65 is the standard color of white reference to use and relates to the .313x, .329y point on the 1931 CIE Chromaticity Diagram. The illuminant upon which the video industry is standardized is illuminant D, which corresponds to a color temperature of 6500 Kelvin. This point is also referred to as D6500 or just D65. Illuminant D represents that color of white most observers perceive as the most neutral shade of white.

It is extremely important not only because it is considered a standard, but because almost all video content creation is referenced to illuminant D. Therefore, to accurately replicate the original intent of the artist, the display system must be calibrated to the same illuminant standard.

CIE Chromaticity Diagram

The ability to reproduce an image electronically requires an understanding of color spaces for individual devices. Each electronic device, whether a display or a printer, has the ability to reproduce a specific color space within the realm of all visible colors that we perceive. Understanding color space attributes and conveying them from one device to another is a complex task.

To simplify it to some degree, the CIE (Commission Internationale de l'Eclairage translated as International Commission of Illumination) developed a two-dimensional color space suitable for describing the limits of color spaces within the visible spectrum without the complication of varying intensity.

The CIE chromaticity diagram provides a method for visualizing what our eyes perceive as the visible light color space within a 2D realm without concern for luminous intensity. The CIE 1931 chromaticity diagram provides a convenient method for charting the color space performance of displays and is an essential guide for attaining some standard color of white.

To describe a color sensation accurately requires three parameters—the coordinates for the red, green, and blue energy comprising the color sensation. A specific method for associating three numbers (tristimulus values) with each color is known as a color space. The CIE 1931 color space provides the stage for describing various color spaces for displays as well as surface colors. Describing colors for video in this two- dimensional space simplifies calibration and is independent of intensity or level of gray.

Display Gamut

A gamut, or color gamut, is a complete subset of colors. In this circumstance, it refers to the subset of colors that can be accurately represented within a color space, such as the CIE color space, or by a specific output device. Generally, the color gamut is specified in terms of hue and saturation. Color gamut standards have been developed by:

- NTSC
- SMPTE and SMPTE-C
- European Broadcast Industry
- Computer Industry sRGB
- ITU-R BT.709 color space—adopted by ATSC same as the computer standard
- ITU-R BT.2020 color space - Ultra HD/4K color space. Will require time to adopt
- DCI-P3 Digital Cinema 4K color space
- Adobe 1998—digital cameras (nearly identical to the original NTSC color gamut)

Display Gamma

Television Gamma is technically referred to as Electro-Optical Transfer Function. It is simply a function of how increasing the levels of electronic signals sent to a TV increases the levels of visible light coming out of that TV. It gets somewhat complex since that function is not a one to one or linear relationship. One simple example of the Gamma function is that 50% strength signal level produces about 18% level light output strength. For almost all of the 80 years of the history of television, we based Gamma functions on the performance of vacuum tube (CRT) television products. We expressed the function of signal in and light out using a Power Law Curve expressed by the number 2.2. That was the specification of professional studio monitors used for content creation in the low light levels in TV studios. Since most consumer TVs are used in rooms much brighter that TV studios, almost all consumer TVs offer Gamma options designed for better performance in brighter rooms. Consumers do not know anything about using these options, but for professional integrators these Gamma options are simply one of the many tools modern TVs offer to precisely optimize TV performance in rooms with multiple ambient light conditions.

For better visual understanding of a display's Gamma options, simply change these settings while watching a dark movie. The dark parts of the images will look different with different Gamma settings. The brighter settings are obviously for brighter rooms. Precise measurements of a display's Gamma functions are now relatively easy with calibration instrumentation.

Since 2008, there have been multiple professional documents from the European Broadcast Union (EBU) and the International Telecommunication Union (ITU) that have impacted studio Gamma. In 2008, the EBU stated that they believed that 2.35 was "appropriate". By 2010, the EBU recommended 2.35. The ITU formal recommendation in 2011 is for a new curve for studio production that is referred to by "BT.1886". It is close to 2.4, but the curve is now specified for flat panel monitors, not CRTs.

In a room with dark studio lighting conditions, simply choosing a studio EOTF or Gamma is the correct setting. With brighter rooms, the following are reasonable approximations:

- Bright room (lots of ambient light or daylight)—1.8
- Average room (some light control, shades)—2.0
- Dim room (quality blinds, some light control)—2.2
- Cinema environment (full control of all lighting aspects, virtually no ambient light)—2.35 for older content or BT.1886 for content created after 2011 on the very newest monitors

Surface Colors

Colors we perceive on the surfaces of objects are called surface colors as opposed to the colors of light. Color printers, such as inkjet printers, deposit inks that reflect light and fall into the category of surface colors. Because inks use the subtractive color process rather than the additive color process used in displays, their gamut is quite different.

Calibrating Color on Multiple Devices

Moving from one device to another involves the careful consideration of working color space and gamut for each device concerned. Most of the time, video technicians work with content based on the SMPTE-C gamut for NTSC and the HDTV (709) color gamut for high definition material.

VIDEO DISTRIBUTION

Video distribution refers to transmitting video from a source to a display or multiple displays. In most cases, this refers to video sources in a remote location distributed to multiple displays via a matrix switch. A matrix switch will allow the source to be shown on any display.

Video distribution's compelling attributes are convenience and organization.

- Convenience, in the sense that it can be integrated into existing automation and unsightly devices can be hidden away in a central location.
- Organization, as a single control system can operate the video distribution along with other functions of the installation. Examples are HVAC, lighting, security, and audio. There can be a cost savings involved as well as there is no longer a need for a source in every location, each user can have an assigned source that can "follow" them from room to room. This is usually minimal and not of the primary reason to use video distribution.

HDMI has presented a far greater challenge in video distribution than the previous analog methods of video transmission. The primary challenges concern HDCP and EDID requests from the panels to the sources. These challenges can be handled in different manners depending on the distribution technology used.

There are several technology formats available when utilizing video distribution. Each has their own characteristics and challenges. These formats are HDMI cables used over distance, HDMI over SDI (Coax), HDMI over RF (Coax), HDBaseT (Category cable), HDMI over IP (Category cable) and fiber. In most cases, there is a switch involved as well and the switched are based on the same technologies as the transmission technologies in most cases.

HDMI

HDMI cables are the simplest method of video transmission as there is no converting of the HDMI format. Simply put, plug the source into a switch or directly into the panel with a long cable. Simple and complex matrix switching can be added as well. There are several technologies involved in HDMI cables as well. This includes a straight "copper" connection involving a traditional HDMI cable just created in longer lengths, "re-equalizing" technology to fix the signal in the signal path of long cables, and fiber HDMI cables.

"Copper" Technology

A traditional HDMI cable has limits on distance primarily due to the properties of the wire. This includes resistance, capacitance, and inductance of the cable creating stress on the transmitting source. As the cables lengthen the resistive, capacitive and inductive properties can create stress that the source was not engineered to deal with.

"Re-Equalizing" Technology

This is essentially utilizing traditional cables with devices inline (either integrated into the cables or an external box). The technology is designed to overcome the electrical properties of the long HDMI cable (resistive, capacitive, and inductive) to allow the source to not be affected by these properties.

Fiber HDMI Cables

HDMI can be converted to fiber and the distances can be greatly increased as the distance is primarily limited by the quality of the fiber and its termination. Since these cables are already created to length, quality is rarely an issue.

Pros

HDMI is simply plug and play, there is no conversion (other than the fiber conversion that is usually small and unobtrusive). HDMI cables will pass uncompressed 1080p and Ultra HD/4K in any format available today (as long as the cable is capable). The distances are only limited to the electrical properties of the cable, the amount of re-equalizers, or the capability of the fiber cable. Costs associated with this type of distribution are typically low as well. One wire distribution is another benefit as CEC[1] can be utilized if you have like or compatible devices.

Cons

HDMI cables can fail or become obsolete. If there is another reformatting of the cable and feature set (Similar to 1.3 to 1.4), the cables may not allow all the features of the new format to be utilized. It is also possible, that as the signals get larger and bandwidth increases the cables cannot transmit the larger signals, becoming obsolete. HDMI cables are created in specific lengths and cannot be re-terminated and any mishaps that damage the cable can result in having to replace the entire cable. Lack of control system's ability to utilize CEC[1] is another issue. This is uncommon so a separate control run is often used. As mentioned previously, the source can have difficulty with long cables as well either by the electrical properties or the inability to drive the re-equalizers that are inline. This also includes, the system working with existing sources and cables and then failing due to an upgrade in sources or technology.

HDMI over SDI (Serial Digital Interface on Coax)

Serial Digital Interface is a technology created by the motion picture industry. There are many formats of SDI. SDI is not often utilized in consumer switch devices. It is most often the case that the HDMI switch is utilized with a SDI technology based extender. The compelling reason for SDI to exist is the utilization of existing Coax in the installation. SDI formats are starting to include more control features often associated with the more common HDBaseT switches and extenders. However bandwidth used for the control features can greatly limit the distance of the signal. There are devices available that can pass RS232, IR, and AV down a single coaxial cable. As mentioned above, the compelling reason to use SDI is existing Coax wire in the installation.

Pros

Uncompressed 1080p signals over existing Coax. Coax has been prevalent in most installs since the 70's. In many cases IR command can be sent to and from the display over the single Coax along with the AV signal. In some

[1] CEC refers to Consumer Electronics Control. This is a feature of HDMI that was designed to send a universal set of commands from one HDMI device to another. Examples are "all on", "standby", "change input", etc. The user can command up to 10 devices in a system utilizing CEC. The biggest issue facing using CEC control is that many devices are not compatible and some sort of CEC manipulation is required in the control equipment. In an HDMI installation, it is unlikely to be used unless all devices are the same brand and are compatible with each other, and in many cases it is best to disable it entirely.

cases RS232, signals can be sent either in lieu of or with IR simultaneously. Technology is improving and it will become possible eventually to transmit 4K/UHD signals. The bandwidth capabilities of Coaxial cable should allow for slightly more throughput than current technologies in other formats. It is possible to buy fairly capable extenders based on this technology today.

Cons

Not many options available, technology primarily used in motion picture industry. Existing coax can be old or have splitter and such in line with poor capabilities. It is possible that the original install of existing coax can be better than 20 years old and poorly done. It is very rare to see switches and matrix devices in this technology available in our market. No 4K SDI products or HDCP2.2 products are currently available.

HDMI over RF

HDMI over RF is most commonly over coax and utilizes QAM[2] or ATSC[3] technology. HDMI is converted to a RF signal that is compatible with the tuner already present in the display. The display is simply tuned to the broadcast channel to receive the distributed signal. There is no receiving device as the display is the receiver.

Pros

No box to hide behind the panel. Typically is cost effective in nearly any size install. This technology can often use existing coax in the installation. It is also easily scalable, if you need to add another panel, simply add it and tune it to the source you wish to see. The same goes for sources, simply add another tuner.

Cons

Lack of control options over the single AV cable, you will have to run another cable for control. Future support for 4K/UHD may be lacking. Counter intuitive for a consumer to tune to a channel for a source. Not many products available to the consumer in this technology. No known HDCP 2.2 products available at this time.

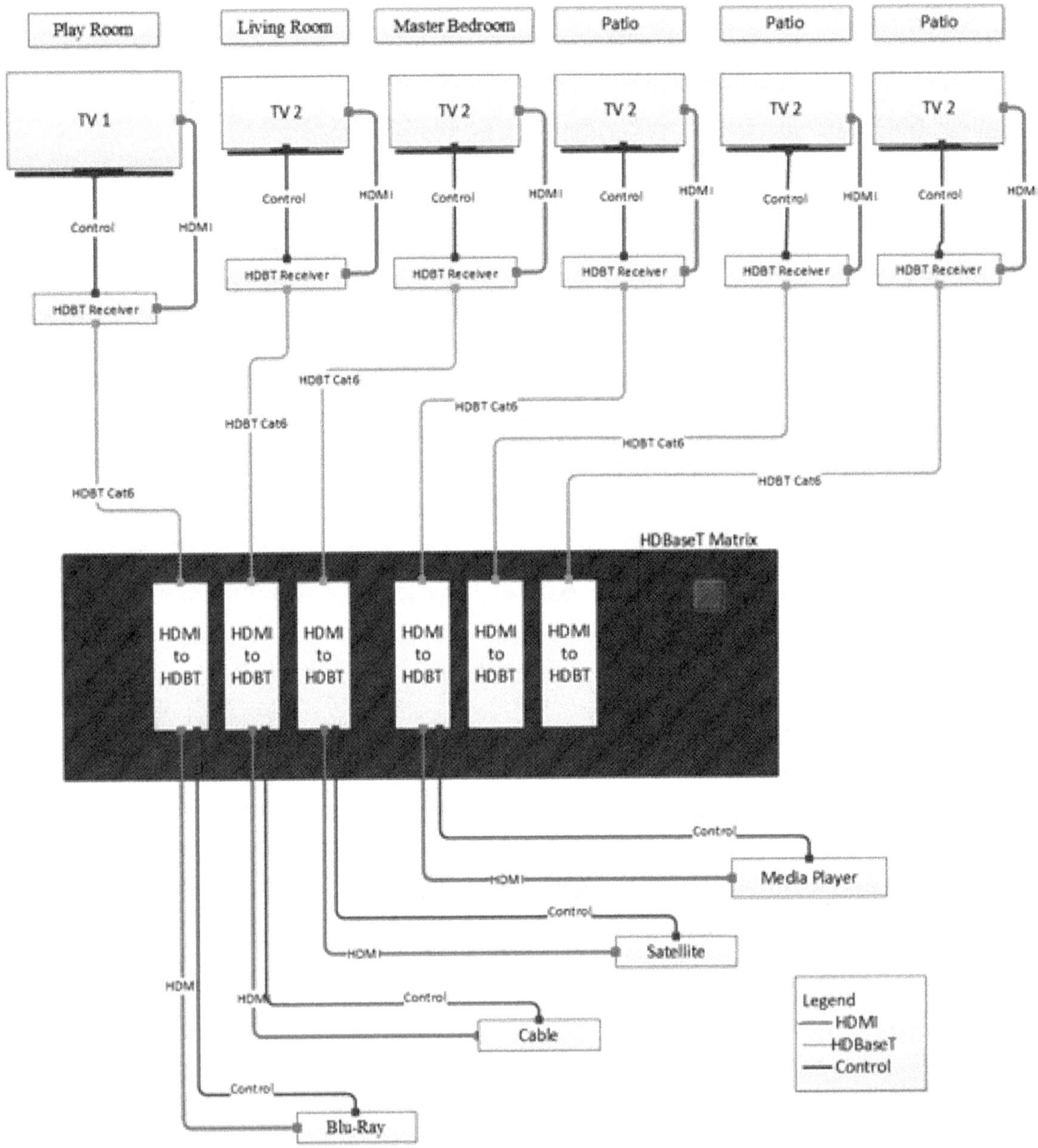

Figure 5-15 *4x6 HDBaseT Distribution System*

HDBaseT

HDBaseT is a relative new comer on the market and is rather complex in how the technology works, but is very flexible and easy to use for the integrator. Because of its encoding and decoding technology, HDBaseT is currently the most capable format available in our market. Over a single category cable, it is possible to send Ultra HD/4K[4] AV, 2-Way IR[5], RS232, USB2.0[6], 100BaseT Ethernet, SPDIF, and 100watts of power (POH[7]) over a single Category cable. The available throughput is up to 10.2 GBps .

HDBaseT is by far the most common used technology in residential applications today. There are 3 available chipsets in HDBaseT technology. Class B (often incorrectly referred to as "Lite"), 5-Play, and the new HDBaseT 2.0. The Class B technology is capable of 1080p up to 70m and 4K/UHD up to

35m. This is very common because of its lower cost. Most 1080p switches and extenders are based on this technology. The most common features are; 1080p up to 70m, 2-Way IR, RS232, and POH[7].

The 5-Play technology is more expensive than the Class B technology, but more capable. The distance is increased to 100m for 1080p and 70m for 4K/UHD. It also has more throughput capability. The most common addition utilizing this throughput is 100/BaseT Ethernet.

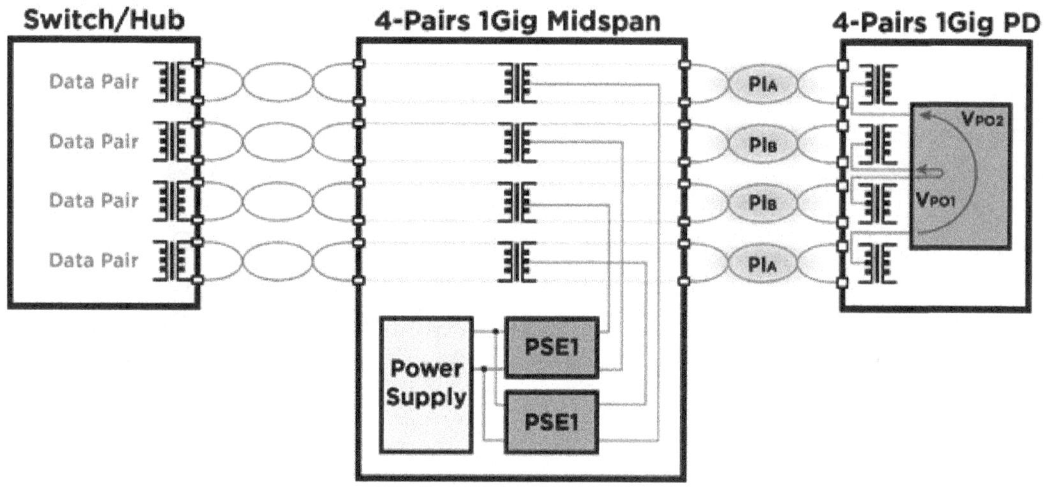

Figure 5-16 *Four-pair Powering*

HDBaseT2.0 has all the features of the 5-Play chipset and adds the ability to make either the transmitting device or the receiving device a server or a client for USB2.0, 2-Way SPDIF, and an audio embed feature are possible as well.

[4]4K and UHD are two different formats. 4K is a cinema standard and is 4096x2160 and UHD is a broadcast standard and is 3840x2160.

[5] 2-Way IR refers to the ability to both send and receive IR signals at the transmitting end and the receiving end of the extension of the signal.

[6]USB2.0 extension is based on one side of the extension being a server and the other being a host. Currently HDBaseT2.0 only supports one side being one or the other. You cannot make each end both a client and a server.

[7]POH is basically double POE+. POE (power over Ethernet) is a standard used in Ethernet networks that provides up to 15.4W in two different formats utilizing one pair of the Category cable. POE+ uses two pairs and is capable of 25.5W. POH (Power Over HDBaseT) utilizes all 4 pairs to allow up to 100watts of power to be transmitted down a single Category cable.

HDBaseT 2.0 is a new more capable chipset that allows even more features. Still utilizing a single Category cable,

Pros

HDBaseT has lots of features, 1080p and 4K/UHD capable along with many control and transmission possibilities over a single cable. Another benefit is because it is a packet based system, electrical interference and such is reduced substantially over other and previous formats. Wide spread availability and often compatible with other brands offering HDBaseT. There are a number of HDCP2.2 compliant matrices and extenders already on the market.

Cons

HDBaseT can get rather costly the HDBaseT2.0 devices are substantially more expensive than the 5-Play device. The cost typically increases per display as the size of the matrix increases. EDID has to be manipulated in many cases. This has become less of an issue in 1080p/720p installations, but has come up again in 4K/1080p installs. A scaling device needs to be incorporated until the display manufactures create 1080p panels that will accept and downscale 4K content.

HDMI over IP

There are several formats of HDMI over IP (Internet Protocol). We will be discussing two technologies as they are the most common available, JPEG2000 and H.264. HDMI over IP offers some things not readily available in the more common HDBaseT devices. It is scalable similarly to the RF system with the exception that you do need a receiver device at each display. It can conceivably be placed in existing IP infrastructures. HDMI over IP often has a video wall function[8] and in some cases multi-view[9] built into the format infrastructure as well. It typically only has 3 parts. A TX device (encoder), a RX device (decoder), and a network switch.

JPEG2000

This is a very common type of encoding and decoding technology. It is a fairly established technology and has been widely in use over a decade and is over 15 years old. It has two modes "lossy" and "lossless". The lossless mode is the most commonly used mode in video distribution. There is some technology where both forms are used simultaneously to create a step between "lossy" and "lossless" primarily in web content. The lossless compression uses more bandwidth than the lossy and the lossy/lossless hybrid. The bandwidth used is about 150Mbs in lossless mode. Because of this, it is easily transmitted over Gigabit networks. HDCP2.2 products starting to show up in this product range.

Pros (both HDMI over IP and JPEG2000)

HDMI over IP (JPEG2000) becomes more cost effective as systems get larger. Typically an HDBaseT system of 16x16 and an IP based system are within a few hundred dollars of each other. It is when the system surpasses 16x16 where the JPEG 2000 product becomes more and more cost effective as the system grows larger. Many HDBaseT matrices are preconfigured in standard sizes 4x4, 8x8, 16x16. IP based matrices are configurable and only limited by the size of the network and its capabilities. Configurable HDBaseT matrices are typically more expensive than preconfigured ones, lowering that 16x16 cost breakeven a little. Fast or instant switching (this is a premium feature in HDBaseT and typically raises the cost of the matrix again) is a common in HDMI over IP solutions. Video walls are easily created with JPEG2000 and many other technology formats of IP based HDMI distribution. Multi-view or preview is often a feature as well. Multi-view can allow several different sources to be decoded at the same time on one screen. The preview is good in control systems for live video feedback. These all can be accomplished in HDBaseT, but at an additional cost. EDID is basically eliminated by the nature of how the system works.

Cons (HDMI over IP)

High cost on smaller systems. Compressed picture (not noticeable to the layman, but where video is being critically watched, can be an issue). You have to have some IP network skills. HDMI over IP, can get really complex in larger systems that require VLANS. Wiring is more particular than HDBaseT.

Cons (JPEG2000 Specific)

In video wall mode, a flaw known as "tearing" occurs in full motion video and has to be corrected by using an extra transmitter per source for each row on the video wall. This can get remarkably complicated in complex video walls where you want several video walls within the wall of panels. Inferior 4K solutions (opinion) when compared to HDBaseT.

H.264

H.264 is a newer encoding and decoding technology that uses less bandwidth than the JPEG2000. It too has two modes lossy and lossless and are used in the same manner as JPEG2000. The biggest difference is the bandwidth and the ad hoc video wall at will capabilities. Because of the lower bandwidth, more devices can be placed on a network. Visually, most people report h.264 to be a higher quality image than JPEG2000 though this is often debated.

Pros (H.264 specific)

H.264 has lower bandwidth requirements. The technology supports ad hoc video wall creation without the "tearing" effects that occur without the extra transmitter in JPEG2000. In short, any picture anywhere easier than other HDMI over IP technologies.

Cons

- Cost, H.264 is often substantially more money than JPEG2000 devices, although there are some products starting to show up priced comparatively to JPEG2000. Inferior (opinion) 4K solutions to HDBaseT

- Future technologies
- Uncompressed 4K in IP is around the corner utilizing 10 gigabit networks.
- Semi-Compressed 4K 60fps/8K 30fps utilizing 10 gigabit networks
- 4K on H.264/H.265/JPEG2000
- Most likely a more sophisticated HDBaseT solution in addition to HDBaseT2.0

Trends

In the home there is a very strong trend to use HDBaseT. This is largely due to cost and convenience over other formats. There is a trend of HDMI over IP happening as well, but it is minimal compared to the HDBaseT sales. With the advent of streaming devices, it is possible that the HDMI over IP systems grow. The wrench in that machine is...

4K content in a disk format is around the corner. This should bode well for HDBaseT systems as they should be superior in quality to the other transmission systems. The lingering question is will HDCP 2.2 stick, and will other devices adopt it? It is already showing up in matrices of all kinds. Will the adoption of it in matrices drive other manufacturers to use the new HDCP chipset and firmware or stay with the backwards compatible previous versions? It can go either way.

Some believe that multi-view will have resurgence into the consumer market. With all of the pixels, multiple pictures on a single screen will look better. This is already a feature on some cable and satellite providers. HDMI over IP is capable as are many outboard devices as well. Expect to see more images on larger screens.

Best Practices

It is a very strong possibility that with the advent of the larger signals that cable certifiers will become a necessity. Right now, the pipeline is not completely used in most cases in HDBaseT systems. Because of the inherent capabilities of HDBaseT to intelligently direct traffic, poor wiring is being overcome by this feature. When that pipeline becomes more filled, it is possible that the systems will not operate as well as they do now. It would be a very good practice to make sure that all of the cabling installed meets the requirements with a cable certifier. This is not a verifier and it is rather expensive. It would be a good idea to rent one and see how your wiring really does stack up as it will matter a lot more very soon.

As with any distribution system, it is highly advisable that all new wire is run and certified. Best practices include avoiding power cables, ideally intersecting them at 90 degree angles. It is another opinion of this author that Category 6 or better cable be used and for the sole reason of reliability and quality of wire. Category 5e is too easily damaged and has many varying qualities of manufacture. Category 6 has not experienced a lot of the low cost poor quality influx that Category 5e has. Is there good Category 5e? Yes, I would verify this with the certifier instead of taking someone's word for it.

Some HDMI cables can have difficulty transporting large signals over long distances. It would be a good idea to use a signal generator and test monitor to verify that the cables will produce the largest signal that the system is likely to produce.

With the advent of 4K panels, it is imperative in HDBaseT systems that the EDID and/or signal size be manipulated. There are some 1080P displays showing up in the market that will downscale 4K to 1080p. There are many that do not. It would be advisable to use a scaling receiver or some sort of in line scaler to solve this issue.

How to Create a Video Distribution System

After choosing the technology and the manufacturer, it is best to create a schematic of what you are going to do. Please see Figure 50-15;

Most modern distribution systems consist of an AV room where all the component and necessary distribution devices are installed in a rack. This alone can be a science. The biggest failure in the design is lack of cooling. Satellite receivers and audio equipment can make an awful lot of heat. Please consult the chapter on rack design. Once the equipment is chosen and the rack designed, it is not a bad idea if this is your first large system to use the expertise of the manufacturer. Have the manufacturers involved look over your design and suggest edits if necessary.

Testing the System

The signal generator mentioned above is a great idea for testing the distribution system. If you are intermixing 4K and 1080P panels, the signal generator will show incompatibilities immediately. Try it on 4K first and then 1080p to make sure all panels display the signal sent to the system

Troubleshooting the System

Troubleshooting is a process. The best practices for trouble shooting is make the system as simple as possible and add devices until it fails. Do you have the same issues with a test monitor plugged into the source? It means it is a bad source or HDMI cable. Again the signal generator and test monitor (available from many) will determine what the issue is pretty quickly. Add components until it fails. The manufacturer of the matrix/ip equipment can help greatly. I have also found that most manufacturers have greatly improved their manuals over the last few years, many are actually worth reading!

Troubleshooting the Network

This is more difficult as network switch settings can cause a lot of issues. It is HIGHLY recommended that you have the manufacturer help you look through your switch with a program like Teamviewer etc. and verify switch settings etc. Again, you can still boil the system down to a point to point and you can still use the test kit to get to the point of adding the switch.

Conclusion

A video distribution system is a matter of convenience, security, and style. Very few interior designers want to work around shelves of video sources and such piled around the display. Hiding them away and using a video distribution system is preferred. The convenience of having your content when and where you want it is exciting and extremely fulfilling to the end user. Imagine not having to leave the room you are in to see who is at the front door? What is going on in your yard? All of these features are part of a secure, convenient, and fun to use video distribution system. There are a plethora of technologies, manufacturers and devices to accomplish this.

CHAPTER 6

HOME THEATER ACOUSTICS AND ROOM DESIGN

Whether used as a dedicated space or a multi-purpose space, a properly designed home theater faithfully reproduces both picture and sound content. In terms of the audio portion of the system, the sound track is developed with the full range of human hearing in mind, both in frequency and amplitude. Therefore it is imperative that we design the room to preserve the frequency response of the sound and to maximize the dynamic range. This means having the ability to hear sounds as close to the threshold of hearing as possible.

When designing a home theater, many factors come into play. Several are interdependent and interactive, and the design process will invariably be iterative or "fine-tuned." This means that at every step, the design is revisited and altered, continuing around the circle of decision points multiple times until the work is finished. Some compromises are inevitable. For example, the picture screen and front speakers will compete for wall space because they need to be in the same location. Of the several ways to deal with this issue, some yield better overall results than others. Ultimately, the best sounding and best looking home theater is the one with the most intelligent set of compromises!

The Amplitude of Sound

A sound wave is caused by increases and decreases in pressure at a certain point in space. Amplitude is the measurement of the maximum amount of pressure at any point in the sound wave where the pressure increases the most. These high pressure points are called crests, or peaks. Tailing the crests are the low pressure points called troughs or nulls. Figure 6-1 shows a diagram of sound waves with high and low pressure points.

Amplitude and sound pressure levels are measured in decibels, or dB. When measuring sound pressure, it is usually measured in reference to threshold of human hearing, which is referenced to 0 dB SPL (sound pressure level).

Decibels

A decibel is a unit used to represent gain, and measures the gain or loss from input to output. The term decibel is a combination of the metric term deci (1/10) and Bel, which is the original unit of amplification measurement. A Bel was named for Alexander Graham Bell, an American inventor well known for his work on the telephone. Bell was the first person to study the logarithmic nature of human hearing.

However, a Bel is too large of a unit for many measuring tasks, so the decibel (dB) is commonly used instead. Decibel is abbreviated dB and the lowercase "d" indicates the fraction of the Bel.

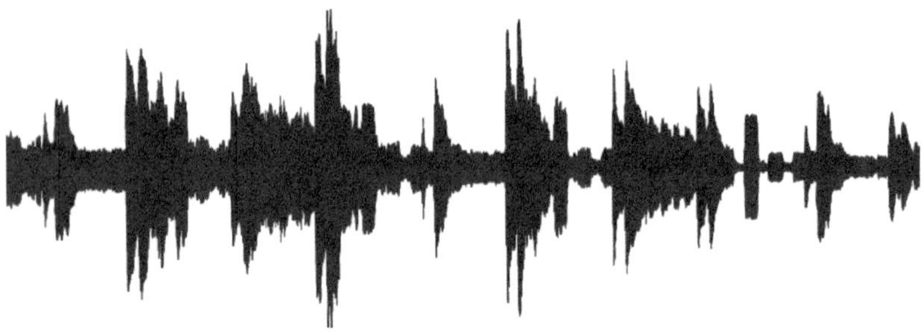

Figure 6-1. *Sound Wave*

The decibel is used effectively with sounds measurements because the human ear responds to sound in a logarithmic manner, and decibels use a logarithmic scale. The decibel is not an absolute measurement, but instead represents a ratio of two power levels as shown in the following equation:

$$dB = 10 \log (P_1 \div P_2)$$

Where:

P_1 is the resultant level

P_2 is the starting or reference level

The logarithmic scale used by the decibel expresses a large range of numbers with relatively small numbers. Table 6-1 shows the log of several numbers and how they relate to decibels.

Table 6-1. *The Logarithmic Scale*

(P_1/P_2)	$\text{Log}(P_1/P_2)$	dB
1	0	0
2	0.3	3
10	1	10
100	2	20
1,000	3	30
10,000	4	40

Loudness

In audio, loudness is a subjective term that refers to the overall audible sound level. When the loudness of a sound system is adjusted up or down, the audible sound level changes in the same manner. A change of about 1 dB is barely detectable to the human ear, but a change of around 3 dB produces a discernible change in loudness. An increase of 10 dB is judged to be twice as loud and a decrease of 10 dB, half as loud.

Equal Loudness Curves

Fletcher-Munson curves represent an average of the frequencies that the human ear perceives as loudness. Over 60 years ago, Bell Labs researchers Harvey Fletcher and Wilson Munson worked to establish equal loudness curves or contours by interviewing people and asking them to evaluate when sounds of two different frequencies were the same loudness.

The answers varied widely from person to person. By averaging the answers, they developed a chart that gives general indicators regarding loudness. Figure 6-2 shows the equal loudness contours or what we commonly call the Fletcher-Munson curves.

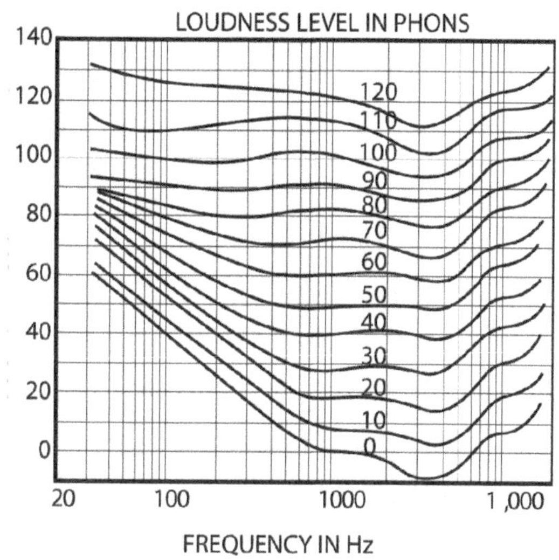

Figure 6-2. *Fletcher-Munson Curves*

Over the years, different sets of loudness curves have been developed in addition to the Fletcher-Munson curves. The most recent research resulted in the Equal Loudness Contours, which are very close to the original models developed by Fletcher and Munson.

For those who work with home theater systems, the most interesting aspect of the Fletcher-Munson curves is that the curves demonstrate that it is more difficult for the human ear to hear low frequency or soft sounds than it is to hear sounds between 1-6 k Hz.

OSHA Noise Exposure Limits

While it seems obvious to anyone who has experienced extremely loud noise that long-term exposure might damage hearing, it is also true that permanent damage can be caused by exposure to different sound levels at various lengths of exposure. To protect workers from permanent hearing damage, the Occupational Safety and Health Administration (OSHA) has established permissible sound level specifications based on an allowable amount of hearing loss over a sustained period of time. It is important to note that these values, as stated by OSHA, are measured using dBA weighting (discussed later in this chapter). Table 6-2 shows permissible sound levels measured by a standard sound level meter using the slow response setting with A-weighting applied.

How Loud Is Too Loud?

The threshold of hearing is the lowest level of sound that is audible to the human ear. In 1933, Fletcher and Munson determined that the threshold of hearing, or where the average human ear begins to sense sound, is at the sound pressure level of 20 μPa (micropascals) and is defined as 0 dB SPL. (When a unit is added to the dB, the value is in reference to that unit, in this case the unit is 20 μPa.) Fletcher and Munson also discovered that the threshold of hearing, as well as the perceived loudness of a sound (the strength or sound pressure level), is dependent on frequency.

Table 6-2. *Permissible OSHA Levels*

Duration per day, hours	Sound level dBA slow response
8	90
6	92
4	95
3	97
2	100
1.5	102
1	105
0.5	110
0.25	115

Once the threshold of hearing is known, other sounds can be established in reference to that value. Figure 6-3 shows some common sounds and their sound pressure levels as compared to the threshold of hearing. These are approximate values because actual values or the exact sound level for any source depends on environmental conditions and distance to the source of the sound, among other things.

When sound becomes too loud, it becomes unbearable. At approximately one billion micropascals, the human ear experiences pain from sound. This is called the threshold of pain. The threshold of pain, which varies slightly from person to person, ranges between 120 dB SPL and 140 dB SPL. The Fletcher-Munson curves show that the human ear is less sensitive to frequency (has a flatter response) as the intensity or level of the sound increases. Extended exposure to high sound pressure levels can lead to hearing impairment or hearing loss.

Frequency

Sounds that are audible to the human ear have a frequency range of about 20 to 20,000 Hz. This range of audible sounds varies from person to person and with a person's age. Generally as people age, the audible sound range gets smaller.

Above this range are ultrasounds, and below this range are infrasounds. The frequency of a given sinusoidal wave is the number of cycles per second. Figure 6-4 shows two sine waves, one with a lower frequency (2Hz) with fewer waves per second, and another with a higher frequency (4 Hz), which has more waves per second. In perfect conditions, sound travels 1129 feet (334 m) per second through 68 degree Fahrenheit (20 degrees C) air. However, actual speed is affected by distance, temperature, humidity, and other factors. When a sound wave strikes a boundary, some of the wave's energy is transmitted through the boundary, some is absorbed by the boundary and some is reflected off the boundary; how much of each is dependent of the frequency of the sound wave and the material of the boundary. A reflected sound wave arrives at the ear of the listener slightly later than a direct sound wave because it travels a longer distance.

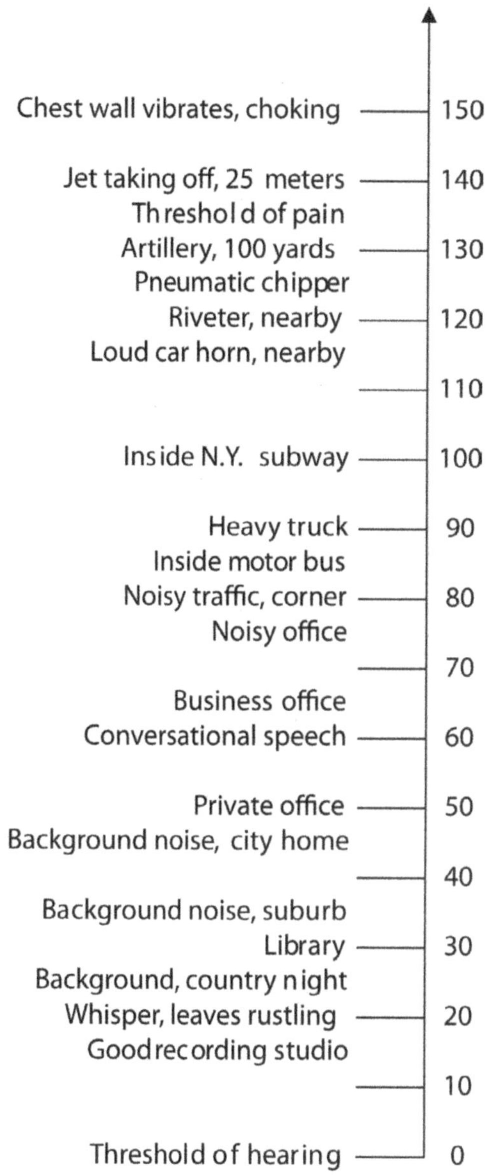

Figure 6-3. *Common Sound Levels*

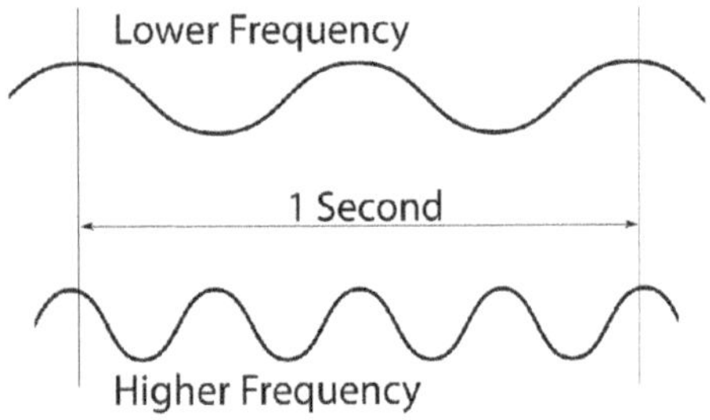

Figure 6-4. *Frequency*

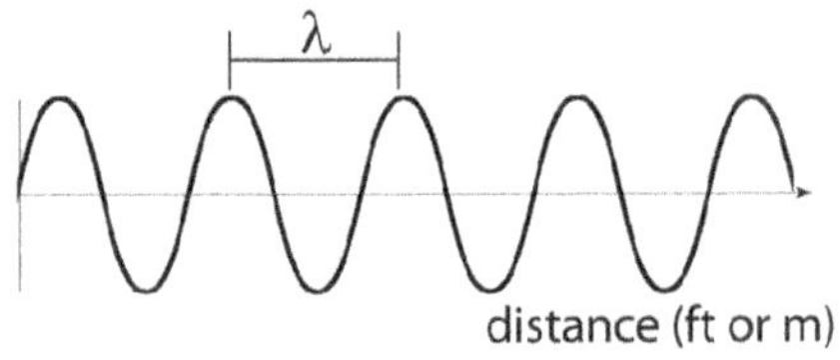

Figure 6-5. *Wavelength*

The wavelength (see Figure 6-5), represented by the Greek letter lambda (λ), of a sine wave is the distance the wave travels during one cycle and is given by the formula:

$\lambda = v \div F$

Where:

- λ is the distance of one sine wave (wavelength)
- v is the velocity of sound (1129 ft/s or 344 m/s)
- F is the frequency of the sine wave

Harmonics

A simple sine wave with a given frequency (f1) can be combined with other frequencies to create complex sounds. When these other frequencies are multiples of f1, they are called harmonics. Harmonic components are integral multiples of the same frequency. They are also periodic at the signal frequency. We describe these multiple frequencies as:

Fundamental Frequency (f1) — The lowest frequency of the combination of sine waves (f1)

Second Harmonic (f2) — The wave with twice the frequency of the fundamental (f2 = 2 x f1)

Third Harmonic (f3) — The wave with three times the frequency of the fundamental (f3 = 3 x f1)

Nth Harmonic (fn) — The wave with n times the frequency of the fundamental (fn = n x f1)

Harmonic Distortion

One of the main uses for harmonics is to evaluate signal distortion. Because the human ear is not linear, harmonics can be heard even with a pure tone. The ear also generates sum and difference tones when two loud tones are received at the same time. In this case, the sum and difference tones, as well as the harmonics, are heard.

Harmonic distortion is the most universally accepted method of evaluating the effects of circuit nonlinearities. It is also the easiest to understand. The device to be tested is driven by a pure, or close to pure, sine wave. If that signal encounters any nonlinearity, the output wave shape changes and harmonic elements appear. Special instruments are then used to measure the amount of harmonic distortion.

Most amplifiers have a specification noting the Total Harmonic Distortion (THD), which is usually less than can be discerned by the human ear.

Octaves

An octave is a doubling of a frequency. This is true in music (one octave up from A440 is A880) and in audio. For example, if the fundamental frequency is 100 Hz, the first octave is 200 Hz, followed by 400 Hz, 800 Hz, 1.6 K Hz and so on. Each of these octaves can be broken into bands on a graphic equalizer. These bands can be 1/3, 1/6, or 1/12 of an octave. At these smaller bands, more control is provided within the equalizer to precisely modify the room frequency response without affecting neighboring frequencies.

Calibration Signals

When designing a home theater it is important to understand how the human ear responds to different frequencies. Once the concept of hearing response is understood, one can begin to understand how to design, install, and calibrate a home theater in order to create a true cinematic experience. To perform system calibration, specialized equipment must be used, along with test patterns and noise generators.

White and Pink Noise

White and pink noises are terms used to talk about sounds in relation to frequency and human hearing. White noise is the sound that includes every frequency in the human range of hearing with equal energy at every frequency.

Because of the structure of the human ear, people listening to the white noise sound will hear the sound as having more high frequency content than low frequency content.

Pink noise is a variation of white noise. Pink noise is created by filtering white noise to reduce the volume at each octave. In pink noise, each frequency is reduced in level with a slope of 3 dB per octave, so the resulting noise sound wave has equal energy in every octave. Figure 6-6 shows

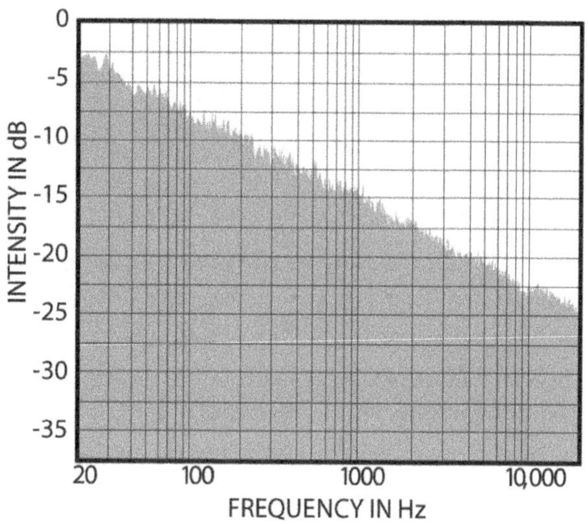

Figure 6-6 *Pink Noise*

pink noise displayed on a logarithmic chart. Pink noise is used with real-time analyzers since it displays a flat response when displayed in octave or 1/3rd octave bands.

Weighted Filters

The human ear is more sensitive to high frequencies than low frequencies, which means that not all sound pressure levels are perceived as equally loud. This is why sound meters are usually fitted with a filter that is designed to respond to the frequency in the same way as the human ear. The filters are weighted to filter out different intensity levels for noise measurement. The most common weightings are called A-weighting and C-weighting.

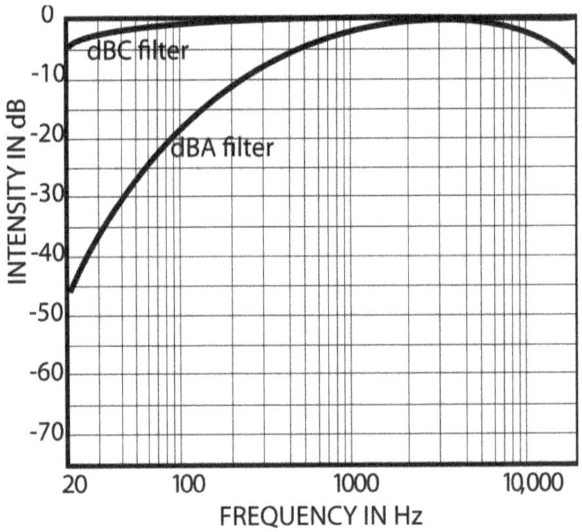

Figure 6-7. *A- and C-Weighted Filters*

A-weighting — follows the frequency sensitivity of the human ear at low intensity levels, 20 to 55 dB SPL. Sound level meters set to the A-weighting scale filter out much of the low-frequency noise they measure, similar to the response of the human ear. Noise measurements made with the A-weighting scale are designated dBA.

C-weighting — follows the frequency sensitivity of the human ear at high noise levels, 85-140 dB SPL. The C-weighting scale is quite flat, and therefore includes much more of the low-frequency range of sounds than the A-weighting scale. Noise measurements made with the C-weighting scale are designated dBC.

Figure 6-7 shows a graph of A-weighted and C-weighted filter curves. It is important to always note the weighting filter used when taking sound measurements, as they greatly affect the interpretation of the data.

Reverberation

When a sound wave leaves a speaker it moves mostly as a spherical pressure wave, with a portion of it traveling in a direct path to the listener. This is called a direct sound wave. But the wave also moves in many other directions. Multiple sound waves can bounce off walls, ceilings, or other surfaces and reach the listener only slightly after the direct sound waves. This longer path is called the indirect path or reflected sound. Reverberation is the effect of the many reflections of sound that occur in a space, and is dependent on the size of the space and the surfaces (objects, people) within that space.

When sound waves bounce off walls and other surfaces in a room, the surfaces absorb some of the energy. As a result, second waves of sound are slightly weaker when they arrive at the listener's ear.

The reflected sound waves can also bounce off surfaces multiple times before reaching the listener. Reverberation (also called "reverb") is made up of this series of indirect sound waves. The more time there is between the different waves reaching the ear, the more obvious the reverberation. As a result, a large room has more reverb than a small room because the sound waves travel farther in a large room. It is also true that rooms that have more hard surfaces have more reverberation than rooms with absorptive materials.

The Precedence Effect

The brain and the human ear perceive the direction of a sound from the arrival of the first sound wave (also known as the incident wave). This is called the Haas effect or the precedence effect - the first sound takes precedence over the weaker reflected sounds. Research has found that the human ear suppresses any sound waves after hearing the first sound for about 40 milliseconds for the purpose of identifying the location of the source of the sound. Based on the speed of sound, that translates to about 45 feet. These "suppressed" reflections are still very much audible, and in fact contribute to fullness and spaciousness, just not localization.

Obviously, this is a big issue for large theaters and auditoriums, but the typical home theater contains much less space. Even though there is some reflection of sound waves from the side walls, the reflection time is not long enough to create an echoed sound. The smaller amounts of reflection that happen in less than 40 milliseconds actually help the ear to decipher sounds. As a result, in home theater applications, side walls usually need much less absorbent material than they do in large auditoriums. In fact, if the sound is deadened too much, the theater loses sharpness and soundstage resulting in a "dead" feeling in the space.

In concert halls, no sidewall absorption is needed (diffusion is still effective, however). In home theaters, a modicum of sidewall absorption (and some level of diffusion) is required, although the amount of sidewall treatment is still somewhat an open issue in home theater design.

Reflections

Reflections take two different forms in reverberation. Early reflections are a set of well-defined and direct reflections that occur for a short period of time after the initial direct sound. Early reflections are related to the shape and size of the room, the position of the source of the sound in the room, and the position of the listener. These are sometimes referred to as "early echoes" even though based on the definition of echo, this is a misnomer.

After the early reflections, additional reflections arrive at the listener's ear at a subsequently increasing rate. The later reflections called diffuse reverberations or late reflections are more random. They are difficult to relate to the room's physical shape. They are, however, directly related to the room's size, and in fact decay exponentially in good home theaters.

Grouped together, early reflections and late reflections are called impulse response of the room. The impulse response of a room is shown on a diagram as a small bit of a sound marked by a vertical line each time that same piece of sound is heard. The height of the line or column indicates the loudness of the sound each individual time it is heard. Figure 6-8 shows how quickly the late sound reflections decay with time compared to the early reflections.

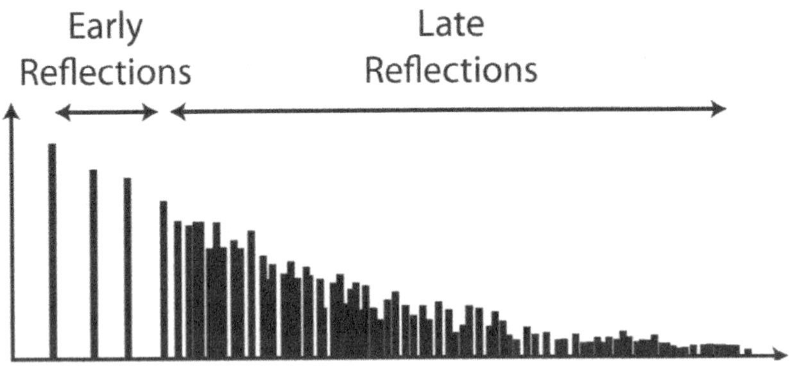

Figure 6-8. *Early and Late Reflections*

Reverberation time is associated with what we call the "size" or volume of the room. The longer the reverberation time, the larger the room size. Reverberation time is sometimes expressed as RT60 which is defined as the amount of time that it takes for the sound pressure intensity to decay 60dB from its original value. Longer reverberation means the sound energy stays in the room longer before being absorbed by the structure and contents of the room.

A time-based analysis system is required for measuring RT60. The RT60 measurement system is very important for extremely large spaces like concert halls and auditoriums. However, RT60 measurements are less important in a home theater, due to its comparatively smaller size. Only in the very largest of home theaters, those larger than 30 feet in any one dimension, does it become an issue. Most well-designed home theaters have a reverb time of less than 0.5 seconds. Any reverberation issues can be resolved by following some simple design guidelines.

Reverberation time is determined by two factors:

- Size or volume of the room
- Absoption of surfaces, including objects in the room

Size — The size of a room is based on the volume of the room measured in cubic meters or feet.

Surface — The surfaces of the room determine how much energy is bounced and how much energy is absorbed. Hard, reflective surfaces like concrete and tile increase the reverb time because sound waves bounce off the hard surfaces repeatedly. Absorptive materials such as curtains, carpet, and people absorb more sound and decrease reverb time. The percentage of energy absorbed by a surface is called the absorption coefficient. In the middle frequencies (usually between 250 Hz and 2 k Hz), the absorption coefficient is almost exactly the same as the Noise Reduction Coefficient (NRC) for a given material.

Calculating RT60

The Sabine Equation is a method for calculating reverberation time (RT) of a room. It assumes that the absorbing materials are reasonably evenly distributed on the room surfaces. The Sabine formula for calculating RT when measuring in feet is:

$$RT = .049\ V/A$$

Where:
V is the total volume in cubic feet

"A" is the total absorption in the room in sabins. "A" is calculated by adding up all of the surface areas (carpet, drapes, walls, and so on) of the boundaries that are covered by materials that absorb sound, multiplied by their individual absorption coefficients:

$$A = (S1a1 + S2a2 + S3a3\ldots)$$

Where:
S is the area in square feet
a is the absorption coefficient for the material covering each surface area.

Absorption coefficient is a measure of the percentage of sound that is absorbed when sound reflects from the material. It is frequency dependent, so we look for materials that have relatively constant absorption over large frequency ranges, ideally, at all frequencies above about 300 Hz. For purposes of this calculation, the absorption coefficient of 500 Hz is used.

The product of "S" and "a" is a number with the unit called sabins. The absorption of some items, such as people or chairs, is sometimes quoted directly in sabins.

The metric equivalent of the Sabine Equation is:

$$RT = 0.161V/A$$

Where the volume is in cubic meters, areas are in square meters, and "A" is in metric sabins.

Absorbers

Absorbers can be added to a home theater to minimize sound reflections in the room. There are many kinds of absorbers, from special ceiling tiles to fabric covered wall panels. In the case of resistive absorbers, how they are mounted in the room influences how effective they are at controlling sound waves. Overall, independent mounting with air space between the surfaces extends the lower frequency performance, however, it is not a direct corollary between say a 4" panel and a 1" panel with 3" of air space. The thickness of the absorbent material and its density are also an indicator of the material's absorption properties. The density of the absorber is typically between 3 and 6 lb/ cubic foot. Typically, adding an air gap behind an absorber will cause it to perform more like a thicker absorber. Thin absorbers are generally effective only at higher frequencies, and thicker ones absorb lower frequencies much better. Broadband absorption is always preferred over absorbing only high frequencies.

Some kinds of absorbers include:

Construction Materials — Fiberglass insulation and acoustical ceiling tiles.

Open Cell Foams — Previously used mainly in cars, airplanes, and machinery, they are now being used in architectural applications.

Drapes — Porous sound absorbers that allow air to flow through. In terms of sounds, fullness has a greater effect than thickness.

Carpet — A key element in both large and small rooms. Carpet absorption levels vary greatly and depend tremendously on the type of underlayment. Often, the carpet absorbs more than its share of sound. It is important to compensate for that and balance the sound throughout the space.

People — An audience adds significantly to the sound absorption in the room.

Air — Usually only a problem in very large spaces, so it is not typically considered in the equation.

Absorbers can be added to a room to increase the room's sound absorption. Some types of absorbers include:

- Bass traps or low frequency absorbers
- Diaphragmatic absorbers
- Polycylindrical absorbers
- Membrane absorbers
- Helmholtz resonators
- Perforated Panel absorbers
- Slat absorbers

Different absorbers work best on certain frequencies. It is vital for the home theater designer to carefully study the absorption coefficients of whatever devices are being specified to understand the effect the device will have on the overall room acoustics. A good understanding of which type will work best for your given issue in essential before adding these absorbers to a room.

Slap Echo

When a room has two parallel hard surfaces, a condition called slap echo can occur with sounds that are primarily mid-range and high frequency that reflect off the two surfaces, as shown in Figure 6-9. The sound reflects back and forth until it finally dissipates. Slap echo can be identified by clapping hands sharply in the middle of the room and listening for the sound of the echo in the mid-range.

Slap echo reduces the sound quality in a home theater by adding harshness to the upper mid- range and treble through energy time storage, and destroying the phase relationships that help to establish an accurate sound stage.

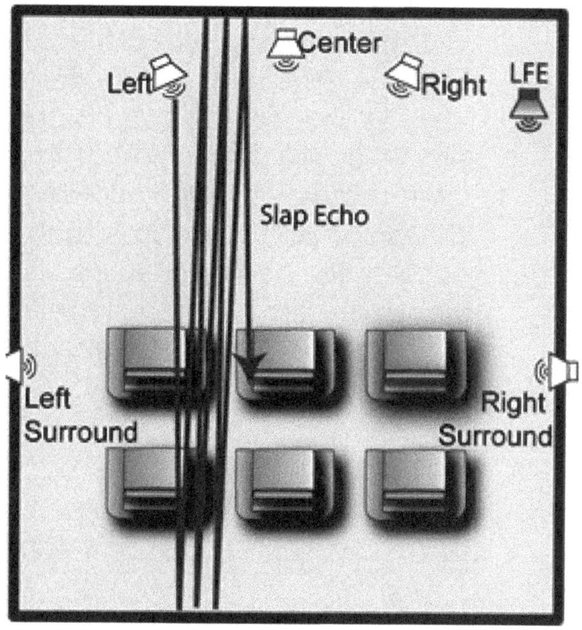

Figure 6-9. *Slap Echo in a Home Theater*

There are several ways to minimize slap echo. These include incorporating absorptive materials like draperies, carpet, fabric-covered wall panels, and seating into the plan, and diffusing the sound with diffusers placed along the back wall of the home theater.

Sound absorbent materials alter the tonal characteristic of the room by reducing the sonic energy in various frequency ranges depending on the absorbent material or device used. Diffusers send sound in many directions, preventing the sounds from returning directly to the front of the room. Diffusers tend to leave the tonal balance characteristics unchanged in the room, but make the sound smoother and more open; although care must be taken to place certain types of diffusers so that they are not in close proximity to listeners as a phase shift phenomenon can occur.

Scattering and Diffusing Devices

Acoustical material placed in the center portions of the front and rear walls should be mostly absorbing, with scattering devices towards the sides of the rear wall. All absorbers, wherever they are located, should not be less than 3 to 4 inches deep. The thickness and density of the absorptive materials will determine how low a frequency the panel will absorb. The use of a thinner absorber, such as a 2" absorber with a 1" air gap, will have an absorption coefficient very close to that of a 3" absorber. However, the designer should analyze the absorption coefficient of each device to assure accurate results.

Side walls should use a mixture of reflection, absorption, and scattering/diffusing devices. Figure 6-10 shows a possible side wall configuration. Diffusers designed to scatter the sound horizontally should be located in the region about 1 foot below and about 3 feet above ear level. Other layouts for front and rear walls are shown in Figure 6-11 and Figure 6-12.

Diffusers can be of the engineered-surface type, as shown in Figure 6-13, that are attached to or built into the walls, or they can be simple geometric shapes that can be constructed on-site using conventional building materials. To assist the illusion of immersion or envelopment, these devices must be effective at lower-middle frequencies. This means that engineered surfaces should not be less than about 8 inches deep, and geometric shapes should not be less than about 1 foot deep. As diffusive materials, and their depth, are proportionally related to a signal's wavelength, the deeper the diffuser, the more effective it is at lower frequencies.

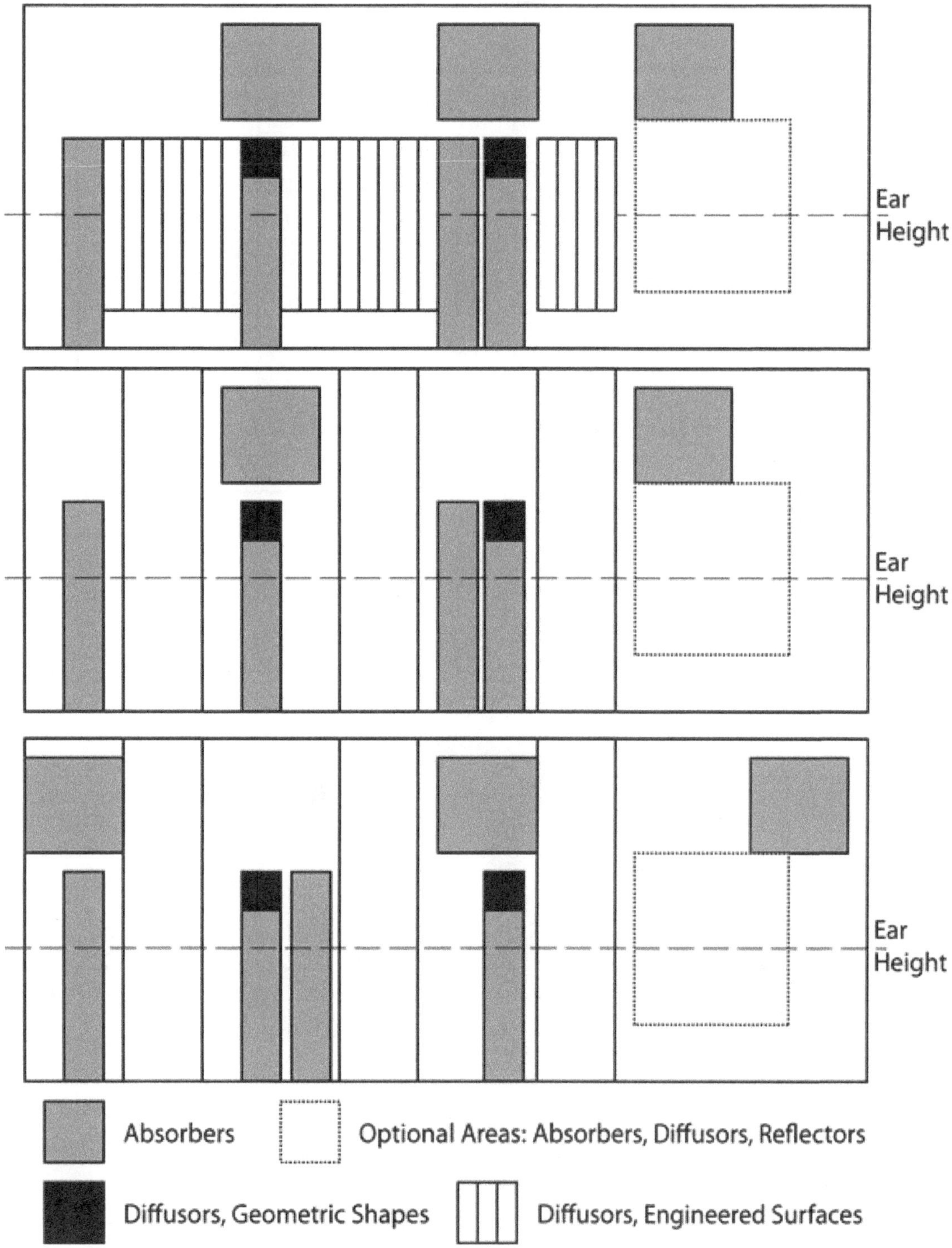

Figure 6-10. *Possible Side Wall Configurations*

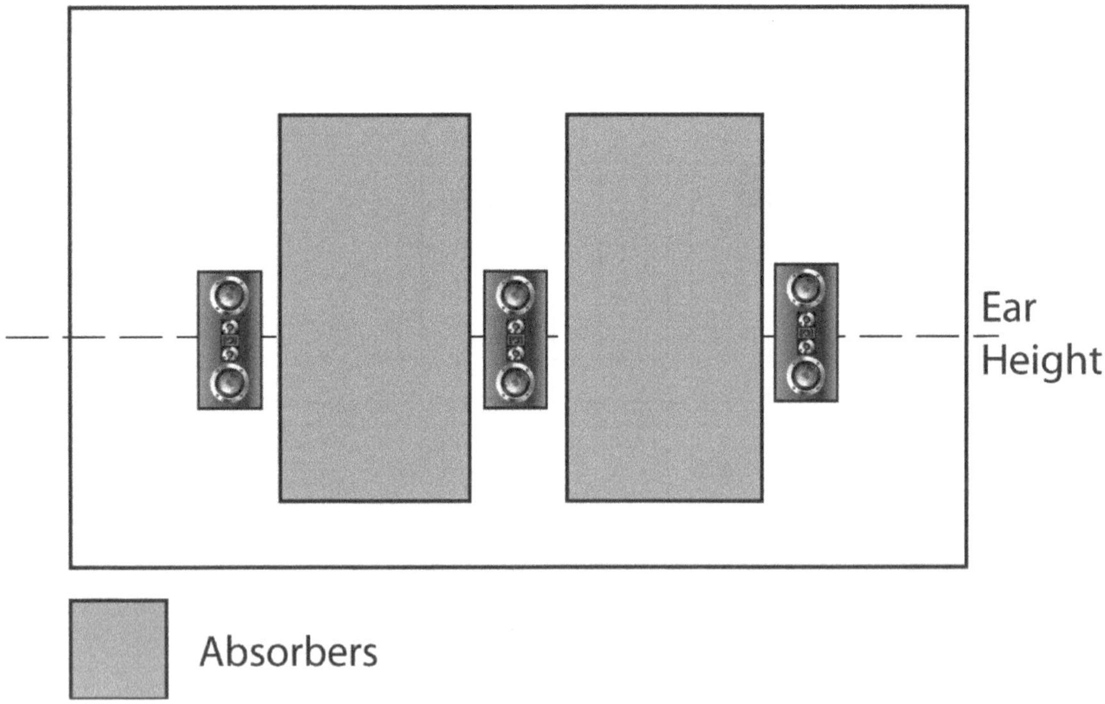

Figure 6-11. *Possible Front Wall Configurations*

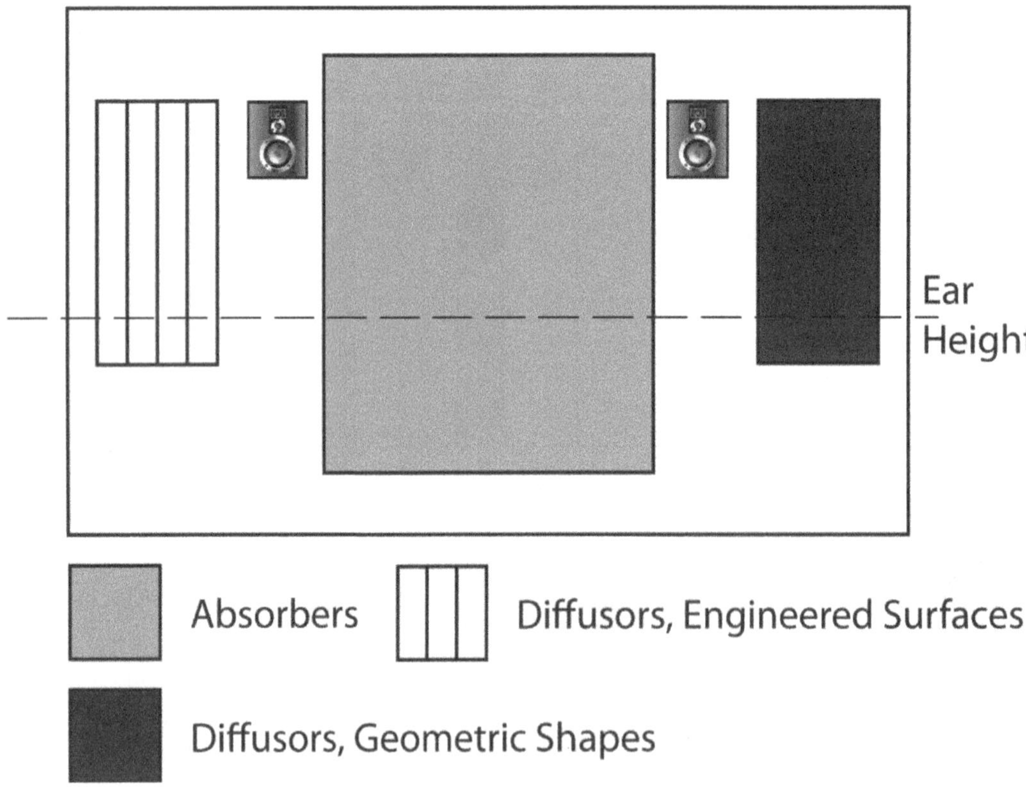

Figure 6-12. *Possible Rear Wall Configurations*

Noise Criteria

Noise Rating Curves (NRC) used mainly in Europe, or Noise Criterion (NC), used in U.S., are part of the family of Balanced Noise Criterion (NCB) curves, an almost universal approach to the critical task of selecting a noise level goal. Figure 6-14 shows NCB curves which are graphed based on sound pressure level and frequency.

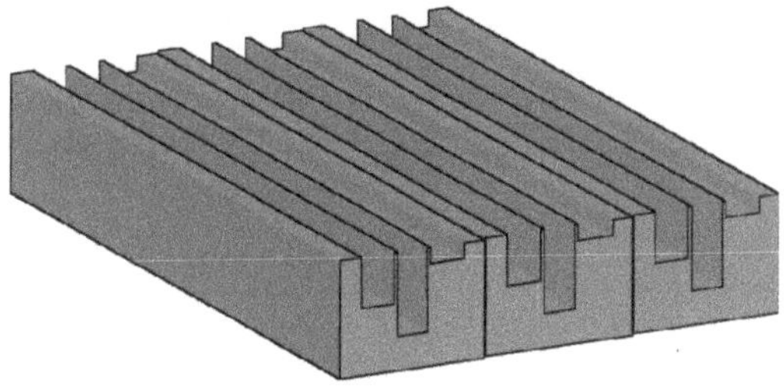

Figure 6-13. *Example of a Diffuser*

Noise Control and Sound Isolation

Noise comes from both inside and outside a room. The term noise control refers to eliminating noise from within a space. The term sound isolation refers to limiting how much noise reaches the room from outside and how much of the sound in the room leaks to the outside.

The goal of the home theater is to reproduce sounds from 0 dB SPL to 105 dB SPL. To do this effectively, the room should be well isolated from interior as well as exterior noises, because these noises will mask the lower loudness sounds within the soundtrack. Locating a home theater in the quietest, most isolated area of the home is the ideal first step.

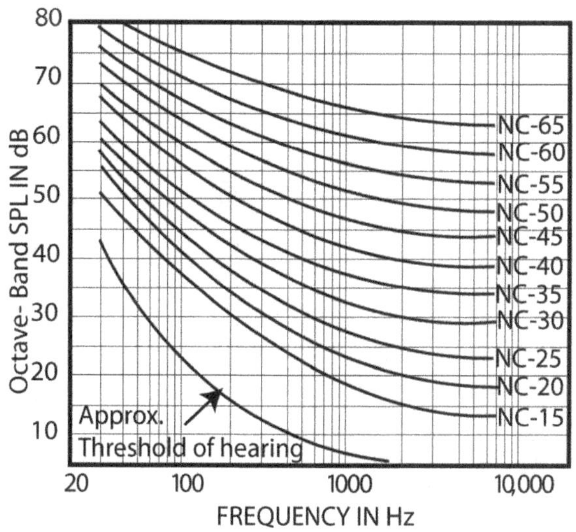

Figure 6-14. *NCB Curves*

Noise Reduction Coefficient (NRC)

The Noise Reduction Coefficient (NRC) is a measure of the amount of sound energy that a surface absorbs when struck by sound energy. An NRC of 0 indicates perfect reflection, like from a glass window or mirror. An NRC of 1 indicates perfect absorption, like sound passing through an open window. Although, don't be surprised to see materials with a NRC above 1, this is possible with some folded or sculptured materials that actually present more surface area per square foot, allowing it to absorb more sound than a perfect absorber. NRC ratings are used to describe acoustical materials in job specifications. Frequency and amplitude charts can be used to determine these specifications, but NRCs are a simpler (though less accurate) way of measuring the sound absorption qualities of a material. The NRC is actually an average of the material's absorption of sound energy at 250

Hz, 500 Hz, 1000 Hz, and 2000 Hz. The NRC works well to measure the absorption qualities of the human voice, but a broader frequency range is usually considered for most audio applications.

Sound Transmission Classification (STC)

The Sound Transmission Classification (STC) is a way to quantify how well a wall, or other construction detail or material can isolate sound. The STC measures the decibel reduction that a partition can provide based on 16 individual measurements across a frequency range from 125 Hz to 4 kHz. The actual transmission loss varies by frequency, but the STC is a single integer average of the overall response curve. While this classification works well for classifying transmission of speech, it is less effective in indicating isolation performance for music and home theater sound that often has significant content below 125 Hz. Transmission loss below 125Hz is not factored into the STC and can vary dramatically with the tested results. Outside the USA, the Sound Reduction Index (SRI) ISO standard is used.

The human ear perceives a reduction of 10dB as a level reduction of 50%. If a 90dB sound is reduced to a 30dB sound on the other side of a wall, floor, or ceiling, then the partition would be considered to have a transmission loss of 60.

Room Shape

The optimum shape of a home theater is a rectangle because it is the best starting point for a creative design, and, with its simple shape, ensures that fewer mistakes are made during construction. Builders and designers are more likely to err in odd-shaped asymmetrical spaces.

A rectangular or symmetrical room provides predictable acoustics due to reflection patterns and voicing. It is also symmetrically acoustic due to imaging and provides fewer acoustical anomalies due to a lack of domes, niches, and obstructions. A symmetrical room also provides optimized traffic patterns to avoid disruptions.

The acoustic benefit of an odd-shaped room is a myth. In reality, an odd-shaped room makes design and acoustic prediction more difficult, if not impossible. For design purposes, a modal analysis and predicting in an odd-shaped or asymmetrical room is not as accurate.

In home theaters, the listener is in the center of a sound field that is modified in the sound track. Asymmetrical rooms cause this effect to be less ideal and more unpredictable. Domes and other concave spaces can cause a very audible distortion, as can niches and obstructions. These details can still be used and their associated problems overcome, but it will require extra attention to the acoustical treatment of the room.

A rectangular shell can be modified with soffits, ceiling details, columns, and prosceniums to create an architecturally exciting interior. But including these details in an odd-shaped room can be very difficult and rather time-consuming.

Walls and Ceilings

The stud and sheetrock walls that are the norm in most homes have a Sound Transmission Classification (STC) of around 33. These provide little privacy and very little noise insulation. Most building standards now require a STC of at least 50 between apartment units. Though this blocks the human voice, it does little for other sounds. Most standards aim for a STC of 70 to properly isolate sound in and from a home theater.

Adding fiberglass insulation to the wall increases the STC anywhere from 3 to 6 points. Doubling the drywall can push the number into the 40s if gaps are properly sealed. The biggest increases in sound isolation will come from decoupling wall or ceiling panels and breaking the sound wave transmission path. In addition, increasing the density of the fiberglass will increase the STC rating.

The STC rating for a single wall construction with insulation and a single layer of wallboard is about 33dB, and this can be increased a few dB by adding a second layer of wallboard. Double wall construction (with 9" of insulation) can provide 52dB of isolation, and adding a viscoelastic compound or mass-loaded vinyl between the layers of drywall will further increase STC values. Remember that STC ratings are an average of several frequencies, and do not provide an accurate description of low frequency performance.

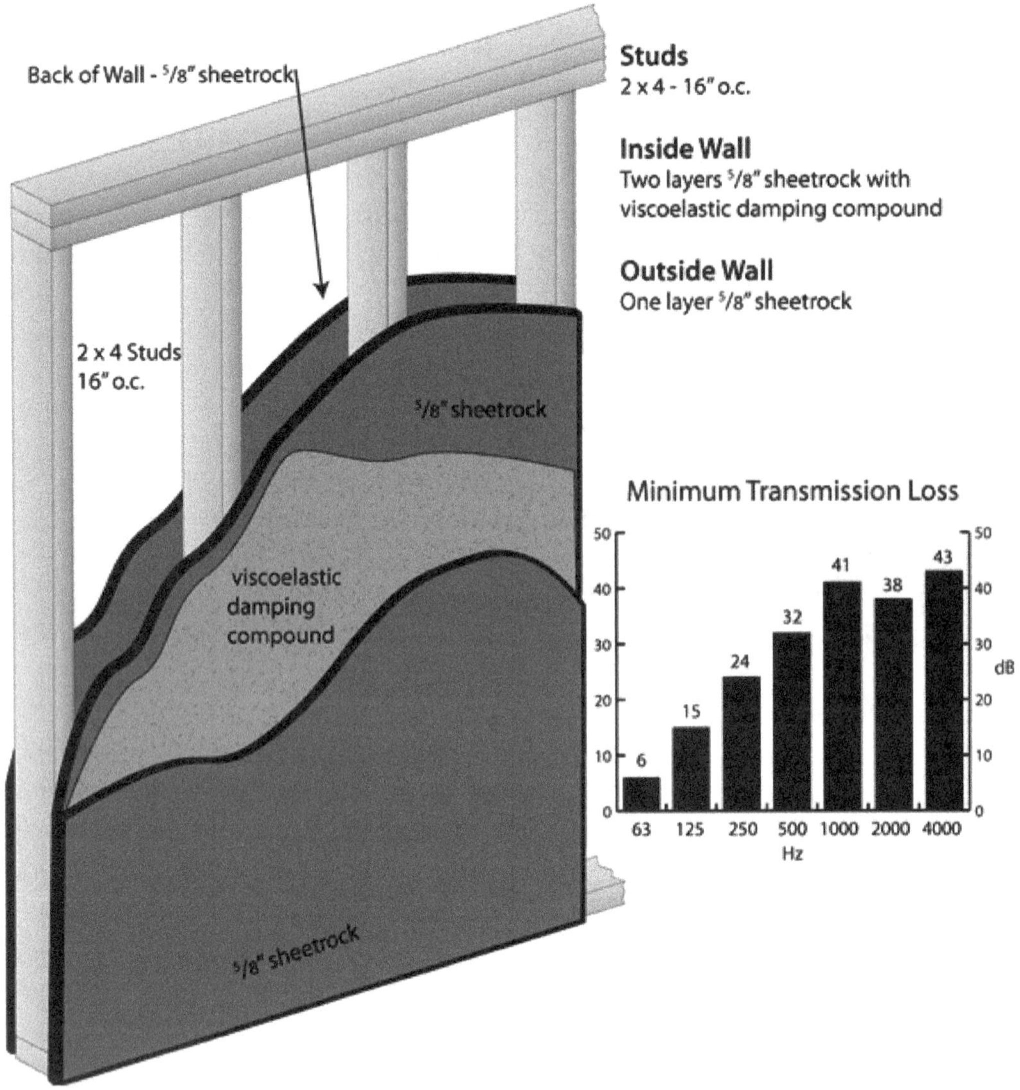

Figure 6-15. *Isolation Level 1 Wall Construction*

Wall Construction Guidelines

Various levels of sound isolation can be achieved through a wall's construction, as shown in Figure 6-15 (Isolation Level 1), Figure 6-16 (Isolation Level 2), and Figure 6-17 (Isolation Level 3).

Sound isolation is achieved through a combination of the mass of the inner and outer wall surfaces (because adding more mass will provide increased isolation), and constraining or damping of either or both of the wall surfaces. This can be accomplished by:

Mechanical Isolation of the Surfaces — Support each surface on a structurally independent frame or provide resilient mounting for one or both surfaces. Resilient decoupling devices must be installed with care to ensure that their function is not negated by screws or nails that bridge the gap between the surface being isolated and the underlying structure.

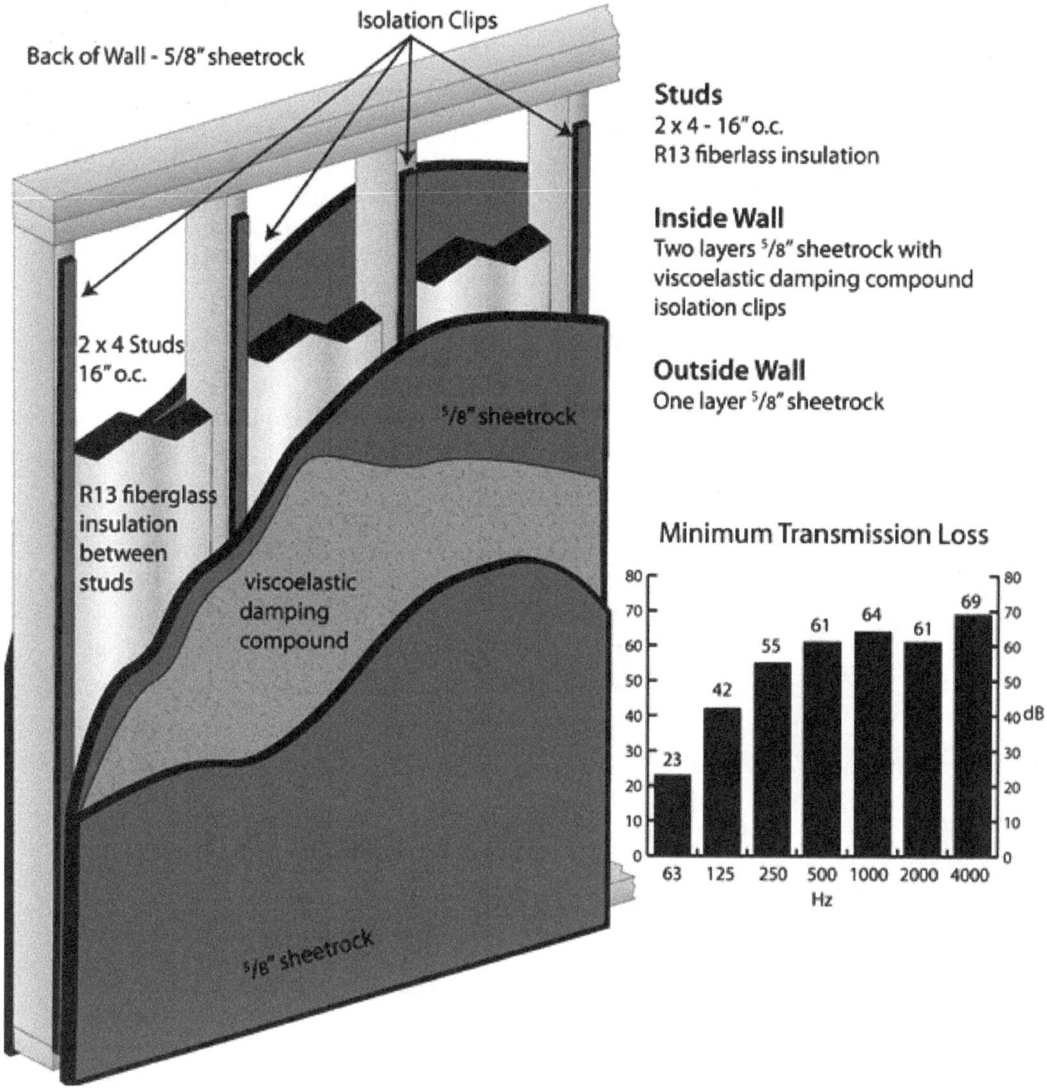

Figure 6-16. *Isolation Level 2 Wall Construction*

Air Gaps — The larger the distance between the inner and outer surfaces, the greater the transmission loss, especially at low frequencies. Several inches to a foot is not an excessive separation if space permits.

Acoustical Absorption — Use flexible batts of fiberglass or mineral-wool in the space between the inner and outer surfaces.

Surface Integrity — The inner and outer surfaces must be continuous, without perforations of the kind created by thoughtless installation of electrical boxes or in-wall loudspeakers. Be careful to avoid accidental mechanical connections between the inner and outer surfaces created by plumbing, electrical conduits, HVAC, and the like. The sound inside the room must stay within the room, and any vibrations within the inner surface must not be communicated to the outside surface—and vice versa. Recessed lighting should be avoided, unless they are completely enclosed. Surface-mounted fixtures are a better choice.

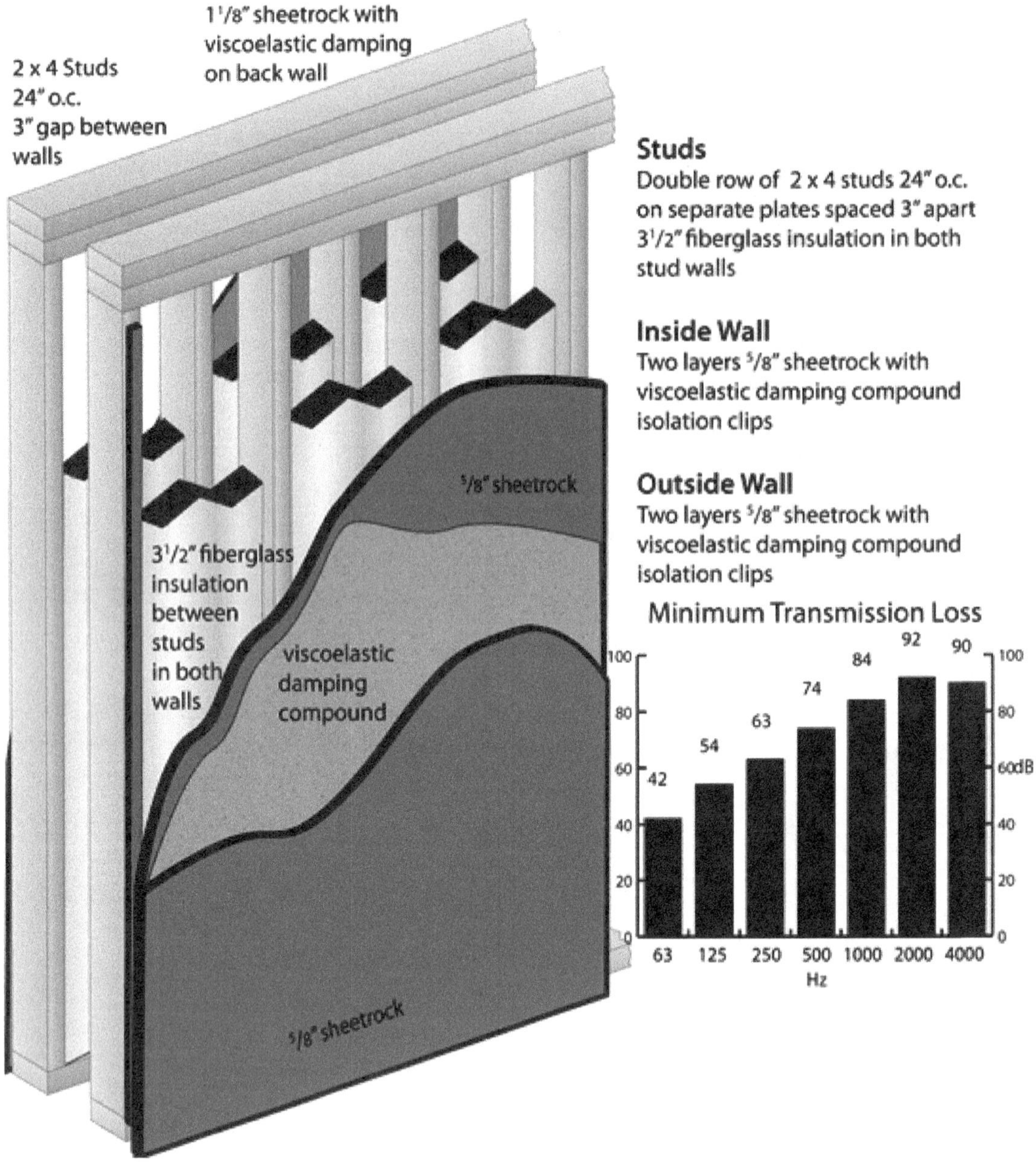

Figure 6-17. *Isolation Level 3 Wall Construction*

Enhancements to Theater-Facing Surface Construction — Additional layers of sheetrock, resilient isolators, or damping materials should be added to walls or ceilings facing into the theater to help avoid flanking path opportunities. Care should be taken as the act of adding a decoupled layer on top of a drywall layer will result in a triple leaf condition that will actually increase sound transference. Careful design and engineering of quiet room construction techniques and the quality control of the installation are essential for good results.

Construction Site Vigilance — Most builders and contractors are totally unaware of the care necessary to construct home theater spaces. All trades operating on site must be monitored and coached to achieve optimum results.

Windows

If windows are a part of the home theater (they are sometimes used between the equipment room and the main viewing area), double pane windows, preferably with entirely separate frames and heavy duty glass, provide the best noise insulating solution.

The windows should all be of sufficient minimum rating to meet the sound isolation requirements of the room and wall class, with STC 60 for typical applications. If windows are required in the STC-75 wall class (try to avoid this), they should be acoustically rated, and have an STC-58 rating, preferably with a transmission loss of 40dB or more at 125 Hz.

Sound Insulating Doors

The ordinary household door offers less than 20dB in sound isolation. Sealing the door well and increasing the weight of the door can add as much as 30dB of sound insulation. The biggest challenge to creating soundproof doors is creating a good seal. Soundproof doors and heavy metal doors are also available commercially.

Door placement helps to control noise levels because distance increases STC numbers. A small vestibule-room with double doors provides optimal noise reduction. Figure 6-18 shows a possible layout where access is provided through the equipment room and the theater from the same vestibule area.

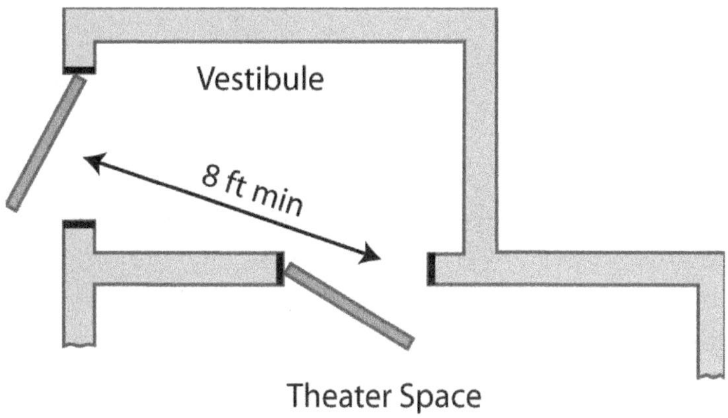

Figure 6-18. Theater Vestibule

Projectors and Other Equipment

The projector contains a fan that can dramatically add to the noise within the room. The best practice is to place the projector outside the room with an optical glass wall separating the lens from the home theater. If the projector is mounted in the electronics closet, be sure the electronics closet has sufficient ventilation. If the projector is housed in its own enclosure, this enclosure will require a separate ventilation system that is triggered based on the temperature inside the enclosure. The goal for any equipment is to maintain room temperature, because increasing the temperature of the components will lower the life expectancy of the equipment. This same idea applies to other heat-generating equipment in the room. Ideally, an electronics closet with a proper cooling system and sound isolation can house all of the home theater equipment. Figure 6-19 shows how this type of design would look.

Transferred Energy or Vibration

Vibration can be a big problem when it comes to creating an ideal audio environment. Vibration creates noise through transferred energy. Transferred energy is energy that is imparted onto the structure, flows through any solid surface connected to it, and then appears in free air as sound. Just about everything in the room can vibrate — including home theater equipment, walls, and ductwork.

Rattles

Rattles appear in the room as a result of loose objects that are physically moved by the high volumes within the space. Rattles can be located by performing a slow sweep test that is generated from a noise generator or a DVD test disk. The sweep test is a slow sweep of all frequencies starting from 20 Hz to 20 K Hz. The sound should be played at the maximum calibrated level of 105dB. Items that rattle should be tightened so there is no audible sound.

Water and Sewer Pipes

In new construction, avoid running pipes through the walls of the home theater whenever possible. In the case where a pipe must be run through the walls, they should be cast iron pipes wrapped in insulation. If there are existing pipes, wrapping them will reduce the noise of running water. In some cases it might be necessary to add additional sound proofing to the walls.

Lighting

When lighting is dimmed to a low level, it can cause the dimmer to buzz. Dimmer interference with audio is only a problem if it is audible. It does not have a negative effect on the equipment. Typically, 50% dimming creates the loudest buzz. The easiest way to avoid this is to place all dimmers and low-voltage interfaces for lighting outside the room or in the equipment closet. Also avoid placing the dimmers on a wall that backs up to the home theater.

Heating, Ventilation, and Air Conditioning (HVAC)

In addition to the sound coming from the equipment, another problem that must be addressed is the sound generated by the heating, ventilation, and air conditioning (HVAC) system. The sound of air rushing into the room can create unwanted noise in the home theater. The fan is the chief contributor to HVAC noise in the home theater environment, but it isn't the only problem.The American Society of Heating, Refrigerating, and Air Conditioning Engineers (ASHRAE) is a good source for designers with little knowledge of HVAC.

In new construction, or if HVAC is being added, plan the equipment location as far from the home theater, or sound sensitive area, as possible. Isolate the equipment from the home structure by placing equipment on a separate concrete slab and using proper vibration isolation mounts.

There is a direct noise relationship between the quantity of air the system is required to deliver, the velocity, and the size of the duct. Unfortunately, high-pressure, high-velocity, small-duct systems are less expensive and therefore more common, but these virtually guarantee noise problems. However, duct work can be installed in ways that minimize noise by slowing down the force and speed of the airflow, as shown in Figure 6-20. The following rules should be followed to minimize HVAC noise in a home theater:

Bends — At least two ninety degree bends should be included in the ductwork between the air exchanger and the room.

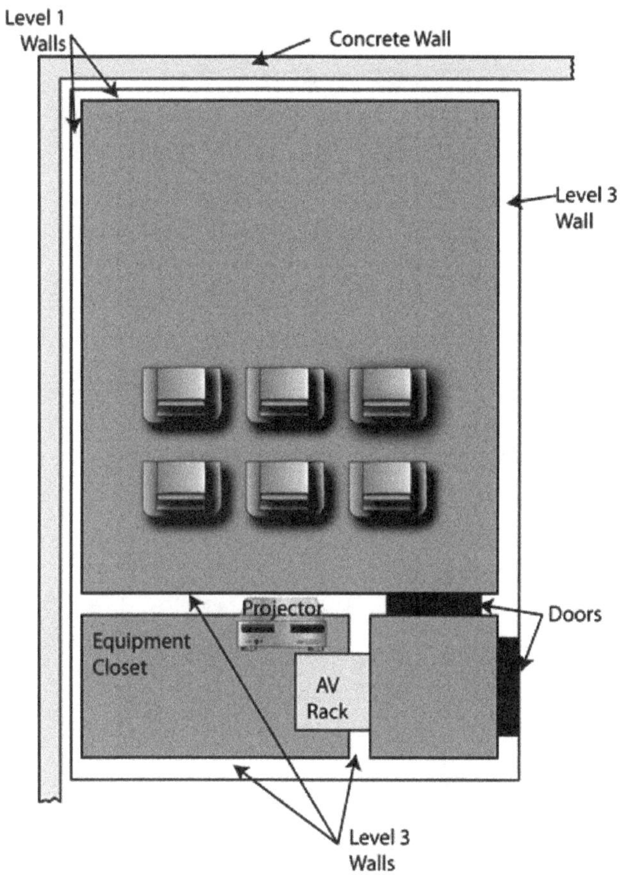

Figure 6-19. *Example Theater Layout*

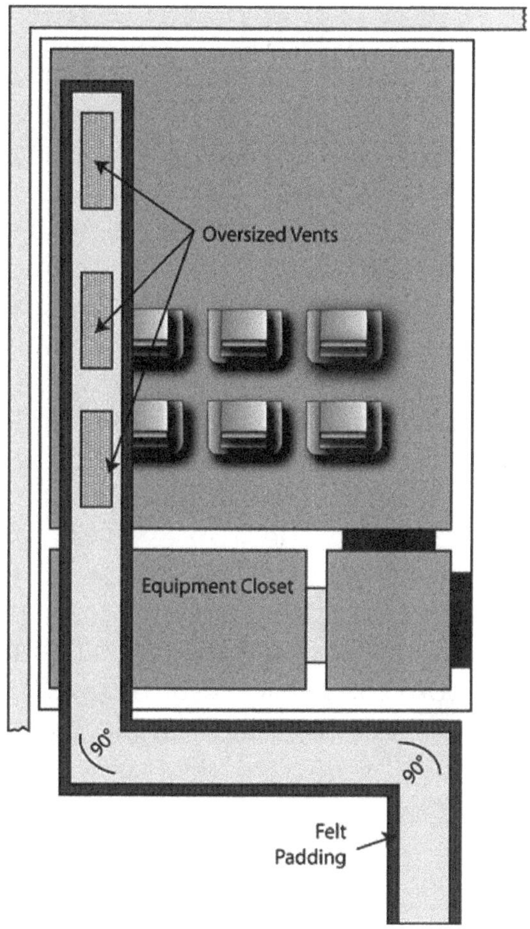

Figure 6-20. *HVAC Noise Reduction*

Lining — The ductwork should have a felt or fiberglass lining to absorb noise.

Oversize Ducts — Oversized ductwork in the room will allow more air to enter the room at a slower speed and thus generate less noise. Vents should not be located between speakers and listeners.

Grills — Large grills reduce vibration and noise.

Foot Fall

Foot fall is the name for the sounds created when someone is walking on a floor above the home theater room. The energy from their steps is transferred to the floor and from the floor into the sound sensitive area. This sound can be very distracting. A suspended ceiling helps reduce the sound transmission from the floor above. A suspended ceiling made of absorbent material will help decrease the noise coming from above and the loss of base from the room.The ceiling can be isolated using z-clips and insulated material. It is more important to provide isolation of the theater structure from the home than to absorb sound. This isolation will minimize the impact of footsteps and other vibrations from the home into the home theater.

A test called the Impact Isolation Class (IIC) is used to measure foot falls. This method, often known as the "tire drop," is a single number rating of a partition's isolation value based on a field measurement of NR at one-third octave bands. The problem with this test is that it can only be done after the room is built. Underlayment in floors can help with this issue, but should be planned in advance and implemented during construction.

One of the ironies of designing and constructing a home theater is that as progress is made in reducing noise inside the home theater, the surrounding noise becomes more obvious and more audible. Things that previously seemed insignificant take on more importance. When the noise from the HVAC system is gone, people walking down the hall can be heard. The best course of action, therefore, is to consider and address all noise sources (no matter how insignificant they seem) at the beginning of the project in order to achieve the best possible results.

THE VIDEO ENVIRONMENT

Just as a home theater must be designed properly to support the audio performance, consideration must also be given to the video environment. There are many comparisons. For instance the ambient light level is comparable to the noise floor and the color and textures of surfaces could be analogous to the reverberation or echo characteristics acoustically. Additionally, just as positioning of listeners and loudspeakers plays a vital role in shaping the quality of our acoustical experience, the video systems and viewers must be positioned appropriately to realize the full potential of the systems.

We will discuss the characteristics of a quality video environment and describe a number of best practices under each category of characteristics. These categories are:

- System positioning & configuration
- Audience positioning & configuration
- Light
- Ambient light conditions
- Lighting design considerations
- Surrounding surfaces

A fundamental characteristic of a good video environment is the ability to properly position and configure the display system. Generally, when discussing a dedicated home theater, we are talking about a 2-piece projection system including a screen and a projector along with all of the necessary hardware needed for support, housing and ventilation. In the case of rear projection systems we will also be considering the projection room environment and the possibility of a mirror system.

Configuration of 2—Piece Projection Systems

The considerations for systems of this type are dependent on a number of characteristics. In turn, many of these choices are also dependent on many other factors.

Screen Size

Also dependent on room size, audience size, ceiling height, projector capacity, aspect ratio(s).

Ultimately the final size will be a compromise resulting from the primary aspect ratio & viewing angle recommendation, number of rows, preference for primary viewing position (there can only be one perfect row!) and the room size.

Recommended Practice, CEA/CEDIA CEB-23:
a. Seating distance at primary view position.
i. 3 × Image Height is ideal
ii. Assumes constant image height in all aspect ratios

Note that 4k systems, with the increased pixel count, allow for larger images (smaller viewing distance), but the designer must keep in mind other factors, such as viewing fatique.

These factors are useful guidelines when determining the ultimate screen size for the theater. The designer will be required to engage in an iterative process. Using the above factors as guidelines the overall room dimensions, audience size, numbers of rows, acoustical impact and other factors can come into play. Many configurators are available on line and from various sources. These may be helpful for limiting the numbers of iterations, but it is advised that the designer carefully design the final screen size by verifying all the relevant standards and performance characteristic within the specific room.

Screen & Projector Location

Also dependent on speaker location, projector characteristics, audience size & configuration, room factors.

Recommended Practice, CEA/CEDIA CEB-23:

a. Vertical viewing angle

i. At primary viewing position, ≤ 5° from orthogonal axis (dead center)

ii. All positions, ≤ 15° from orthogonal axis

Obviously, the location of the screen is directly associated to the factors determining screen size. For instance, in a room where a 138" D 1.78: 1 screen is selected (selection based on the preferred viewing angle, number of rows and projector output), we now have to look at the room itself and integrate the screen with the equipment and the environment.

Equipment — The screen must be within the optical range of the projector. In other words, depending on the technology and the optical system, the special relationship with the projector has to be verified to be within the operational range. The considerations are:

- *Throw Distance* — Most projectors offer various lens options. The position of the projector and the screen must be matched with the range of available lenses. Verify the measurement reference points (midpoint of chassis, endpoint of chassis, end of lens) and carefully select the right equipment and position.
- *Offset* — All projectors have a maximum vertical and horizontal offset range. Most projectors calculate that range from dead center on the projected image. So if a projector states the vertical offset is +.5 screen height, it means it can be positioned half the vertical dimension of the screen above the center point of the screen (or flush with the top of the image). Verify the projectors reference point (i.e. center of lens). It is never advisable to position the screen outside the optical offset range of a projector (using digital keystone correction) as this will always result in a loss of resolution. Another consideration regarding offset is whether an anamorphic lens assembly is being utilized. Check the manufacturer information to see what impact a specific anamorphic lens has on offset range.
- *Speakers* — If the speakers are being placed behind the screen (acoustically transparent screens), make certain adequate space has been allowed for the speakers, driver excursion and

accommodation of acoustical energy from the woofers. The dimensional requirements and acoustical impact of placing speakers behind screens is controversial as many differing opinions exist. Certainly all screen materials will have some acoustical impact and the designer must research each materials impact and make accommodations accordingly. Keep in mind the area surrounding the speakers, even if not visible, must be considered in the overall acoustical design.

Projector Positioning — The location of the projector is dependent on room construction, screen size and location, screen configuration, projector performance and requirements related to ventilation and noise control. Many of the considerations will already be determined by the screen size and position. Every projector will have operational ranges of offset, throw and size capacity, however, the physical and aesthetic characteristics of a room may have overriding considerations. For instance, a room with very high ceilings where a projector would be required to hang on a long mounting assembly may be unacceptable aesthetically. Additionally, the need to contain the fan noise of such a projector would require ventilation. Additionally, the throw distance and ambient light characteristic of the room will have an impact. This is generally a function of the screen size increase at greater throw distances. Again, use the factors noted above and look at all the parameters before making a final design decision.

Special considerations for 2-piece rear projection systems - Many rear projection systems have projection rooms which are limited in space. This characteristic requires careful engineering of the projection system.

Some of these applications will require short throw lenses which will limit the location of the projector as such lenses generally do not allow offset positioning. Additionally many screen surfaces are not acceptable for short throw lenses. If mirror systems are being engineered, other complexities arise such as duplicate reflections and other distortions. Some can be addressed with optical coatings or proper surface specification. Other environmental considerations for rear projection systems are ventilation, ambient light conditions and noise control.

Audience Configuration & Positioning

Just as many of the system configuration & positioning decisions are interdependent, audience configuration and positioning are as well. For instance, if a projector will drive a 138" diagonal 1.78:1 screen and can be positioned properly in the room for optimal results, can a viewer (or multiple viewers) be placed in that room in positions to benefit from the system? Again, careful design investigation of all characteristics, including the audience must be performed by the designer. Calculation of viewing angles and sight lines for all rows is essential and these results must also be weighed against environmental and ergonomic factors. For instance, seating has significant impact on screen size, vertical positioning and ultimately viewing angles when multiple rows are specified. This is a function of geometry as the further rows are separated, the higher the screen or platforms must be to provide clear sightlines for all rows. The more rows that are in consideration, the more critical this becomes as the vertical viewing angle for front rows becomes close to or over the maximum 15 degrees to center. Additionally, the more widely spaced rows in a theater, the greater the difference between the front and rear rows viewing angle. These are considerations the clever designer must work out and describe to the client so it is clear that while one or two rows may have ideal viewing positions, one or more may have less than ideal.

How wide should the seating area be? Again, this could be one way of achieving high audience numbers but certainly there will be acoustical considerations. But how about visually? Depending on the environment and the equipment specified, the viewing angle will have more or less impact. In a dark room where a diffuse screen surface can be used effectively (providing the appropriate screen contrast without narrowing the viewing angle), a wide seating area can work well. However, the designer must carefully review the room ambient light condition and screen material to assure all viewers are within the half-light viewing angle of the screen.

Achieving the ideal viewing positions in a home theater is best done with early planning and involvement. If the designer is faced with a situation where seating platforms have been constructed arbitrarily without the considerations noted above, the potential for optimal seating positions are likely greatly reduced. Generally, for viewing placement optimization, just like for acoustical optimization, seating positions should be a result of the acoustical and video engineering studies and not a hurdle for acoustical and video engineering to magically overcome.

Light

Many home theaters are highly designed spaces which feature beautiful interior design and many are multi-use spaces which serve multiple purposes. All are residential spaces where illumination, both artificial and sometimes natural, is present. However,the presence of light will have an impact on the image. Some of the most critical considerations for light in relation to home theater are:

Ambient Light Level – a low or nonexistent level of natural ambient light is generally considered to be a good thing for home theater. This is generally, but not always, achievable in dedicated rooms. The higher the level of natural ambient light, the greater the potential image degeneration due to loss of screen contrast. This can be overcome with rear projection screens of specific design and also some front projection screens. Generally these solutions will limit the horizontal viewing angle or half-light angle for the audience.

Ambient Light Direction – if ambient natural light is positioned in such a way that the light path hits the image, it will either wash it out (loss of contrast) or cause glare. This is always a condition that must be controlled and avoided.

Ambient Light Location – ambient natural light which directs the light path into the viewer's eyes or distractingly close to the viewer's field of vision will be a distracting characteristic which must be controlled.

Control of ambient light by using black out shades with side pocket designs are effective methods of controlling ambient natural light. Many creative solutions now exist which offer multiple levels of ambient light control from moderate screens to blackout within a single controllable device. These are effective methods of ambient light control for lifestyle type theater environments.

Artificial Light Levels - it is rare and even of questionable value to have a purely black room with no light. Safety alone dictates some level of path lighting in a theater. However,even the existence of low levels of light in a room will effect contrast. For example, a 2000 ANSI Lumens projector on a 138" diagonal 1.78:1 screen with a unity gain will have a theoretical screen contrast of 42 in a perfectly dark room. If we add just 5 footcandles of light into the room, the contrast ratio drops to 7.

Artificial Light Direction – just like natural light, artificial light if directed onto the screen surface will destroy contrast and cause glare. This must be avoided.

Artificial Light Location – a good lighting design in home theater allows for various levels or scenes of lighting for different activities. A generally dark scene may be best for movie viewing However,a social gathering such as sporting events may be best served with a higher degree of ambient light. Creating well segregated and placed lighting and combining them effectively can achieve this goal. In our previous example of the ambient light study above, if we maintain the added 5 footcandles at the audience, but cut it at the screen, our contrast ratio is improved almost back to the original 42.

Artificial Light Color – As we are experiencing not only black, but all the colors of the spectrum as reflected off a white screen surface, the color of the artificial lighting in the space can alter the image color. Incandescent lighting is skewed strongly to the red spectrum and as the most commonly used lighting in residential design may be present. LED lighting is now available in many color temperatures and, while white color light (5500 Kelvin and above) is generally not pleasing aesthetically, most LED manufacturers have light engines in multiple color temperatures.

Control of Artificial Light – it is essential that the lighting in a theater environment have some level of integrated control. The effective combination of light loads into useable and performance enhancing scenes as noted above can only be accomplished in this manner.

Additionally, the simple, well-conceived menu of scenes guarantees a repeatable light environment and thus experience.

Surrounding Surfaces

While this subject may seem obvious, it is worth mentioning. The essence of a video image is of a light source. Whether 2-piece front projection, rear projection or direct view, the image is a light and can be reflected. Ironically, and similarly to an acoustical phenomena, the better the basic environment the more critical this can be. In other words, if we have a room with high levels of ambient light, viewed in the daytime, light colored walls are less of a noticeable issue. That same room however, viewed at night, or a dedicated room with absolute light control with light walls will suffer from a mirroring effect. The light walls become a projection surface where the image reflected (or projecting from direct view) will be visible on these light colored surfaces. Selection of darker and non-reflective fabrics and finishes is essential to elimination of these phenomena. A simple test is to place examples of finishes (this must be roughly a square foot or more) at a 90 degree angle to a video image in a light controlled room. If you can see light movement on your sample, you will see it on your wall, ceiling, or floor. Additionally, the larger the surface (i.e. a wall rather than a sample), the greater the visibility of the reflection.

With surrounding surfaces, it is important to take care and avoid glossy and even semi glossy finishes. Even a satin finish panel will reflect light. The areas directly surrounding the screen must be a non-reflective and ideally a light absorptive material in order to provide a sharp mask and optimum experience.

Planning

The creation of an optimized environment for video, just like the design of an ideal acoustical environment, takes planning, engineering, creativity and skill. It is a task worth every penny charged and often worth many times more than charged! The conditions are independent and there is much iterative process and engineering involved in putting the right set of systems, design and engineering together for the best results. The room plays an integral role in overall system performance, both audio and video. Therefore, every aspect of the configuration must be designed to work together. Do not underestimate the importance of this process and the value to your clientele and ultimately your reputation.

CHAPTER 7

CONTROL SYSTEMS AND USER INTERFACES

OVERVIEW

In recent years, control and integration have become the largest segment of the average CEDIA member company's revenue. Control systems represent a specialized discipline which requires the expertise of an experienced integrator to be implemented properly, which allows the home technology professional to leverage their expertise as the "added value" which is not available at a retailer or online. A full understanding of the control system content found in the Fundamentals of Residential Electronic Systems is assumed for those reading, or referring to, this chapter.

Before we begin, it is important to review a few definitions:

Control
In its most basic form, a single room solution which allows the user to use one device, rather than several, to control something like a media room system. This may seem like a simple task, but to the user it can be a huge enhancement to their lifestyle.

Integration
When multiple subsystems are controlled, lifestyle is further enhanced. For instance, a single user interface to address audio, video, HVAC, lighting, and security means not only simplified operation, but a much cleaner wall surface. Systems integration reduces the number of actions needed by the homeowner, which provides a higher level of convenience, security, and even energy savings.

Automation

When integration is taken one step further, certain functionality no longer requires any input from the user. Examples; outdoor lighting that turns on at sunset, air handlers that are turned off if a smoke sensor goes into alarm mode, and lighting events which sequence themselves to make the home look occupied when the homeowner is away on vacation.

The goal of any control system is to provide the homeowner a simple, easy-to-use way to control the electronic systems in the home, which is rock solid in its performance, dependable over time, and allows for upgrades and enhancements as the needs of the client change.

SYSTEM SPECIFICATION AND DESIGN

The Starting Point

The designer's role begins with client discovery; asking those open-ended questions that will guide the system design to the right functionality. This conversation allows the designer to understand a great deal about the client, including;

- Their past experience with control systems, good and bad
- Who will be using the control system
- What level of complexity the users will be comfortable with
- What functions are the most important/critical
- What possibilities the client may not be aware of

All of this information will be valuable as the designer determines what type of control system will best meet the needs of the client, as well as providing clues about what will be an appropriate budget for the system. The control system itself needs to meet the current needs, and have scalability for the future, but will not always be the fully featured, fully flexible, system necessary for the most complex applications.

Specifying User Interfaces

Next, the designer needs to begin the process of selecting the right user interface for each application within the project. This will be determined by not only the task at hand, but who the users are. Basic users will be most comfortable with the simplest interface possible. Power users require access to much more features. In some cases both of these user types can be served by one interface. In other cases it may be better to provide two different devices.

Personas

While every client is different, it is important to have a good understanding of your most common client types. A persona is a "virtual" person, created and defined to represent a typical client type which you deal with often. This concept allows the company to establish some standardized design goals which can be repeated and modified only as needed, creating consistency over time and a more predictable workflow for programmers, engineers, and technicians in the field. Once you have built and defined a few personas, each new project can use one of them as a starting point for design and functionality.

Interface Types

The pros and cons of handheld remotes, keypads, and touch panels are covered in Fundamentals of Residential Electronic Systems. These basic characteristics must be considered from the very beginning of the design phase, along with the overall control system type. The needs of the client must be carefully considered and the control system selected based not only on functionality, but how well its user interfaces will work for that particular client.

INTERFACE DESIGN

Most sophisticated interfaces allow for a great deal of flexibility in how they are configured, laid out, and programmed. This flexibility can often lead to designs which are too complex and convoluted for the user to be comfortable with. Remember that the more simple and usable an interface is, the more it will be used. The designer must determine exactly what features the user needs access to, and make those features available and intuitive. The more critical the function is, the easier it must be to access. When a user enters a command, be it via a hard button or a tap on a touch panel, there should be some kind of feedback which lets them know the command has been sent. This can be a screen change, button color change, or a tactile cue the user feels. When a control device does not interact with the user, this causes frustration and even misuse of the device.

Minimizing Errors

Frustration can also be caused when errors are made by the user. There are a few ways to minimize user error:

- Avoid having too many features available. Limit the choices, especially on the pages first accessed. Just because something is possible doesn't mean it should be there!
- Organize the control environment. Grouping or modularizing functions together can reduce the likelihood of error. There are some functions which are often seen in similar locations, and many users are already accustomed to this type of layout.
- Automate command strings. This is one of the keys to simpler operation. When one button push can initiate several commands (macro) this makes everything more simple and error-free for the user. For instance, two commands, "Watch" then "Satellite" can replace several different commands.

- Make the operation intuitive. A good user interface will require little or no training, because its functionality is well aligned with the way the user, even a first time user, expects it to work.

Client Approval

Early in the process, the client should see some examples of the user interfaces you will be recommending. Full size printouts of remotes, keypads and touch panels will allow the users to see exactly what their control environment will look like. As part of the design and implementation process, detailed mock-ups should be created, and approved by the client. This should take place before programming begins. This step will help the client understand what is being done as well as manage expectations. Getting their sign-off will help prevent "feature creep", and ensure that everyone is on the same page.

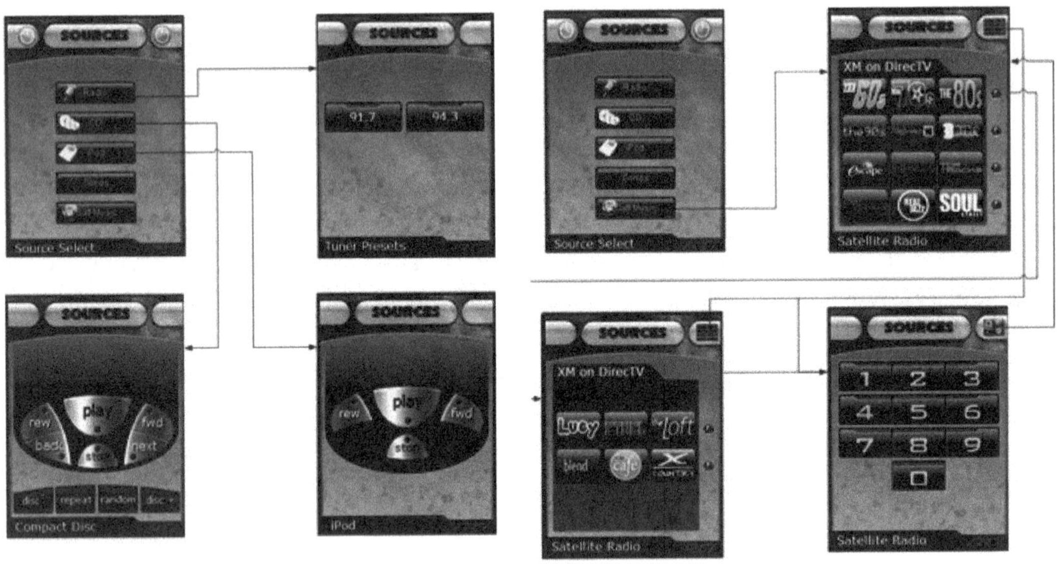

Figure 7-1. *UI Mock-Up Examples*

Standardizing the Process

It is imperative that there is a well-defined process regarding how the designer's vision moves through interface design, system design, and control system programming. In addition to mock-ups, these documents can help greatly in this communication.

- *Menu Trees;* These provide a visual representation of each page's function, and should be blocked out prior to programming. They serve as a guide which will make sure the final functionality is in line with the user's needs and expectations.
- *Flowcharts;* more complex systems may require full-blown flowcharts, showing many pages and many links between the pages.
- *Programming Worksheets;* these are more comprehensive documents, showing specific buttons, component status, macros, and page flips

- *Equipment Test Worksheets;* there are many variations of this document, but the key is to have tested every component to make sure they respond properly to commands. Certain components may not have the functionality needed for a specific application. These limitations sometimes rear their ugly heads near the end of a project. A worksheet for each component, which spells out its capabilities and caveats, can be referred to the next time that model is being considered for a system, minimizing guesswork and saving a great deal of time and head-scratching.

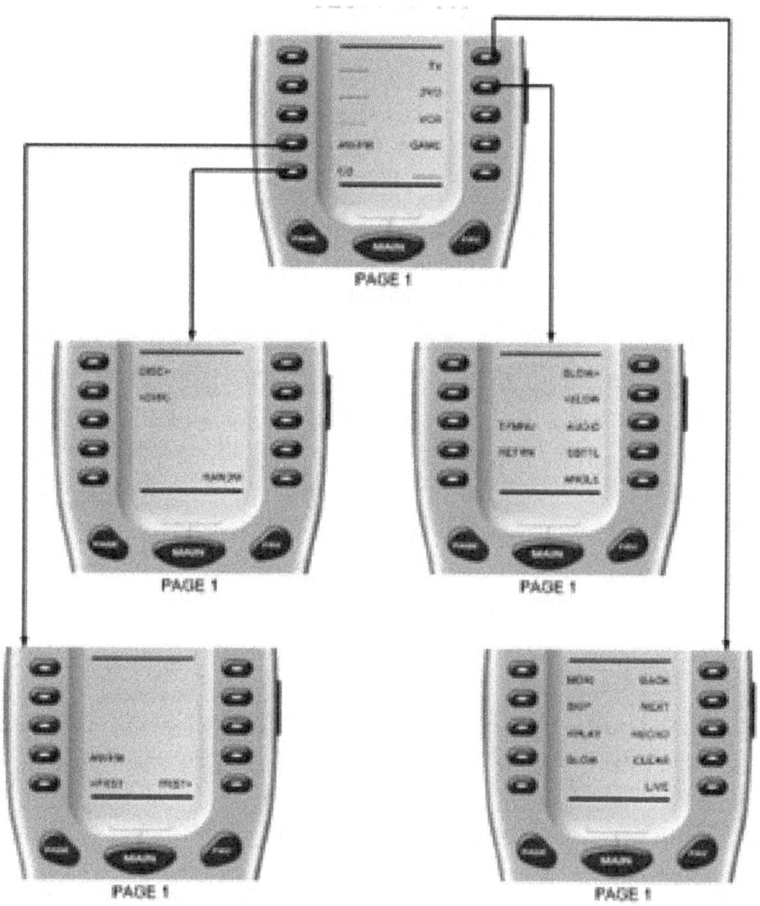

Figure 7-2. *Menu Tree*

As the programming moves forward, the communication should continue, noting any design changes, model changes, etc. and ensuring that the process is still in line with the functional and aesthetic goals set forth initially.

Mobile Devices as Control Interfaces

The rapid growth and mind-boggling developments in smart phones, tablets, and wearables have brought a heightened awareness of what is possible using apps, the internet, and network-enabled components and systems. The sheer number of devices in use means a huge part of the population is intimately familiar with how they work. In one recent year, over 2 billion smart phones and tablets were sold worldwide. Since so many end users are familiar with the "app environment", it is easy to see why they are coming to expect their mobile devices to be able to control just about anything.

Users may be able to download an app and start using it, but to craft a useable "ecosystem" of apps related to systems in the home often requires the expertise of a systems integrator.

As we will see, there are some very compelling arguments for the App-Based smart home system, but it is important to understand that this approach works better for some applications than others.

App-Based Control Disadvantages

While it may be tempting to provide all control functions on the wireless device platform, using apps, there are some situations where this is just not ideal. Some functions simply lend themselves to the physical touch of a hard button, either on a keypad or a hand-held remote. Most people can control their TV and/or set-top box via a handheld remote control, without even looking at it; channel up, channel down, volume up, volume down, guide, mute, last channel etc. We have memorized where these buttons are and don't need to look at the remote to find them. In this case, switching to an app on a smart phone would be inefficient, cumbersome, and frustrating. (Some innovative companies are offering hardware solutions like sleeves that fit around an iPad and provide a "button" type experience.)

There are actually a number of scenarios where a small touchscreen, dependent on cellular or Wi-Fi, is not ideal;

- Some control functions are often done in the dark. Hard buttons are convenient in this situation, and in fact many users prefer not to look away from the TV to initiate common commands.
- A keypad on the wall is a control option everyone is accustomed to, because they have been turning lights on and off all of their life. If there are a few simple functions that can be incorporated into that same location, this is often a good choice.
- Getting to an app can take time, even if it is only a few clicks away.
- Wireless and cellular networks are not always dependable. If the control system requires Wi-Fi, and the Wi-Fi is down, so is the user interface. This underscores the importance of designing and configuring a bullet-proof network for the home. The integrator must also be able to implement good roaming performance on the wireless network.
- The end user has access to settings on the device, which can lead to errors and failures. Even with safeguards built in, automatic OS and app updates can create issues.

App-Based Control Advantages

On the other hand, some control functions are perfect for mobile device apps. And there are some inherent advantages to investing in software, and not just hardware. If implemented correctly, this approach offers a wide variety of advantages:

- Using apps provides the user with "best in class" products and solutions. This means for each type of subsystem (music, lighting, access, HVAC etc.) the design can utilize the established leader in that particular discipline. Devices can be specified based on not only their feature set, but the philosophy and reputation of the manufacturer.
- Updates to functionality are often done via simple app updates. So rather than becoming outdated, the experience often improves over time....at no cost.
- Cloud-based platforms allow for easier integration/automation of various subsystems and apps. A URL call from one component can trigger a certain response from another.
- New hardware developments will extend the reach and scope of an App-Based system in ways we are not even aware of yet. Example; the iWatch was adopted by over 20 million people the first year and those users now have a completely new way to access the same systems they have been using.

As always the key to success is good design, based on good client discovery. In many cases the right solution will be a hybrid approach, using a solid control system as the backbone but also incorporating mobile devices to provide more remote access (and ease of access).

PROGRAMMING

Programming refers to the process of creating instructions (or programs) that are used by a computer, such as a control system, to accomplish a particular task. In general, programming encompasses the overall design, writing, testing, debugging, implementation, and documentation of these programs. Programs can be as simple as basic functions on a keypad or as complicated as creating whole-house themes for an integrated lighting system. There are literally hundreds of different programming languages used to translate logic into instructions that computers can understand, and each was created to solve a particular type of problem. Some are created by individuals, while others are created by colleges and standards committees, but all offer a method that humans can use to communicate with machines.

At the root of our communication with computers or control systems, we find a fundamental, universal concept: mathematics. The ability to count in a sequential order is the precursor to mathematical functions such as addition and subtraction, which are the building blocks of computer languages and at a higher level, programming itself.

Numbering Systems and Logic

A numbering system allows the measurement of something in exact, quantitative terms. A numbering system must have a sequence of unique identifiers that reach a certain point and then repeat in some predetermined fashion.

For example, the numbering system we are most familiar with is the decimal numbering system, which is also called the "base 10" numbering system because it uses ten unique characters (0,1,2,3,4,5,6,7,8,9). These numbers represent different values depending on the position (or column) they appear in. For example, 9 is a different value than 90 or 900.

To count sequentially in any numbering system, the numbers increase in any given column until it reaches its maximum value (which in a base 10 numbering system is 9). To create the next number in sequence, that column becomes a 0, and the column to the left of it is incremented by one.

Decimal

For example, to add 1 to the number 19, the ones column rolls to 0 while the tens column is increased from 1 to 2 to make the number20. The same process happens for any base numbering system.

The numbering systems covered are:

- Decimal ("base 10")
- Binary ("base 2")
- Hexadecimal ("base 16")

In the decimal system, each column represents a ten-fold increase of the next lowest column, as shown in Table 7-1.

Although this process is easy to understand with the decimal system, it is important to illustrate these steps in order to understand less familiar systems such as binary and hexadecimal.

Table 7-1. *Decimal Numbering System*

Power of 10	10^3	10^2	10^1	10^0
Column	Thousands	Hundreds	Tens	Ones
Value	1,000	100	10	1

Binary

The binary numbering system (also called "base 2") consists of only two unique digits: 0 and 1. Although decimal numbers are easy for humans to read and perform calculations with, computers use the binary system. Computers represent these two values using two voltage levels; most commonly 0 V to represent 0, and+3.3 V or 5 V to represent 1.

Each digit represented by a column is called a bit. Every four bits are called a nibble, and they are separated by a space for better readability. Two nibbles are called a byte. Bits, nibbles, and bytes do not vary in their respective lengths. However, the next larger grouping is called a word, which is set by the CPU processor of the system. A double word is two words; therefore, words and double words can vary in size from system to system depending on the processor (CPU). For example, if a word is defined as 32 bits for a certain system, then a double word on that same system is defined as 64 bits. The binary system truly is "the language of computers."

Hexadecimal

The hexadecimal numbering system (often referred to as "hex" or "base 16") is based on 16 characters: 0-9 and A-F. These digits represent the numbers 0-15 as follows: 0-9 represent themselves, A=10, B=11, C=12, D=13, E=14, and F=15. Counting in sequence yields the following: 001, 002, 003, 004, 005, 006, 007,008, 009, 00A, 00B, 00C, 00D, 00E, 00F, 010, 011, and so on.

Note that the column reaches its maximum value at F, rather than at 9 (as seen in the decimal system), or 1 (as seen in the binary system). Table 7-4 lists the maximum values for the first four columns in the hexadecimal system. Also, note that each column can represent a much larger number than is seen in the decimal system

Table 7-2. *Power of 2*

	2^7	2^6	2^5	2^4	2^3	2^2	2^1	2^0
Column	One Hundred Twenty Eights	Sixty Fours	Thirty Twos	Sixteens	Eights	Fours	Twos	Ones
Value	128	64	32	16	8	4	2	1

Hexadecimal notation is denoted either by preceding characters "X" or "0x" or a suffix character "h." Using this notation is especially important when the number does not contain any letters (A-F), because it looks identical to a decimal number.

Table 7-3. *Grouping into Number of Bits*

1	0	1	0
8 X 1	4 X 0	2 X 1	0 X 0
8	0	2	0

Table 7-4. *Max Values Per Hex Column*

F	F	F	F
4096 X 15	256 X 15	16 X 15	1 X 15
61,400	3,840	240	15

These basic logical operators are:

- AND
- NAND (opposite of AND)
- OR
- NOR (opposite of OR)
- XOR (exclusive OR)
- XNOR (opposite of exclusive XOR)
- NOT

The result of a binary test is always a single state — either a 1 or 0 — which can be designated by on/off or high/low. The term "high value" is commonly used to represent a 1 and "low value" to represent a 0.

Conditional Logic

Conditional logic uses the various operators mentioned previously to compare bits and arrive at a single output, no matter how many inputs are processed. The use of these operators allow for logical comparisons of data within programs that can direct programs to perform functions and complete tasks based on the results of those comparisons.

Boolean Logic

Boolean logic is a method of testing for desired outcomes or "states" by combining binary data using logical operators. Understanding Boolean logic allows programmers to form fundamental logic required in all programming.

Truth Tables

A truth table shows the result for a given set of inputs for a Boolean logical operator. Although truth tables are normally shown with only two inputs, the same rule would apply for multiple inputs for any given operator.

AND Operator

The AND operator, shown in Figure 7-3, returns a high value (1) only if all inputs are high values (1s). If any of the inputs is a low value (0), the result of the AND operation will be a low value (0).

NAND Operator

The NAND operator, also shown in Figure 7-3, produces results that are the exact opposite of the AND operator. Only in the case of all high values (1s) will this operator return a low value (0) result.

OR Operator

The OR operator, shown in Figure 7-4, returns a high value (1) if any one of the inputs is a high value (1). Only in the case of all inputs being low values (0s) does the OR operator give a low value (0) result.

NOR Operator

The NOR operator, also shown in Figure 7-4, results are the exact opposite of the OR operator.

Only in the case of all low values (0s) will this operator return a high value (1) result.

XOR (Exclusive OR) Operator

The XOR operator, shown in Figure 7-5, functions much like the OR operator, but it has one more stipulation applied to it. Like the OR operator, if at least one input is a high value (1), the result will be a high value (1); however, if ALL of the inputs are high values (1s), the result will be a low value (0) result.

XNOR (Exclusive NOR) Operator

The XNOR operator, also shown in Figure7-5, gives results that are the exact opposite of the XOR operator. If at least one input is a high value (1), the result will be a low value (0); however, if ALL of the inputs are either high values (1s) or low values (0s), the result will be a high value (1).

NOT (Inverter) Operator

The NOT operator, shown in Figure 7-6, is the only operator that requires a single input. It returns a value opposite of the single input. Its partner operator is the buffer (also shown in Figure 7-6), which passes the same state as it receives. Note that both operators can be applied to the result of any other logical operation, because the result of that operation will always be a single state value.

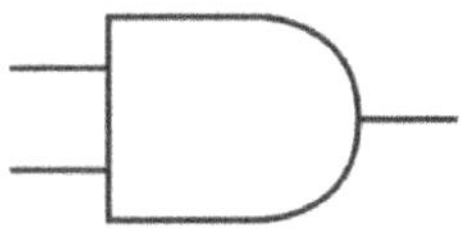

AND

A	B	OUTPUT
0	0	0
0	1	0
1	0	0
1	1	1

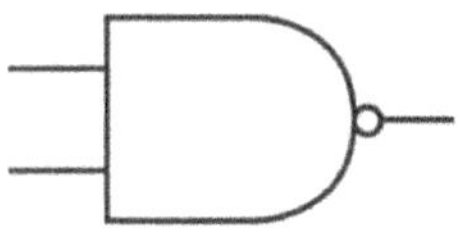

NAND

A	B	OUTPUT
0	0	1
0	1	1
1	0	1
1	1	0

Figure 7-3. *AND & NAND Truth Table*

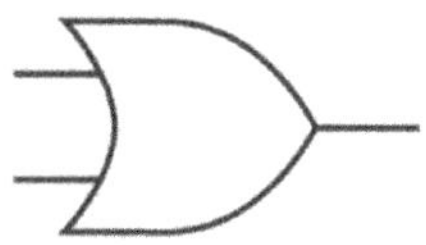

OR

A	B	OUTPUT
0	0	0
0	1	1
1	0	1
1	1	1

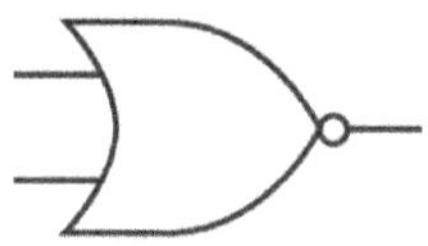

NOR

A	B	OUTPUT
0	0	1
0	1	0
1	0	0
1	1	0

Figure 7-4. *OR & NOR Truth Table*

XOR XNOR

A	B	OUTPUT
0	0	0
0	1	1
1	0	1
1	1	0

A	B	OUTPUT
0	0	1
0	1	0
1	0	0
1	1	1

Figure 7-5. *XOR & XNOR Truth Table*

BUFFER INVERTER

A	OUTPUT
0	0
1	1

A	OUTPUT
0	1
1	0

Figure 7-6. *NOT Truth Table*

This same type of IF/THEN logic is widely applied in control system programming, in sequences such as the one shown in Table 7-5, which illustrates a typical ON sequence for a theater system. It looks at the ON/OFF state of various components, ensures that they are turned on, then does input selections etc. A good understanding of this type of sequence is critical for anyone who is programming any type of control system.

Table 7-5. *Example of an If/Then Sequence*

Home Theater ON Process
If Projector is Off then
Turn On Projector
If DVD is Off then
Turn On DVD
If Receiver is Off then
Turn On Receiver
SELECT Projector Input 1
SELECT DVD Input on Receiver
Press PLAY on DVD Player

File Types

Files contain data that computers use to perform their intended functions. For example, a file may contain credit card transaction data, student test scores, medical directory information, and so on.

Like storage containers for various types of data, are associated with programs that know how to interpret the specific file type. In this example, a .doc document could be processed by a word processing program such as Microsoft Word, while a .jpg file would be processed by an image editing software program such as Adobe® Photoshop.

In the programming world, there are three basic types of files that are commonly used:

- Source
- Object
- Executable

Programming Methodologies

Programming methodology addresses the analysis, design, and implementation of programs. Programs must be organized to accurately and efficiently process data and produce the desired results, but there are several ways to accomplish these goals. Program methodology offers different sets of rules and practices that programs can follow on their way to becoming a live application:

- Structured programming
- Object-oriented programming
- Event-driven programming

Structured Programming

Structured programming is a process that uses a set of well-defined structures, such as conditional statements and loops. There is only one entry point and one exit point for the program and no branches or "GOTO"s, which represent breaks in the logical flow of the program. Program tasks are split into smaller sections (known as functions, modules, or subroutines) that may be called when they are required.

This approach is often associated with a top down design methodology, where programmers map out the large-scale structure of a program in terms of smaller operations, implement and test the smaller operations and then tie them together into a whole program. It is possible to do structured programming in almost any procedural programming language. Some of the better-known structured programming languages are Pascal, COBOL, PL/1, Ada, and C.

In electronic systems, a procedural task may appear as in Table 7-6. In this example, the house is placed into "Home" mode when the homeowner has arrived at the end of the day.

Table 7-6. *Example of a "Home" Mode*

Main Subroutine
RUN HVAC System "Home Mode"
RUN Lighting System "Home Mode"
RUN Music System "Home Mode"
Music "Home Mode" Subroutine
TURN ON all common area zones
SELECT all digital radio as a source
SELECT the "Hits" channel

Programming languages can also be unstructured. Unstructured programming is identified by having code that is one continuous block and does allow for the use of unconditional branching (most commonly for exception handling) to change execution flow to jump to a specified section of code. The "GOTO" command is an example of a command that will branch to a given location. Unstructured programming is viewed as a sub- standard method of programming in most applications.

Object-Oriented Programming

Object-oriented programming (OOP) is a programming methodology that is very different than structured programming, because it changes the focus from procedural logic to a focus on the data that interacts with a program. OOP is based on the concept of a modular, reusable entity called an object.

Objects are defined as standard classes that contain all the properties of an object. As a simple example, an object class could be a point on the globe and would contain the latitude and longitude of the point, a feature code for the point, such as "radar beacon," and any necessary text to describe the object. All of this information is defined and assigned to the object.

The OOP approach to programming is often simpler to develop and maintain than other programming methods, which enables it to support more direct analysis, coding, and understanding of complex situations and procedures.

Object-oriented programming is very popular in large-scale software engineering projects. C++ and Java are examples of object-oriented programming languages. In electronic system contracting, an object-oriented approach may look like the code shown in Table 7-7.

Table 7-7 *Example: Keypad*

Keypad(1).Button(3). PressRelease

In this example, Keypad is a collection of objects and Keypad (1) is the first keypad in that collection. The object keypad has multiple buttons associated with it, and for the third button the method PressRelease will be executed, which simulates the pressing and releasing of that button.

Event-Driven Programming

In event-driven programming, external events are the primary drivers behind the control of the flow. With the two styles previously discussed (OOP and structured programming), programs generally have their own control flow pattern. However, event-driven programs can be written with either structured programming languages or object-oriented languages. Systems that are event-driven usually have an event loop running that constantly looks for information to process, such as a keypad press. When an event occurs, the program calls a trigger function to process it. This is also called polling for events (triggers).The trigger functions are written to match the desired behavior of the system.

There are different ways that the system can obtain information about the events. For example, all inputs can be polled for events in an event loop, or interrupt handlers (small subroutine that runs when triggered by a hardware interrupt) can process specific hardware events. Systems may also use a combination of both methods. Graphical user interface (GUI) programs are usually programmed in an event-driven style. In electronic system contracting, an event-driven task might look like the example in Table 7-8.

Table 7-8. *Lighting at Sunset*

When Sunset
Press Keypad 4, Button 3 /* this activates outside lighting scene

Software Designer's Role

Software design is a process of defining and documenting a process that will become an automated software solution. The software designer's role is to accurately define one or more of the system components or applications.

This is accomplished through the following stages:

- Pre-design
- Domain Analysis
- Design and Development

Pre-Design

The pre-design phase is one marked by information gathering: meetings with the customer to thoroughly understand the project's requirements and scope, setting of project expectations and goals, and publishing all pertinent information. Key project players are identified, information is assembled, and a project schedule may be set based on the information.

One of the byproducts of the pre-design phase is a requirements document that clearly spells out the functions that the customer wishes to automate.

Domain Analysis

Domain analysis covers the analysis, description, and understanding of the sphere of influence of where the application will actually be deployed. The designer needs to thoroughly understand and adequately document the areas (domains) for which a system will be built.

In domain analysis, the designer outlines the desired behavior of the system and accurately defines the domain terms and concepts. Design diagrams (discussed next) are useful for depicting the domain characteristics of the system. Prototypes can be effective tools at this stage as well.

The goal of domain analysis is to identify, capture, and organize information for the purpose of making it reusable when creating new systems. The information generated; from requirements, to specific designs, to source code; needs to be viewed within the context of the domain being studied to see if parts or segments can be reused in an efficient manner.

Design and Development

Design and development is where the bulk of the work is completed. The software designer creates, modifies, and obtains approval for the project designs and development. This can be an iterative process in which the designer codes a little and then tests that code before the next round of coding and testing, or it can take on more of a waterfall process, where each phase is completed before the next is begun. In either case, the designer builds the components one at a time until the system is complete and performs necessary testing and verification prior to implementation.

Design Diagrams

Software design diagrams are visual representations of the process flow of a computer program. They show, through the use of graphical icons and pathways, how data is to flow, the behavior of objects, where reports are to be generated, and how different parts of the program will interact.

Three common types of software design diagrams are:

- Flowcharts
- State Diagrams
- Sequence Diagrams

Flowcharts

A flowchart illustrates the many steps and decisions in a process. By visualizing the process, a flowchart can quickly help identify bottle necks or inefficiencies where improvements can be made. Programmers use flowcharts to show the logical flow of data through a program to be sure requirements are clearly understood and the program will function correctly according to those requirements.

There is one starting point, but a flowchart may have various ending points. The shapes in a flowchart all have certain functions; for example, a diamond represents a decision-making step, while a cylinder may represent a table or database. An example of flowchart icons is listed in Figure 7-7.

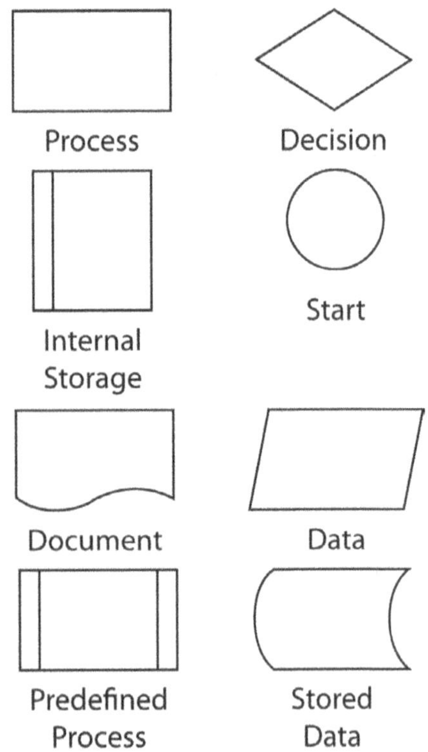

Figure 7-7. *Flowchart Icons*

State Diagrams

State diagrams are used to convey the behavior of a system by describing all of the possible states of an object as events occur. A state represents a stage in the behavior pattern of an object. State diagrams show the dynamic behavior of a system by showing the various states that an object can fall under and the transitions that occur between those states. A transition is a progression from one state to another and will be triggered by an event that is either internal or external to the object.

Figure 7-8 shows a state diagram of how a light is activated based upon information from a security system. In this case, the light will only come on when the system is armed and a motion is detected that triggers that event.

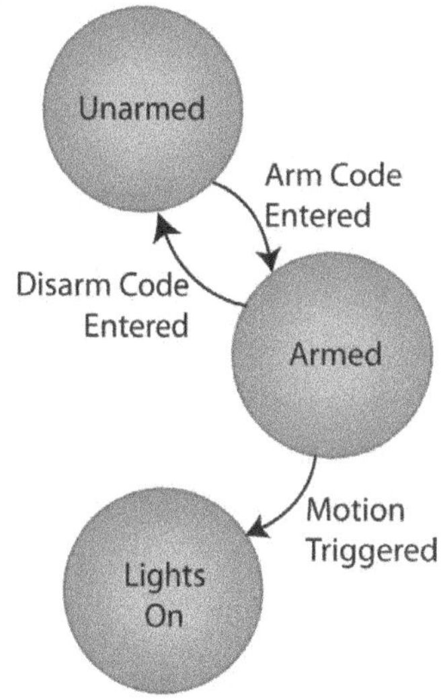

Figure 7-8.
Sample State Diagram

Sequence Diagrams

A sequence diagram can also represent the dynamic behavior of a system by depicting the sequence of actions that occur in that system. It illustrates the invocation of methods in each object and the order in which the invocation occurs. Graphically speaking, a sequence diagram is two-dimensional in nature, with the horizontal axis representing the life of the object that it represents, and the vertical axis showing the sequence of the creation or invocation of these objects.

Because it uses class name and object name references, the sequence diagram is very useful in elaborating and detailing the dynamic design and the sequence and origin of invocation of objects. Hence, the sequence diagram is one of the most widely used dynamic diagrams in the Unified Modeling Language (UML), which is a standardized specification language for object modeling.

Strategies for Successful Programming

There are programming pitfalls, such as inadequate requirements, misunderstood functionality, and poor testing that can quickly sabotage a project.

The following are some strategies intended to help designers avoid such pitfalls:

- Design up front and follow a design methodology
- Start small and add as technical challenges are resolved
- Test the complete system

Design Up Front and Follow a Design Methodology

The project design must address all requirements adequately. The difficult part is when the requirements are sparse, incomplete, or incorrect. To avoid this pitfall, the software designer must wholly understand the user's intended process and communicate in such a way as to help the customer identify all important facts in order to ensure requirements are complete.

Following an established design methodology will not only reduce the temptation to design on the fly, but it will provide a concrete guide to follow. Basic system design should not begin until the requirements are clearly defined. Design diagrams are essential tools for this step of the design process.

Start Small and Add as Technical Challenges Are Resolved

Program code should be as efficient as possible by reusing common modules and creating generic subroutines that can be used between applications. As these components are built, they should be added to the overall system to provide new functionality. Examples of these common modules or generic subroutines would be the routines used to control a TV or DVD. Although they may be specific by manufacturer; they can often be built once and reused for each new control system.

Prototype systems lend themselves well as a proof of concept system. Although code may have to be written for this system that does not ultimately end up in the production system, the benefit of seeing a portion of the system "in action" should prove itself in a higher-quality design, since more fine-tuning can occur.

Test the Complete System

Software testing is a crucial part of the development process and involves many different types of testing, each with its own goal.

Some common forms of software testing are:

- White box testing
- Black box testing
- Regression testing
- Unit testing
- System testing

White Box Testing — is based on knowledge of the internal logic of an application's code. Tests are based on coverage of all code statements, branches, paths, and conditions.

Black Box Testing — is based on an analysis of the input and output specifications of a piece of software without reference to its internal workings.

Regression Testing — is the retesting of previously tested programs following modification of some part of the system to ensure that errors have not been introduced or uncovered as a result of the changes made.

Unit Testing — is the specific testing of the smallest parts of a system. It requires knowledge of the internal code of the program in order to write valid test cases.

System Testing — is the large-scale testing that attempts to discover defects that are properties of the entire system rather than of its individual components.

Testing is usually accomplished by a variety of methods. Using manual and automated testing tools that can simulate a production environment, provide debugging information, and help identify the source of an error are all helpful to the programming team.

Unless test cases are carefully written that test the program code correctly and robustly, testing is no more than a rubber stamp on a shaky program. Great care and diligence must be taken to create test cases that test both the expected and unexpected scenarios, that are not too simple or too complex, and that test the programs completely.

Documentation

Documentation is the process of describing, in common everyday language, the processing that is occurring in a program or application. Documentation that is internal to the program is written for programmers as they navigate through the source code itself. This documentation is usually in the form of comments embedded within the code on a line-by-line basis. Comments are not executable code; they exist only for the purpose of making the coding easier to understand.

Documentation that is external to the program may be in the form of programmer specifications, data and table layouts, and other such technical documents to aid the programmers in the overall support and maintenance of the system. See Chapter 15, Design and Engineering Documents, for more information on specific documents and their functions.

Revision Control

Revision control, also called version control, is the management of multiple versions of the same piece of information. In this case, that information is source code.

This method of safeguarding code is commonly used in engineering and software development to manage ongoing evolutions of source code that may be worked on by a team of people. Changes to a library of files can be controlled in a number of ways; one of which is to apply a number or letter code as a revision identifier. The revision identifier tells the programming team that the file has been changed and can convey the current state of the program— whether it is currently being coded, has already been tested, or is ready for deployment to the production environment.

Some library control systems also track additional information such as what change request by the user initiated the change, which programmer made the change, what other modules are included in the change, the date the change was made, and so on.

One benefit of version control is that it allows developers to return to any earlier version of code. This is especially useful for cases in which a particular addition or modification interferes with or breaks another feature of the system. It is also used in cases where multiple versions of the same code are distributed to different customer sites with custom modifications made for each particular site. There are many free and open source software programs used for revision control.

Some of the more widely used free programs include:

- CVS – Concurrent Versioning System
- Subversion
- CVSNT

Some of the more popular proprietary software programs include:

- Rational Clearcase
- Serena Version Manager; formerly PVCS
- Microsoft Visual Source Safe

Functional Specifications

Functional specifications are formal written descriptions of a software system used as a blueprint for implementation into the production environment. Specifications should state the purposes of the program, provide implementation details, and describe the specific functions of the software from the user's perspective. For example, a lighting control function spec explains in customer language how the lighting control system will be programmed but leaves out all the technical jargon. A simple example of functional specs is shown in Table 7-9.

Table 7-9 *Example of Functional Specs*

At sunset, outside lights will come on.
At midnight, a low lighting scene will be started for the outside lights.
At sunrise, all exterior lights will be turned off.

Programming Specifications

Programming specifications are more technical than functional specifications. If functional specs tell what the project will address, programming specs tell how the project will be coded. Detailed data-level information such as new table and database layouts, definitions for variables, and data files are all part of a programming spec document. For the example in Table 7-9, the associated programming specifications might appear as in Table 7-10.

Table 7-10. *Example of Programming Specs*

Sunset
Press keypad 4 button 6 /* this turns outside lights on
Sunrise
Press keypad 4 button 7 /* this turns outside lights off

Software Development Process

A software development process is an organized set of activities performed in a linear fashion to translate user needs into software products. This process provides guidelines that help to ensure efficiency and accuracy at every stage in the development of a piece of software. Commonly used terms in the IT industry that refer to this process are software life cycle, software development methodology and software process.

Two widely accepted software development processes are:

- Waterfall Development Process
- Iterative Development Process

Waterfall Development Process

The waterfall development process provides an orderly sequence of development steps that are completed in a linear fashion, one after another; with one phase beginning only after all prior phases are completed.

Each phase has a definite start, a definite end, and a quality metric used to measure progress. Documentation and design reviews are conducted to ensure the quality, reliability, and maintainability of the developed software. These reviews represent junctures to assess the quality of the product being produced and offer decision points for continuing the project.

Although different developers may modify the process to suit their specific projects, generally the following steps are included in the waterfall development process:

- State the requirements
- Analyze the requirements
- Design a solution
- Develop a software framework
- Develop the software
- Test the software
- Deploy the solution
- Maintain the software

One of the challenges of this methodology is that there are no provisions for correcting errors in earlier steps. For example, if the requirements were not accurate or if they changed in the middle of the process, the end product may have unusable or unnecessary software features.

Many software engineers believe the waterfall model is not the most effective model to use. However, many software managers still prefer it because it is easy to predict and plan. It is easy to measure progress as there are a fixed number of steps that must be completed in order.

Iterative Development Process

The iterative development process, also called the incremental build model, advocates the building of small but ever increasing portions of a software project. This helps the developers uncover important, often hidden, issues before those issues lead to major problems.

Developers using this model; design, implement, and test incrementally until the project is completed. They declare the project complete only when it satisfies all of its requirements. Many commercial software developers prefer the iterative process because it enables them to reach the design goals of customers who may not have initially defined their needs clearly, which is a frequent problem.

Using the iterative process allows developers to build small parts of the project that customers can use to help further define requirements beyond their initial request.

It is strongly recommended that programmers build flexibility into their development program to allow for changes that will inevitably come after a system has been in use for some time. The end-user's use of the completed system is another iteration that a programmer must accept will point out flaws or missing functionality in the existing software. Modular and flexible software design will allow the programmer to quickly and easily update the current system code to meet the customers' needs.

COMMUNICATION PROTOCOLS

In order to in integrate various devices and subsystems into a seamless, easy to operate, system, it is imperative that communication between the various parts is robust and dependable. As more and more devices in the home become network enabled, many might think that IP will be the only language needed. This is far from true. Many control functions will continue to be done over the tried-and-true protocols even if only in the last leg of communication. And, the demand for less intrusive retrofit techniques has driven innovation in the form of new ways to carry data and control information over existing infrastructure, as well as wirelessly. So it is extremely important to understand ALL of the various protocols and platforms, old and new. Many of these protocols and standards will be addressed in this chapter, but this is an area which is constantly changing so today's professionals need to keep up with the industry through trade magazines and various forms of training.

Interface standards define the specific infrastructure that data travels on, much like one might define the kinds of roads (dirt, asphalt, concrete, and so on) on which people may travel. But defining the road is not enough; there must be rules that govern a person's actions on the roads. These rules take the form of traffic signs and signals so that multiple people may use the infrastructure safely and without traffic accidents. The same is true for data. Communications standards function as the "rules of the road" to define how data should travel. Communications standards define voltages, cable lengths, bit representations, speeds, and access methods for data. Sometimes, the standards also define the mechanical interfaces. Communication systems can use a variety of media to provide the infrastructure needed including wired copper cables, fiber optic cable, RF wireless systems and Power line technology. There are many different communications standards defined by the EIA/TIA, such as EIA/TIA-232 (the most common), EIA/TIA-422 (RS-422), and EIA/ TIA-485 (RS-485). All of these standards are for serial communications, but have different features and capabilities.

Fundamental Elements of a Protocol

A protocol is an accepted method or standardized procedure that is agreed upon by multiple parties. Protocols require essential components in order to address the needs of various applications:

1. A physical connection
2. The structure of the data packets
    - Start Byte
    - Length
    - Command/Response Code
    - Additional Data (0 or more bytes)
3. Checksum
4. The meaning of the data in the packets
5. How the data packets may be used

Protocol Models

A communications protocol is a protocol that is used for transmitting or storing data, especially those used in regulating data transmission between computers and/or peripherals. Protocols exist at many different layers. The Open Systems Intercommunication (OSI) model defines seven layers, starting at the lowest level with the physical (hardware) layer, and progressing through the data link, network, transport, session, and presentation layers to the highest level called the application layer.

Protocols apply to services (e.g., e-mail) and to many applications in the consumer electronics (CE) industry such as lighting control and automation. Initially, CE protocols used primarily the physical and application layers, but with the advent of networked components using TCP/IP, CE protocols now reach into two more layers: the link layer and the networking layer. For the most part, however, CE programmers typically focus only on the application layer.

Protocol Layers

Various protocols are implemented in both hardware and software to facilitate communication between devices with different hardware or software components. Protocols enable one component in one host to interact with a corresponding component at the same ISO/OSI layer in a remote host. For more information on ISO/OSI Layers, see Chapter10. Protocol layering divides a protocol design into smaller parts, each of which performs closely related sub-tasks and connects to other layers of the protocol in precisely defined ways.

Digital and Analog I/O

Analog input and outputs (I/O) from a control system to a sub-system come in the form of mechanical or solid state relays. A relay is an electromagnetic device used for remote or automatic control that is actuated by a variation in conditions of an electric circuit, that in turn, operates other devices (as switches) in the same or a different circuit.

Table 7-11 *EIA/TIA-232/422/485*

	RS-232	RS-422	RS-485
Max Data Rate	Up to 20 kb/sec	Up to 10 Mb/sec	Up to 35 Mb/sec
Max Length (ft)	Up to 50	Up to 400	Up to 4000
Balance/Differential	No	Yes	Yes
Connections	Point-to-point	Multi-point	Multi-point

A dry contact closure is created when two contacts close to make electrical continuity in a circuit. If the sub-system uses a dry contact closure, it detects the short circuit caused by the contact closure. Some sub-systems will require a wetting voltage, typically 5V to 24V (usually DC, but occasionally AC). In this case, the sub-system detects the presence of an external voltage source. It is usually up to the integrator to provide a suitable power supply to switch the voltage to the sub-system. The typical usage of analog output using a wetting voltage is the 12V trigger sometimes used to control A/V equipment functionality. Many integration controllers provide both a number of analog inputs and outputs and may also provide the wetting voltage.

Another analog I/O uses a transmitter, receiver, power supply, and the connecting loop wire. A single transmitter can be connected to multiple receivers on the same loop, as long as there is sufficient power supply voltage to drive the loop current.

Typically, the transmitter is a sensor providing measurement information about a physical parameter (e.g., fluid level, temperature, pressure, and so on), but the transmitter can be a controller that sets the desired physical parameter rather than reading it. Other methods of analog I/O control based upon voltage can be used in short- range scenarios similar to the 4-20 mA loop. Usually, the voltage measurement is simply a resistance measurement from sensors. These sensors are often located remotely from the controller, requiring each sensor to be calibrated to take into account the wiring resistance between sensor and controller. The most common example of this type of control is remote temperature sensors for an HVAC controller.

RS-232

RS-232 (also known as EIA/TIA-232) is a "complete" physical layer specification, encompassing electrical, functional, and mechanical components. The latest revision is EIA/TIA-232-F. The most common EIA/TIA-232 signals are present on both EIA/TIA561 and EIA/TIA 574 connectors, but they do not support the same complement. Not all sub-systems or controllers support them. The simplest RS-232 connection typically requires only three signals: TX, RX, and signal GND. However, some devices require additional signals, for example RTS/CTS and DSR/DTR.

RS-232 is a point-to-point standard, which means that only one connection can be made on one cable. In other words, there is one receiver for each sender. When there is one transmitter and multiple receivers, the standard is a multi-point standard. EIA/ TIA 422 is a multi-point standard, and it can accommodate up to 10 receivers. Table 7-11 outlines some additional performance specifications for these standards.

It is important to note that the data rate does decline as the cable length increases, so the maximum data rate is not upheld at the maximum length. However, this also means that the cable length can be stretched if the data can be processed at a low rate. Balanced, or differential, lines are capable of transmitting over longer distances and are less susceptible to interference or noise.

I'm ready to communicate	DTR	⟶	DTR
I'm ready to communicate	DSR	⟵	DSR
Telephone line ringing	RI	⟵	RI
Modem connected to another	CD	⟵	CD
RTS/CTS flow control	RTS	⟶	RTS
RTS/CTS flow control	CTS	⟵	CTS
Transmits bytes out of PC	TX	⟶	TX
Receives bytes into PC	RX	⟵	RX

Figure 7-9. *RS-232 Signal Flow*

Figure 7-9 shows the functional flow for an RS-232 signal. A common misconception is that transmitted data is data that is "sent", and receive data is data that is "received." However, the actual definition of "transmit data" is data that is sent from a DTE (Data Terminal Equipment) to a DCE (Data Communications Equipment), while "receive data" is data sent from a DCE to a DTE. DCE refers to the equipment which carries the communication while DTE refers to the actual "end point" of the communication path.

Connectors

Commands from the input devices must travel via a hardwired connection or a wireless signal to the system hardware in order to be processed. For wired connections, there are different ways to both carry the information (cables) and connect the input device and the system hardware (interface).

The amount of data, its speed, and the distance to travel are all factors in determining which exact components to choose. Typically, system control does not require the transfer of large amounts of data.

The most common serial connector is the EIA/TIA-574, which is referred to as DB-9. It is a D-shell with nine conductors. Although technically the DB-9 connectors are not an approved connector per the RS-232 standard, it is very common within the CE industry. Figure 7-10 shows a DB-9 connector with its RS-232 pin assignments.

The RS-232 Mechanical specification calls for a DB-25 serial data connector. It is a D-shell with 25 conductors. It is not used much anymore because only three wires are needed for RS-232 serial communications. Figure 7-11 shows a DB-25 connector with its RS-232 pin assignments.

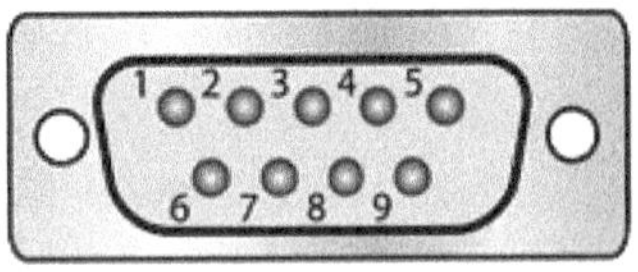

1	DCD	Carrier Detect
2	RxD	Receive Data
3	TxD	Transmit Data
4	DTR	Data Terminal Ready
5	SG	Signal Ground
6	DSR	Data Set Ready
7	RTS	Request To Send
8	CTS	Clear To Send
9	RI	Ring Indicator

Figure 7-10 *DB-9 Connector*

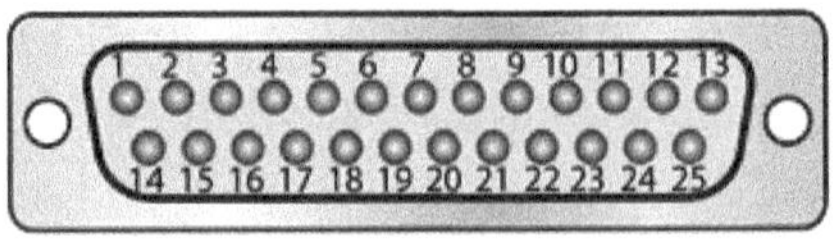

1		Chassis Ground
2	TxD	Transmit Data
3	RxD	Receive Data
4	RTS	Request To Send
5	CTS	Clear To Send
6	DSR	Data Set Ready
7	SG	Signal Ground
8	DCD	Carrier Detect
20	DTR	Data Terminal Ready
22	RI	Ring Indicator

Figure 7-11. *DB-25 Connector*

The 8P8C connector (sometimes called an RJ-45, although that is technically inaccurate, as RJ stands for Registered Jack, which is no longer the case) is a standard twisted-pair networking cable connector for legacy 10/100/1000BaseTnetworks and new 10 Gigabit Ethernet systems. It designates an 8-position/8-conductormodular connector. RJ-45 is the telephone industry's designation for the Universal Service Ordering Code (USOC) wiring pattern with an 8P8C connector, and should not be used in referencing a data connector.

Wiring for data networks uses either the T568A or the T568B wiring pattern, as shown in Figure 7-12. Many legacy networks are wired in the T568B pattern however the US government calls out the T568A pattern for all of its offices, and the EIA 570B Residential Structured Wiring standard does as well. So in the home, the recommended practice is always T568A. This makes the jacks easily repurposed for telephone service. Either pattern can be used as long as both ends of the cable are wired the same.

The 8P8C connector can be used for RS-232 serial communications through the EIA/TIA- 561standard. EIA/TIA-561 assigns RS-232 signals to the eight pins of the 8P8C connector. It then uses any straight-through networking cable for connecting a DCE to a DTE device. In addition, it is better to use NULL-modem adapters where necessary rather than using a different 8P8C pin-out to create a NULL- modem cable.

Cables are the physical means by which the data is communicated from one device to another. It is important to choose the right cable for each application because there is a wide difference in the electrical capabilities of different cable types, even if they are physically similar.

Category 5e, Cat 6 or Cat 6a cables are commonly used for data transmission for computer networks (Ethernet). Depending on the cable type, it may be used for data transmission up to 500 MHz. twisted pair cable of this type consists of four twisted pairs housed under one jacket. Cat 5e, Cat 6 and Cat 6a cabling used in networks are typically terminated with the 8P8C connector. Technicians must be sure to use a connector that is rated for the cable; and that proper termination techniques have been followed to ensure system performance. Figure 7-13 shows the Cisco 8P8C standard for RS-232 signals.

RS-485

RS-485 (also known as EIA/TIA 485) is a physical layer multi-point standard, which allows multiple receivers to connect to a single sender over the same cable. It allows up to 32 devices to connect on the same cable. EIA/TIA 485 also has the ability to have up to 32 receivers and transmitters on the same cable, but only one transmitter at a time can talk.

RS-485 Converters

An RS-485 converter is a device that translates voltage levels between RS-485 and another protocol, usually RS-232. An automatic switchover monitors the transmit data on the RS-232 side. When the start bit appears, it switches the transmit drivers onto the cable. Switchover is also only needed for 2-wire RS-485. This is not an issue for 4-wire communications.

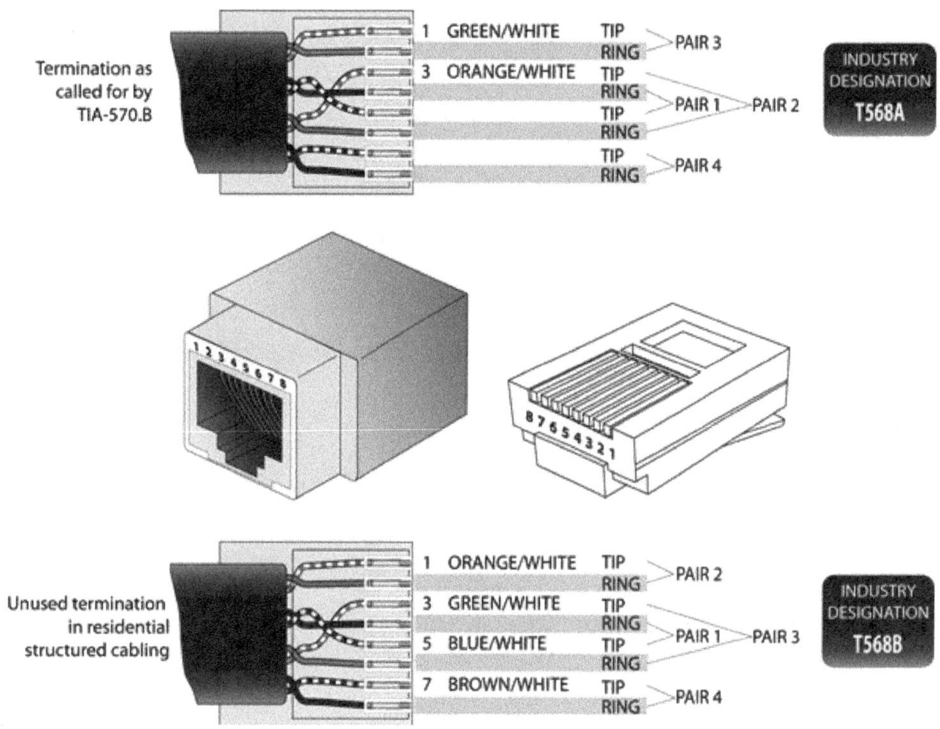

Figure 7-12. *8P8C Connector*

Converters usually require configuration for a specific baud rate for functionality. This baud rate configuration determines how long the transmitter stays active after transmitting a "1" bit. Alternatively, a 232-to-485 converter can switch based on the RS-232 RTS signal.

By monitoring the RTS signal from the RS-232 device, the converter will turn the 485 transmitter:

- On when RTS is active
- Off when RTS goes inactive

Whichever method is used, timely switching of the transmitter is important especially if the devices being communicated with are quick to respond back. If the converter's transmitter is still active when the device begins responding, a collision will occur and delay the reception of the response due to retries.

RS-485 Communication Methods

Since every device transmits and receives on the same cable, there must be a control that dictates which device speaks, and when. Three popular methods for controlling device-to-device communication are:

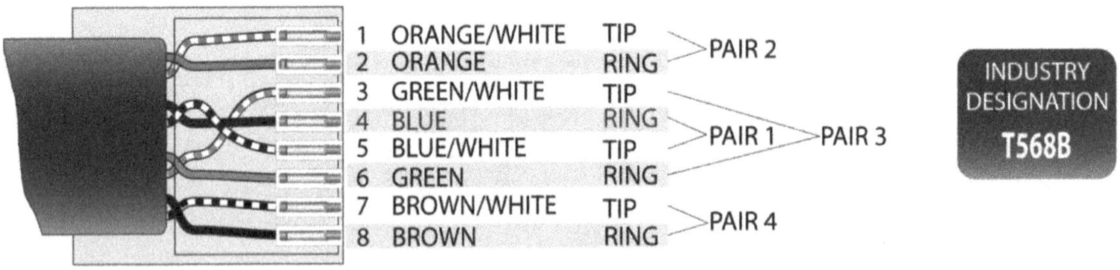

Common Ground(G)	4,5
Transmitted Data(TxD)	3
Received Data (RxD)	6
Data Terminal Ready (DTR)	2
Data Set Ready (DSR)	7
Request To Send (RTS)	1 (Aux only)
Clear To Send (CTS)	8 (Aux only)
Carrier Detect (DCD)	-
Ring Indicator (RI)	-

Figure 7-13. *Cisco 8P8C Connector for RS-232 Signals*

- Polling
- Collision detection
- Token passing

RS-485 Polling Method

Because the master device has to ask each attached device for data, it has to know which devices are available.

This is accomplished by two methods:

- Discovery mechanism
- Pre-configuration

A discovery mechanism uses a procedure defined by the application layer protocol or one that the developer designs to detect what devices are present on the bus. Alternatively, the developer or installer can provide pre-configuration information to the application. This provides the addresses of available devices and any other necessary information (e.g., a device is a contact input or output).

RS-485 Collision Detection

As bytes are transmitted, they are also received by the transmitting device, but if two devices transmit at the same time, the read back will be incorrect; which indicates a collision. A collision requires at least a re-transmission of the last byte sent, but may require the re-transmission of the entire last packet, depending on the particular system.

KNX

KNX is a standardized (EN 50090, ISO/IEC 14543), OSI-based network communications protocol for intelligent buildings. KNX is the successor to, and convergence of, three previous standards: the European Home Systems Protocol (EHS), BatiBUS, and the European Installation Bus (EIB or Instabus). The KNX standard is administered by the KNX Association.

KNX is a standardized and open protocol that is embedded in a chipset, and then installed in to a product. This is what makes it so unique. There are more than 300 manufacturers who have products that can communicate on the KNX bus; including companies such as AMX, Crestron and Control4.

With its roots originally in the commercial market place, it is now becoming more established in residential systems. It uses a two wire bus that is hugely scalable up to 58,399 devices. The cable can run in the same bundle as mains voltage and can power devices up to 350 meters (1,148 feet) away.

The programming is really no more than parameterization, with the parameters being previously agreed and signed off by the KNX Association in Brussels. A dimmer switch can send a dim up/down, on/off or percentage command and a dimming actuator can receive and act upon those commands.

The KNX standard allows multiple product sets from manufacturers to live on a single bus cable and communicate to each other. HVAC, smart meters, weather stations, lighting controllers, blind actuators, PIR sensors, security devices, door intercom and touch screens coexist using one communications protocol. There are fewer system interfaces, a single programming environment and one platform that can interlock the heating and cooling elements, making them compliant with new European building regulations.

Ethernet

Ethernet is the networking technology that today's computer networks are based on. It was introduced in 1980 by Digital, Intel and Xerox and has become the standard worldwide.

IEEE 802

The most popular Ethernet standard is IEEE 802.3 and was developed in 1985. It is a collection of standards developed by the Institute of Electrical and Electronic Engineers (IEEE). It describes the physical layer and the media access control (MAC) sub-layer of the data link layer of the OSI (Open Systems Interconnection) model.

Wired runs can transmit data up to 297 feet (90 meters as specified by TIA-570C) from a network switch to the wall outlet. The bit rate does not decrease with distance. The consumer is allowed a total of 10 meters in patch cords at the outlet and at the switch or router for cross connecting of equipment. Total cable distance of 100 meters or 328 feet. By contrast, IEEE 802.11 a, b and g wireless networks have a typical inside-the-home farther away from an access point a receptor is, the slower the transmission speed, until the signal is lost entirely.

Table 7-12. *Common Standards*

	802.3 Wired
802.3	10 Base-5 10 Mbps over Coax
802.3i	10 Base-T 10 Mbps over UTP
802.3u	100 Base-T 100 Mbps Fast Ethernet over UTP
802.3z	1000 Base-X 1000 Mbps over UTP
802.3ab	1000 Base-T 1000 Mbps over UTP
802.3an	10G Base-T Gbps over UTP
	802.11 Wireless
802.11	1 or 2 Mbps at 2.4 GHz
802.11a	54 Mbps at 5.4 GHz
802.11b	11 Mbps at 2.4 GHz
802.11g	54 Mbps at 2.4 GHz
802.11n	72.2 Mb/s at 2.4 o2 5 GHz

The frequency spectrum used by wired and wireless networks is different. Wired runs are dedicated to only the transmission of data and are highly resistant to interference from other signals, unless they are run in parallel and are too close to high-voltage power lines. However, most wireless signals operate in the unlicensed frequency spectrum 2.4 GHz (gigahertz); although a new technology is currently available that operates in the 5+ GHz range. Because the 2.4 GHz spectrum is unlicensed (as is the 5+ GHz spectrum), it is also a spectrum frequently used by wireless phones and microwave ovens. This frequency sharing can cause interference and dropped wireless data connections. Wireless systems also introduce security concerns that are not as common with wired Ethernet connections. This is due to the fact that they are broadcasting signals into the air which are potentially open to being decoded by others. By enabling and properly configuring Wireless Security, integrators can help prevent the unauthorized access or use of the wireless system. The most common types of wireless security are Wired Equivalent Privacy (WEP) and Wi-Fi Protected Access (WPA & WPA2). WEP is the least protected, while WPA2 is the most secure.
Table 7-x lists the more common wired and wireless communications standards.

Internet

Internet protocols are the most well-known protocols today, although they are not proprietary, meaning they are not protected by trademark, patent, or copyright. They can facilitate communication across networks that are connected to each other, and are widely used for local area networks (LAN) and wide area networks (WAN). There are actually many different Internet protocols, but Transmission Control Protocol (TCP) and Internet Protocol (IP) are the most recognizable.

HTTP

Hyper Text Transfer Protocol (HTTP) is the protocol used to carry requests from a browser to a Web server in order to transport pages from the server back to the requesting browser. The Internet uses this protocol quite extensively, even though it does not have very robust security features. There are variations of HTTP, such as SHTTP (Secure HTTP) that adds a layer of security encryption, and HTTPS
(HTTP Secure) that provides for encryption and transmission through a secure port.

FTP

File Transfer Protocol (FTP) is a protocol used to move files either individually or in groups to another computer on the network. FTP allows a user to connect to another computer and "push" (upload) or "pull" (download) files in a straightforward way using a simple F TP application.

SMTP and POP3

SMTP (Simple Mail Transfer Protocol) is a TCP/IP protocol used in the delivery of electronic mail (e-mail). Its primary function is to transfer mail between MTAs (Mail Transfer Agents), which actually move mail over the network. Because SMTP has a limited capability to queue messages at the receiving end, it is usually used with one of two other protocols, POP3 or IMAP. This allows the user to save messages in a server mailbox and download them periodically from the server to free up server space.

Most mail programs allow a user to specify both an SMTP server and a POP server. SMTP is usually implemented to operate over TCP port25. The details of SMTP are in RFC 821 of the Internet Engineering Task Force (IETF).

Other Protocols and Platforms

There are several other protocols and platforms used to carry information in a variety of ways.

In some cases they are specialized "languages" which travel over cable to allow devices to communicate. In many cases a new platform has been established which allows an already widely used protocol such as IP to travel around the home in a new way (such as over existing cabling or wirelessly).

CEBus/EIA600

Consumer Electronic Bus, or CEBus, (ANSI/ EIA-600) is a communications standard released in 1992 by the Electronics Industry Association (EIA) to govern communications between consumer electronic devices, such as appliances, lighting, HVAC equipment, and soon. CEBus is no longer an active standard.

X10

X10 was another industry communication standard used by electronic devices to communicate with each other. This technology represented a basic form of home automation allowing remote control of home devices and appliances using existing power line wiring for signaling and control by sending brief RF bursts of digital information. The X10 standard is no longer supported.

IEEE 1394

IEEE 1394, originally developed by Apple, is the IEEE standard for high-speed data transmission on local cable networks (LANs) as well as home networks. Also known as Firewire, it supports data rates up to 3.2Bbps (IEEE1394c). The IEEE 1394 multimedia connection enables simple, high-bandwidth, low-cost, isochronous (real-time) data interfacing between computers and many different kinds of consumer electronics products such as camcorders, VCRs, printers, PCs, TVs, and digital cameras. It is mainly used in professional video applications.

Z-Wave

Z-Wave is a wireless RF-based, two-way mesh networking protocol that is designed to allow wireless control of devices such as:

- Thermostats
- Garage door openers
- Light switches
- Residential appliances

Z-Wave technology is also designed to provide interoperability between home control systems made by different manufacturers. Z-Wave's mesh networking capability allows for the wireless signals to be routed from device to device until the target device is reached, allowing for control of devices from a farther distance away, extending the Z-Wave system beyond the range of one wireless device. It operates in a frequency range around 900 MHz, which is in the range of many cordless telephones but avoids the crowded 2.4 GHz range.

ZigBee

ZigBee is another low-power, wireless mesh network standard. It is a low cost technology used for wireless control and monitoring applications. It features low power but long battery life. ZigBee is based on the IEEE801.15.4 standard and uses radio bandwidth allocated for industrial, scientific and medical purposes; 915 MHz in the USA and Australia, 868 MHz in Europe and 2.4 GHz in most other parts of the world. Transmission rates vary from20 to 900 Kbps. Individual devices must have a battery life of at least two years for ZigBee certification.

A ZigBee network may consist of three different types of devices:

- ZigBee Coordinator (ZC): One per network, it forms the root of the network tree and may bridge to other networks.
- ZigBee Router (ZR): Runs application functions and can act as an intermediate router.
- ZigBee End Device: (ZED): Communicates to a ZC or ZR, but cannot relay data from other devices.

The ZigBee Home Automation application profile was released in November of 2007. The typical transmission range of a ZigBee device is 10 to 75 meters, with the ZigBee pro version capable of a maximum 1500 meters. Typical radio output level is just 1 mW.

HomePlug

The HomePlug Powerline Alliance has released a series of communications specifications, beginning in 2001. This platform allows for the existing electrical wiring in the home to be used to extend the home network without installing new twisted-pair cabling infrastructure. In 2010 the IEEE

1901 Broadband Powerline Standard was approved, making HomePlugAV an international standard. HomePlug AV2 (2012) provides speeds up to 1.8 Gbps.

HomePNA

This standard, developed by the Home Phoneline Networking Alliance, uses existing coaxial and twisted pair cabling in the home for networking, without interfering with the primary functionality of that cable. AT&T is an alliance member and uses this standard for their U-Verse IPTV system.

MoCA

The Multimedia over Coax Alliance introduced a specification in 2004 which allows existing coaxial cable to support networking, internet access, multi-room DVR, etc. MoCA 2.0 (2010) operates in RF frequency ranges from500 - 1,500 MHz and provides speeds up to 1.4 Gbps. Supporters include Comcast, Verizon, Time Warner Cable, and Cox Digital Addressable Lighting Interface (DALI) Digital Addressable Lighting Interface is an open standard protocol for lighting control that is contained in the technical standard IEC 62386. DALI addresses lighting components, such as electrical ballasts and dimmers, and can be used for automated scene selections as well as for getting feedback regarding faulty light sources. Used in conjunction with building automation systems, DALI makes remote supervision of lighting systems easier to manage. It requires a two conductor control cable from the processor to each load. This standard is used primarily in commercial applications.

DMX512-A

DMX512-AisanRS-485-based communications protocol developed by the Engineering Commission of USITT that addresses the entertainment technology industry (e.g., stage lighting). This asynchronous serial digital data transmission standard applies to control for lighting equipment and accessories such as fog machines and moving lights. DMX512 has some limitations; for example, it does not include automatic error checking and correction.

LonWorks

LonWorks is a protocol created by the Echelon Corporation that allows network devices to communicate without knowing each other's network topology, names, or addresses. These networks may be connected via a wide variety of cabling (twisted pair, coaxial, fiber optic, and power lines) and other methods such as radio frequency (RF) and infrared (IR). LonWorks networks are specifically suitable for control applications because the protocol was developed to address the unique needs of such applications. This standard is used for a wide variety of commercial applications, and has been adopted for residential applications in Europe and China.

CHAPTER 8

EQUIPMENT INSTALLATION

One of the most important "added values" provided by the home technology professional is the custom installation of components. A well designed and executed residential system delivers the technology-driven user experience AND meets the aesthetic sensibilities of the client. The work of the best integrators always reflects a strong commitment to quality work in everything they do:

- Flawless fit and finish
- Attention to detail
- General neatness
- Adherence to industry best practices

A technically superb system cannot be considered successful if its appearance is amateurish. Remember, the homeowner (and their guests) will always be immediately impressed by quality workmanship, regardless of the minutiae of the technology behind the scenes.

Another important consideration relates to how the technician is perceived when working in the home. Most final phase installation takes place when the house is occupied. For this reason, a high level of professionalism and extreme care must be standard operating procedure when installing A/V components. More detail regarding jobsite professionalism and safety, as well as the basics of equipment installation, can be found in Fundamentals of Residential Electronic Systems.

SAFETY FIRST

Nothing is more important than the safety of employees and clients; both in the installation process, and the way equipment is installed. Every technician should be trained in the fundamentals of jobsite safety, first aid, and the proper installation of equipment.

A Company Culture of Safety

Establishing a culture of jobsite safety within the company is not just the right thing to do, it is good business. In most jurisdictions, employers are required to have a well-documented plan which ensures that employees are well-versed in workplace safety requirements, electrical safety, and personal protective equipment (PPE). Having this type of program in place, including regularly scheduled safety meetings, distribution of safety-related information, and enforcing safety standards, not only minimizes the chance of an accidental injury or death, but serves to demonstrate the company's broader intention to ensure jobsite safety. If an accident does occur, producing documentation which clearly shows the safety program will go a long way to protecting the company from fines and civil liability.

In the U.S. the Occupational Safety and Health Administration (OSHA) estimates that every dollar spent on workplace safety programs will save companies an average of $4-6 in the long term. They also state that injured employees miss an average of eight workdays following an injury. In a small company, this can have a serious impact on timely project completion. In addition, fines and shut-downs can seriously affect profitability.

Know the Rules - And Design to Them

The first step in adhering to safety rules, regulations, and codes is knowing them. Familiarity with local codes is critical. And just as important is researching and applying any codes or regulations in effect when you do a project outside of the municipality, state, or province where you normally work. There should be one person whose responsibility it is to research and assess the rules and regulations which apply when working in an unfamiliar location.

The application of best practices related to homeowner safety must begin in the system design. The designer must apply rigid safety standards to the way equipment installation is specified. This is especially important with equipment which can be accessed by children. For instance, a video display which is wall mounted can often be reached by tiny hands, which can apply a great deal of additional strain to the mounting system. Depending on your region, there will be different codes and standards which need to be referenced when specifying mounting hardware, mechanics, fasteners, etc. Remember the wall or ceiling structure is also part of the mounting system. The overall integrity of the installation is only as good as its weakest link, and oftentimes the wall or ceiling itself must be reinforced before installation can take place. It is the responsibility of the systems designer to take all of these factors into consideration and specify a safe and functional installation.

Jobsite Threats

Electrical Safety

One of the most dangerous types of jobsite injuries is also one of the most common. Electric shock can cause burns, impact injuries from falling, nervous system disorders and death. Technicians in the field should take basic precautions at all times to avoid electrocution:

- Do not use frayed, damaged, or spliced extension cords
- Do not hang cords over metal objects
- Only use approved, grounded cords and equipment (see local codes)
- Test all outlets before use
- Use approved power tools which are properly grounded or double-insulated

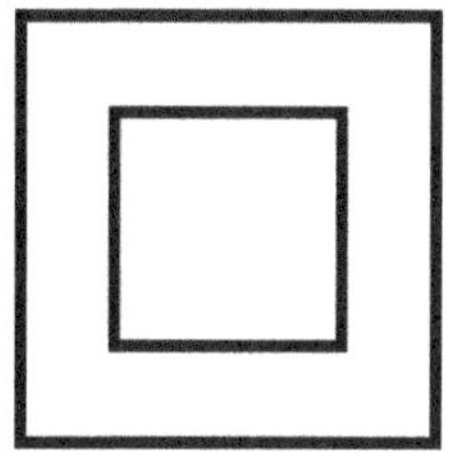

Figure 8-1
Symbol for Double-Insulated Power Tool

Verifying that an outlet is wired correctly not only protects the technician from shock, it also ensures that the power for the installed equipment is correct. Improper power can cause impaired performance or complete failure of an electronic component.

Hazardous Materials

New construction sites generally utilize materials which meet current safety standards, however when working in an existing home there may be some threats which are not easily identified.

- *Lead-Based Paint* – Use of lead-based paint varies in different parts of the world but is now generally only found in older buildings. In the U.S. its use was banned in 1978. Lead can cause serious health problems, especially for children, and when surfaces with lead-based coating are disturbed special precautions must be taken. In the U.S. this is mandated by the EPA's Lead Renovation, Repair, and Painting rule of 2010.
- *Asbestos* – Use of asbestos in homes was also stopped in 1978 in the U.S. but other regions vary. For more information see publications from the EPA or the similar agency in your country.
- *Vermiculite* – This material was once used for insulation and it was discovered that much of it was contaminated with asbestos, making it a threat for workers working in walls and attics. The same steps used to avoid or deal with asbestos should be used when vermiculite is found in a home.

Guidelines

Perhaps the most critical part of installing projectors, screens, and displays is choosing the right fasteners for the job, and using them correctly. A good technician will be familiar with all of the hardware used to properly attach mounts to walls and ceilings.

In order to ensure the safety of the user, and protect the integrator from liability, great care must be taken when both specifying and installing mounting systems. In order to do this you must understand the concept of load limits.

Every piece of hardware and fastener has a stated load limit, and walls and ceilings also have a limit as to how much weight they can support. The Total Working Load (TWL) is the total of the weight of the equipment, cables, and accessories. When the load is static (no movement), a good way to plan the mounting system is to have every element of the support system, including the wall or ceiling, capable of supporting 5 times the TWL. So the system needs to be able to support 5 times the actual weight to be considered safe. This formula has been published in various documents, including the InfoComm/BICSI AV Design Reference Manual. In the past, UL 1678 has been referenced, which uses a recommended safety ratio of 4:1 for static loads.

For any installation which is moveable or motorized, the potential for failure is much greater. UL 1678 recommends a ratio of 8:1, TWL to SWL. Using this same approach with the accepted 5:1 ratio for static loads, a good guideline for fully articulating mounts would be 10:1.

The bottom line on this topic is this: The entire system must be over-engineered. The mount and fasteners need to be properly specified for the application (static, dynamic, and what structure they are being attached to). The wall or ceiling must be capable of supporting the Total Working Load. In residential settings, this often means the installation of blocking prior to the drywall being installed, to provide more mass and the ability to spread the load out over more locations. In nearly all situations, it will be necessary to have all fasteners connected directly to solid framing members (studs, joists). Additional fastening to sheetrock is OK but should not be considered a dependable, safe means of support. Fasteners such as plastic sleeve anchors and small molly bolts should never be used. Remember, the entire systems is only as good as its weakest link.

Fasteners

No matter how well-made a mounting apparatus is, or how robust the wall or ceiling might be, if the fasteners are not properly selected and installed, the overall system will be compromised. A good technician will be well informed about a wide variety of fastening hardware, and experienced in their proper use.

Mounting to Wood Framed Structures

IThe most widely used fastener used for attaching through sheetrock and into wooden framing members is the lag screw. These screws are rated for heavy loads and do a great job when used correctly. Installing them incorrectly can give the impression of a solid mounting system, but fail over time. General guidelines for lag screws include:

- Make sure you find the exact center of the stud or joist
- Pre-drill to prevent splitting
- Do not overtighten. It is not hard to break off the hex head.

In some cases, smaller toggle bolts may be used for very small displays, and as extra mounting points along with lag screws.

Mounting to Metal Studs

Metal studs are widely used in light commercial and MDUs (Multi-Dwelling Units). They provide strong and lightweight vertical support but can be less than ideal for wall mounting equipment. Heavier displays will require solid wood blocking be specified and installed prior to the installation of sheetrock. For lighter displays, toggle bolts can be used to go through the sheetrock, and through the front surface of the metal stud, then expand to provide good support. A specialized type of toggle bolt known as a "snaptoggle" works very well.

When using a "snaptoggle" bolt into a metal stud:

- Carefully locate the center of the stud
- Drill the recommended sized hole through the sheetrock and through the face of the stud
- Insert the toggle as recommended, and align it so that the "T" expands vertically into the stud cavity
- Break off the excess plastic
- Do not overtighten the bolt when installing the mount

Mounting to Brick or Concrete

Brick walls are often found in living spaces and concrete walls are common in basements. Poured concrete and concrete block walls are widely used in residential construction in many parts of the world. Proper mounting to these surfaces requires specialized hardware, powerful tools, and high quality drill bits. The most widely used fastener for this type of wall is the expanding wedge anchor:

- Predrill
- Follow manufacturer's directions
- Take care not to overtighten/break

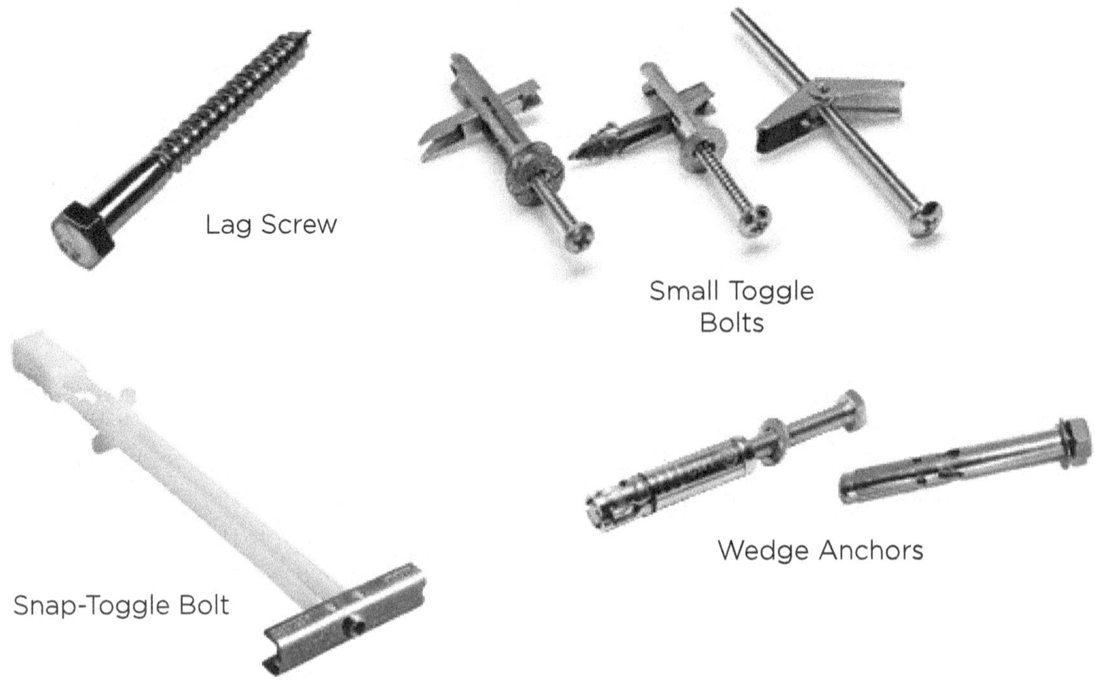

Figure 8-2 *Fasteners*

FLAT PANEL DISPLAYS

Design

As part of the system design, not only the display technology but the location, angle and mounting type should be determined based on several criteria:

- Type of viewing (cinema, casual, larger group)
- Ambient light, angle of sun at different times of day and year
- Viewing distance, sight lines
- Geography (some displays sensitive to altitude)
- Surface to be mounted to
- Size and weight of display

Mounting Techniques

Video displays are mounted on a wide variety of surfaces, using many different types of mounting hardware. As mentioned above, the most important issue is making sure the entire mounting system (display, mount, hardware, and wall construction) is able to dependably hold the display and not allow it to fall or be pulled down. Remember a flat panel display poses the greatest risk of an accident because it is often positioned in such a way that it can be grasped and pulled on by individuals, especially children. Other components, like projectors and speakers, are usually out of reach, so unlikely to be touched.

VESA FDMI

In order to facilitate easy interface between displays and wall mounts, the Video Electronics Standards Association (VESA) has established a standard set of mounting hole patterns. The Flat Display Mounting Interface (FDMI) standard designates the following configurations which most manufacturers conform to:

Table 8-1 *VESA FDMI Standards*

	DISPLAY SIZE (DIAGONAL)	MAX WEIGHT	THREAD	PATTERN
MIS-D 75	12" (305mm) - 22.9"(583mm)	17.5lb (8kg)	M4	75mm X 75mm, 50mm X 75mm
MIS-D 100	12" (305mm) - 22.9"(583mm)	30.8lb(14kg)	M4	100mm X 100mm, 50mm X 100mm
MIS-E	23"(684mm) - 30.9"(786mm)	50lb (22.7kg)	M4	200mm X 100mm, 50mm X 200mm
MIS-F	31"(787mm) - 90"(2286mm)	250lb (113.6kg)	M6, M8	Multi-hole Configuration, 200mm X 200mm and up

Installation Tips:

- Take pictures of blocking and wiring before sheetrock goes up.
- Make sure area is free of obstacles.
- Establish a nearby staging area for TV.
- Use a dropcloth anywhere you are working.
- In retrofit situations, verify the location with the client before drilling
- Never rely only on sheetrock, always find studs.
- Center and predrill for lag screws in wooden studs.
- Use a long level, not a torpedo level, for more accurate results.
- Clean screen surface with non-ammonia cleaner (remind client of this, too).
- Always do at least a basic video calibration

PROJECTORS

Design

The precise location of the projector must always be determined as part of the design process. Also important to consider are proper ventilation, noise levels, and conditioned (UPS) power. In general, the lens should be located near the rear of the zoom range, to use the most accurate part of the lens. A full understanding of available vertical lens shift is critical.

Projector mounts have become more sophisticated and user-friendly in recent years. Be sure to keep up with these advancements and choose models which work well for you, and try to stick with those models. Familiarity leads to quicker, more accurate, installations.

If fan noise is a problem, an enclosure may need to be specified. This must be done in advance, and included in the proposal and budget.

Installation Tips:

Same as with wall mounted displays, plus:

- Double check the location for distance and centering.
- Always use solid studs and find the center (other mounting options in commercial spaces)
- Never, ever, use keystone correction.
- Make sure power and signal terminations and plate-work are well-coordinated.
- Theaters and media rooms should be thoroughly calibrated.

SCREENS

A wide variety of projection screens are now available, with many different types of mounting options. The designer will determine the correct size and screen material as part of the overall system design. Design considerations include:

- Front vs rear
- Flat vs curved
- Masking

Installation Tips:

Same as above, plus:

- Make sure there are no marks or smudges on the screen surface.
- Double check for wrinkle or waves in the screen. This may mean coming back in a few weeks to make sure everything is perfect.
- Verify perfect operation of the control system on motorized or masked screens.

CAMERA SYSTEMS

Designing and installing residential camera systems is a relatively new and expanding market. Reductions in pricing and the proliferation of home networks have contributed to this growth. There are several key elements that go into any system design. Among those are:

- Placement of camera
  - Coverage (Field of View)
  - Pixels on Target
  - Lighting Environment
  - Alignment of Aesthetics
- Specifying the right type of camera for each application
- Signal Transmission and Power
  - Power
  - Data
- Installation

Placement of Cameras and Lighting Considerations

When choosing the placement of any camera, the most important factor is the Field of View (FOV) that the camera is afforded from the chosen location. Obviously, having a camera does relatively little good (with the possible exception of preventing an incident) without an effective field of view. Factors that affect a camera's field of view are: the lens type and obstructions that may be in the FOV.

Many cameras have a varifocal (zoom) lens, which means that the lens can be adjusted (typically between 2.8 mm to 12 mm). With an average distance to object in the field of view of 10 feet, the size of the FOV can range from 12' x 16' to 3' x 4'.

Obstructions in the FOV also need to be taken into account. These may include items that will change over time, for example trees, plants, and shrubs that grow during the year. One must also think ahead about what is portable in a home, and the areas where these types of items may get moved to.

In addition to the FOV, one must also take into account what type of information that is required from the picture. There are different types of informational needs in video; General Scene, and Forensic (Personal and Details). In a residential setting, you will most likely want to be able to recognize the person in the picture. Therefore you need to make sure that you have at least 40-60 pixels on target (per square foot).

The lighting environment is also always a key factor. You should be sure to either know that you will have enough ambient light at the time of the picture (remember to think about both day and night), or supply enough light, or specify the proper type of camera. If you are only concerned about pictures in daytime, generally the ambient light will be sufficient. However, if you may require pictures at night, you must be sure that the artificial light supplied will meet the camera's specifications. All cameras will have a specification of the light required, measured in units of lux (lx) which is one lumen/m2.

Figure 8-3 *Wide Dynamic Range Camera*

Figure 8-4 *Infrared Camera*

If neither ambient nor artificial light can be supplied, then an IR (Infrared) camera will supply enough IR illumination for a useable picture. If IR is required, you need to check the specifications of the camera to determine the effective distance. Also remember that when using an IR camera, all pictures will be only black and white at night. This will certainly affect your ability to differentiate detail on the picture.

Also remember that there can be too much light in some cases. Examples include: a camera in a home looking out a sliding glass door or an outside camera. For these types of cases, one must specify a Wide Dynamic Range (WDR) camera, which can compensate for too much ambient light and still give a quality picture.

Of course since we are speaking about a residential setting, the aesthetics of the unit are also important. Features such as color, size, mounting location and type can make or break the acceptability of the camera to the end user. Housings can be found to match white ceilings and in some cases could be painted to match wall color. Current electronics make the cameras much smaller than in the past. Locating cameras in corners may not only help with coverage, but also make them appear less intrusive.

Figure 8-5 *Attractive Camera Design for Indoor Use*

Types of Cameras

As discussed, camera types may be specified based on lighting considerations (IR and WDR). There are also various types of cameras that have functional differences that must be considered. For field of view, there are 360° cameras, multi-camera units, and Pan/Tilt/Zoom (PTZ). If the camera is going to be outside or inside a dusty garage, or any extreme temperature location, be aware of the specified operating temperature range of the camera and make sure it is IP66 rated.

Signal Transmission and Power

Traditionally, getting power to the camera and the video data from the camera has been accomplished via electrical conductors. In many cases, coaxial cable has been replaced by either twisted pair wiring or network cable. Care must be taken to not exceed the specification range of the cable chosen. Data losses can be seen if wire runs exceed specification. When running cable, be sure to minimize the bends, and keep away from high voltage wiring (especially fluorescents). Be sure to pay close attention to all wiring terminations, as these often are found to be the weakest link of the transmission media. Be sure to pay close attention to all wiring terminations as these often are seen to be the weakest link of the transmission media. All wiring should be completed following all applicable NEC standards.

The industry is expanding to include wireless transmission of video signals. Infrastructure in the home must be considered. All wireless technology is dependent upon effective signal penetration and has range limitations. Concrete construction, metal studs in walls, large mirrors, competing wireless signals, and metal objects can all can reduce the effective range of wireless products. The security of the wireless channel is also of great importance.

All of the normal security precautions should be taken to ensure the wireless connection is private. These include, but are not limited to; changing the SSID, engaging security protocol, and changing all default passwords.

In conclusion, the residential video market is growing rapidly. This is due to a number of factors, including the lower prices of the equipment, the reduced physical size of the equipment, and maybe most importantly, the need in our society for instant information and the acceptance of video in our lives generally. Following the guidelines given above will help to ensure that the installation will be accepted by the end user and effective in practice.

WIRELESS ACCESS POINTS

Proper access point (AP) placement and installation is critical to the success of a wireless network. In smaller installations, it's okay to place an access point in a central location in the home to ensure adequate coverage. In larger installations which may see more network traffic, simple AP placement isn't enough. Instead, it's important to properly design the wireless network for smaller cells, even coverage, and proper channel-planning. Don't give in to the temptation of simple scattering access points around the building. Instead, seek proper design guidelines, and let that dictate careful AP placement.

Access points can usually be mounted either on walls or ceilings, but check with the AP manufacturer to see what their recommendations are, as some AP antennas are polarized to perform better when mounted a certain way. If the AP uses external antennas, don't point them away from each other, or at 45 degree angles. Keep all of the antennas oriented vertically, and most importantly parallel with each other. This will help clients and APs hear each other more easily, and it will allow MIMO devices to function properly.

Keep in mind that certain materials can attenuate (block) or reflect RF signals. Avoid placing wireless accent points near metal (like a refrigerator) or water pipes. Some homes may use 3" diameter cast iron drain pipes to drain water from upper floors. Metal and water will both attenuate 2.4 and 5 GHz signals, so try to be aware of the plumbing and HVAC systems in the building when designing the network.

EQUIPMENT IN RACKS

The most professional and efficient way to install several electronic components in a single location is to use equipment racks conforming to the EIA (Electronic Industries Alliance) standard. An introduction to this concept can be found in the Fundamentals of Residential Electronic Systems book. This section will expand on that knowledge with information valuable to designers and lead technicians. We will cover the management of cabling, power, and heat and present some best practices and methods for proper design.

Ergonomics

The location of components within the rack should be established early in the design phase, and indicated clearly in the rack elevation drawings. It is important to locate each piece of equipment carefully. Some general guidelines:

- Hottest components at the top and bottom (heavy on the bottom)
- Equipment with a display that needs to be seen often - near eye level
- Devices with trays (Blu-ray, game console) at a convenient height for loading
- Components which rarely need user interaction - low and out of reach
- Down-firing lights - top of rack

These are general guidelines. More specific requirements will be dictated based on the method used to manage heat in the rack (covered later in this section).

Cable Management

Poor design and sloppy wiring says a lot about the installer, and none of it is good. Conversely, when an equipment rack is neatly dressed, the result is an impressive reflection on the integrator, as well as being functionally superior. Attention to detail is a benchmark of quality work, and should always be a standard feature of every project. When the wiring in a rack or cabinet is clean, and well thought out, the advantages are numerous:

- Neat, organized appearance reflects positively on the integrator and drives referrals
- A well-done rack is easy to service and upgrade
- Performance is improved;
    - NEXT (Near End Crosstalk) is reduced in data cabling
    - EMI (Electromagnetic Interference) and RFI (Radio Frequency Interference) is reduced in audio and video cabling
    - Avoidance of cable pinches and kinks ensures proper performance

Figure 8-6 *Award Winning Equipment Racks*

Entry of Cable to the Rack

A large rack will have many cables connected to it. Managing these bundles properly will have a positive impact in both appearance and performance over time.

- Top entry may be through rack top or top opening on the rear.
- When a rack is located next to a wall and can be rolled out for service, bring cables into the rack at the top of the rear and bring cables out of the wall at the same height, with the drop being just above the floor at its lowest. This allows for the rack to be pulled away easily.
- Some commercial installations may allow for cable entry through the bottom. Follow best practices.
- When conduit is used, utilize the knock-outs for standard size openings.

Internal Cable Dressing

The way the cabling is arranged and secured within the rack will determine how easy it is to identify cables, troubleshoot problems, and do replacements/upgrades in the future. The best integrators always adhere to strict guidelines in order to ensure the best possible outcome:

- Isolate AC and speaker cables from data and coax (high power speaker signals can act like AC and interfere with A/V and data signals)
- Use vertical lacer strips to manage vertical bundles
- Use racks with flanged rack rail to provide more space when bundles are large (4" diameter).
- Use horizontal lacer bars for horizontal runs in and out of components, to provide:
    - Strain relief
    - Enhanced visibility of labels
    - Easy servicing
- Use hook and loop Velcro; no pinching, easy removal/replacement
- Use 3/8" rack screws (10-32) to prevent damage when cables are dressed in tight spaces.

Managing Power in Racks

A/V signals are always susceptible to noise induced by Electromagnetic Interference (EMI) and Radio Frequency Interference (RFI). In order to minimize these problems (and ensure safety for technicians and homeowners) several best practices can be followed:

- Always observe local codes and recognize they may vary from larger standards (NEC, CEC, etc.)
- Know who the Authority Having Jurisdiction (AHJ) is. The title may be different (ie; "electrical subcode official")
- Always check for proper AC wiring before doing any kind of installation. Avoid circuits with ground/neutral reversal or a "bootleg ground".
- Long run signal cables with SCIN (Shield Current Inducted Noise) are susceptible to ground loops. Consider lifting the shield at the destination. To reduce RF interference, a 0.1μF capacitor can be added between the shield and the chassis of the receiving end component.
- Keep unbalanced cables as short as possible, and separated from AC and speaker runs.
- Use high-quality signal isolation transformers to eliminate hum if necessary

- Use signal AND power cables that are twisted to reduce the effect of magnetic fields.
- Never, ever, lift or bypass a power cable ground.
- Loads which operate for three hours or more are considered "continuous loads". The power available to this type of load should be 125% of its anticipated draw. Make sure to specify adequate power.
- Use a power sequencer system to eliminate "pops" and troublesome in-rush current draw.
- Ground multiple racks together.
- Use power conditioners which regulate voltage and filter line noise and have surge protection.

Thermal Management

The single factor which most often causes equipment failure is heat. Most studies tell us that 85°F (29.4°C) should be the maximum continuous operating temperature for electronic equipment. For every 10°F (5.6°C) increase in temperature, digital equipment life is reduced by approximately 40%. Power amplifiers are especially problematic, as they often run at very high temperatures, even under normal conditions.

The overall thermal system that must be considered has three different airflows:

1. How the heat travels through the rack
2. How the heat moves around the room
3. How the heat is removed from the room

The cooler the room the rack is in, the easier it will be to keep the equipment cool. An ambient temperature of 75°F (23.9°C) provides a good supply of cool fresh air to the rack. In fact, even cooler air is desirable, as long as the temperature is not below the dew point (where condensation takes place).

Thermal management is complex and can be quite challenging. Comprehensive articles and white papers have been created which focus on this subject. See the References section at the end of the chapter for a variety of resources related to rack-related practices.

Calculating Heat

Equipment generated heat is measured in British Thermal Units per Hour (BTU/hr). Most equipment is very inefficient, converting most of the current it draws into heat. A quick heat calculation can be made, knowing that at 117 volts, each ampere of current draw will create about 400 BTU/hr of heat. Also keep in mind that the current draw on the component's nameplate is there to indicate the MAXIMUM draw, for safety purposes. In normal use the draw may be much less. Calculating the HVAC requirements solely on nameplate ratings may result in vastly over engineered ventilation. The designer should use accurate current draw figures, based on normal operation, which could be as little as 25% of the stated maximum draw.

Power Amplifiers require a completely different approach to heat calculation, depending on the type of amplifier and its application. Most large systems use Class B amplifiers.

Table 8-2. *Component Efficiency and Waste Heat*

AMPLIFIER CLASS	EFFICIENCY	CONVERTED TO HEAT
A	20%	80%
AB	≥ 50%	≤ 50%
D	≥ 90%	≤ 10%

Many amplifier manufacturers will provide specifications related to current draw and heat generated, based on the type of program being amplified. Table 8-3 shows an example of this type of chart.

Table 8-3. *Example of Information Provided by an Amplifier Manufacturer*

PROGRAM MATERIAL	PROGRAM DUTY CYCLE	WASTE HEAT BTU/hr	CURRENT DRAW 120V AC
Individual Speech	10%	390	1.6A
Acoustic/Chamber Music	20%	460	2.2A
Full Range Rock Music	30%	540	2.9A
Compressed Rock Music	40%	620	3.5A
Pink Noise	50%	700	4.2A

Passive Convection Cooling

In most situations, where ambient air is at a comfortable temperature and equipment heat is not extreme, a passive convection approach is adequate. In this scenario, the natural tendency for warm air to rise, and draw ambient air in to replace it, is enough to keep the operating temperature in a safe range. This design is highly dependable because it does not depend on fans, which could fail. In general, cooler air needs a way to enter the rack at the bottom, and exit at the top. Equipment that has no built-in cooling fans can have vented blank panels between them, to allow airflow around them. Components with built-in fans will generally have the air intake on the front panel and exhaust on the rear. This equipment can be installed with no spaces between them, as long as there are no vents on the top or bottom. The components which generate the most heat will drive the upward movement of air best when installed at the top or bottom of the rack (heavy on the bottom, light weight near the top).

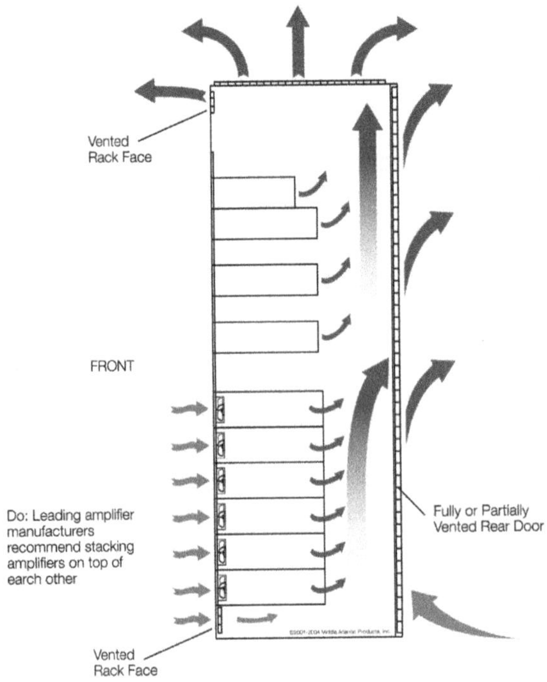

Figure 8-7 *Passive Convection*

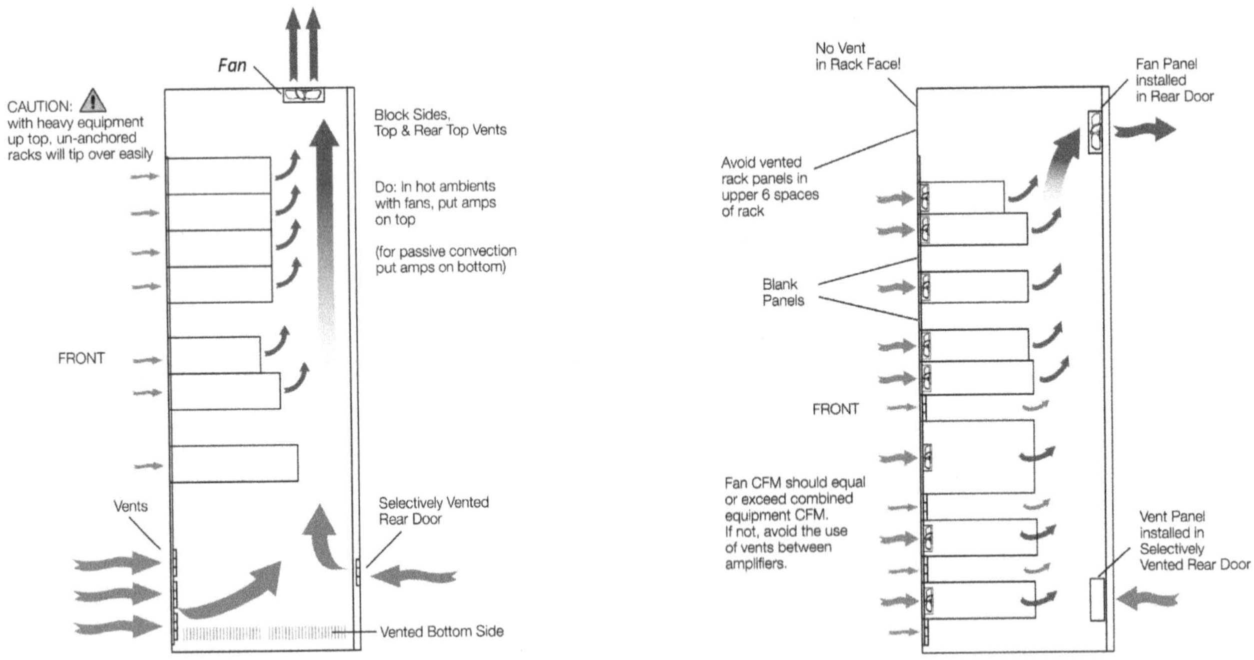

Forced Air w/Top Fans

Forced Air w/Equipment Fans

Figure 8-8 *Active Cooling*

Active/Forced Air Cooling

In some situations, the heat generated is too great for convection cooling to be adequate. In these cases, active thermal management (forced air) is required. In a forced air design it is imperative that the system is sealed, with only specified locations where air can enter and exit. The fans are typically at the top of the rack, pulling out warm air. The ambient air enters at the bottom, passes by the equipment, and is exhausted through the fans. Some recommended practices related to active thermal management:

- Equipment with front air intakes may be separated by vented blank panels.
- The CFM (Cubic Feet per Minute) rating of the rack exhaust fans must exceed the total CFM of the equipment fans, to ensure that all warm air is exhausted.
- There should be no vented panels or uncovered rack vents near the top of the rack.
- Any vent in the rear door should be near the bottom.
- Adequate intake venting is necessary to prevent "starving" the airflow
- Deep rack shelves should be vented near the back.
- Beware of improper venting, which can cause "hot spots"
- Fan operation must be monitored. A failed fan can create a "short circuit" and rack will overheat
- Extend fan life by installing proportional speed thermostatic fan control.
- Inlet filters are recommended, but must be checked and cleaned regularly

How to Calculate Ventilation Needed

Figure 8-8 shows a chart which will allow the designer to determine what type of thermal management to use and how much heat must be removed from the interior of the rack (and the surrounding space). Only use this method when accurate figures are available for the amplifiers and the current draw of the other components.

To calculate total waste heat:

1. Determine total waste heat output of amplifiers, based on published specs.
2. Add up total MEASURED amperage draw of other equipment (at 117v) and multiply by 400 to get total BTU/hr
3. Combine these two totals and mark on column C.

To find minimum ventilation requirements:

1. Mark ambient room temperature in Column C and connect points B and C with a straight-edge.
2. The minimum cooling requirement will show where the line extends on to column A.

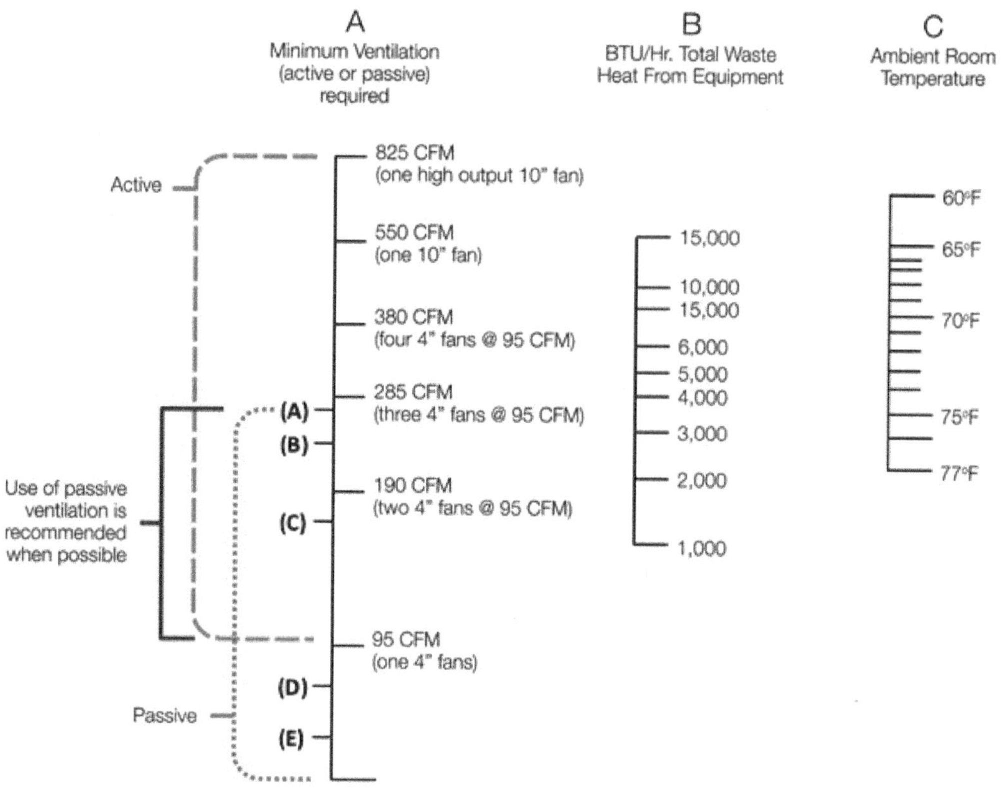

PASSIVE VENTILATION REQUIREMENTS

(A) Fully vented rear door, vented rack top, in vented-face rack
(B) Fully vented rear door, vented rack top, in solid-face rack
(C) Solid rear door, vented rack top, in vented-face rack
(D) Solid rear door, 4 space vent in upper rackspace, solid top
(E) Solid rear door, 2 space vent in upper rackspace, solid top

Figure 8-9 *Guide for Calculating Ventilation Requirements*

Rack Pre-Configuration and Installation

A professional racking system allows equipment to be organized, connected, and kept cool. It also provides an opportunity for the technicians to re-configure and test the system before installing it in the home. This minimizes the amount of time onsite and allows for troubleshooting and testing in the privacy of the shop. The entire system can be racked up, wired, and tested. Then, when the rack is delivered and installed during the final phase, it can simply be interfaced with the prewire and retested. If the rack includes very heavy components such as power amplifiers and power conditioners, these may be removed and transported separately, to make the weight more manageable.

REFERENCES

Middle Atlantic Products White Papers

http://www.middleatlantic.com/resources/white-papers.aspx

Power Distribution and Grounding

Cable Management Guide

Thermal Management

Middle Atlantic Products Thermal Calculator

http://www.middleatlantic.com/resources/thermal-calculator.aspx

CHAPTER 9

TROUBLESHOOTING

In this book, troubleshooting is defined as the use of a logical, systematic process to efficiently and accurately diagnose and repair electronic system failures.

PHILOSOPHY OF TROUBLESHOOTING

Troubleshooting, like most other forms of problem solving, may have more than one path that can lead to a correct solution. Therefore, when performing troubleshooting procedures, it is extremely important to stay organized, think logically, and be patient.

It is critical to keep a level head when things go wrong, because with electronics (or anything with moving parts), something will eventually go wrong. More often than not, there will be struggles and frustrations during the course of a project, and accepting this fact and working through unforeseen obstacles methodically and objectively will increase the likelihood of a successful outcome.

From another perspective, troubleshooting can be quite beneficial. A successful outcome while troubleshooting can be an opportunity to improve the customer experience. While a client can become frustrated by a problem, a timely and successful resolution can quickly create a happy customer, and a happy customer can be a loyal customer; providing both referrals and additional revenue opportunities.

Having an efficient and organized approach to troubleshooting will save time, which in turn protects the profitability of a project and the company itself. Defining a troubleshooting methodology and sticking to it will ease frustration and increase productivity.

Finally, keep in mind that the first rule of customer support is to not make the situation worse. If the cause of the problem cannot be found or fixed during the initial service call, have a backup plan to get the customer's system up and running.

PREQUALIFICATION

Troubleshooting can be a very time consuming and costly process. For this reason, it is highly recommended that integrators PREQUALIFY systems prior to installation in the field. By prequalifying the entire system exactly as it will be installed in the customer's home, technicians will likely uncover any unknown variables (i.e. device interoperability issues), design flaws, or malfunctioning equipment problems before heading to the job site. This would then leave only those issues that are unique to the customer's environment. Once a system has been installed, it "become more difficult to diagnose and problem solve, and the client may become upset. By bench testing the system in a controlled environment, it not only allows for much easier system diagnosis, but significantly simplifies the process of implementing a solution.

THE TROUBLESHOOTING PROCESS

Proper troubleshooting is not a guessing game of which part to replace or which cable to re-terminate. Technicians should establish and use a specific methodology with repeatable step by step procedures whenever faced with a situation requiring them to repair a system issue. This will increase the likelihood of correctly diagnosing and permanently repairing the problem, while also greatly increasing the accuracy and efficiency of the overall troubleshooting process. Establishing this process, and ensuring that each of your technicians involved in troubleshooting maintain this process, you will not only greatly increase the success rate but also subsequently reduce costs. The CEDIA recommended process for troubleshooting can be outlined in five steps.

The Five Steps of Troubleshooting

1. Analyze
2. Diagnose
3. Repair
4. Verify
5. Prevent

Analyze

Oftentimes, it is all too easy to skip this first step of the troubleshooting process, and jump stage. However, without accurate data and proper analysis, this may lead to hours of wasted time and ineffective testing procedures. Therefore, prior to making any changes to the system, it is critical to gather all the data available and form an accurate analysis of the situation. This means understanding the true nature of the problem as well as knowing the full extent to which it is affecting the system. Being patient and taking the time to fully analyze the situation will help to define an efficient troubleshooting path for the other four steps of the process and drastically reduce the time necessary to bring the situation to a resolution.

Another point to remember during the early stages of troubleshooting is to stay objective and not jump to conclusions. Do not make assumptions about the source of the problem based solely on customer reports. Also, having observed similar symptoms in a previous troubleshooting situation may help to identify the cause of the symptoms in the current system, but it will by no means lead to a guaranteed solution. In almost all cases, there is more than one possible cause for any given symptom and it is important to consider every variable before ruling them out.

Table 9-1. *Recommended Interview Questions*

Interview Questions
When did the problem first begin?
When does the problem normally occur? (Time of day)
What exactly is the system doing or not doing?
What other equipment is in use at the same time?
What exactly have you experienced?
Have you noticed any pattern in the problem?
Have you smelled any unusual smells or heard any unusual noises when this problem has occurred?
What is different about the circumstances when this problem occurs and when it does not?
How long has this problem been occurring?
When the problem occurs, how long does it last?
Has the problem increased in frequency or duration?
Did the problem begin during a lightning storm or power outage?
Did the problem manifest itself all at once or did it occur over time?
Can the symptom be reproduced?

Methods For Gathering Data

- Interview the client
- Review system documentation
- Observe the system

Interviewing the Client

Interview all parties. Talk to the people who use the system regularly about what is actually happening. Remember, some things may only occur under specific circumstances that may be difficult to recreate during service calls scheduled for short periods of time. Ask for exact details about what else was happening in the client's location, what other equipment was being used simultaneously, and if the client has noticed any pattern in the problem. If possible, ask the client to perform the actions that lead to the problem as this may lead to a user created problem versus equipment or programming. The problem will not always turn out to be what the customer believed it to be. Be ready for anything.

Review System Documentation

Develop a complete system description. If available, use existing diagrams, wire schematics and blueprints as well as, if available, previous work orders to help evaluate the system. If these documents are not available, new ones should be created during the system review process. Question anything on the existing drawings that doesn't look right.

Know what the product is intended to do and what the client was expecting to occur. Locate and gather the appropriate manufacturer documentation such as owner/installation manuals for each system component. These documents can provide valuable information about the specifications for the equipment and what the equipment is truly designed to do. It may be that the problem exists as a misunderstanding of proper use and is not related to equipment at all.

Often, documentation from the manufacturer will have a list of the most common problems as well as suggestions to correct them. The documentation will at least provide the operating specifications, which may give helpful information about the problem or the ideal environmental conditions. If the documentation does not provide useful information, consider contacting the manufacturer directly and asking for their technical support department.

Observe the System

It is not uncommon to receive inaccurate or inadequate information regarding problem symptoms from a client interview. This makes it extremely important to fully observe the system and the environment independently of the client feedback. Observations include using all senses. Visual cues can provide valuable information, but so can smells, touch and sound.

Table 9-2 *Recommended Observation Questions*

Observation Questions
Do you feel any heat or vibration in the equipment?
Do you smell smoke or burning insulation?
Do you see any flickers in the lighting or brightness of the equipment?
Do you see any scorch marks or discolored areas on any cords or cabinets and housing?
Do you hear any unusual system noises, like rattles, whines, whistling etc.

When dealing with a problem that is constant, it typically makes things much easier to identify and diagnose. However, in many cases the problem will be intermittent, which makes it extremely important to observe and document all aspects of the environment when the problem occurs. This will help to ensure that the problem can be recreated during the diagnostic process which will in turn help to ensure that the solution implemented will be permanent.

Analyze the Data

Once the data gathering process is complete, it is necessary to analyze the results and document all of the known possible causes for the symptoms. By theorizing about the possible causes for the system failure, a more efficient diagnostic procedure can be chosen.

Diagnose

The second step in the troubleshooting process is to diagnose the problem. With the list of possible causes established during the system analysis phase, it is critical to identify which one is truly the culprit of the system failure in order to implement steps to correct it.

To diagnose the problem:

- Recreate the symptoms (if possible)
- Test different hypothesis
- Document all steps

Recreate the Symptoms

Reproducing the symptoms in real time will offer the opportunity to make new observations about the problem (and possibly gain new insight as to the cause) while also increasing the accuracy of the diagnostic process. In order to recreate the symptoms; reset the system to the same operating environment and circumstances in which the problem first occurred. It is important that the problem can be recreated repeatedly-that is the only way to confirm it isnot a fluke and that, indeed, this problem occurs in a specific set of circumstances.

When trying to recreate the symptoms, it is important to observe all recommended safety practices. When dealing with electrical faults, there is a very real possibility of danger due to electricity or fire. Recreating the symptoms must be done with careful planning and forethought to safety.

Test Different Hypothesis

Using the previously determined list of possible causes, diagnostic procedures can be focused on the component(s) identified as the most likely source of the system failure. Often there is more than one test that can be used in order to confirm that a component is the cause of the problem. Therefore, it is best to identify and use the diagnostic procedure that provides the most insight but also the one that is the easiest and most convenient to complete.

"Occam's Razor"

The concept of "Occam's Razor" states that usually the simplest solution is also the correct one. For this reason, when trying to recreate the symptoms, it is helpful to start testing with the most obvious problems. These are problems that tend to recur or are the standard, usual issues to go wrong. Experience and system analysis will assist in identifying the most likely malfunctions. Use the checklist in Table 9-3 of some common, easily identifiable occurrences.

Table 9-3 *Common Problem Checklist*

Common Problem Checklist
Is the component or equipment connected to an electrical outlet?
Is the breaker active?
Do other electrical devices work in the same plug?
Is the component plugged into a power strip or surge protector that may not be functioning?
Is the component or device turned on?
Are the batteries in the component or device fresh?
Are all cables and connectors firmly seated?
Is the wire kinked or bent?
Are all safety interlocks closed?
Is the device getting enough ventilation so as not to overheat?
Is the client using the equipment properly?
Does it work without the remote? (take manual control of volume and tone controls)
Does the equipment have adequate power?

Efficient Diagnostic Procedures

When working with a partner or installation crew, never allow two or more people to unplug and move cables and devices around at the same time. Troubleshooting is not a race, and if more than one person begins attempting to diagnose the system at the same time, no one will know what worked or what was changed by the other technician. The best way to approach the troubleshooting process in this scenario is to have the second person document steps. This will help both parties work together to come to the correct diagnosis.

It is also important to consider the entire signal path (from source to output device) prior to starting the diagnostic process and the physical troubleshooting. With this in mind, don't ever start in the middle of the signal path. Pick the end (either upstream or downstream) of the signal path where the problem is most likely originating and begin testing the system in the other direction.

Make a mental or written logical flow chart to map all testing procedures. This will help to ensure that as the troubleshooting process proceeds, there will be no steps repeated, no unnecessary steps taken and significantly lessen the possibility of overlooking a possible diagnostic outcome. See example in Figure 9-1.

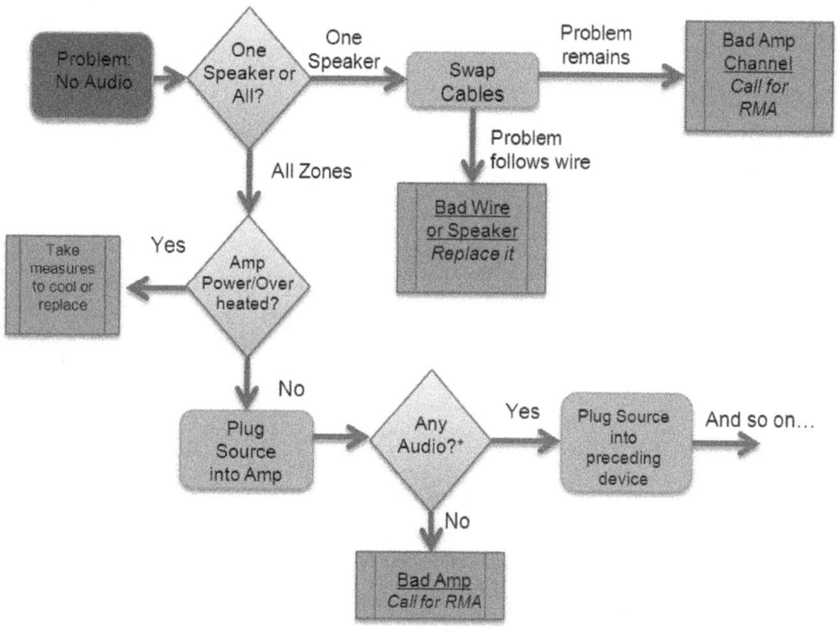

Figure 9-1. *Sample Troubleshooting Chart*

Table 9-4 *Recommended Test Equipment*

Recommended Test Equipment
RF Analyzer
Digital multi-meter
CAT5 tester
Laptop
HDMI tester
Tone generator and inductive noise amplifier
Video Test Pattern Generator
Line voltage circuit tester
WiFi Sniffer/analyzer

Table 9-5 *Recommended Assortment of "Known Good" Cables*

Recommended Assortment of "Known Good" Cables
Optical Cable
HDMI
CAT5e
VGA
Serial 9-pin
1/8" to stereo RCA
Stereo RCA
Null modem adaptors

Diagnostic Software

Many software tools exist today for diagnosing common problems. Some manufacturers also include error logs in their equipment that can provide helpful information. If it is possible to include outside internet access to the system, be sure to stress the importance and convenience to your customer for adding it.

Testing Procedures

Once the problem has been defined, all possible causes have been documented, and the diagnostic process has been planned out, it is time to begin the actual testing.

Substitution

When working with a residential electronics system, one of the simplest ways to test the signal path is through the method of substitution. By using a known good cable, a known good source/display device or test equipment capable of emulating (mimicking) a known-good device, to replace suspect components or cables within the system, it is possible to verify proper operation and to discover where/when the problem goes away.

It is critical when using this diagnostic process that only one change is made at a time. For example, if both a cable and a device are replaced at the same time and when the system is retested the problem has gone away, there is no way to know whether it was the cable, the device, or both that were causing the problem in the first place.

Simplification

By reconfiguring a system to a more simplified connection path, it is possible to effectively remove external variables that could be compounding the problem and increasing the difficulty to troubleshoot the system. Prior to implementation of this procedure, it is important to remember to document the system completely before proceeding. Make a record of all equipment settings, levels, and component connections. If this procedure does not provide a solution, you will need to restore the system to its original state.

Remember to only make one change at a time and test the system in between changes. This will allow for troubleshooting the system at the same time it is being simplified. If a device or cable is removed and the system begins working properly, there is a very high likelihood that the last device removed was the problem.

Deductive Reasoning

"When you have eliminated the impossible, whatever remains, however improbable, must be the truth" -Sir Arthur Conan Doyle. In other words, as various hypotheses are tested, the pool of possible causes will begin to narrow down until ultimately the process comes to and confirms the actual cause of the problem.

Document All Steps

As the diagnostic process progresses and hypothesis are tested, it is of the utmost importance to document the steps taken. Documentation will reduce the expense of needless time and energy repeating the same tests or steps. It is important to remember that the troubleshooting progress may exceed a single visit and documentation can prevent double work due to duplicating previously performed tests. In addition, it provides a great starting point for any future technicians who may become involved in this project, as it helps them understand what has already been done.

Save all documentation created during the troubleshooting process as it may prove useful in future troubleshooting scenarios. If, in the future, a similar problem occurs, it may be possible to implement the same steps and locate the problem more efficiently. Troubleshooting documentation can also be used as a training tool for new technicians in the future.

Troubleshooting documents may include the following types of items:

- Work Order with Explanation of the Problem. Always document the site visit, describing the problem that existed and the resolution that was used. This document should also list any components installed or replaced during this visit with the appropriate serial numbers.
- As-Built Drawings or Cabling Diagrams. If changes are made to the system layout, wiring or components during the site visit, all affected documentation and as-built drawings should be updated for future use
- Product Manuals
- Building Blueprints

Keep all documentation with the equipment from the un-boxing process to delivery and sign-off; including all small, extra parts that were included.

When the job is complete, it is highly recommended to combine all manuals and cut-sheets into a binder with instructions for the customer. Include how to clean and care for touchpanels and equipment (filters, bulbs), as well as contact information for future service needs. Clients should be instructed to keep the binder with the equipment so that it is easily accessible on future visits.

Repair

Once the problem has been located, the third step in troubleshooting is to correct or repair the problem. Depending on the type of problem, it is possible that a faulty piece of equipment or an entire component may need to be repaired or replaced. Determine the best solution based on the part of the system causing the problem.

- Hardware
- Repair
- Replace
- Software/Firmware
- Update or reprogram
- Design
- Rewire/Reconnect
- Ensure the solution is implemented accurately
- Document changes

Hardware: Repairs

Consider these key factors when determining how to make the repair.

- Determine if the item should be replaced or repaired. If the component is old or inexpensive, it may be more cost-efficient to replace the item than to repair it. Check the documentation for the product to determine if it is still under warranty. Keep in mind that many warranties are void if the component is opened or repairs are attempted by anyone other than an authorized repair center.
- Ensure the job is done correctly. If the proper technique is unknown, ask for assistance from another professional. No one wants to have another problem because of an incomplete/incorrect repair.
- Determine the time requirements for the repair. The goal is to be as unobtrusive as possible in a client 's life. If the repair is extensive, it may be beneficial to repair it off-site and return it to the client's site later. If the repair is not too time-consuming, or cannot be moved, be sure to clean up the mess made during the repair, and restore the client 's location to the condition in which it was found.
- If the component needs to be returned for replacement or repair, make sure you have a replacement unit or a substitution, that way the client doesn't experience excessive down time.

Always keep the client informed of the repair or replacement, so he or she knows exactly what was done and why. It is also important at this point to provide any necessary training to the client. This is especially important if the problem was due to something the client did or could have prevented, or if any new equipment has been installed.

Prior to implementing a solution, make sure there is an agreement on any charges that will result from the repair. If there will be a charge, be sure to get a signed authorization.

It may be possible to repair a piece of equipment or bad cable on site if the problem is blown fuses, iffy wiring or clogged air vents, but if an RMA is necessary, advise the customer of the time frame. If an RMA, return material authorization is needed; the authorization should be obtained while in the field. Many manufacturers require that the technician "call" while on site; so that they may ensure that the problem is not coincidental with any other conditions. Failure to follow this step may result in a trip back to the site, reinstalling the device and re-testing before it can sent back for repair. Check to see if it is possible to get them a loaner during the repair time.

Hardware: Replacement

If replacement is necessary, determine what, if any, changes will need to be made to the programming, connections and documentation; depending on whether of not the same model is available. If changes do become necessary, allow for additional time to complete the programming, cabling and documentation changes. Confirm that IP, IR, or RS-232 modules are available.

Software

Software or firmware updates may be available to fix known issues. Always check with the manufacturer to see if a fireware update is available prior to attempting to repair or replace a device. Also, be sure to discuss the impact of any firmware updates with the manufacturer before simply implementing the new software.

Programming issues such as buffer overflows are possible over time. Check control processor for error logs. Always remember to back up programming files while on-site prior to making changes to the system.

Design

In some situations, it may be necessary to alter the original system design in order to get the system to operate properly.

An example of this situation could be a grandfathered, first generation HDMI receiver installed with all new sources and a new flat panel that's having problems processing HDCP with the new devices around it. In this case, the best solution may be to reroute the HDMI signal from the sources around the receiver directly to the TV and then use an optical or digital coax cable to the receiver for audio.

It is critical that whenever faced with changing the original design of the system, a full evaluation of all aspects that the change may affect is performed. This includes updates to remote programs, charges for additional/new cabling, and especially documentation changes/updates.

Documentation

As mentioned previously, it is extremely important to document the repair or replacement. This includes documenting changes on as-built diagrams as well as any other appropriate places within the job folder. Also be sure to update warranties or service contracts.

Keep a copy of the updated documentation on file, and leave a copy with the client. This will ensure the information is available for future warranty claims on the equipment, as well as to assist in any future troubleshooting scenarios. Make sure the documentation is detailed, and provides information about the actual problem and the scenario surrounding it.

Verify

It is important to perform verification testing of the equipment after the repair has been completed. This process will make sure the system works properly and the repair or replacement that was performed really fixed the problem. Check to ensure that the repaired or newly installed equipment performs as designed for the system.

The repair verification testing is similar to the testing that should be done for each new installation. Specifically, test the repair by recreating the environment in which the problem first surfaced. The circumstances may not be typical for the test environment; however, recreating those circumstances is the only way to ensure the repair has eliminated the problem.

Once it has been established that the problem has been corrected, it is important to recalibrate and verify performance of the entire system. Be sure and reach out and touch all systems. Do not assume that the repairs performed on one system or device could in no way affect anything else. Remember the old adage referring to "assuming". Prior to leaving the jobsite, the system should be performing as intended.

Workarounds

In some cases, there may be a limited number of things that can be done on-site to correct a problem. Typically these actions should be assessed as to which are the most likely to fix the problem as well as the most simple to complete. In some cases these corrective measures only get a system working for a single instance of a problem, in other words, they are workarounds. These workarounds may not be acceptable to a customer. For example, when dealing with HDMI, unplugging and then plugging a cable back in or initiating a power up/down sequence may free up a stuck HDMI port on an HDTV, but if the HDTV exhibited that problem once, it is likely to reoccur. Therefore, the "I've got sound and picture" test may not be an adequate indication that the repair will be permanent.

Replacing cables, equipment or updating firmware may be more involved than some of the workarounds previously discussed but are solutions that are much more likely to resolve the problem permanently.

An important thing to remember is that test equipment can confirm the root cause of a problem and verify that a solution is not simply a work-around.

Customer satisfaction is the ultimate test! Be sure to check in with the customer to make sure the problem is resolved. Don't forget the importance of asking questions, and possibly providing additional training.

Prevent

After the repair is complete, take steps to prevent and defend against future problems. Clients are not happy if the same or similar problem occurs soon after it was repaired.

The types of preventative measures that can be implemented will depend on the system and the original problem that was repaired. General maintenance is always a good idea, as well as client training.

Maintenance

Some equipment and components require regular maintenance, such as changing filters or lubricating components. It is a good idea to perform this type of maintenance while on-site at the client's location. Also consider creating a checklist of general maintenance that should be performed. This checklist should list the frequency of the maintenance as well as the items that may require maintenance.

Example Checklist

1. Clean all equipment
2. Test all connections
3. Battery checks (remotes, UPS, etc.)
4. Physical inspection (dust, rust, cracks, IR emitters) – "white glove" test
5. Tidy wires
6. Firmware upgrades
7. Reboot devices
8. Clean equipment (screens, vents, dust, speakers)
9. Review system logs
10. Backup all programs
11. Check temperatures
12. General check of all functionality (lighting, alarm, AV, etc., shades, keypads, speakers)

Other common preventative maintenance ideas include:

- Removing dust from all electronic components.
- Ensuring there is adequate air flow around all electronic components.
- Removing items that may be stacked on top of the devices, such as DVDs, CDs, etc.
- Ensure all connections to all components are tight.
- Change any filters as appropriate.
- Lubricate any components that require lubrication.

These issues may not have caused the current problem, but if left unattended, they may cause future problems. This is also a good time to make sure all other parts of the system are meeting specifications.

Maintenance Recommended Practices

It is important to establish and follow a set of standard operating procedures when performing a maintenance call. Creating a checklist of maintenance steps for every technician to follow will ensure that all customers receive the same treatment and that a small unnoticed problem does not become a full blown system failure.

Having a carbon copy of the checklist to give to the customer can be an excellent added value piece. This will show the customer all of the work being done and help them to see the value of continued maintenance.

Client Training

Educating the client on a few key indicators that may be built into the equipment they have purchased can streamline the service process. If remote diagnostics are not an option, making the customer aware of error lights can help them pre-diagnose the system and save you time on service calls.

Common equipment with indicator lights:

- Projectors
- Amplifiers
- Power products
- Network switches
- Equipment network cards

If the original problem was the result of misuse by the client or a lack of understanding by the client, then training is critical to prevent the same issue from occurring again. Take time to educate the client in the proper use of the equipment, or in how to avoid causing damage to the equipment.

Proper client orientation is important, whether it is during a service call or after finalizing the initial installation. By taking the time to ensure the customer understands their system and showing patience while answering all of their questions, the likelihood of avoiding phone calls later will be exponentially increased. Recommending that your client take notes during orientation can be very helpful. Many companies will write out system instructions which can be very effective. However notes taken by the client during orientation tend to be more helpful as these notes are written in a language and style more attuned to the client.

Client orientation can be time consuming (especially on larger projects) so be sure to include this consideration when evaluating how to charge your customers. It is recommended to include a few training sessions with the initial contract as well as including them in service contracts during regular maintenance. Be sure to make the client aware that if they do not opt for a service contract they will have to pay for your time to re-train them later.

Remote Diagnostics

There are many methods of remote diagnostics that can be incorporated into a system in order to receive alerts about temperature issues, projector bulb life and communication interruptions. By utilizing the ability to monitor a system remotely, it may be possible to preemptively correct problems before the customer even knows they have occurred.

Troubleshooting a system remotely is much the same as troubleshooting a system when physically on site. The first place to begin is with the basics.

- Hard/Soft reboots
- Basic network troubleshooting
- Try to emulate problem remotely
- Check system logs

Once these common issues have been ruled out, move on to troubleshooting individual devices on the network.

During this phase of the troubleshooting process:

- Look at device online status
- Check command flow
- Send manual commands to test response

There are many tools available when dealing with IP connected equipment. These tools have been around for a long time and are free for anyone to use or troubleshoot with.

Common IT diagnostic tools include:

- Remote desktop solutions
- Remote support solutions
- Remote access (VPN, SSH, Telnet, Port Fwd.)
- Standard network troubleshooting tools
- WiFi sniffer /analyzer (inSSIDer for example)

In addition to the common software and IT troubleshooting tools, many manufacturers have their own software that is designed to troubleshoot and diagnose problems with their products. For more information on these types of software, taking courses provided by specific manufacturers is highly recommended. These manufacturer product trainings can offer a wealth of knowledge and are oftentimes, free.

Along with the "right now" troubleshooting tools, these software solutions can also provide long term reporting and historical insight into how a system is behaving and what may have caused the problem.

All of these tools put together can provide an extremely powerful diagnostic system that will allow for the opportunity to provide the ultimate care and support to your customers.

CHAPTER 10

NETWORKING FUNDAMENTALS

In recent years, the network has emerged as the backbone of just about everything an integrator does in the home. Therefore it is critical that every company have someone who is well-versed in network design and configuration. The three chapters found in this book provide an overview of CEDIA's network training track, but does not attempt to be a comprehensive source of all needed knowledge. They will, however, assist someone in preparation for the ESC-N certification, and will be a great resource for technicians and designers as they learn more about this critical topic

By definition, a network is a collection of computing devices connected by a physical infrastructure. Networks can be broadly defined on the basis of scope, topology, protocol and architecture. Active devices (devices powered by electricity) connected to the network are referred to as nodes.

NETWORK SCOPE

The scope of a network is defined by the size of area it which it operates:

Personal Area Network (PAN)

A network used by devices to communicate on a personal scale such as devices within a room, on a desk, in a car or on a person. Range is usually limited to around 10m and includes the following technologies:

- Bluetooth (Wireless Radio)

- IrDA (Infrared)
- ZigBee (Wireless Radio). Also applicable for LAN usage.
- 6LoWPAN (Wireless Radio) - Ipv6 over Low Power Wireless Personal Area Networks

Local Area Network (LAN)

A network covering a contained geographic area such as a house, office, campus or factory. These networks are typically high bandwidth and includes the following technologies:

- Wi-Fi (IEE 802.11)
- Ethernet (IEE 802.3)

Municipal Area Network (MAN)

A typically wireless network covering a defined geographic area. Today, these are considered 4G cellular Mobile Communications. Typically, the following technologies are used:

- WiMAX (IEEE 802.16m)
- LTE - Based upon GSM/EDGE and UMTS/HSPA cellular mobile communications

Wide Area Network (WAN)

A network spanning regions, countries or the globe. WANs can either be private, built by companies to allow for inter-office and inter-country communications, or they can be public built by Internet Service Providers (ISPs) providing a connection from the user's LAN to The Internet.

The

A global collection of interconnected WANs used by devices that all support a common protocol - TCP/IP

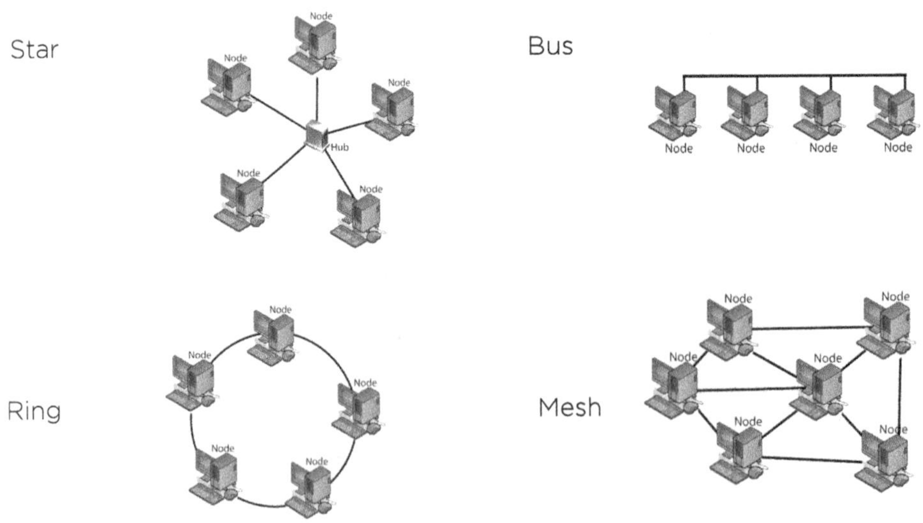

Figure 10-1. *Network Topologies*

CLASSIFICATION BY TOPOLOGY

Networks may be classified by their topology, the way the elements are arranged and connected. These topologies are shown in Figure 10-1.

Star Topology

A network with a star topology has a single central node that is connected to each end node (user) by a single, point-to-point link. Communication from one end user to another must pass through the central node, which coordinates all network traffic. The star topology by far the most used network topology used today, as Ethernet typically uses this topology.

Bus Topology

A network with a bus topology is arranged in a linear fashion where end nodes are connected to a single cable line. The line may be extended at either end to add new users to the network. Bus topology, though used for other communications standards such as RS485, is seldom now used for networking.

Ring Topology

Ring topology is one in which the network is essentially a closed loop, with no beginning or end. End nodes act as repeaters along the cable to enhance a signal as it comes across the network on its way to another destination. Ring topologies are now seldom used for networking.

Mesh

Networks with a mesh topology are designed with redundancy in mind. Devices are connected with many interconnections between end nodes, so that if any cable or node fails, there are other options for network traffic to reach its intended destination. Some wireless technologies, such as ZigBee, create mesh networks.

Backbones

Backbones are high-capacity parts of the network that collect traffic from smaller connected segments. A distributed backbone, which typically has a copper or fiber optic core, has a physical infrastructure connection between smaller network segments that are found in different locations. A collapsed backbone "collapses" the distribution network to the switch itself. This has the advantage that the backplane speed (the speed at which the ports connect to each other internally within the switch) is much higher than is possible over copper or even fiber Ethernet channels. A collapsed backbone topology will look like a star topology.

CLASSIFICATION BY PROTOCOL

The network protocol defines a common set of rules and signals that devices on the network use to communicate. The most common way to represent network protocols is the OSI Model (Open System Interconnection) as shown in Table 10-1.

Layers one through four are functions of the network whilst layers five to seven are usually functions of the device connected to the network and the software running on it. Data is passed down from layer to layer. Each protocol layer takes the data received and encapsulates it into its own data format. This takes the form of the layer adding a header and possibly a footer to the data it receives before passing it down to the layer below. Once the message gets to the physical layer, it is converted into electrical signals and passed through the network. At the receiving device, the process happens in reverse with each layer stripping off its part of the message until the data eventually gets to the application in its raw format again. See figure xx for an example of encapsulation within the TCP/IP model.

Transmission Control Protocol/Internet Protocol (TCP/IP)

TCP/IP is a collection of data communication protocols developed to standardize data transfer between systems and networks that were operating with dissimilar protocols. See Table 10-1 for an explanation of the different layers in the TCP/IP model.

The TCP/IP model consists of four layers with each layer having a specific set of responsibilities. Breaking the tasks into separate layers also simplifies troubleshooting and modification. The TCP/IP model has worked so well since it was started that with a few exceptions, it remains as it was originally designed and is the Internet standard.

The IP portion defines the means to identify and reach a target computer on the network, in this case, the World Wide Web. Each network node connected to the public Internet has a unique IP address that identifies it.

The TCP portion of the protocol provides the services enabling a computer to send data to a remote computer.

OSI (Open Systems Interconnect) Model

The International Organization of Standardization developed a standard in competition with the TCP/IP model. Their model breaks down data transfer services into seven layers to enable efficient management of services and future development. This model is known as the Seven Layer Model or the OSI (Open Systems Interconnect) Model, as shown in Table 10-1 and can be applied to any protocol. The OSI model is fee-based, whereas the TCP/IP model is open-source.

Both the TCP/IP and OSI models are extremely useful when problem solving a fault on a network. Always start from the bottom (Layer 1, Physical Layer) and work your way up. Protocols higher in the model depend on those lower in the model to work correctly. The first step in problem solving a network issue is to always check that the physical layer is operating correctly by using the correct test tool.

Table 10-1. *OSI Model and TCP/IP*

OSI Model	TCP/IP Model
Layer 7: Application Layer	
Layer 6: Presentation (or Syntax) Layer	Application
Layer 5: Session Layer	
Layer 4: Transport Layer	Transport
Layer 3: Network Layer	Internet
Layer 2: Data-Link Layer · LLC · MAC	· Network Access · AKA Network Interface
Layer 1: Physical Layer	

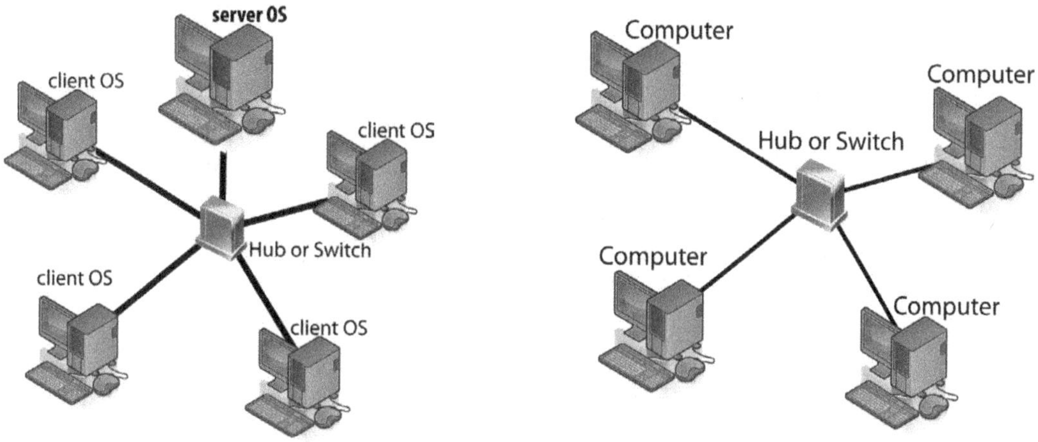

Client-Server Peer-to-Peer

Figure 10-2. *Network Architecture*

CLASSIFICATION BY ARCHITECTURE

Networks may be classified by the type of architecture they use:

Client-Server

The classic definition of a client-server network is where one computer is chosen to be a dedicated server (or "host"), which executes the main computer applications and delivers services back to the other computers on the network (clients), as shown in Figure 10-2. Clients get most or all of their information from the server, and they rely on the server to perform many tasks.

Peer-to-Peer

A peer-to-peer network (P2P) is one without a designated server, also shown in Figure 10-2. It allows all computers connected to the network to communicate and share resources (such as shared data, video and audio files, and printers) on one level, called a "peer-to-peer" level. The network simply provides the mechanism to allow the devices to communicate with each other. Most of the systems that we install in a home are peer to peer networks. Although there may be a server on the system for a specific sub system (such as a movie server), this is sharing the network with many other devices.

NETWORK TECHNOLOGIES

Ethernet

Ethernet is the most common type of networking technology used to connect networked devices together. It is a collection of standards defined by IEEE 802.3 that describe the Physical Layer (The signaling used over copper or fiber) and the Data Link Layer's Media Access Control (MAC). Ethernet usually uses a Star or Backbone physical topology.

Though Ethernet has used a number of different physical layer types in the past, today it is dominated by UTP (Unshielded Twisted Pair) copper cable. Fiber optic cable is often used for backbone connections over greater distances than possible with copper.

The speed of an Ethernet connection is defined by the standard used. Only the currently most used standards using UTP cable are listed.

100BaseTX

Uses one pair of twisted wires in each direction to provide 100Mb/s of throughout in each direction (Full-Duplex) using at least CAT5 cable. There is a maximum Ethernet channel length of 100M for all xBaseT standards.

1000BaseT (1GBaseT)

Uses all four pairs of twisted wires to provide 1000Mb/s of throughput in Full Duplex. CAT5 cable can be used but CAT5e or above is strongly recommended.

10GBaseT

Provides 10Gb/s of throughput. CAT6A cable is required to carry 10GBaseT over the full 100m Ethernet channel length. CAT6 cable can be used over much shorter distances but is not recommended.

Other standards exist for Ethernet over Fiber. Most Ethernet connected hardware uses auto-negotiation to set the highest speed and duplex supported by both connected devices at each end of the channel.

Power over Ethernet - IEEE 802.3at-2009

Is the current standard for Power over Ethernet (PoE). Equipment operating to this standard can pass power over the cable up to a maximum of

25.5W as well as the Ethernet data. Power is supplied by using either a PoE Ethernet Switch, or a mid-span Injector that sits between the Ethernet Switch and the device needing power. Uses include powering IP Cameras, VoIP (Voice over IP) Phones and Wireless Access Points. There are, and have been, many proprietary standards for PoE so ensure that the equipment you wish to use is compatible.

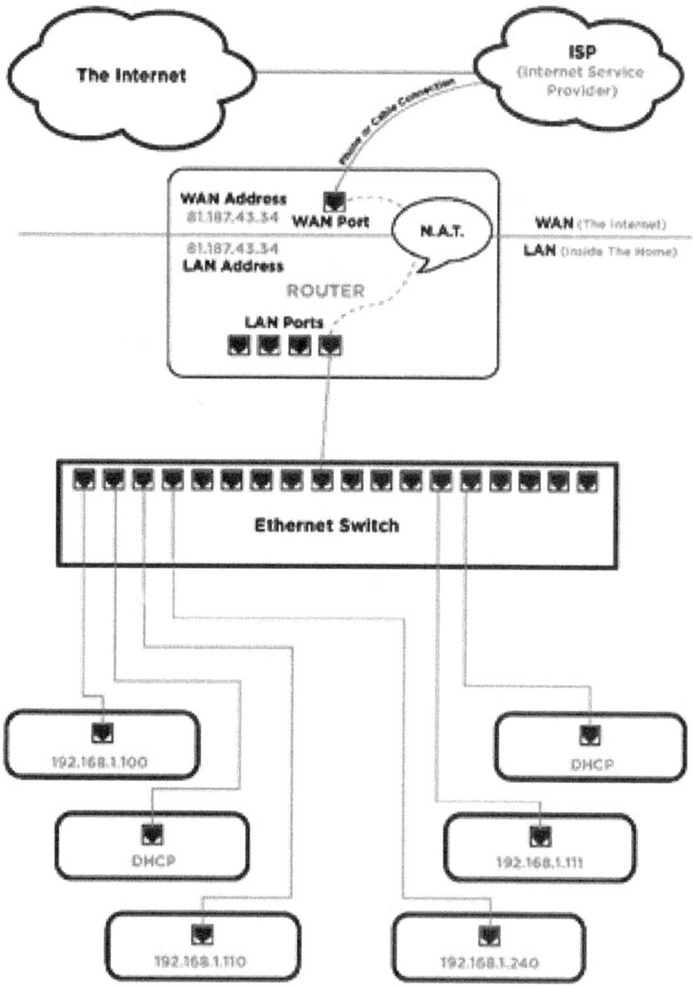

Figure 10-3. *Typical Home Network*

ACTIVE NETWORK COMPONENTS

There are a number of active (those that need an electricity supply to operate) components that are used to create a network.

Network Interface Cards

A network interface card (NIC) is installed into a device (such as a computer or printer) to communicate with a network. Acting as the point of connection between the device and the network, the NIC is designed to interface to a specific physical media such as twisted pair cable and optical fiber cable for Ethernet, or using wireless radio for Wi-Fi.

Hubs

The term hub is used in two ways. Generically, the term hub refers to a location which is a termination point for the network cables. A hub is also an active network device (largely obsolete now having being replaced by far more efficient switches) that takes data input on any port, regenerates and re-times it, and sends it out on all ports to all connected nodes. It is up to the node to determine if the data was meant for it or not.

Switches

A switch provides internal network connectivity between Ethernet devices. Although consumer routers have multiple ports built into them, it is advisable to use a single LAN port on the router and connect to a multi-port switch, which may offer up to 48 additional ports.

Several multi-port switches may be employed to accommodate the network as it grows in size. As the name implies, a switch looks at the data packet and sends the data to the desired attached node instead of just repeating it to all attached ports.

This data switching is accomplished by the switch mapping the location of each attached node's MAC address to its associated port on the switch. The switch only sends data specifically addressed to the MAC address out that port of the switch. This function reduces overall network traffic, and on Ethernet switches, great reduces the chance of a data collision and thus increases overall speed of the network. All switches are not created equal and there are large variations in both performance and functionality. Additional features that a switch may have include:

Layer 3 Switching - Most switches are what we call Layer 2 devices and switch the data based on the MAC address only (Layer 2 of the OSI model). Some switches are Layer 3 devices that function similarly to a router and look at the IP address attached to a data packet and makes switching decisions based on routing tables similar to network routers.

Managed Switch – All layer 3 switches are managed switches as they have the ability to be configured. Not all managed switches are layer 3, however as layer 2 switches can also have the following functionality:

VLAN (Virtual LAN) – Where configured on a single switch, VLANs allow the single physical network to be split logically into a number of "virtual" networks. Devices can be grouped together not on the basis of either their physical location or the port on the switch that they are connected to. Each VLAN created on a switch is a separate network. This means that a separate broadcast domain is created for each VLAN that exists. Network broadcasts, by default, are filtered from all ports on a switch that are not members of the same VLAN and this is why VLANs are useful in keeping certain subsystems apart on a network so they do not interfere with each other.

Routers

A router (or gateway) is a network device that connects two networks together. The most common router in the home is one that connects the Internet to the LAN. A router will have one or more ports that connect to the WAN (or Internet) and one or more ports that connect to the LAN. Rules set in the router's configuration allow it to inspect packets of data and then take a decision on if to pass the packet from one network to another. Although there are many types of network protocols that can be routed, we generally associate routing with TCP/IP networks. A router is not needed on a LAN, but as soon as we need to interconnect the LAN with another network or the Internet, the router is the device we must have.

Types of Routers

ADSL Router/Modem - The WAN port is usually an RJ11 connector that connects to the phone line via an ASAL splitter. Though often called an ADSL router, they will have an ADSL MODEM built in. These routers typically have one WAN ADSL port and four LAN ports. It is good practice to connect only one of the LAN connections to a switch to allow for the required number of Ethernet connected devices.

Ethernet Router - The WAN port is an Ethernet (RJ45) port. This type of router is often used to connect a Cable Modem to the LAN.

NETWORK ADDRESSING

Media Access Control (MAC) Address

The Media Access Control (MAC) address is a globally unique 40-bit address consisting of a manufacturer's code and a serial number. This is comparable to a citizen's social security number in that no two citizens (or computers) will have the same number/address. There are 281 trillion possible combinations. The MAC address provides networked devices the ability to communicate directly with each other using a switch. The switch keeps a table (directory) of the devices connected to it using the MAC address. When the switch receives a transmission request, the table is checked and a virtual connection between the two devices is created. Networking using MAC addresses works well on local area networks where information on locally attached devices can be easily stored and accessed, but when interconnection to larger networks is required, the MAC addressing scheme does not lend itself to be easily routed. The need to internetwork many dissimilar networks located across the nation required the development of a new network addressing method.

IP Network addressing

Is the ability of the network to identify a node, much like a postal worker identifies a house by its address. There are several protocols that can be applied to network addressing, but the most common is the TCP/IP suite of protocols. An IP address is assigned to each device to be connected to the network and it consists of a series of numbers separated by dots or periods, for example: 174.24.61.13.

Internet Protocol (IP)

IP addresses are used to identify data as it travels across a network or the Internet. Every device connected to a network (including Web and e-mail servers, PCs, and web-enabled telephones) must have a unique IP address. This unique address makes it possible for two devices on the Internet to locate each other. The Internet is one network so every device directly connected to The Internet must have a unique IP address.

An IP (IPv4) address is a series of four-sets of three numbers between 0 and 255, separated by periods. Each of these four numbers is called an octet, as each number is an 8-bit binary word, or one byte. Another example of an IPv4 address would be 192.168.1.100

Because of the pending depletion of available IPv4 addresses, IPv6 was released to increase the number of devices can have a unique IP address. IPv6 uses eight groups of four hexadecimal digits separated by colons allowing it support approximately 340 Undecillion or 3.4×1038 addresses. An example of an IPv6 address would be 2002:0db7:85a2:0000:0000:8a2c:0371:7335. Efforts are ongoing to transition from IPv4 to IPv6 addressing, and you should be seeing that most of the newer network devices will support both addressing schemes. However, for the purposes of this manual, network addressing information will be based on IPv4 only as it will be at least 2016 until we start seeing IPv6 addressing in the home.

IP Addressing

Private and Public Addresses

Most IP addresses are what are known as public addresses, meaning they are unique and assigned for use on the public Internet. However, a number of addresses have been reserved for use on private networks where the nodes are not directly connected to the public Internet. The Internet Assigned Numbers Authority (IANA) has set aside addresses just for this use to prevent possible conflicts. These addresses will never be used or found on the public Internet.

The router connecting the Internet to the home LAN has two IP addresses. The address on the WAN port is a public address that is usually allocated by the ISP (Internet Service Provider) whilst the Router's LAN address will fall into one of the three ranges discussed below. The only IP address visible from the Internet is the WAN IP address.

Routers designed for small networks use a technique known as Network Address Translation (NAT) to allow traffic from multiple private IP addresses to use a single public address. NAT ensures that when a device on the LAN wishes to communicate with a device or server on the Internet, the router 'translates' the LAN address of the device into the WAN address of the router for communication over the Internet. Once the requested data has returned to the router from the Internet, NAT then forwards this data to the device that requested it.

It should be noted the NAT works well with most Internet services, but there are a few services that require a direct connection to an internal private address that may not like being translated through the NAT process.

Private Addresses

As mentioned, all devices on the IP network must have a MAC address and an IP address bound to it. Because networks, even private ones, vary in size, several classes of addresses were reserved for private use.

Class (number of nodes in block) – Range of addresses

- *1 - Class A (16.8 million)* — 10.0.0.0 through 10.255.255.255
- *16 - Class B (1 Million)* — 172.16.0.0 through 172.31.255.255
- *256 - Class C (65,536)* — 192.168.0.0 through 192.168.255.255

Network devices do not use the 0 and 255 addresses. For instance, you would never give a device an address of 192.168.1.0. Here's why:

- 255 in the last octet is a Broadcast Address – A packet sent to, for instance, 192.168.1.255 will be sent to every device on the network as a broadcast.
- 0 in the last octet would be used to Identify the Network – For instance, 192.168.1.0 identifies the 192.168.1.x network.

IP Address Allocation

A device may be given a ***static*** (fixed) or a ***dynamic*** address. Static addresses are entered manually into devices and are used when you require the IP address of a device to be constant through its operation. For instance, you may wish to allocate a media streamer a static IP address in order to control it over IP from a control processor. The processor needs to know which IP address to always send packets to when controlling that particular Media Streamer. When inputting a static IP address, you will need to enter an IP address, subnet mask, gateway address and DNS server address.

Dynamic Host Configuration Protocol

Dynamic Host Configuration Protocol (DHCP) allows for allocating IP addresses dynamically so that addresses can be reused. When these IP addresses are no longer needed, they are released and reused when a new request for an IP address is received. DHCP is a service of TCP/IP and provides a method for individual devices to request and obtain a temporary IP address.

As well as for use on a LAN, many Internet Service Providers (ISPs) use DHCP to provide users with a reusable IP address. When the user's router connects to the Internet using a cable modem, DSL, or dial-up access, the router makes a request for a public address from the ISP. The ISP owns a block of addresses, so the ISP assigns the IP address for that connection time. This is a unique, but temporary, address. This recycling of IP addresses allows a large number of nodes to share a limited pool of addresses.

There should only be one device, like a router, providing DCHP services on a local area network. If more than one exists, a duplicate or un-routable address may be assigned to a node causing a connection failure. Most devices are initially set up to receive their IP addressing information from a DHCP server, so you will need to override this setting in the device's configuration if you want to assign static IP addresses. The DHCP server will typically assign the device's IP address, subnet mask, gateway address, and DNS server addresses, although a DHCP server can be set up to assign additional parameters as well.

When setting up a home router that will act as the DHCP server for the network, it is important to reserve a range of IP addresses that will be used as the DHCP pool of addresses. This ensures that the DHCP server will never give out an IP address in the range that you might be using for static IP addressing. Two devices on a network may NEVER have the same IP address.

The Subnet Mask

An IP address has two components; the network address, and the host address. A subnet mask separates the IP address into the network and host addresses. A '1' in a subnet mask sets network bits, and a '0' sets host bits. The most common subnet mask used in the home is 255.255.255.0

As each octet of an IP address is an 8 bit word, writing out the above subnet mask in binary and applying it to an IP address of 192.168.1.100 gives us:

Table 10-2. *Subnet Masking Detail*

	Binary Notation	Decimal Notation
IP Address	11000000.10101000.00000001.01100100	192.168.1.100
Subnet Mask	11111111.11111111.11111111.00000000	255.255.255.0
Network Prefix	11000000.10101000.00000001.00000000	192.168.1.0
Host part of address	00000000.00000000.00000000.01100100	0.0.0.100

A device will use its subnet mask to determine what network another device it wishes to communicate with is on. The device will apply its subnet mask to the IP address of the other device. If the network prefix of the other device is the same as the network prefix of its own IP address, then the two devices can simply communicate over the same network. If the network prefixes are not the same, the device will need to communicate via the router, as that is the only device on the network with connectivity to another network (usually the internet). When configuring a device with its settings, the gateway address is the LAN address of the router.

If you ever encounter a LAN that uses a subnet mask other than 255.255.0.0 or 255.255.255.0 for its devices, it is best to consult a qualified network specialist.

IP Address Lookup

Even though we have become quite good at remembering telephone numbers, it is known that people remember names much easier than a series of numbers like an IP address. To allow IP addresses to be referenced by a name, a service known as the Domain Name System (DNS) stores an online database of host names and addresses and converts the host name you enter into the IP address required by your network device to make a connection. For example, an organization such as CEDIA would have an address of www.cedia.net instead of 66.39.126.203.

The Domain Name System is a hierarchy of DNS servers that store and forward domain name information as it is request by a local computer. The IP address of your local DNS server is part of the network information you will need, to properly setup a device on a network. It is considered good practice to always reference two or more nearby DNS servers in the network setup, to allow for fast response even if one of the servers fails. Without a DNS server to resolve web names, also called uniform resource locators (URLs), connections to other network nodes cannot be found and the device fails to make a connection.

TCP and UDP

The TCP in TCP/IP stands for Transmission Control Protocol. Whereas IP handles the actual delivery of the data, TCP is the protocol that keeps track of the data and guarantees delivery. It will deal with timeouts, out of order delivery, lost packets and re-transmissions. It is called a reliable delivery protocol. Due to all the overhead that TCP requires to ensure integrity of the messages, it does not guarantee timely delivery and is therefore not always suitable for time critical applications such as video streaming or video conferencing. For these applications, UDP (User Datagram Protocol) is often used. UDP is a best effort protocol and does not guarantee delivery. It is, however, faster than TCP due to reduced overheads and no error-checking.

Table 10-3. *TCP vs. UDP*

TCP	UDP
Guaranteed delivery through error correction (segment retransmission, flow control, and segment acknowledgement)	No error correction makes for faster speed than TCP
Connection-oriented · Requires a logical connection to be established between two devices before transferring data.	Connectionless · Protocols do not establish a connection between devices. · As soon as a device has data to send to another, it sends it.
Commonly used for streaming audio and video. Because UDP is concerned only with speed, streaming media does not always have high quality	Commonly used to send important data such as webpages and database information.

SERVICES AND PORTS

A device with a single IP address is able to run many services simultaneously all connecting to and communicating on the network. Services include web browsing, sending e-mails, receiving e-mails, sending E-Mails and FTP. Messages intended for a certain service are tagged with a port number. The IANA (Internet Assigned Numbers Authority) is responsible for the coordination of port numbers for Internet services. Port numbers ranges are broken down into three ranges, well-known ports, registered ports and dynamic ports.

Examples of well-known ports include:

- Port 25 – SMTP (Simple Mail Transfer Protocol). Used for sending e-mails
- Port 110 – POP (Post Office Protocol). Used for receiving e-mails
- Port 143 – IMAP (Internet Message Access protocol). Used for receiving e-mails
- Port 80 – HTTP (Hypertext Transfer Protocol). Used to render web pages.

Examples of registered ports include:

- Port 1319 – Used by AMX
- Port 41794 – Used by Crestron

Firewalls can be set up to allow incoming connections based on the port number of the service. This, for instance, could be set up so that when a firewall (inside a home router) receives an Internet request on Port 80, it forwards this request to an IP address on the LAN for an IP camera. This will then allow the camera to be viewed from the internet.

SECURING THE NETWORK

Securing networks is a critical installation process and must be considered for every network. The installation of software to protect against viruses and other destructive bugs must be set in place prior to accessing the Internet.

Some of the more common threats include:

- Viruses, worms, and Trojan horses
- Identity theft
- Spam and scams
- Phishing schemes
- Spyware

VIRUSES, WORMS, AND TROJAN HORSES

Viruses, worms, and Trojan horses are all considered ***malware***, or malicious software. This software is designed to cause damage or disrupt a single computer or a whole network. Some malware may be more dangerous than others. A ***virus*** is a self-replicating program that spreads itself by inserting copies of itself into other program code or documents.

Viruses can only spread when computer systems interact in some way, such as when communicating over a network or the Internet, or sharing media storage items such as CDs and flash drives. Once spread, the virus tends to cause some type of damage, such as overwriting files, deleting files, accessing private information, and sending it to others, or just using up the computer processing power so that it cannot work as intended. Viruses need some sort of program or document (known as a host) to replicate itself.

A ***worm*** is similar to a virus in that it uses computer networks and security holes to replicate itself. One difference, however, is that a worm does not need to be a part of another program to run itself. Worms often are designed to exploit certain security holes that can be found in many software programs. Like a virus, in addition to replicating itself, a worm is likely to cause specific damage to a computer.

A ***Trojan horse*** is software that disguises itself as legitimate software, but is actually malicious. Unlike viruses and worms, a Trojan horse does not replicate itself. The software appears to be valid, so an unsuspecting user may install the software. A common disguise is a "helpful" toolbar addition to the browser. Once the software is installed, it does something other than expected. Some of the common functions are to collect information (such as passwords or account numbers) or to install a backdoor on the computer, which makes it easy for someone to gain access to the system later.

IDENTITY THEFT

Identity theft is the process of assuming someone else's identity, usually for financial purposes. Identity theft generally involves stealing credit card or banking information in order to withdraw money or apply for additional credit cards. Identity theft can leave a person's credit score ruined and leave behind large amounts of debt.

Some malware programs are responsible for gathering this information. A virus or Trojan may load a keystroke logging program onto the user's PC. This type of program might log every keystroke that the user makes in order to steal passwords and account numbers. The program then periodically transmits the gathered information back to the criminal.

In other cases, the hacker may capture the information as it transmits from one computer to another over unprotected data lines. This is becoming more common as retail establishments, such as local coffee houses, switch to wireless networks.

Spam and Scams

Spam is unsolicited e-mail that is sent out in bulk to many e-mail addresses at once. Spam is usually a type of advertising. Large amounts of spam can slow down networks and increase processing time. Spam often includes links to websites that, when accessed by the user, will install spyware or viruses onto the computer. Some spam will imitate legitimate e-commerce websites and encourage the reader to buy a product that never arrives. Instead, the order forms are designed to capture the buyer's credit card information in order to perpetrate identity theft.

Phishing Schemes

Phishing is the process of directing someone to a website with the purpose of collecting personal information. The e-mail, which appears to be from a legitimate business with which the individual has a relationship (for example, a credit card company or bank) directs the victim to a false website.

The websites to which the victim is taken often look remarkably like the company's real website. They are so authentic in appearance that it is often very difficult, even for experts, to tell the difference.

The fake website then captures the information given and uses it to gain access to the individual's bank account, or to perpetrate identity theft. In addition to banks and credit unions experiencing this problem, other websites such as PayPal and eBay have been targeted. In response to this threat, banks and other major companies now advise against clicking on a link that appears in an e-mail. If users receive an e-mail requesting them to verify their account information or other similar request, they should open an Internet browser window and type the name of the website directly into the URL address field. This ensures that they are indeed going to the authentic website of the company, rather than a fake website.

Spyware

Spyware is a type of software that is loaded onto a computer typically without the user's knowledge. Sometimes, it comes bundled with another program that the user intends to install; other times, it is loaded when the user opens an attachment or clicks on a banner advertisement. Spyware does exactly what its name implies; it spies on the computer's activities. It may do nothing more than record which websites are visited, or what topics are searched for in order for a company to collect consumer behavior data. Frequently, this information is resold to bulk spammers and is used for "targeted spam marketing."

PROTECTION AGAINST NETWORK SECURITY THREATS

There are many tools in the arsenal against network threats. Some of the more common ways to combat them are:

- Proxy servers
- Firewalls
- Spam filtering
- Antivirus software
- Wireless Data Encryption (WEP)

A proxy server sits between an end customer application (such as a web browser) and a server on the Internet. Its function is to "pre-process" requests from the customer to see if the request can be handled locally; if not, the request is forwarded to the remote server. To do this, a proxy server keeps track of Internet activity in temporary files for a certain amount of time. If duplicate requests come in to the proxy server, it can fulfill the request with information that it has stored locally. This improves network performance and response time. Proxy servers can also be used to filter requests and block certain websites from being accessed on a network. A proxy server is unlikely to be implemented on a home LAN but there are companies on the Internet that offer this feature.

Firewalls

The easiest and least expensive hardware solution for many security threats is using a router with a firewall. A firewall is a device that uses a set of rules to allow or block network traffic. They protect the LAN from unauthorized access from the Internet (WAN) whilst allowing legitimate traffic to pass. Most home routers have firewalls built into them, so always ensure that you install a home router that has firewall functionality. In addition to the hardware solution of a firewall on a router, there are software versions of firewalls that allow parents to restrict access to specific types of content, and allow filtering of content based on certain flagged words.

Spam Filtering

Spam filtering programs are designed to limit the amount of spam e-mail that a user receives. Some of these are stand-alone programs, and some run as part of various e-mail applications. There are different ways of curbing the tide of spam e-mail. Some spam filtering software will not allow the user to receive any e-mail from an unknown source, thus requiring senders to fill out a request form along with their e-mail the first time they send an e-mail to the person with this service. The recipient must approve this form before they can accept e-mail from the sender.

Other types of programs will look for key words in the e-mail to determine if it is spam, and either stop the delivery, receive it into the Junk e-mail folder instead of the Inbox, or delete the message.

Antivirus Software

Antivirus programs work to stop viruses, worms, and Trojan horses. They can be configured to automatically scan all incoming e-mail for viruses, and to scan the whole computer regularly to ensure nothing is infected. Because hackers develop new viruses daily, antivirus companies publish daily fixes to their virus definitions that should be downloaded from the Internet to be sure the antivirus program will recognize all the current threats. Most antivirus programs perform this function at least once per day. Ensure that if antivirus software is used, that it is kept up to date.

NETWORK SECURITY

Now that you know about the potential threats that exist, how do you protect against them? No network can be protected completely. However, there are steps you can take to minimize the threat. These s suggestions can be organized into three categories:

- Hardware
- Software
- Wetware

Hardware Suggestions

- Enable all firewalls on all devices that support them.
- Use VPNs when possible or Port Address Translation (PAT) when not. Re-number ports to less common ports to prevent hackers from discovering them.
- Configure routers so their configuration settings cannot be accessed via the WAN port.
- Change all default passwords to something not publicly posted on the Internet.
- Change the default SSID and add a password. Use WPA2, WPA, or WEP in that descending order.

- Be sure you know where all network cabling terminates and be sure no jacks are left on that you don't intend to have left on. This prevents hackers from entering a place of business and plugging their notebook into a network jack.
- Configure a VLAN on wired and wireless public-access networks to separate them from your main business network.
- Do not use inexpensive consumer routers. They can be hacked easily and are often unreliable.
- Keep all firmware and software up to date on all devices to match and fix new security risks before they can be exploited.

Software Suggestions

- Install antivirus software, turn on firewalls, and set up limited user accounts.
- Configure software applications to for automatic updates. This includes the firewall, operating systems, and antivirus and other software installed on all computers.
- If a company runs FTP, mail, and web hosting services in house, consider sourcing them to companies designed to accommodate them.

Wetware Suggestions

"Wetware" refers to the users of the network. Even though your client (or wetware) has the intent of providing security to the network, they are also the biggest security risks to it. To minimize the risk advise them to:

- Follow safe browsing habits. Be concerned about where you browse, just as you're careful what parts of town you drive through.
- Decrease reliance on antivirus programs. Just as the black box or airbag won't save you from driving off of a cliff, an antivirus program will not stop your client from making improper security choices.
- Do not download files from people you do not know.
- Do not depend on your client to secure their system. Build it in. For example, use automatic updates, so your client is not accountable for additional network security that can be handled automatically by hardware or software.

What to Do if All Else Fails

- Disconnect from the Internet.
- Turn off the computer to isolate the virus and prevent infecting the network.
- Contact an IT specialist.

NETWORKING PCS AND HOME AUTOMATION DEVICES

Networking is the process of connecting devices on a network (Ethernet or 802.11x) so they can communicate data, information, resources, and files. There are various methods of networking PCs, as well as different levels of networking. For example, the Internet is one big network, where computers around the world are connected in such a way that information can be shared. This section will discuss some of the aspects of home networking that are important to the homeowner, and therefore the integrator.

AVAILABLE INTERNET CONNECTION SERVICES

There are different ways to connect to the Internet:

- Telephone Modem
- Broadband Internet Access (DSL, Cable Modem, and Satellite)
- Not all methods are available in all locations. Generally, larger cities have access to more options than people who live in rural areas.

Telephone Modem

A telephone modem is a device that allows transmission of digital data over an existing telephone circuit. The data is modulated into an analog signal and transmitted over the telephone line. The signal is then demodulated into a digital data signal at the receiving end. Using this method, the computer must be hardwired to the modem that is connected to the telephone line. An Internet Service Provider (ISP) must provide a call-in number to access the ISP computer system for connectivity to the Internet. This method of connecting to the Internet is often referred to as "dial-up" or "narrow band" and is seldom used now as most people have access to a Broadband Internet service.

Broadband Internet Access

Broadband access is often referred to as "high-speed access." Broadband Internet Access speeds vary from around 2 Mbps up to 1 Gbps in some parts of the world. Speed is dependent on the type of network being used, as well as the distance from the broadband equipment to the customer's home.

The most common types of broadband technology are:

- Digital Subscriber Line (DSL)
- Cable Modem
- FTTH - Fiber To The Home

Each type of service requires special equipment and has its own advantages and disadvantages.

Digital Subscriber Line (DSL)

Service uses a DSL modem connected to a telephone line to provide Internet service, without the installation of a second phone line. The same phone line may be used for traditional voice calls, but a low-pass filter must be installed to filter out the digital signals. Normal voice calls may be made and received while the network is simultaneously connected to the Internet. DSL Services are usually Asymmetric Digital Subscriber Lines (ADSL) meaning that the download speed is greater than the upload speeds. Speeds vary from around 2Mbps up to 24Mbps for ADSL2+.

In some regions, VDSL (Very High Speed Digital Subscriber Line) is available where the connection from the exchange to the cabinet in the street is a fiber optic connection. The connection from The Home to the cabinet is then made with existing telephone twisted pair cable. Maximum real-world speed for a VDSL connection is around 50Mbps.

Cable Television Service Companies

Provide Internet access using a cable modem connected to the cable line entering the home. The cable modem should then be connected to an Ethernet Router to enable the connection to be shared amongst multiple devices. This router should also offer firewall functionality. The Internet signal is handled on a different frequency than the standard television signal, and generally provides high-speed, reliable connectivity. Typical connection speeds can range from 2Mbps up to 100Mbps.

Connecting to the Internet Service Provider

Most Internet Service Providers (ISPs) require that subscribers enter a user name and password each time they log into the provider's services. Normally, the Modem/Router (For DSL services) or the Ethernet Router (For Cable Services) provides this functionality. These devices have the capability to keep the connection 'Always On.' As well as enabling near instant access to the Internet form any devices on the LAN, this will also keep the connection open to access the Home from the Internet. This may be useful to access resources in the home from the Internet, as well as to allow remote diagnostics and programming.

CHAPTER 11

WIRELESS NETWORKING IN THE HOME

A wireless network connects computers, printers, gaming consoles, home theater systems, network storage devices, surveillance cameras and monitoring systems without cumbersome cabling. In place of cables, a wireless network uses radio waves to send and receive data, similar to cell phones, televisions, and radios. This implementation takes place at the physical level (layer) of the OSI model network structure.

RF SPECTRUM

The radio-frequency (RF) spectrum consists of electromagnetic radiation and frequency bands. In North America, three unlicensed radio bands are used for IEEE 802.11 wireless LAN transmissions.

- 2.4 GHz band — More densely populated by wireless LAN devices, providing the potential for more interference among competing devices in this band.
- 5 GHz band — Less populated, with more room (about 20 MHz) per channel than the 2.4 GHz band.
- 60 GHz band — Newest spectrum to relieve potential congestion in the 2.4 GHz and 5 GHz bands.

WIRELESS PROTOCOLS

Table 11-1 *Wireless Protocols*

Protocol	Description
IEEE 802.11a	· Frequency Band: 5 GHz · Speed: 54 Mbps. · Range: 100 ft.
IEEE 802.11b	· Frequency Band: 2.4 GHz · Speed: 11 Mbps. · Range: 100 ft.
IEEE 802.11g	· Frequency Band: 2.4 GHz · Speed: 54 Mbps. · Range: 125 ft.
IEEE 802.11n	The most widely available wireless standard. · Backward-compatible with 802.11a, b, and g. · Frequency Band: 2.4 GHz and 5 GHz. · Speed: 600 Mbps.
IEEE 802.11ac	· Frequency Band: 5 GHz. · Speed: 1 Gbps. · Range: 90 ft. · Backward-compatible with 802.11a, b, g, and n.
IEEE 802.11ad	Newest IEEE standard. · Frequency Band: 60 GHz. · Speed: 7 Gbps. · Range: 3 - 33 ft.
ZigBee	Short-range wireless technology. Based on the IEEE 802.15.4 personal-area network (PAN) radio standard. · Frequency Band: 5 GHz. · Speed: 250 Kbps. · Range: 33 - 328 ft. line of sight.
Bluetooth	Short-range wireless technology using UHF radio waves. · Frequency Band: 2400 - 2483.5 GHz · Speed: 24 Mbps · Range: 16 - 98 ft.
Z-wave	Short-wave mesh-networking technology added to the ITU G.9959 standard. Supports up to 232 nodes. · Frequency Band: 908.42 MHz · Speed: 9.4/40 Mbps · Range: 98.4 ft.

WIRELESS NETWORK COMPONENTS

The following devices are common in a wireless network:

Table 11-2 *Wireless Network Devices*

Device	Description
Modem or gateway	· Connects the home network to the Internet. · A gateway combines a modem and router in one device. · Modems and gateways can be rented from the ISP, or purchased from a computer or electronics store.
Wireless router	Links Internet-connectable devices together so they can communicate with each other.
Wireless adapter	Plugs into a computer, giving it the ability to receive and transmit wireless networking signals.
Access point	A device that allows wireless devices to connect to a wired network using Wi-Fi or related standards. The access point usually connects to a router using a wired connection, but it can also be integrated into the router.
Repeater	· A wireless network device that repeats wireless signals to extend range without being connected by cable to a router/modem or client devices (for example, to allow a signal from a router on the first floor of a 3-story house to reach the second and third floors). · Must be installed in an area that already has a solid wireless signal. · Some routers and access points can be configured to act as a repeater.
Antenna	· Picks up incoming radio signals and radiates outgoing signals wirelessly. · Antennas can be external or internal to a device. · There are different types of antennas for different purposes. · Omni-directional antennas receive signals in all directions, whereas directional antennas work more like a flashlight - point it in a given direction to gain visibility in that specific area · Omnidirectional antennas are commonly used on wireless routers and adapters, because these devices must support connections from multiple directions. · Directional antennas are typically used to extend the range of a Wi-Fi network into hard-to-reach areas.
Bridge	· Some routers and access points can be configured to act as a bridge.

AVAILABLE WIRELESS CHANNELS

Like channels on a traditional TV, all wireless network equipment, including client devices and routers, communicate over specific channels.

- Each channel is designated by a number that represents a specific radio communication frequency.
- Wireless devices set and adjust their channel numbers automatically as part of the communication protocol.
- Operating system and utility software on computers track the channels being used at any given time.

2.4 GHz Wi-Fi Channels

Wireless equipment in North America features 11 channels on the 2.4 GHz band.

- Channel 1 operates at a center frequency of 2.412 GHz.
- Channel 11 operates at 2.462 GHz.
- All other channels operate at frequencies in between, evenly spaced at 5 MHz (0.005 GHz) intervals.
- Because each 2.4 GHz Wi-Fi channel requires a signaling band roughly 22 MHz wide, radio frequencies of neighboring channels numbers overlap each other.

5 GHz Wi-Fi Channels

5 GHz offers significantly more channels than 2.4 GHz Wi-Fi. To avoid issues with overlapping frequencies, 5 GHz equipment restricts available channels to certain numbers within a larger range. For example:

- 5 GHz channels include channels 36, 40, 44, and 48. Other numbers in between are not supported.
- Channel 36 operates at 5.180 GHz, with each channel offset by 5 MHz, so that Channel 40 operates at 5.200 GHz (20 MHz offset), and so on.
- The highest frequency channel (165) operates at 5.825 GHz.

Reasons to Change Wi-Fi Channel Numbers

- Many home networks use routers that by default run on channel 6 in the 2.4 GHz band.
- Neighboring wireless home networks that run over the same channel generate radio interference that can slow network performance.
- Re-configuring a network to run over a different channel minimize these slowdowns.

How To Change Wi-Fi Channel Numbers

To change channels on a home wireless router:

- Log into the router's configuration screens and look for a setting called "Channel" or "Wireless Channel."
- Most routers provide a drop-down list of supported channel numbers to choose from. Other devices will detect and adjust their channel numbers automatically to match that of the router or wireless access point with no action needed.
- If devices fail to connect after changing the router's channel, use their software configuration application and make matching channel number changes there.

Choosing the Best Channel Number

No single channel number is inherently "best" relative to the others. For example:

- Some users prefer to set their 2.4 GHz networks to use the lowest or highest channel to avoid midrange frequencies because some home Wi-Fi routers default to channel 6.
- If neighboring networks do the same, severe connectivity issues can result.
- In extreme cases, users may need to coordinate with their neighbors on the channels each will use to keep separation between them.
- A network analyzer test can be run to test a local area for existing wireless signals and derive a safe channel to use based on the results.
- An easier way is to simply try and test each channel individually, and pick one that seems good; typically more than one will work equally well.
- The effects of signal interference vary over time, and what appears to be the best channel one day may turn out later to be not good. Monitor the environment periodically to see whether conditions have changed that would require a Wi-Fi channel to change.

WIRELESS NETWORK TOPOLOGIES

Wireless networks have two topologies:

- *Infrastructure* — Point-to-multipoint (one-to-many) topology typically used for permanent networks.
- *Ad hoc* — Multipoint-to-multipoint (many-to-many) topology typically used for temporary networks.

Infrastructure Network Topology

- A single central wireless access point acts as the hub in the network.
- All the other client devices connect to the access point.
- Typically offers high speeds and strong security.

Ad Hoc Network Topology

- There is no central access point.
- Every computing device in the network communicates directly with every other device in the network.
- Typically offers only a few security modes and lower network speeds.

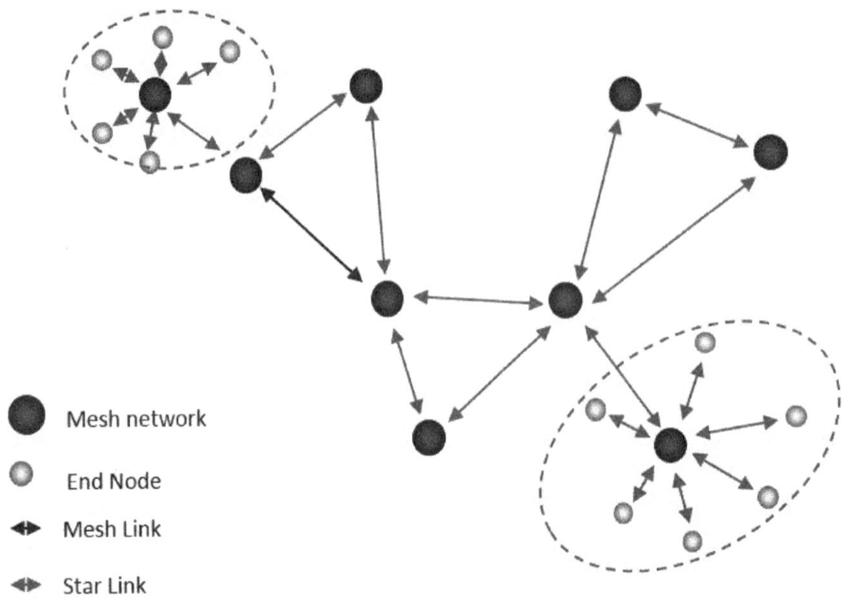

Figure 11-1 *Ad Hoc Network Topology*

Wireless Mesh Network

A wireless mesh network is a form of ad hoc network in which dozens or hundreds of wireless mesh nodes "talk" to each other to share the network connection.

- Mesh nodes are small radio transmitters that function in the same way as a wireless router.
- One node is physically wired to a network connection and shares its Internet connection wirelessly with all other nodes in its vicinity.
- Those nodes share the connection wirelessly with the nodes closest to them.
- The more nodes, the further the connection spreads, creating a wireless "cloud of connectivity."
- Mesh networks are self-configuring and incorporate new nodes into the existing structure automatically.

- Mesh networks are self-healing because the network automatically finds the fastest and most reliable paths to send data, even if nodes are blocked or lose their signal.
- ZigBee is an example of wireless mesh architecture.

Configuring Multiple Access Points in the Same Network

When configuring more than one access point in the same network:

- Configure all access points to use the same SSID, security type, and password.
- Configure the access points to use different channels to minimize interference.
- Change the IP address of the each additional access point by 1 to whatever the IP address was for the first access point. For example, if the first access point has an IP address of 192.168.10.11, configure the IP address of the second access point to 192.168.10.12.

Bridging Techniques

A wireless bridge is a device that plugs into this Ethernet network and connects two or more LAN segments on the same subnet. Most wireless game adapters are transparent bridges as well.

Because the computers in the bridged LAN segments are on the same subnet:

- Broadcasts will reach all machines.
- DHCP clients in one segment can obtain IP addresses from a DHCP server in a different segment.
- Computers in one room can communicate with computers in a different room.

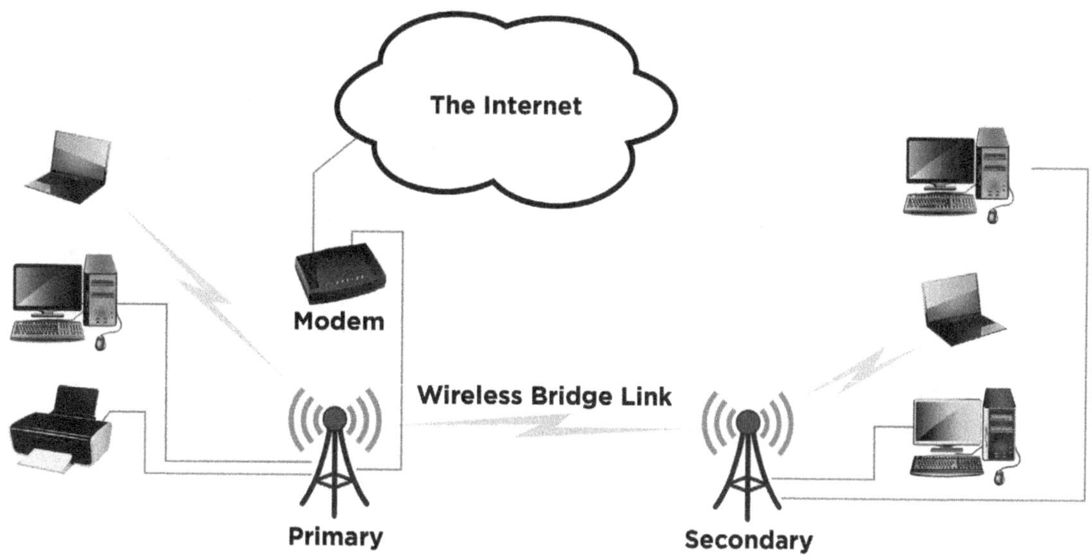

Figure 11-2. *ESS Client Bridge*

Wireless Distribution System

Some wireless devices support Wireless Distribution System (WDS) bridging.

- WDS creates a transparent Level 2 wireless bridge between two or more points.
- Its notable advantage over other solutions is that it preserves the MAC addresses of client frames across links between access points.

Access Point as a Bridge

Some access points can be used as bridges to connect networks and to form a mesh network.

- Use the same model access points with the same firmware.
- Some access points support only a single point-to-point connection to another access point.
- Other access points support point-to-multipoint connections to several other access points.

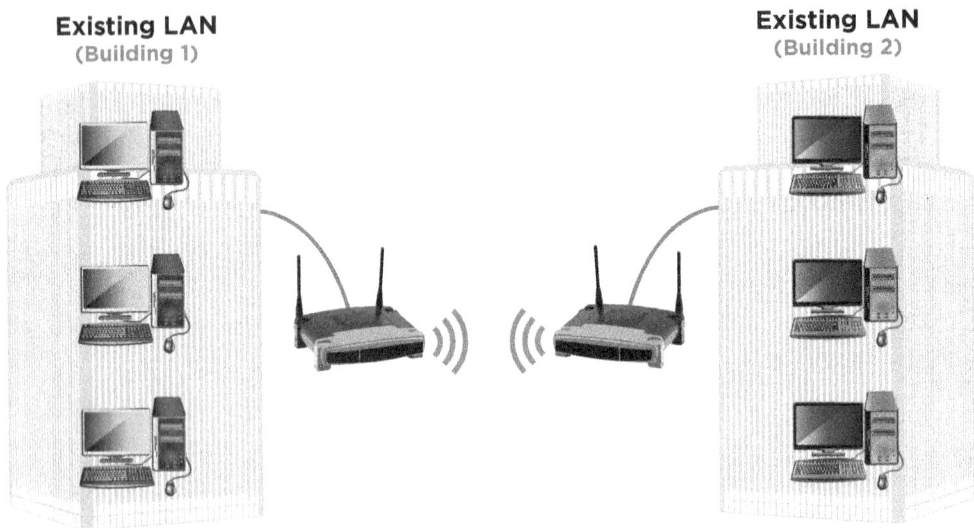

Figure 11-3 *Access Point as a Bridge*

Access Point as a Repeater

Some access points can be used as repeaters to the range of the wireless network.

- As a repeater, the access point can be used to boost a weak signal onto another access point connected to the network.
- It is better to have sufficient access points connected to a cable infrastructure than to use repeaters.

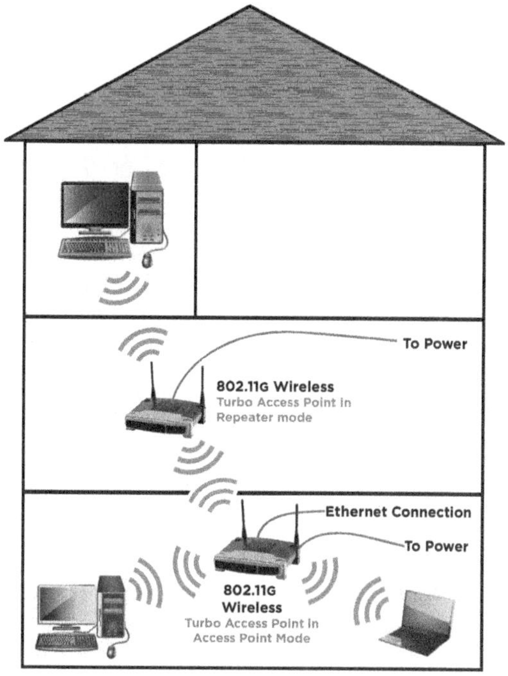

Figure 11-4 *Access Point as a Repeater*

SITE SURVEY

With wireless networks, it is hard to predict the propagation of radio waves and detect the presence of interfering signals. Performing a site survey can prevent a wireless network from under-performing.

Site Survey Goals

A site survey should:

- Reveal coverage voids.
- Recommend access point locations to ensure adequate network coverage (i.e., good data rate, signal strength, and signal quality).
- Detect potential sources of interference that can degrade network performance.

How Complex Must the Site Survey Be?

The complexity of a site survey depends on the size and layout of the home. For example:

- A small, single-floor house might get by with a single access point located anywhere within the residence and still maintain adequate coverage. If this access point encounters RF interference from a nearby wireless network, a different channel can be used to eliminate the problem.
- A large, multi-floor residence might need multiple access points and repeaters to maintain adequate coverage and high performance.

What Should a Site Survey Contain?

When conducting an RF site survey, consider these general steps:

1. *Obtain blueprints* — Locate a set of blueprints. If none exists, draw a floor plan that shows the location of walls, walkways, and other potential obstacles to wireless signals.
2. *Visually inspect the house* — Walk through the house to verify the accuracy of the blueprints. Record potential barriers to RF signals that generally are not shown on blueprints, such as metal racks and partitions.
3. *Identify user areas* — Note areas where wireless users will and will not go. Fewer access points might be needed if the roaming areas can be limited.
4. *Obtain a site-survey tool* — Site survey software applications can be loaded on a notebook PC or mobile device to test the coverage of each preliminary access point location. Alternately, handheld site survey tools are available that provide advanced site-survey functions.
5. *Mount access point at each preliminary location* — Use the site-survey tool to record data rates and signal readings while walking varying distances away from the access point. A poor signal quality reading can indicate RF interference and might require a spectrum analyzer to characterize the interference.
6. *Site-survey findings* — Based on the results of the testing, access points might need to be relocated. After finalizing the access point locations, identify the mounting locations on the blueprints or floor plan.
7. *Post-deployment survey* — After deploying the wireless network, perform a post-deployment site survey to ensure that performance and coverage meet the design requirements. Keep the site survey in a safe place so that it can be accessed at any time.

RF Spectrum Analysis Tools

Finding sources of interference often can be a cat-and-mouse game. A spectrum analyzer can be used to find the source of the interference.

- Spectrum analyzers measure the power of the spectrum of known and unknown signals.
- Most provide a "waterfall view" that shows a window amplitude history or RF activity over time.
- A network installer is able to see fluctuations in signal amplitude.
- It is possible to focus on one signal by walking around with the spectrum analyzer and honing in on the signal of the offending device.

Analyzer Readouts

An RF spectrum analyzer will allow you to see the amplitude of interference at different frequencies. Most analyzers have full color readouts, where red or some other color indicates the highest amplitude. In the upcoming examples you will see how different types of interference have very different displays.

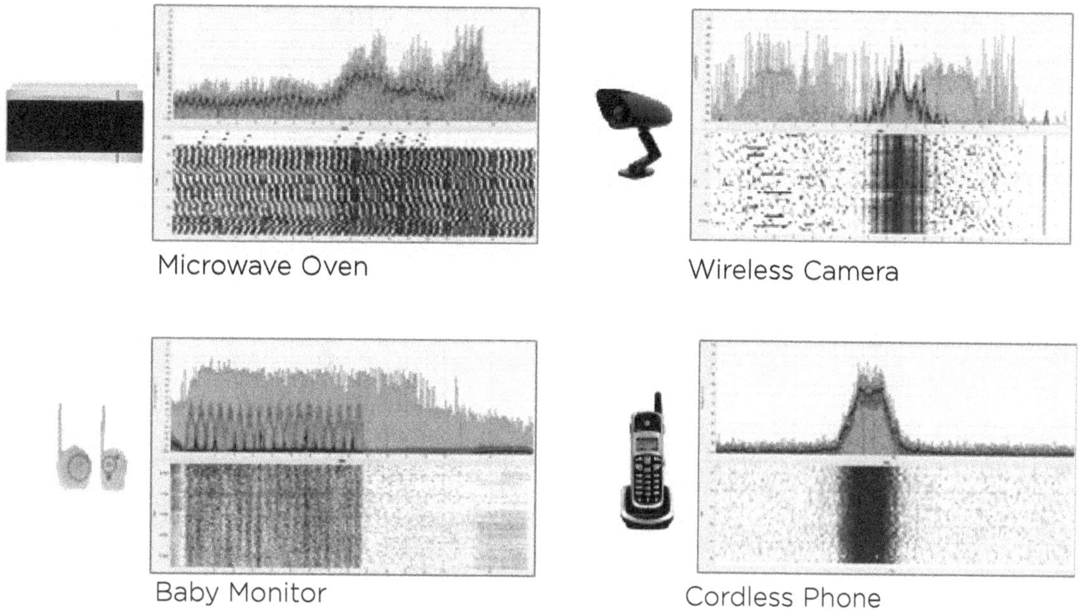

Figure 11-5 *Wireless Interference*

Interference from Microwave Ovens

- Some wireless audio devices that transmit lossless audio over the radio waves use the same frequencies as Wi-Fi.
- These can cause interference with Wi-Fi and ZigBee wireless networks.
- They tend to have a curved shape similar to 802.11b networks, but with smaller spikes.

Interference from Video Cameras

- Wireless security cameras typically have high utilization, as they transmit constantly.
- These cameras typically have three spikes in the spectrum.
- The image below shows two brands of wireless video cameras.
- The wide signals indicate high utilization (duty cycle) that affects Wi-Fi severely.

Interference from Baby Monitors

- Wireless video baby monitors typically occupy 50 MHz-wide swaths of the 2.4 GHz spectrum and only leave a single Wi-Fi channel available, channel 11.
- Very creative spectrum management may be required to have video baby monitors co-exist with wireless networks.

Interference from Cordless Phones

- Older analog cordless phones transmit nearly 100 percent of the time
- They can exist either in the 2.4 and 5 GHz bands
- Generally make a narrow spike in the band

INSTALLING WIRELESS HARDWARE IN THE HOME

Gather requirements from the customer and document his/her objectives for the installation. Often, a customer's request will have to be balanced with what can actually be achieved. The following table lists factors to consider.

Table 11-3 *Design Considerations*

<table>
<tr><th colspan="2">Scenario</th><th>Resolution</th></tr>
<tr><td>Wide-covering signal vs. high throughput</td><td>A wide-covering signal can cause slow throughput due to the inverse relationship between range and data rates.</td><td>Use more access points to keep the data rates high.</td></tr>
<tr><td>Large number of clients</td><td>A wireless network can support different types of devices. Examples include laptops, tablets, smartphones, TVs, control systems, photo frames, and media players.</td><td rowspan="2">Use SMB or enterprise-grade hardware, not SOHO-grade, to accommodate high-capacity environments.</td></tr>
<tr><td>Roaming and VoIP</td><td>A wireless network might need to support reliable roaming, voice, and video applications</td></tr>
<tr><td>Wired LAN</td><td>Installers might be replacing a pre-existing wired network with a wireless network.</td><td>Assess whether any existing hardware devices can support the new wireless deployment.</td></tr>
<tr><td>Selecting the right hardware</td><td>Should the networking hardware be from one or various vendors?</td><td>Although wireless gear can be mixed and matched, the better choice is to use gear from the same manufacturer to utilize proprietary features that are highly desired.</td></tr>
</table>

Design Strategies

Wireless networks can be designed for coverage or data rate.

Design by Coverage

A network that is designed for coverage simply provides adequate signal strength for every location in the coverage area. It doesn't take into account co-channel interference from adjacent cells that need to take turns talking, and it doesn't ensure that clients can talk quickly and efficiently with fast data rates.

A network that is designed by coverage:

- Requires very little planning

- Can result in decreased performance for distant client devices, who will connect at slower data rates
- Can result in adjacent coverage cells suffering from co-channel interference due to channel sharing

Note: Having a large coverage area increases the potential for interference.

Design by Data Rate

If the customer prefers fast data rates for streaming or data transfers rather than a large coverage area,

- Create small cells that have a low transmit power to reduce the chance for interference.
- Reduce the number of clients connected to access points.

Materials and dB Loss

Wireless signals fade over distance. They also experience (attenuation) loss at a higher rate when they travel though materials. As the signal is attenuated, the data rate suffers. For these reasons, observe the following guidelines when installing a wireless network:

- Different materials cause different rates of loss.
- 2.4 and 5 GHz wireless signals do not penetrate materials such as steel roofing, aluminum siding, and elevator doors.
- Materials such as chicken wire used in older plaster-and-lath walls impede or block wireless signals.
- Concrete and brick are very dense and create a significant loss for carrier signals. Concrete block construction and cast concrete are almost always accompanied by steel re-bar, which intensifies RF blocking.
- Framed walls with drywall or plaster are less dense than brick and concrete. Therefore less loss occurs to radio waves as they pass through these types of walls.
- Cubicle walls contain less material and are less dense, causing higher rates of RF propagation.

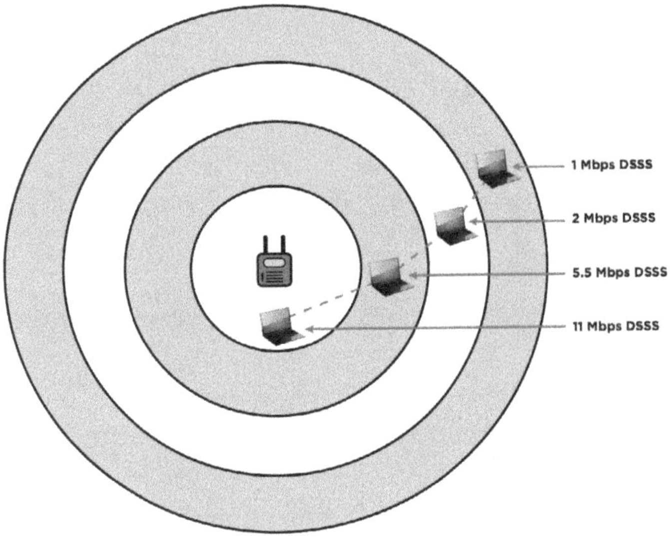

dBm Power Level	Data Rate
-94 dBm	1 Mbps
-93 dBm	2 Mbps
-92 dBm	5.5 Mbps
-86 dBm	6 Mbps
-86 dBm	9 Mbps
-90 dBm	11 Mbps
-86 dBm	12 Mbps
-86 dBm	18 Mbps
-84 dBm	24 Mbps
-80 dBm	36 Mbps
-75 dBm	48 Mbps
-71 dBm	54 Mbps

Figure 11-6 *Attenuation and Data Rates*

The RF Budget

The RF Budget is an accounting of all the gains and losses from the transmitter, through any medium (cable, fiber, free space, walls), to the destination.

Received Power (dBm) = Transmitted Power (dBm) + Gains (dB) - Losses (dB)

For instance, an access point may boost the signal 20dB, the loss in the air may be 75dB, and the laptop antenna may boost the signal by 2 dB. The effective signal level at the laptop would then be -53dB. A typical laptop will communicate with a signal level of -75, so in this scenario the signal is adequate.

Aesthetics

When installing a wireless network, observe the following aesthetic guidelines:

- Use water-based paint only. Do not use paint with lead, metal, or other reflective materials.
- Outdoor enclosures are a great way to hide wireless equipment so they blend into an environment. Choose an enclosure rated for wireless equipment. The enclosure should be plastic-based and must not have metal, reflective, or RF-absorbing properties.
- Consider environmental factors when placing wireless equipment. The most aesthetically pleasing location might not offer the best performance. Reflective obstacles and devices that cause interference can reduce the overall performance of the network.
- Locate power cables out of sight, while preserving the aesthetics of the environment. Avoid placing stress on the connectors.

ROAMING

Roaming is the process where a wireless client device moves its communications from one access point to another while staying connected to the network.

Roaming Standard

- Roaming is covered by the IEEE 802.11r-2008 standard (also known as "fast BSS transitions").
- IEEE 802.11r-2008 is an amendment to the IEEE 802.11 standard that permits the continuous connectivity of wireless devices in motion, with fast and secure handoffs from one access point to another in a seamless manner.
- Under IEEE 802.11r-2008, the client device decides when to hand off and to which access point it wants to hand off.
    - Some devices pre-authenticate and pre-associate before being handed off to another access point.
    - Some devices wait until they lose minimum signal, and then tear down and re-establish the connection — a process that can take 5-15 seconds.
- IEEE 802.11r-2008 is not widely implemented, with roaming handoffs based mostly on proprietary solutions unique to each wireless vendor.

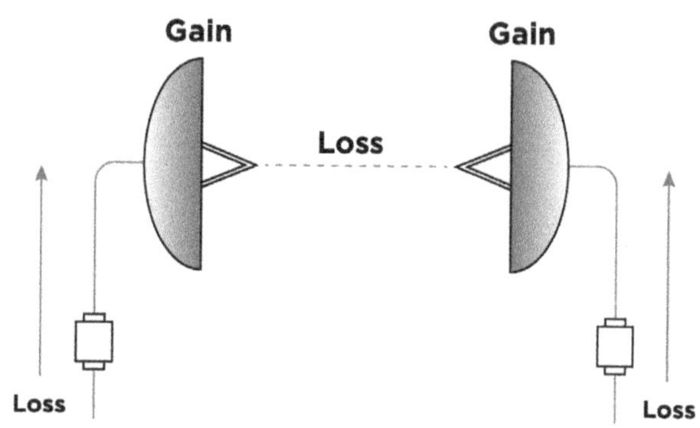

Figure 11-7 *Gains and Losses*

Understanding the Roaming Process

After a client moves from one access point to another, it transmits a re-association request to an access point that meets its roaming criteria. The roaming process includes 6 frames.

Table 11-4 *The Roaming Process*

	Station	New Access Point	Original Access Point
1.	Sends a re-association request to a new access point under the same SSID.		
2.		Sends an ACK in response.	
3.		Notifies the original access point (or wireless controller if present) about the roaming station.	
4.			
5.		Sends the re-association response.	Delivers buffered data to the new access point.
6.	Sends an acknowledgement frame.		

Wireless Controllers

Wireless controllers are physical devices that are rack-mounted in the core data room and communicate with each access point at the same time. The key benefits of using a wireless controller are:

- Centralized configuration, management, and firmware updates can be performed for multiple access points, without having to configure each one manually.
- Allows roaming clients to authenticate only once, reducing lag time when going between access points.
- Optimizes client distribution and channel utilization to maximize efficiency of the available wireless spectrum.
- Limits the maximum bandwidth to avoid overloading the wireless network.
- Improves scalability by allowing more access points to be installed onto the network while reducing deployment and management complexities.
- Some controllers can limit the maximum bandwidth used by individual access points to avoid overloading the wireless network.
- Some wireless controllers perform functions such as a stateful firewall between the wired and wireless networks, VPN connectivity, intrusion detection and prevention services, spectrum monitoring and analysis, and more.

WIRELESS NETWORK SECURITY

Wireless SSIDs

Because multiple wireless networks can coexist in one airspace, each network needs a unique name. This name is the service set ID (SSID) of the network.

- All access points and devices on a wireless network must use the same SSID to communicate with each other.
- An SSID is a sequence of case-sensitive, alphanumeric characters.
- SSIDs have a maximum length of 32 characters.

Because the SSID differentiates one wireless network from another, all access points and all devices attempting to connect to a specific wireless network must use the same SSID to enable effective roaming. As part of the association process, a wireless network interface card (NIC) must have the same SSID as the access point or it will not be permitted to join the BSS.

BSSIDs

The BSSID is essentially the MAC address of each unique access point on the network. A BSSID names an individual access point, an SSID gives the access point a human-readable name, and an ESSID is a collection of access points with the same SSID. The BSSID is included in all frames to define which access point they are intended for.

Wireless Encryption Standards

Wireless routers use encryption protocols to encode information in a way that allows only authorized parties to read it. The three most common choices for encrypting data are:

- Wired Equivalent Privacy (WEP)
- Wi-Fi Protected Access (WPA)
- Wi-Fi Protection Access 2 (WPA2)

Implementing the appropriate encryption protocol is the difference between offering someone easy access to a home network and sitting secure.

WEP

- Defined in the 802.11b standard.
- Designed to provide the same level of security as a wired LAN.
- Encrypts data over radio waves to protect transmitted data as it is sent from one end point to another.
- Used at the two lowest layers of the OSI model, the data link and physical layers, and does not offer end-to-end security.
- Suffers from well-known security flaws, is hard to configure, and is easily broken.

WPA

- Designed to replace WEP.
- Works with existing Wi-Fi products that have been enabled with WEP
- Includes two improvements over WEP:
  - Improved data encryption through the temporal key integrity protocol (TKIP), which scrambles the keys using a hashing algorithm and to ensure that the keys have not been tampered with.
  - User authentication through the extensible authentication protocol (EAP) to ensure that only authorized network users can access the network.
- Designed to be an interim standard that will be replaced with the IEEE 802.11i standard.

WPA2

- Provides government-grade security by implementing the National Institute of Standards and Technology (NIST) FIPS 140-2-compliant AES encryption algorithm and 802.1x-based authentication.
- Backward-compatible with WPA.
- May not be supported by older equipment.
- Has 3 versions:
- *WPA2-Personal* — Protects unauthorized network access by using a set-up password.
- *WPA2-Enterprise* — Verifies network users through a server.
- *WPA/WPA2 Mixed Mode* — Uses WPA2 if possible, but falls back to WPA if necessary. Because WPA2 is a better choice, do not use this mode. If the network has devices which are incompatible with WPA2, upgrade that equipment.

Table 11-5 *Encryption Protocols*

	Encryption Protocol		
	WEP	WPA	WPA2
Initialization keys:	24-bit	40-bit	48-bit
Possible combinations:	16.7 million	500 trillion	500 trillion
Number of bits:	64/128	64/128	64/128
Keys:	Static	Unique	Unique
Computing power:	Low	Medium	High
Master key:	Used directly	Never used directly	Never used directly

Recommended Encryption Settings

- Use WPA2-Personal whenever possible, since it has the strongest encryption.
- WPA should be a far second choice.
- Do not consider WEP due to its flaws.
- If the network has an old router, consider upgrading the device to a newer one that can be better secured.
- After configuring the encryption setting on the router, reconfigure all of the wireless devices on the network.

Configuring Secure Network Passwords

Most routers require an administrator password to access the setup and configuration settings. However, the default passwords for these routers are generally weak, and some have none at all.

- Change the default network name (SSID), administrator name, and password to something strong.
- For older routers that support WEP only, use 128-bit WEP keys. Check the manufacturer's web site for a firmware update that will add WPA support. If none is available, replace the router with newer models that support WPA.
- Change passwords often.

What Makes a Password Strong?

A strong password:

- Is at least eight characters long.
- Does not contain a user name, real name, or company name.
- Does not contain a complete word.
- Is significantly different from previous passwords.
- Contains characters from each of the following four categories:
    - Upper-case characters **A** through **Z**
    - Lower-case characters **a** through **z**
    - Numbers **0** through **9**
    - Special symbols **` ~ ! @ # $ % ^ & * ( ) _ - + = { } [ ] \ | : ; " ' < > , . ? /**

What Makes a Password Weak?

A password can meet all the criteria above and still be a weak password. For example:

- **Hello2U!** meets all the criteria above, but is weak because it contains a complete word.
- **H3llO 2 U!** is a stronger alternative because it replaces some of the letters in the complete word with numbers and includes spaces.

Remembering Passwords

To remember strong passwords:

- *Create an acronym* — Select a meaningful phrase. For example, My son's birthday is August 12, 2004 can become Msbi12/Aug,4.
- *Substitute numbers, symbols, and misspellings for letters or words* — For example, My son's birthday is 12 August, 2004 can become Mi$un's Brthd8iz 08124.
- *Relate the password to a sport or hobby* — For example, I like to play baseball can become ILuv2PlayB@seba1l.

CHAPTER 12

ADVANCED RESIDENTIAL NETWORKING

In this chapter, we will explore some of the key techniques used to take the home network to the higher level of performance, dependability, and security which is necessary to meet the demands of today's integrated home.

The network must now support multiple systems, including streaming HD video, control systems, distributed audio, and more.

It is up to the integrator to design and implement a powerful, robust network which is capable of delivering this new level of performance.

VIRTUAL LOCAL AREA NETWORKS (VLANs)

VLAN is short for "Virtual Local Area Network." A VLAN consists of group of hosts with a common set of requirements that communicate as if they were attached to the same broadcast domain, regardless of their physical location.

- VLANs create independent logical networks within a physical network, thereby improving security by limiting the broadcast domain.
- A VLAN has the same physical attributes as a physical local-area network (LAN), but allows devices to be grouped, even if the devices are on different network switches.
- Devices in one segment of a VLAN are not visible to devices in other segments. This limits which devices can communicate with each other.
- By segmenting devices, VLANs can be used to separate logical

segments of a LAN that should remain secure, such as segments that support IP security cameras or network video recorders.
- With VLANs, issues such as viruses, worms, and trojans can be contained to affected segments only, without allowing them to spread to devices on other segments.
- A network can have multiple VLANs.

VLAN Security

Since 802.1Q relies on modifying frames, a hacker can modify the frames and inject VLAN IDs to traverse unwanted parts of the network. However, this is unlikely because the hacker must have:

- A deep understanding of the network, including the MAC address of the target machine on another VLAN he wants to target.
- Physical access to the network switch.

Although it is hard to exploit 802.1Q VLANs, do not use VLANs by themselves as a way to enforce security policy.

VLAN Implementation

In 802.1Q VLANs, each frame gets tagged with a VLAN ID between 1 - 4094 so that the devices that support 802.1Q will forward the frame appropriately.

- The tag is a 32-bit field that is added between the source MAC address and the Ether Type/Length fields of the original frame.
- The tag is added by a source device, such as a VOIP phone, wireless access point, or 802.1Q switches and routers between the sending and receiving devices.
- Each frame can be a member of a single VLAN only.

Untagged and Tagged Ports

- VLANs are created and managed using the software on managed switches. This software allows switch ports to be configured as tagged or untagged ports.
- *Untagged Port* — Used to connect VLAN-unaware devices such as computers, TVs, and gaming systems. Packets received at an untagged port are assigned a port VLAN ID (PVID), stripped of any VLAN tag, and forwarded to the appropriate member ports. An untagged port can belong only to a single VLAN specified by the PVID.
- *Tagged Port* — Used in a VLAN trunk port. A tagged port expects received packets to have a VLAN tag. Packets received at a tag port are forwarded to the appropriate VLAN member ports with the tags in place, so they can be processed by the receiving device.

Trunk Ports

Managed switches also provide a trunk port. A trunk port allows multiple VLANs to send data through a single network link. Typically, the ports connecting the network infrastructure (router, switches, access points) are configured as trunks.

- Use a trunk port when a port is expected to be a member of multiple VLANs or when connecting VLAN-aware devices together.
- Trunks preserve the VLAN information between the devices and pass all VLAN-tagged frames.

Example of 802.1Q Frame-Tagging Network on the Same VLAN

In this example, PC 1 and PC 2 are on the same VLAN and want to communicate with each other.

- Two switches are used to forward the data between the PCs. The ports connecting the two switches are configured as trunk ports that are members of VLAN 1 and VLAN 2.
- PC 1 is not 802.1Q-compliant and can send only untagged data frames to PC 2.
- The Switch1 port connected to PC 1 is configured as an access port or untagged member of VLAN 1. This switch port is untagged because it is not expecting received frames to have a tag, since PC1 does not support 802.1Q.
- The Switch 2 port connected to PC 2 is configured as an access port or untagged member of VLAN 1.

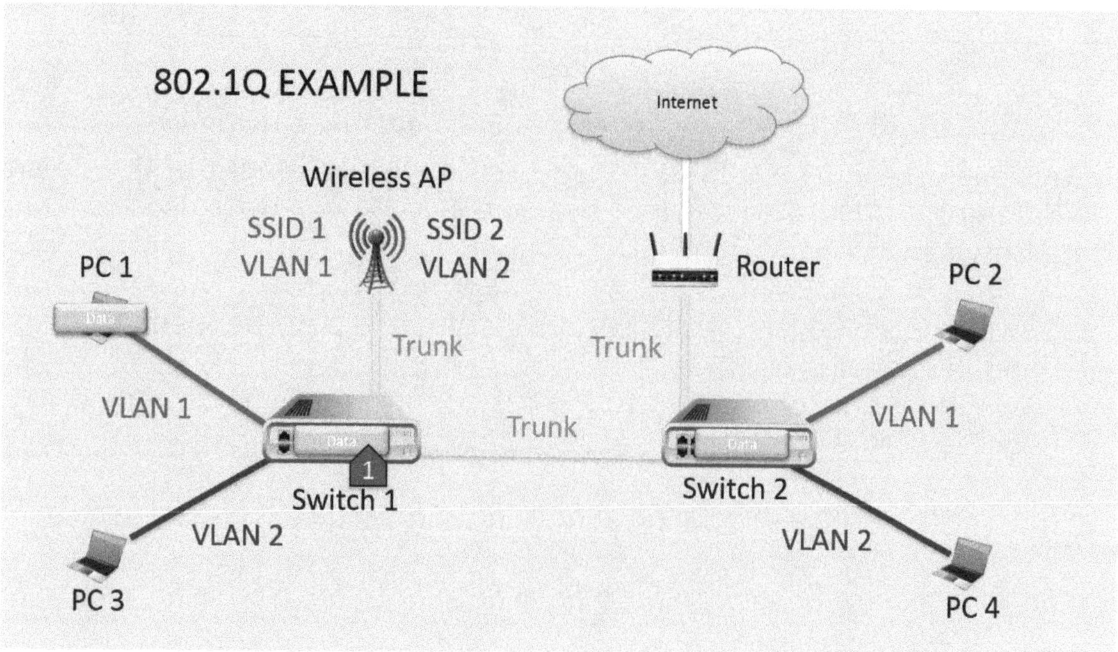

Figure 12-1 *Frame-Tagging*

The following table describes how data moves from PC 1 to PC 2 via Switches 1 and 2.

Table 12-1 *Data Movement from PC 1 to PC 2*

	PC 1	Switch 1...	Switch 2...	PC 2
1.	Sends the data frames to Switch 1.			
2.		Receives data frames from PC 1.		
3.		Tags the frames with the VLAN ID of VLAN 1.		
4.		Forwards the frames to all ports that are members of VLAN 1.		
5.			Receives the data frames on the trunk port.	
6.			Reads the VLAN ID of VLAN 1.	
7.			Removes the VLAN tags.	
8.			Forwards the frames on to PC 2	
9.				Receives the data and processes it accordingly.

Example of 802.1Q Frame-Tagging Network on Different VLANs

In this example, PC 1 wants to communicate with PC 4, but both PCs are on different VLANs. A router that supports 802.1Q VLANs is used to route data between the VLANs.

- Switch 2 is a Layer 2 switch and cannot route data between VLANs and IP subnets.
- Switch 2's port connected to PC 4 is configured as an untagged access port.

The following table describes how data moves from PC 1 to PC 4.

Table 12-2 *Data Movement from PC 1 to PC 4*

	PC 1	Switch 1...	Switch 2...	Router...	PC 4
1.	Sends the data frames to Switch 1.				
2.		Receives data frames from PC 1.			
3.		Tags the frames with the VLAN ID of VLAN 1.			
4.		Since the ports between Switch 1 and Switch 2 are configured as tagged trunks to carry all VLANs, Switch 1 forwards the frames to Switch 2.			
5.			The trunk port receives the data frames from PC 1. The frames are tagged with a different VLAN ID than the VLAN ID on the port connected to PC 4.		
6.			Forwards the data over the tagged trunk port to the router.		
7.				Receives the data on its VLAN 192.168.1.1 interface and knows that the data is destined for PC 4 at 192.168.2.20.	

	PC 1	Switch 1...	Switch 2...	Router...	PC 4
8.				Replaces the VLAN 1 ID with the correct VLAN 2 ID for the 192.168.2.1 interface.	
9.				Routes the data from its 192.168.1.1 interface to the 192.168.2.1 interface, and then sends it back to Switch 2.	
10.			Receives the data with the proper VLAN 2 tag. The data and switch port are both on the same VLAN.		
11.			Removes the VLAN 2 tag.		
12.			Forwards the data to PC 4.		
13.					Receives the data and processes it accordingly.

BANDWIDTH

Bandwidth refers to the amount of data that can be transferred or moved through the network cables, generally twisted-pair cables. Different applications will require different bandwidths.

Table 12-3 *Bandwidth Requirements for Various Applications*

Application	Bandwidth
Internet access	Up to 2Gbs in some areas
Computers on LAN	As much as possible, limited by cable and NIC type
VoIP	100 Kbps
Video conferencing	512 Kbps
Closed-circuit television (CCTV)	2 Mbps
Control systems	Less than 1 Mbps (transient)
Music	Less than 1.5 Mbps
Video	Approximately 20 Mbps (HD) - changing rapidly with 4K/UHD

QUALITY OF SERVICE

Bandwidth can be managed using Quality of Service (QoS).

- QoS is the ability to provide different priority to different applications, users, or data flows, or to guarantee a certain level of performance to a data flow.
- For example, a required bit rate, delay, jitter, packet dropping probability, or bit error rate may be guaranteed.
- To use quality of service, a router or managed switch is required that supports QoS.

QoS and Bandwidth

The interplay between QoS and bandwidth is notable in various applications. The following table summarizes this interplay:

Table 12-4 *Applications, Bandwidth, and QoS*

Sub-System	Application	Bandwidth	QoS
Standard computer applications	· Network printing · Network scanning · Reading or writing to storage devices	Becomes noticeable.	Not critical.
Communications	VoIP	Not an issue.	Very important, as delays of 250 ns or longer can affect voice quality.
	Video conferencing	Bandwidth is usually limited by Internet connections rather than the LAN. But this is changing rapidly.	Very important to ensure good picture and voice quality.
Cameras	CCTV	Check specific camera requirements.	Check specific camera requirements
Control systems	Can use IP over Ethernet to interconnect devices.	Not critical Check requirements for video on touch screens.	Not implemented
Media streaming	Music	Not intensive	Most systems use buffers. QoS is not needed.
	Video	Intensive	Most systems use buffers. QoS is not needed.

Layer 2 (Port-Based) QoS

In port-based QoS:

- Each physical port on the switch or router is assigned a priority level (for example, low, normal, medium, or high).
- Data from devices on high-priority ports is serviced first followed by medium, normal, and low.
- Most managed switches allow maximum upload and download rate to be set for each physical port. The aggregate bandwidth of all devices on the port cannot exceed these limits.

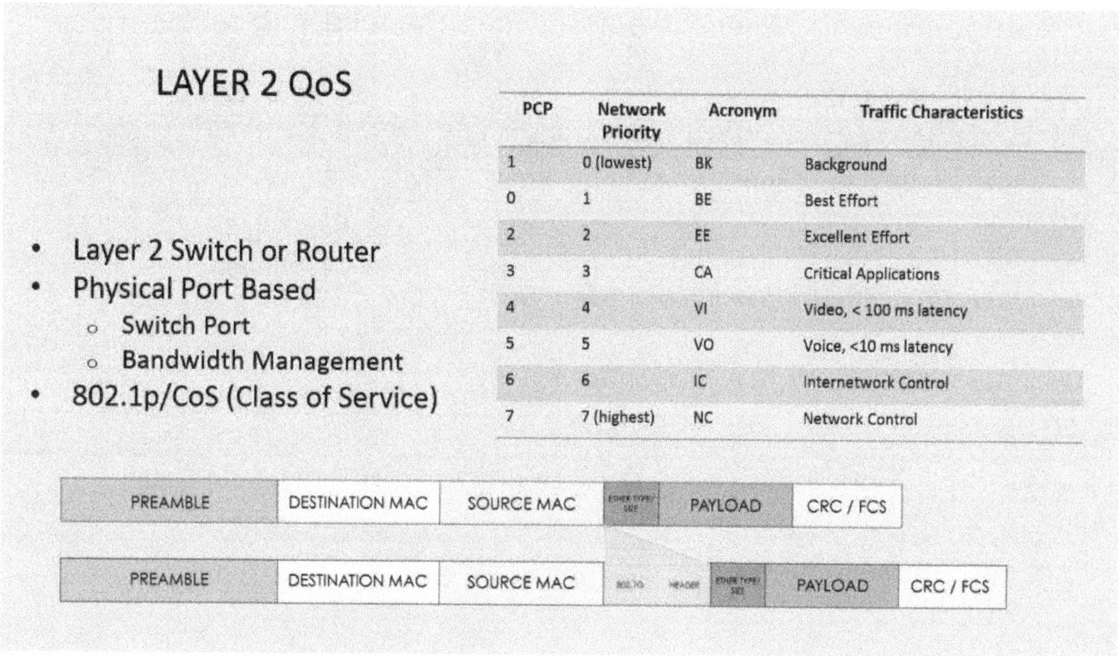

PCP	Network Priority	Acronym	Traffic Characteristics
1	0 (lowest)	BK	Background
0	1	BE	Best Effort
2	2	EE	Excellent Effort
3	3	CA	Critical Applications
4	4	VI	Video, < 100 ms latency
5	5	VO	Voice, <10 ms latency
6	6	IC	Internetwork Control
7	7 (highest)	NC	Network Control

Figure 12-2 *Layer 2 QoS*

Layer 3 QoS

- Layer 3 QoS manages or throttles bandwidth using more options than Layer 2 in order to implement a very granular QoS. Layer 3 QoS typically is found on smarter Layer 3 routers and switches. With Layer 3 QoS:

- Bandwidth can still be limited.
- Priority can be given based on IP address, IP ports, or protocol. For example, network priority can be given to:
- Real Time Streaming Protocol (RTSP) port 554 for video streaming.
- Point-to-Point Tunneling Protocol (PPTP) VPN service.
- Windows Remote Desktop Protocol (RDP) port 3389.
- QoS can be applied to individual or groups of IP addresses to guarantee all the services on a device (such as an Xbox or Apple TV) get network priority.
- QoS can be applied to protocols such as Session Initiation Protocol (SIP) for VOIP-enabled phones.

DSCP

Differentiated Services Code Point (DSCP), or "DiffServ," is a 6-bit field in an IP packet that enables different levels of service to be assigned to network traffic.

- DSCP is complex and only used by large enterprise networks and Internet service providers.
- DSCP marks each packet on the network with a DSCP code and appropriates to it the corresponding level of service.
- With DSCP, network traffic can be categorized into four application categories, with 10 service classes (see the following table).

Table 12-5 *DSCP*

Application Category	Service Class
Application Control	Signaling
Media-Oriented	Telephony
	Real-Time Interactive
	Multimedia Conferencing
	Broadcast Video
	Multimedia Streaming
Data	Low-Latency Data
	High-Throughout Data
	Low-Priority Data
Best Effort	Standard

Class of Service

The QoS technique 802.1p is also known as class of service (CoS). CoS is a 3-bit Priority Code Point (PCP) field added to an Ethernet frame header when using VLAN tagged frames as defined by IEEE 802.1Q.

- CoS specifies a priority value of from 0 to 7 that can be used by QoS disciplines to differentiate traffic.
- 802.1p is neither a standard nor an amendment published by the IEEE.
- Rather, 802.1p is incorporated into the IEEE 802.1Q standard, which specifies the tag inserted into an Ethernet frame.
- 802.1p works best when supporting devices on the network can tag their own packets with the appropriate priority level.
- Packets that come into an 802.1p switch with a PCP defined will be respected and serviced in the appropriate order.
- If some devices on the network do not support 802.1p, the physical switch port can be configured to tag any packets with a default priority level.

PORT TRANSLATION AND PORT FORWARDING

Port address translation is an extension to network address translation that allows multiple devices on a LAN to be mapped to a single public IP address in an effort to conserve IP addresses.

Port forwarding allows an outside computer from the Internet to connect to a computer or computing device on a private LAN. Port forwarding is configured at the router or firewall level. Port forwarding is common for the following reasons:

- It is widely supported.
- It requires no special software.

Port Forwarding Precautions

There are precautions to take with port forwarding.

- Port forwarding allows any machine in the world to connect to the forwarded port at will, making the network more insecure and vulnerable to hackers.
- Only one port can be used at a time by one machine.
- The port forwarding technology itself is built in a way so that the destination machine will see the incoming packets as coming from the router rather than the original machine sending out the packets.

SEGMENTATION

"Network segmentation" refers to splitting a network into smaller sub-networks, each being an independent network segment or network layer. Segmentation offers several advantages:

- *Optimized performance* — Improved performance is achieved because a segmented network has fewer hosts per subnetwork, which minimizes local traffic.
- *Improved security* — Limits users to just the segment that they are on. A guest network for WIFI is a good example of segmenting for security.
- *Reduced local traffic* — Provides more capacity for network services and applications, especially low-latency services like VoIP and streaming media, which are susceptible to network congestion.

REMOTE-ACCESS TOOLS

There are many ways to gain access to devices on a remote LAN. Some require port forwarding or VPN connections to be established before connecting. Once established, a variety of devices can be accessed, and detailed and real-time status can be obtained about the devices.

Standard Methods

The following table describes standard tools for remote access and the ports they use.

Table 12-6 *Frequently Used Port Numbers*

Tool	Description	Port
Telnet	Terminal-based connection used in LANs and WANS.	23
Secure Shell (SSH)	UNIX-based command interface and protocol for securely accessing a remote device. SSH commands are encrypted and secure because both ends of the client/server connection are authenticated using a digital certificate and passwords are protected by being encrypted.	22
Remote Desktop Protocol (RDP)	Microsoft-specific connection that connects to a Windows desktop or server remotely. This tool is handy for upgrading device firmware as it should not break the connection to the remote device during the upgrade. Also known as Terminal Services.	3389
Virtual Network Computing (VNC)	Similar to RDP. However, if VNC is used to connect to a remote machine running Windows Media Center, the remote machine does not need to be rebooted before it can play video files. There are different types of VNC software. For example, Real VNC is not compatible with 64-bit versions of Windows, but Ultra VNC is.	5900
File Transfer Protocol (FTP)	Provides access to file stores in a remote location.	20 and 21
Secure Copy Protocol (SCP)	Secure copy or SCP is a means of securely transferring computer files between a local host and a remote host or between two remote hosts. It is based on the Secure Shell (SSH) protocol.	22

The following table lists ports for additional remote-access methods.

Table 12-7 *Ports for Remote Access*

Tool	Port
HTTP	80
Alternate HTTP	8080
HTTPS	443
FTP	20, 21
SFTP	115
SNMP	161
AMX	1319
LT2P	1701 (usually configured by the router automatically)
PPTP	1723 (usually configured by the router automatically)

Device Tools

Devices on the home LAN might have their own remote-access tools for testing, configuration changes, and firmware upgrades. Examples include:

- Crestron - Toolbox, Test manager (ports 41794, 41795)
- C4 - Composer, Detective Suite (Control4 discourages port forwarding for remote access)
- AMX - Netlinx Studio (1391)
- Savant - System Monitor
- URC
- RTI
- Lutron
- Vantage

To use these tools:

- The device one is connecting to must be on the LAN.
- The device's network configuration is correct.
- The LAN subnet mask and gateway must be configured properly.

Proprietary Tools

The following proprietary remote-access tools can be used without having to change firewall or other settings on gateways and routers.

- CrossLoop
- GotoMeeting
- Join.Me
- LogmeIn
- TeamViewer
- WebEx

Custom Tools
Custom solutions offer flexibility in accessing and servicing a remote site. Once in place, the tool offers an experience similar to being on site. However, specialized configuration, operating systems, hardware, and preloaded software might be required and the tools can be complicated and expensive.

Examples include:

- Server with GotoMyPC or LogMeIn
- Server with VPN
- Server with port forwarding (VNC or RDP)

Hybrid Tools
Hybrid solutions remove complexity and save costs. Hybrid tools fall into the following categories:

- Cloud-based remote desktop solutions
- Remote power management
- Industry-specific tools

Industry Tools
There are many industry-specific solutions for hybrid remote access. Examples include:

- Ihiji Invision
- Pakedge Bakpak
- Panamax BlueBolt
- SnapAV OvrC

Dynamic DNS
Dynamic DNS (DDNS) allows connection to remote sites using hostnames instead of IP addresses.

- Because DDNS uses host names, it allows connections to a remote site even if the site's IP address keeps changing.
- DDNS is useful for sites that have dynamic (DHCP-assigned) IP addresses.
- DDNS is also useful if a site has a static IP address because it is easier to remember a hostname than an IP address.

Examples of DDNS services include:

- DynDns.org — A famous and well-implemented service found on most routers.
- no-ip.com

- Proprietary DDNS services — Found on devices such as cameras, DVRs, and control companies such as Crestron to help installers find a remote location quickly and easily.

Virtual Private Networks

A Virtual Private Network (VPN) is used to create a tunnel from the home to remote networks for remote access. VPN functions are built into many commercial-grade routers that support VPN endpoints. The PPTP VPN protocol is also built into all PCs.

VPNs offer the following features:

- Generally easily to implement.
- Standardized and widely adopted.
- Security — Best practices include a pre-shared key and/or a username and password before access is granted beyond the router and onto the network. After access has been granted, the remote user can access all the devices on the LAN that his account allows.
- Encryption — If configured properly, traffic in the tunnel is encrypted, protecting the data from others. VPN encryption adds bandwidth overhead that can reduce the data rate slightly within the secure tunnel.

VPN Encryption

VPNs offer different types of encryption:

- DES
- 3DES
- SHA1
- MD5
- AES-128
- AES-256

Higher encryption provides better security, but requires more processing power.

- On less robust devices, this can cause slowdowns.
- Choose an encryption method that balances compatibility with connecting devices and the available resources of the connecting hardware.

Configuring VPNs

When configuring VPNs, observe the following guidelines:

- To avoid routing issues, the subnet/IP scheme should be different on both sides; for site-to-site VPNs, each site must be on its own subnet.

Create a new network that is different than the default for most networks.

Avoid using the following networks:

- 192.168.0.0/24 (Default D-Link, Ruckus and others)
- 192.168.1.0/24 (Default Linksys, some Cisco, and others)
- 10.0.1.0/24 (Apple default)
- Depending on the setup, allow for DHCP over VPN when connecting with client software. This can provide an IP address on a preferred subnet within the connecting network and allows for features that are unavailable through a virtual NIC.
- For multi-layered network, configure routing rules and firewall access rules to be able to access more than just the primary network. For instance, to access three subnets remotely, specify which subnets the connecting user or device has access to. Some more basic VPNs will provide access to all subnets by default, but more advanced, security-minded devices will force one to specify them. SSL VPNs will even allow the specification of applications, ports, and protocols that a user has access to.

Split Tunneling

Split tunneling allows a user to connect to resources on the remote site through the VPN while still maintaining general Internet access at the local site. If the user tries to access resources on the internet, the traffic will be forwarded through the local ISP.

- Split tunneling is the preferred VPN configuration, as it allows for faster Internet browsing locally, without creating additional load on the remote network.
- Without split tunneling enabled, all traffic, including internet traffic, passes through the remote site unnecessarily causing slow-downs on either end.
- In some situations, split tunneling should be disabled. For instance, if an administrator wants to maintain the security rules of the firewall to protect the client, all traffic will pass through that firewall utilizing the security services within. Or if a client would like access to resources only allowed through their remote firewall IP (eg. A home in the UK may have better access to Netflix media through their UK IP address.)

Remote Network Troubleshooting

When troubleshooting a remote network:

- Enable device logs and review them to spot the cause of the problem.
- Many common issues can be caused by incorrect gateways, IP or subnet configurations.
- The inability to make a remote connection might be due to incorrect subnets, IP addresses, configurations, or incorrect or missing firewall access rules.

FIREWALLS

A firewall transfers traffic between computer networks of different trust levels and block unwanted intrusions to the LAN. Every home network should have a properly configured firewall between it and the Internet. Tips for security measures on routers include:

- Activate firewalls on all routers.
- Deactivate port translation and port forwarding unless absolutely required.
- Ensure the router is not configurable from the Internet.
- Change default passwords.
- Ensure firmware is up to date regularly.
- Configure the firewall to log access attempts. This can highlight problem areas in security.

ACCESS TO THE CLIENT'S HOME

Having remote access to systems in a house via the Internet provides several advantages:

- Access to stored media while on the road
- Remote access to live and stored CCTV images
- Control of functions such as temperature control, lighting, and TV recording while away from home
- Installing security patches and upgrading firmware for networked devices
- Ability to perform remote diagnostics
- Ability to monitor and reset equipment remotely
- Ability to program system changes to a control system and/or load new graphics files to touch panels

CHAPTER 13

SUBSYSTEMS & INTEGRATION

Systems integration can be defined as the interconnecting of all subsystems to provide useful, intelligent, and simplified control for the home owner. Successful integration requires knowledge of all electronic systems installed in the home, their components, communications protocols, standards, and maintenance needs. Combine this with a company-wide desire to establish best practice and regulatory compliance for all elements of the integrated system, and you have the wherewithal to create elegant integrated solutions that enhance the homeowner's lifestyle.

Critical elements for successful integration include:

1. An in depth knowledge of each subsystem
2. A clear understanding of lines of demarcation between subsystems
3. The ability to define and convey the added value that integration provides for the homeowner
4. The skill and knowledge to design, install, and maintain robust systems which perform as intended, with great reliability

Before we can truly integrate we must first understand each system, its primary function, the elements that make up the system and the value they add to the 'integrated system'. In most cases, the fundamentals of key systems have been covered very well in the Fundamentals of Residential Electronic Systems book, and this knowledge is assumed to be a prerequisite for anyone using this book at a more advanced level.

GENERAL GUIDELINES FOR INTEGRATION

Integrated...But Separate

Where do you draw the line between two systems? In simple terms, this might be understood as the boundaries or the interconnecting points. If, for example, some of the lighting keypads buttons are being used for simple heating control, are you able to demonstrate that the new desired set point of 21°C (68.9°F) was generated, and then travelled down the wire and arrived at the point where the heating system receives the command. It is in essence the NTTP (Network Test & Termination Point). This is analogous to the Point of Demarcation (at the Network Interface Device) where a service provider would test to determine if a problem is in the home or in the provider's system. Knowing where your system ends and another begins, and being able to have them operate independently, is critical to the troubleshooting process as well as ensuring that all individual systems are able to operate independently, if necessary.

Keep It Simple

We all like to think that we are able to make an integrated system do amazing things. However, JUST BECAUSE IT CAN DOESN'T MEAN IT SHOULD. Systems integration should provide simplification and intelligence, and above all, enhance lifestyle. We are able to simplify the homes operation because we remove the need for our client to go to each system and "tell it" that they are leaving the home. But after that, what we do with that information provides the intelligence - making useful decisions based on time, temperature, date or day, client preferences, or weather. Storing this information and then creating variables and subroutines that make informed decisions on behalf of the client is where the intelligence lies. A one-way IR code such as "TV ON" is not intelligent, the intelligence comes by adding a video or mains sensor to the TV and feeding the status of that device back in to the control system. Once you know if the TV is on, you can then choose whether you need to send it an ON command. Likewise if you know it has been raining for 3 days because you have information from a weather station, then you are able to make an informed decision about turning the sprinklers on. I think most would agree that most intelligent people wouldn't water their backyard if it had been raining for 3 days. An intelligent, automated system can make these decisions without user input.

Our role as integrators is to simplify our client's life, and that really means simplifying the systems we install. A quick count of the buttons on a TV remote might tell us there are fifty, and there's a shift key too, for DVD control. Of these, the user uses five every time they watch TV, and an additional fifteen only periodically. Many projectors enable access their menu for brightness, contrast, and specific user profiles via an RS232 module. But choosing which commands to provide your customer is part of the skill when designing systems. Just because you are able to write a driver that plumbs the depths of the projector's menus doesn't mean you should. Adding value by removing unnecessary functionality, automating the necessary, and making informed decisions (within the system) to simplify many other tasks are skills which come with experience. Whilst gaining that experience, you'll hear many a programmer say something like, "I just need to...reset/change a code line/ask the manufacturer why that doesn't work properly". If you hear problems like this, it means the customer's system is not operating properly, which is unacceptable.

Make it Solid

Robust design requires a system to be installable, repeatable, maintainable and above all safe. Knowledge of, and compliance with, local standards and safety codes is critical. NEVER compromise safety.

Also, there is much to be said for a bit of over-engineering. The systems that are not robust will become the bane of your service department's life, and none of your engineers will thank you when they are swapping out inadequate relay boxes that keep welding shut due to the inrush current of the roller blind's motor. Use properly rated, professionally manufactured components.

In conclusion, keep these three ideas at the forefront when designing integrated systems;

1. Individual systems must operate first as a complete stand alone system capable of performing their own tasks without dependency upon any other system.
2. Maintaining system integrity is a fundamental requirement for all subsystems.
3. A simple and robust system is always preferable to complex and crashing system.

With those three principles as your focus, you won't go wrong. Keep them in mind as you learn more about the individual subsystems covered in this chapter and the rest of this book. A full understanding of how each of them work, on their own and as part of a larger whole-home system, will ensure your continued success as a home technology professional.

INTEGRATING LIGHTING AND MOTORIZED SHADES

In this section, we will discuss some of the technical and design considerations which are critical to the successful installation of lighting systems, as well as the energy saving benefits and overall design philosophy. This information builds on the basics presented in the Fundamentals of Residential Electronic Systems book, and is intended for experienced technicians and designers.

Load Types

In the world of residential lighting, there are a few key lighting load types:

- Resistive lamps – Incandescent and Halogen
- Low Voltage – Magnetic or Electronic Transformer driven
- Fluorescent
- Light Emitting Diodes

Resistive Lamps

Resistive lamps are incandescent or halogen. The lamp produces a warm light but has a low lumen per watt ratio and, as a result of this inefficiency, has been taken off of the market for wattages above 40W.

Halogen lamps operate similar to an incandescent lamp but have halogen gas encapsulated within the lamp to aid in bulb life extension by re-depositing the tungsten back onto the filament after the lamp has been turned off and improving efficiency, increasing the lumen per watt ratio.

Resistive lamps are less complex from a control perspective due to the fact that the voltage and current are in a linear relationship to each other (as current increases across the load, the voltage will increase too).

Low Voltage Lighting

The lamps commonly used with low voltage lighting tend to be resistive in nature (they may also be LED). The difference between a standard resistive lamp and a low voltage one is that there is a transformer which provides voltage and current to the lamp. The primary side of the transformer will take in the full line voltage of the circuit. The secondary side will output a lower voltage, typically 12V or 24V AC, to power the lamps.

There are two types of transformers: magnetic and electronic.

Magnetic transformers:

- Typically larger, bulkier
- Metal core with wire wrapped around the primary and secondary sides
- Turns ratio of wire from the primary to the secondary side determines output voltage to load

- Commonly used for landscape lighting but sometimes for other fixture types (downlights)
- Electrically similar to an inductor
- Electronic transformers:
- Typically smaller
- More efficient than magnetic transformers
- Made up of solid state electrical components using buck regulation to transform the line voltage to the lower output voltage
- Electrically similar to a capacitor

Fluorescent

Fluorescent loads use an electric arc to force a combination of an inert gas and mercury to radiate UV which the phosphor coating of the lamp then uses to emit a visible light into the space. The light output tends to be a cooler color temperature than the low voltage or line voltage resistive lamps. The electric arc is produced by a ballast which takes line voltage in and produces the arc to strike the lamp.

There are multiple forms of fluorescent lamps from the linear (tube) style to compact.

LEDs

Light Emitting Diode (LED) lighting uses an array of diodes that, when they are forward biased by passing a direct current and voltage through them, produces illumination. LEDs are very energy efficient and provide a large lumen per watt ratio. They can also span a wide variety of color temperatures and produce light as warm as a standard incandescent lamp or as cool as a fluorescent tube lamp. The LED is provided its DC current and voltage from a driver, similar to the ballast in a fluorescent fixture.

Dimming

Forward Phase Control (Leading Edge)

Forward phase dimmers utilize solid state electronics to achieve the dimming by switching the load on and off 120 times per second, imperceptible to the human eye. Current is not conducted to the load for a portion of every half cycle of the line voltage sine wave.

The most common component for performing the switching is a semiconductive switch called a TRIAC. Once the TRIAC is switched on and conducting to the load, it must remain on until the zero cross (transition point from one half-cycle to another). The TRIAC unlatches at the zero cross and remains unlatched until it is told to latch on again.

- Shorter ON time, load less bright
- Longer ON time, load brighter

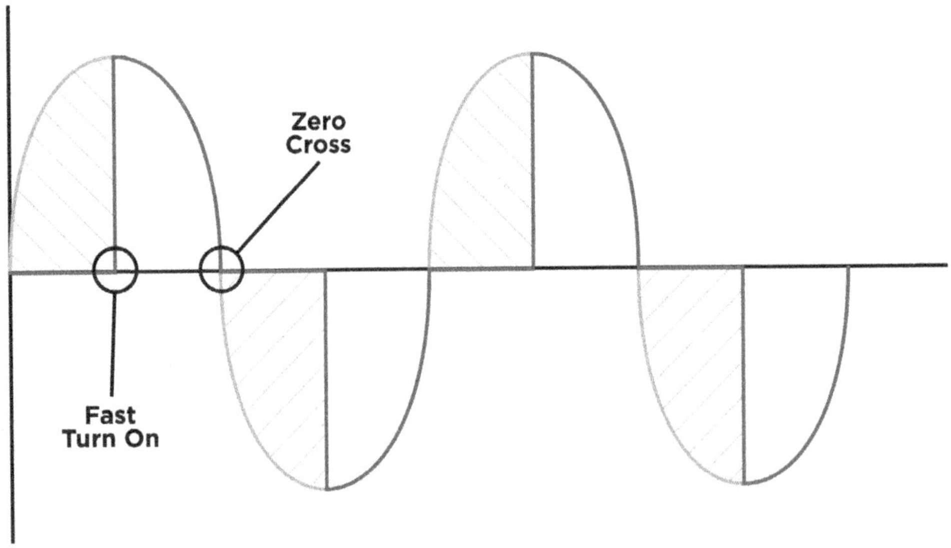

Figure 13-1 *Forward Phase Control*

Forward phase is useful for resistive load types and inductive loads (MLV). Not all forward phase dimmers can control MLV. MLV requires symmetric forward phase dimming. The positive and negative half cycles of the dimming signal need to be symmetric to each other. Asymmetry introduces DC currents to the MLV transformer which will lead to the transformer becoming very hot and can cause transformer damage. A dimming control capable of symmetric forward phase must be used for MLV.

Forward phase control is also capable of controlling certain compatible LED loads. Compatibility depends upon the driver.

Reverse Phase Control (Trailing Edge)

Reverse phase dimming is similar to forward phase dimming except that the back half of each half cycle is where there is no conduction to the load, exactly the opposite of forward phase. Instead of a fast turn on edge and gradual turn off edge, there is a smooth turn on edge and rapid off edge.

The most common component for performing the switching is a semiconductive switch called a FET (field effect transistor). FETs are used instead of a TRIAC because once the TRIAC is on it only unlatches at the zero cross. FETs can be switched off at any point of the half cycle which allows for use in reverse phase control, providing:

- Shorter ON time, load less bright
- Longer ON time, load brighter

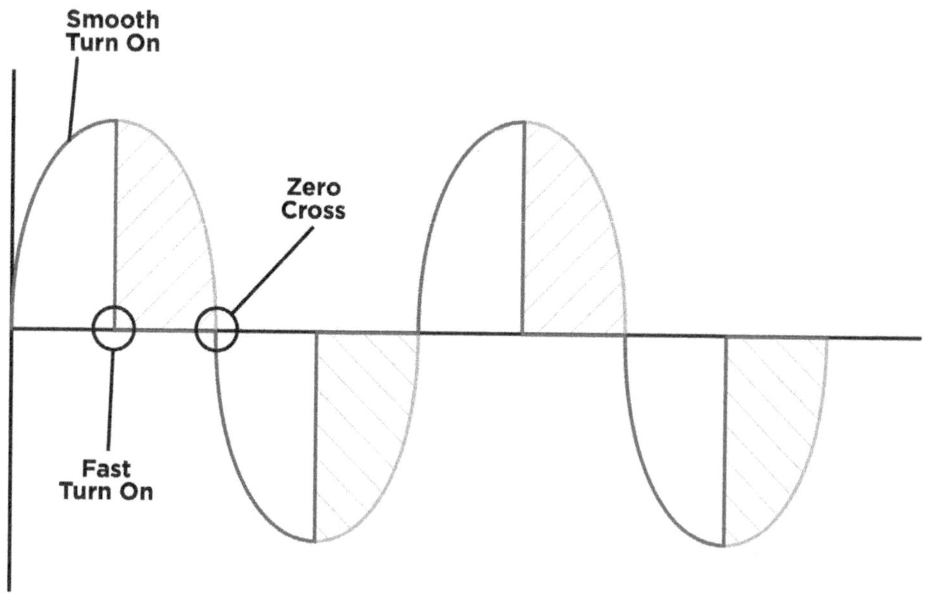

Figure 13-2 *Reverse Phase Control*

Reverse phase is typically used for capacitive load types (ELV) but can also be used for resistive load types (incandescent and halogen). Forward phase dimmers rarely work with ELV loads unless specified by the transformer. The reason is that a rapid change in voltage over a small period of time results in the potential for current spikes which can overload the dimming control. Also, the rapid turn on edge, rapidly switching at 120 times per second can cause the transformer to produce acoustic noise or buzz. Hence the need for a smoother turn-on edge for these transformers.

Reverse phase control is also capable of controlling certain compatible LED loads. Compatibility depends upon the driver.

Phase Adaptive Controls

For low voltage transformers buried out of sight, it became important for some dimming controls to have the capability of being phase adaptive. Phase adaptive controls use FETs for dimming, since they must be capable of reverse phase when required. They often can be forced into forward or reverse phase through software, but commonly are in auto-detection mode where the dimmer looks for specific load conditions to determine when to change to forward phase from reverse.

Phase adaptive controls are capable of controlling certain compatible LED loads. Compatibility depends upon the driver.

Dimming LEDs

Phase Control Dimming

Many LED drivers work well with phase control dimming. Some require forward phase, others will require reverse phase. The performance of the light engine is a function of the driver. The driver must be able to understand the phase control signal and correlate that to the proper constant current DC or pulse width modulated output. This is one of the key areas where compatibility issues may arise. The driver may not be designed to properly handle the input signal leading to poor aesthetic qualities such as flicker or shimmer.

Many of these drivers have electrical characteristics similar to that of a capacitor and, as a result, forward phase dimming can lead to repetitive peak inrush currents (RPIC). RPIC occurs every time the forward phase dimmer turns on in every half-cycle with its rapid turn-on edge. The large change in voltage over a very short period of time causes the driver circuitry to respond with RPIC. While energy savings are not affected due to the instantaneous nature of the spike, the dimmer will carry additional load, well above the rating of the lamp and could become overloaded.

Quality phase control dimming of LEDs is achievable, but requires the driver to be compatible and due to a large variety of drivers and lamps on the market, there are a lot of incompatible lamps and fixtures.

3-Wire

3-wire dimming helps to reduce challenges with phase control dimming by placing the phase control signal onto a separate high impedance wire into the driver. Power is provided by a constant hot to the driver, separating the function of control and power.

0-10V

0-10V dimming is a low voltage analogue standard where the control signal voltage level determines the light output of the fixture. The driver is provided with line voltage for power. The challenge with 0-10V dimming is that there are two versions of the standard and it is important to make sure that the appropriate control is chosen for the driver. It is often difficult to determine the standard used by the driver. In one standard, a 0V control signal indicates full off of the fixture. In the other, 0V is equivalent to low end and a switch is required to fully turn off the fixture.

0-10V is a control standard, not a performance standard, so features like low end will vary from driver to driver.

Digital Lighting

Where 0-10V is an analogue standard, there are also digital control standards for lighting. These include DALI and manufacturer specific versions of DALI where extensions have been added to the control protocol. Digital control of lighting allows for a number of benefits over traditional control schemes from a number of standpoints, including wiring. With DALI, drivers are wired on what is referred to as a loop and each loop can contain up to 64 ballasts or drivers. The control wire gauge can vary depending on the length of run needed to wire to all of the drivers on the loop. All drivers are provided with constant hot and use the control signal to determine what level to turn onto. The drivers on the loop are then grouped into zones.

Zoning is not determined by power wiring but rather on the digital grouping. Performance of the lighting, low end for example, are not set by the standard and will vary from driver to driver.

Load Calculations

Resistive Loads

Load calculations for resistive loads, such as incandescent lamps, are relatively simple. The total load on the dimming control is equal to the sum of the wattage of each lamp.

Low Voltage Loads

Low voltage lighting involves the use of a transformer to transform the line voltage amplitude down to 12 or 24 volts. If we consider the lighting load to be more resistive in nature, the total circuit load in watts is equivalent to the sum of the wattage of all lamps on the circuit plus the loss of power in the transformer.

Dimming controls that are UL listed for control of MLV lighting will have a total wattage rating for resistive loads and a volt ampere or VA rating for MLV loads. A dimmer that can control 600W of incandescent load may be capable of controlling 600VA of MLV. The wattage rating for MLV lighting would be lower than 600W because some of the wattage is lost in the transformer. The VA rating combines transformer and lamp power.

LED Loads

LED load calculations can be challenging for a number of reasons when dimming. It is not as simple as summing the total lamp wattage as indicated on the lamps themselves. There a various electrical characteristics which can complicate load calculations. It is best to follow the recommendations of compatibility and loading for each specific LED fixture or lamp as per the dimming control manufacturer. Due to variations in LED driver technology, interactions with dimming and subsequent load calculations can vary from dimmer to dimmer.

Energy Saving

Saving Energy through Lighting Control and Automation

Lighting control can maximize the energy savings for each zone of lighting. It provides aesthetic benefits through setting the right light levels for viewing a movie or bringing out the finest qualities of art. It also aims to save energy.

Phase control dimming lights, even an incandescent lamp, saves energy by not conducting energy to the lamp during portions of every half-cycle. Lamp life is extended since the filament is not getting as hot when dimmed to lower levels and thus not evaporating as much. Dimming down to 50% light level can extend the lamp life of an incandescent lamp to 20x its normal life.

Saving Energy by using Automated Window Treatments

Electricity savings through lighting, while important, is a relatively small portion of the electricity bill of a residence when compared to HVAC. Not only can smart thermostats be employed to maximize energy savings, automated shading control can be leveraged to take HVAC energy savings to the highest level possible. Consider a sunny, warm day in the summer time. The shades can be lowered during certain portions of the day so that the natural heat of the sunlight could be reflected away and prevented from entering the space. This would provide natural cooling and help prevent the HVAC equipment from turning on as often as it normal would. The opposite would be true on a sunny day in the colder winter time.

Designing the Optimal Whole House Lighting Control Experience

A well designed lighting control solution is one that maximizes and cohesively blends all of the benefits of the system together in a way that enhances the quality of life for the end user. It is a system that looks elegant and is aesthetically pleasing. For instance:

- Keypads and window treatment fabrics that complement the look of the room while providing the intuitive and responsive control of the system.
- Using only the number of buttons required at every control station
- Programming of scenes that enable one button press to control multiple system components to set the perfect environment for watching a movie or entertaining guests
- Time-clocks programmed to remove the manual processes of lighting control such as the control of landscape lighting, tied directly to the local astronomic time for an area
- Occupancy sensors that automatically turn on lights in a bathroom to the appropriate level depending on the time of day and, perhaps more importantly, automatically turn the lights off after a programmable time to save energy
- Light sensing equipment that can monitor light at the window to determine whether or not to automatically raise or lower automated window treatments, maximizing the energy savings as described in the previous section
- Integration with security systems which, when an alarm is triggered, turn interior lights to full on, exterior lights flashing to alert emergency personnel and neighbours, window treatments all raised to the open limit, and the system locked out to prevent the burglar from altering the lighting levels.

Several key technologies are transforming residential security today and are poised to have a significant impact in the future. The integration of residential security systems with home automation has never been more prevalent than today as platforms develop to enable the previously disparate technologies to integrate. The opportunities for custom installers in this area are boundless.

The emergence of interactive services has been driven by a steady drumbeat of technology innovation during the past 10 years. What began as the core ability to send commands to the security panel from a computer interface and get notifications has given way to today's systems that are far more sophisticated, offer better security and have made it easier to service and support customers. The evolution of interactive services from early adopter phase to a 'must-have' technology can be attributed to multiple factors.

First, explosive growth of mobile devices has led consumers to rely increasingly on their iPhones, iPads, BlackBerrys, Android phones and other Internet-enabled mobile devices for day-to-day activities such as monitoring and securing with their property.

The quantity and quality of interactive services continues to evolve from basic real-time text notifications to today's set of home energy management, integrated video, and new location-based capabilities. Also, the rise of interactive services reflects the extent to which consumer perception of what security means has progressed from traditional arming and disarming to an expectation for day-to-day property awareness and peace of mind. Notably, the price point for many interactive services has come down to a level that many consumers can afford and are willing to pay for.

Interactive services technology has also driven great advancements in the service and support of customers. Interactive services has made it possible to access and change most panel settings from a Web site, greatly reducing the need for a truck roll and increasing customer satisfaction with the ability to address request almost immediately. This has resulted in decreased customer support costs for accounts with interactive services and reduced attrition due to higher engagement and overall customer satisfaction.

All of this means the integrator is well positioned to merge the various security subsystems (access control, deadbolts, and cameras) into a seamless whole house control. For example, when an alarm activation takes place on a motion sensor, commands make interior lights go on, exterior lights flash, all interior and exterior IP-based cameras begin recording at higher frame rates, the HVAC system shuts down, the multi-room audio system shuts down music and annunciates an emergency notification message (if it is a fire), and the entertainment video system cuts off.

The ultimate goal being driven by the integration of security and home control is a sensor-based "conscious" home that learns the behaviour patterns of a family for setting the thermostat, activating the lighting levels, turning on and off the intrusion alarm, activating IP camera image capture and more based on simply walking into the home.

Mobile Apps Improve Retention

Mobile apps for security are also changing the landscape. For example, when the first Alarm.com app was released in the spring of 2009, the overwhelming majority of logins to an Alarm.com interactive account were through the company's Website. One year later, 50% of logins were through a mobile device and now more than 75% of remote access events for those interactive service accounts are through a mobile app.

Nearly all of the other key technologies are either enhanced or enabled by the ability for consumers to access these features via mobile apps. The traction mobile apps have gained for controlling and monitoring security, video, lights, thermostats, and locks reflect their ability to keep customers engaged with the system on a regular basis. This has, in turn, proven effective for security dealers and integrators in improving retention of existing customers, driving new customer acquisition, and delivering additional revenue-generating services.

Mobile apps have also proven transformative for the ability to change how customers interact with their home systems. Not only have mobile apps been relied upon by users remotely (at work, on vacation, etc.), but customers also are drawn to the ability to change thermostat settings, lock doors or arm the security system from the living room couch or bedroom rather than having to do so from the physical keypad. This behavioral shift positively impacts dealers, who could see equipment costs go down as customers use products they already own — for example, smartphones and tablets — to get more out of their systems.

Video in the Home Is More Common

Video as a Service (VaaS) has added a highly disruptive element to traditional home security, with both its both its technology and its price point, VaaS refers to an integrator's opportunity to, in essence, lease for a monthly fee a residential video surveillance system to a customer, following much the same mass-marketing model for burglar alarm/intrusion systems that has been in place for decades. For the integrator, it often means cloud storage of images off-site, which in turn adds more recurring revenue.

The end result is that video monitoring is no longer relegated to high-income individuals willing to spend tens of thousands of dollars for a custom installation of surveillance equipment. Everyday consumers can now take advantage of wireless IP cameras for a few hundred dollars, and because video can be stored remotely in a cloud environment, there is no need for consumers to incur a local storage device.

For security dealers and integrators, affordability, higher quality IP cameras, and the ability to deliver live or motion-triggered video clips directly to the customer translate into expanded RMR (Recurring Monthly Revenue) opportunities. At the same time, the ease at which some video monitoring solutions can be installed and compatibility with analog security cameras eliminate historical hurdles around the upgrade process. This unlocks a broader set of potential customers who have video cameras, but need interactive monitoring features that can lead to greater revenue.

Mobile apps have served as a true catalyst for generating greater value out of video for the customer by allowing for live video feeds, motion and alarm-triggered video clips, and the ability to remotely adjust pan-tilt cameras. This has transformed video from an experience that required poring through hours of video in front of a screen to being able to receive video clips to a mobile device exactly when the customer wants it and how they want to receive it.

The camera market is further adapting with the advent of cloud storage.

Tapping Into Energy Management

By 2017, an estimated 90 million homes worldwide will employ home automation systems. These projections by ABI Research hint at where this market is headed, but the fact is home automation technology is already making its presence felt with residential security today.

The flood of products and technologies dangling before security dealers and integrators, ranging from smart thermostats to wireless keypad door locks, offer multiple paths to consider when creating customer solutions for consumers. While the full potential of home automation and home energy management is not close to being realized, evidence suggests the greatest perceived consumer value to be when home automation is tightly integrated with an underlying security platform. Research by Parks Associates backs this up, finding that 40% of consumers with security systems are interested in energy management compared to 25% of those without.

By integrating home automation with the security platform, data becomes a valuable asset for customers to make more informed decisions on their use of lights, thermostats and locks for energy savings and improved security. By leveraging sensor data from the security system and setting sensor-triggered optimization rules, customers gain insight on activity in the home and can more accurately control home thermostats via 'smart schedules' or automating lights to turn on when a customer disarms the security system at night upon returning home.

The whole is greater than the sum of its parts — an end-to-end integrated solution delivers significantly enhanced value to the customer compared to a set of standalone products unable to communicate with one another.

Monitoring External Conditions

One of the more recent technologies changing residential security is the shift from simply monitoring events that occur inside the home to systems that can account for external factors and conditions ranging from weather to power outages. External condition monitoring technology has emerged over the past 12 to 18 months, allowing consumers to receive alerts to their security panel if extreme weather is approaching, so there is time to act before disaster strikes.

Integrators can now also layer in technology for consumers to automatically set thermostats during periods of extremely hot or cold weather, which helps individual consumers save money by reducing energy consumption.

Another technology innovation now working its way into residential security is the use of a person's location to trigger security system events, a.k.a. Location-Based Services (LBS). Security dealers and integrators now have access to LBS technology that is integrated with the security platform, providing customers with the ability to automate system rules and notifications for the security system, lights, locks, and thermostats based on their mobile phone location.

For example, based on the physical location of a smartphone, LBS enables a reminder notification to be sent to the customer if they move a certain distance (one mile, five miles, etc.) from their house and forget to arm the security system or turn off the lights.

Somewhat in the same vein, GSM (Global System for Mobile Communications, originally Groupe Spécial Mobile), cell backup devices are becoming prevalent in alarm systems to prevent line-cuts. These systems untether the alarm system from the plain old telephone service (POTS) to be cellular based. But, they also enable dealers to sell upgrade GSM modules and/or increase monthly monitoring fees. Many installers are already using these as the primary means for emergency communications with monitoring stations. Others are using it as a backup in case something was to disable the regular landline. Regardless, the solution is easy to install and gives the customer additional reassurance that their property is secure.

Key Technologies

- *Smartphones* — With consumers increasingly relying on smartphones, tablets and other mobile devices for home security and automation, mobile apps can help increase customer interaction and keep them "sticky" while serving as a valuable sales tool to close prospective customers.

  Also, since cell phones mostly include GPS monitoring, the technology enables geo-locating services for integrators. In this, the cell phone acts a locator that automatically activates the alarm system when the smartphone is a certain distance from the home, such as one miles radius.
- *Residential Access Control* — Residential access control is a limited, but growing market. Today, it primarily exists in gated communities or multi-dwelling units (MDUs) where homeowners need proximity cards are pushbutton codes to enter the parking facility or the condo complex. In single-family residences, it is relegated to ultra-high-end homes where the homeowner has an interest in denying access to certain family members or service staff such as maids or gardeners.

- *Smart Deadbolts* — For many years, oddly, security systems controlled everything but the deadbolt to the home. Today, smart locks from various manufacturers, including Schlage, Yale and Kwikset/Black & Decker, have made their way onto the market. These units often use wireless communications via Z-Wave or ZigBee, for example, to communicate door entry and exit information for generating open/close reports and tracking the card user. Moreover, homeowners can unlock the front door from their cell phone or iPad, allowing housekeepers or emergency personnel access to the home at their discretion. Automating these locks means that every door can be secured immediately upon arming the alarm or at a certain time of night. These devices have filled the gap that existed between motion sensors, door and window contacts, and other devices controlled by the intrusion panel to the front door.
- *Driveway Sensors* — One commercial product that's now making its way into home installations is the wireless driveway sensor or vehicle detection device. Installers simply hook up a wireless receiver to the automation controller and mount the detection device near the driveway. Now, when a vehicle is detected using earth's magnetic field, the automation system can automatically activate lighting, video surveillance or an alarm. That automation was simple and required no digging or extreme wire runs.
- *IP Cameras* — Interior and exterior IP cameras have opened up a barrage of possibilities for integrators and homeowners. Cameras can automatically transmit images onto a homeowner's TV set, smartphone, PC or tablet. Even better, cameras can include motion analytics that isolate certain zones of the image (or the entire image) and activate recording functions and transmission functions only when motion is detected. This reduces recording space onsite via a DVR, off-site on an NVR or in the cloud.
- *Home Robots* — What is the next paradigm for security in the home? Some believe it could be robots. Robots could someday be fully integrated with the smart home operating system and help manage it, along with providing assistance doing manual tasks. Further robotics technologies of sensing, learning, and adapting will be crucial to enhancing the underlying functions of the smart home.
- *Home Health* — The integration of health monitoring equipment could be on the way. Personal Emergency Response Systems (PERS) aimed at the elderly or disabled have been on the market for years and they are growing in use, especially as the U.S. population ages. The next generation of these devices can monitor heart rate, blood pressure, blood sugar and more. Systems are already on the market that include bed pressure sensors, cabinet sensors, oven sensors, and refrigerator sensors to monitor the daily activities of loved ones remotely.

HVAC SYSTEMS

HVAC systems provide a comfortable environment in the living spaces of the home. Though the installation of the HVAC system is not part of the integrator's role, the integration of the HVAC system controls to other systems is a frequently requested task in the industry. To accomplish this, a basic knowledge of the different types and functions of HVAC systems is needed.

HVAC systems include the following functions:

- Heating
- Cooling
- Air filtration/ventilation/quality
- Humidification/dehumidification

The equipment chosen to maintain a comfortable living environment is based on the type of home construction and the climate in the region.

Types of HVAC Systems

Before considering integrating different types of HVAC systems, the designer should be familiar with the various system types and the typical applications in which they are used. Although HVAC systems are uniquely configured to support varying technologies and individual building requirements, they all perform very similar functions. Remember that the focus is not to provide an HVAC system, but to be able to successfully integrate the particular type of HVAC system with other systems in the home. The first step is to understand a little about the systems and how they work. There are a variety of system types which an integrator might run across. Some homes may have a steam boiler system and radiators (the heat source may be coal, oil, or natural gas), others may have radiant heating in the floors (electric or heated fluid). Some Multi-Dwelling Units (MDU) share a large chiller on the roof for cooling. In some locales, geothermal subsystems moderate the home's temperature by taking advantage of the constant temperatures below ground level, making it much easier and cost effective to heat or cool the home to the desired goal temperature.

The most common HVAC system, however, is the forced-air system, where an air handler moves conditioned air (temperature, humidity) throughout the home. In this case, the system may have the capability of controlling air flow to different parts of the home, and the user often has some direct control of the fan and whether heat or cooling is desired.

These systems are generally configured as a "split system" with the air handler located inside the strucure and an outdoor unite to either dissipate heat or harvest heat from the outside air, or both.

Heat/Cool System

In this type of system, the indoor unit handles the heating (may be electric, oil, natural gas, or propane). Cooling is accomplished with evaporator coils within the air handler unit (absorbs heat as refrigerant changes from liquid to gas) and an outdoor unit with condenser coils (releases heat as refrigerant changes back to liquid). In both cases, the air handler (fan) moves this warm or cool air to the rooms in the house.

Heat Pump

A heat pump system is configured basically the same as the Heat/Cool system, however the indoor and outoor coils can reverse their function, depending on the need for heating or cooling. The outdoor unit is able to either dissipate heat or absorb heat from the ambient air. This makes the heat pump system very cost-effective in moderate climates, where the temperatures do not get below freezing. In cooler climates, supplemental heating technologies are implemented.

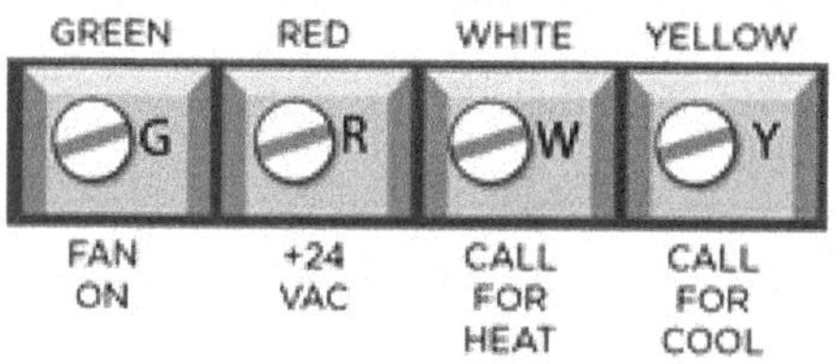

Figure 13-3. *Four-Wire Thermostat Wiring*

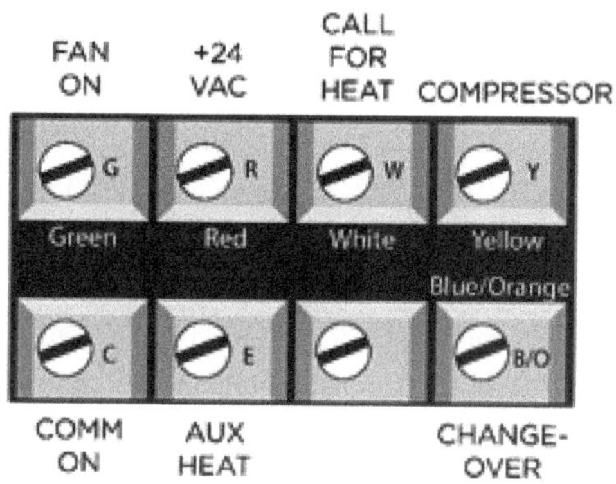

Figure 13-4. *Heat Pump Thermostat Wiring*

Zones

Zoning allows control of two or more areas from the same HVAC unit, rather than having completely separate systems. Motorized dampers that are inserted in-line in the supply ductwork control airflow to zoned areas. Requests from each zone thermostat go to a zone controller that manages the requests and ensures that the appropriate damper or dampers are fully open and that the unit is running. The zone controller also manages safeguards, such as ensuring compressors are not turned on while the fan is off thus potentially freezing supply pipes

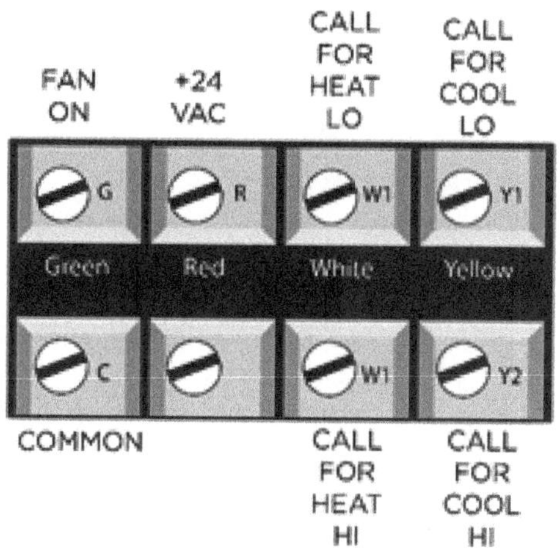

Figure 13-5. *Multi-stage Thermostat Wiring*

and coils. Traditional wiring connects the thermostats to the zone controller and the zone controller to the HVAC unit. The exceptions are systems that integrate the thermostats with the zone controller and, sometimes, the zone controller with the HVAC unit. In these cases, the manufacturer's thermostats and sensors must be used. Either way, understanding the options for interfacing to the proposed control system is very important.

Theater and Equipment Considerations

Home theater systems can present special challenges for HVAC systems because they include a lot of heat-generating audio, video, and computer equipment in one location. Amplifiers, integrated receivers, media centers, computers, plasma TVs, projectors, lighting, and even humans all contribute to the heat load in a space. The challenge is to remove the heat and keep the equipment cool and running properly without adding a lot of noise. The goals of Home Theater HVAC design are:

- Occupant Comfort
- Acceptable Equipment Environment
- Acceptable Noise Floor

Acceptable occupant comfort is created by having the HVAC designed to deliver an ambient temperature of 60°–75°F (20°–23.9°C) with a relative humidity between 30%–60%. The equipment rack or room should have an operating temperature ≤ 85°F (29.4°C).

The additional heat loads, background noise specifications, and ventilation requirements should all be considered and discussed with the HVAC designer or installer early in the project. Maintaining the comfort and keeping the equipment cool is important, but hearing the HVAC equipment any more than necessary is to be avoided. Care must be taken to design the HVAC to minimize noise. Typically noise generated by the HVAC should have an RC(N) < 25, with total noise being ≤30dB/A. The systems designer must serve as the driving force to ensure that the theater space is quiet and comfortable. This often means providing specific requirements to the HVAC contractor.

Thermostats

HVAC systems are controlled by thermostats. A thermostat monitors the ambient temperature and sends commands to the system in order to maintain a desired temperature. In its simplest form, the user must select either heat or cool manually. More sophisticated thermostats may be programmed for different goal temperatures for heating and cooling, and for different times and days of weeks. Some will automatically switch from heating to cooling as needed. These often have a feature which prevents the heat/cool temperatures to be set too close together, resulting in frequent switching between heating and cooling. Sometimes, the reading on the thermostat does not accurately reflect the temperature in the room because of the thermostat's location or simply the thermostat itself. There is no problem with adjusting the setting on the thermostat to lower or increase the actual temperature of the area. Additionally, there is no negative effect on the economy of the system because the actual temperature of the room isn't warmer or cooler, just the setting required to achieve that temperature. A room that has many inefficient windows, for example, may be warmer or cooler throughout its space than the location of the thermostat.

Communicating thermostats allow home technology professionals to integrate HVAC systems with the other systems in the home. For example, the security system indicates the presence of smoke in the home and sends a signal to the central control system, which can shut off all HVAC fans to minimize the spread of smoke throughout the home. Most communicating thermostats, like regular thermostats provide local setting of:

- Heat and cool set points
- Thermostat mode: heat, cool, auto, and off
- Fan mode: on, off

Humidistats

Humidistats provide area control of relative humidity. Maintaining the relative humidity between 30% and 60% can improve comfort as well as prevent damage to the home and its belongings. Most of us have experienced the differences between a humid and a dry climate. The same can apply in the home if the humidity is not controlled. If the normal process of the heating or cooling a room removes too much humidity, then it may be necessary to add a humidifier. On the other hand, in more tropical climates where there is too much humidity, a dehumidifier might be needed. Special areas such as wine cellars, home theaters, or rare book collections often need special humidity controls.

HVAC Integration

The HVAC system and its controls must be able to stand alone and be maintained without the constant involvement of the integrator. The best option is to have a communications interface that, when disconnected, does not affect the operation of the HVAC system. This precaution will require pre-planning of the system interface in close collaboration with all parties involved. Understanding what kind of HVAC system has been installed is extremely important so that the correct communicating thermostat can be installed that will both match the HVAC equipment and service the integrator's equipment and applications as well.

Adding a layer of energy monitoring and HVAC control to the control system can result in significant savings, especially if the client has access to "time of use" utility rates. An intelligent system can perform demand management, which allows the client to cut down on simultaneous power use during utility peak hours (usually described in the utility rate plan). HVAC is the biggest "offender" and can often be shut down for brief amounts of time without impacting client comfort, thus reducing load on the grid and minimizing the "demand charge" on the utility bill.

The control system can integrate with the HVAC system in a variety of ways depending on the HVAC and control system manufacturers. Most control systems will integrate directly with the manufacturer's thermostats, third party thermostats, or with the control system vendor's thermostats. The thermostat is the most obvious point of interconnect since the control system is able to simulate human input at the thermostats. While it is possible to control HVAC systems by directly interrupting connections between the thermostats and the HVAC systems, it's not advised as it could make troubleshooting difficult for the HVAC technician and the integrator. This configuration also ensures proper operation of the HVAC system in the event of control system failure.

A user interface must also be provided either by the control system vendor or a third party. The user interface allows for access to all thermostat settings including cool set point, heat set point, hold modes, HVAC modes, fan modes, and schedules. If mobile access is permitted, a smart phone user interface can provide for easy remote access to the control system to set back heating and cooling set points while away or restore them before arriving home.

Programming Scripts

A key benefit of control system integration to HVAC systems is the ability to automate tasks using programming scripts. Most control systems permit custom programming, allowing the integrator to tailor custom HVAC control strategies for the client. Energy Management with HVAC HVAC accounts for over 50% of energy consumption in a home. With a control system integrated with HVAC, several advanced energy savings strategies can be created.

House Modes — House modes involve basic programming which allows the client to activate scenes such as "Home", "Away", "Vacation", etc. An "Away" scene could adjust thermostat set points one or two degrees to achieve some energy savings while away from home for short periods of time. A "Vacation" scene could adjust thermostats more aggressively while away for extended periods.

Schedules — Some basic schedules can be programmed from the user interface but are usually stored locally on the thermostats. This way, if the control system becomes disabled, the thermostat schedules will continue to run.

Online Cloud Energy Services — An emerging area of energy management is the integration of control systems with online energy management services. A driver added to a control system can allow communications with the online energy service, to track energy usage and thermostat settings.

Clients and integrators can access the online service to create unique energy savings rules that will control the HVAC system to minimize energy usage and demand on the utility grid.

Working with HVAC Contractors

The objective in integrating HVAC with other subsystems is to provide customers with the ability to control and monitor their HVAC systems from many of the same integrated controls, such as touch panels, remotes and smartphones used to control lighting, audio/video, security, and other systems in the home. To accomplish this goal, discussions must take place with the HVAC designer and installer to find the best method to link the HVAC system to the home's automation system. This may be as simple as replacing the standard thermostat with a communicating thermostat. However, as HVAC equipment becomes more sophisticated, the interface options are also becoming more complex. The key to working with any outside contractor is clearly defining responsibilities. For example, the integrator might have the HVAC contractor design and install the system without any automation. After the system is fully functional, the thermostats can be upgraded to communicating thermostats. The integrator can then communicate with the thermostats through the control system. The integrator needs to provide a means to disable this communication and restore local control for the purpose of servicing the HVAC system and troubleshooting any problems that might come up.

TELEPHONE SYSTEMS

Telephone systems and services remained relatively unchanged for nearly 100 years, but in the last few decades, that landscape has evolved rapidly. Today the integrator must be able to navigate a virtual "wild west" of voice options. In 1984, the regulated monopoly in the US known as the Bell System was broken up into regional operating companies and the door was opened to competition, not only among those "baby Bells," but to a wide variety of other innovative companies. Even in countries where the telecommunications industry is owned by the government there are ways of getting around that monopoly, and new communication options are being offered, giving the consumer more choices. These choices create challenges for the integrator who is coordinating the technologies in the home.
These changes have made the systems integrator even more important in helping the end user select the best options for their voice service. As part of the design process, the integrator's first task is to fully understand the requirements of the customer.

POTS

The term has been used to describe the traditional analog telephone system for many years. The acronym is widely considered the abbreviation for Plain Old Telephone System, however, since many of the first telephone exchanges were housed in the local post office, that may be the actual origin of the nickname. If the home is going to be served by this type of telephone system, the following things need to be understood:

- How many voice lines will be needed?
- Will DSL or FAX services be on these lines?
- How many telephones will be needed?
- Will the combined total of all devices exceed an REN Of 5 per line?
- Will the system include cordless handsets?
- Will intercom or door stations be part of this system?

The answers to these questions will direct the design and installation of the telephone system in the home. If DSL, fax, or security is part of the system, then filters or switches might be needed to ensure proper operation of the equipment. The number of lines and locations of the phone equipment will direct the pre-wire requirements. If intercom and door station features are desired, a commercial style telephone system may be required.

REN

The Ringer Equivalence Number (REN) is a measurement of the electrical loading effect of one basic telephone on the telephone line. A total load on a telephone line which is too high can affect services like call waiting, caller ID, and ADSL. For this reason, most traditional systems are limited to 5 telephones. If the system includes cordless handsets or other modern devices, the number can often be expanded without impact on the REN load on the line. Many new analog telephones have an REN of less than one some even less than .5 so the limitation to the total REN of 5 not the number of telephones.

VoIP

Voice over IP has become a popular option for not only commercial but residential installations. Rather than using dedicated lines tied to the telephone infrastructure, this type of system utilizes the internet and is dependent on the network in the home.

If VoIP is chosen as the solution these questions need to be covered:

- Who will be the service provider?
- Will the system be hosted or will it require premises located equipment?
- Will the IP network be able to support the addition of VOIP services?

The answers to these questions will have an impact not only on the installation of the phone system and the network resources needed to ensure a properly functioning phone system, but also on the user's satisfaction with the system.

There are a large number of VoIP service providers, they include the cable company, the local phone company and a myriad of independent providers who use the "always on" broadband connection to the customer's home to ensure connectivity to the cloud. In order to use the network for VoIP, there must be enough bandwidth available to transport the voice packets. This is where the value of a properly built robust enterprise grade network is made evident. The use of residential grade networking equipment will not allow for the proper transport of VoIP services. Most networks can handle the larger TCP (Transmission Control Protocol) data packets used for many of the services utilizing the network, but VoIP uses many small UDP (User Datagram Protocol) packets to transport its data. This method of transport is used to reduce the delay time in the network as the packets transverse the many routers, switches and media converters necessary to make the trip from the speaker to the listener and for the listener to respond. In order to accomplish this, it does not have the error correction features of TCP. If the delay or latency in the network is 150ms or greater for the data to get from the speaker to the listener, it can create an echo in the audio. When the round trip for the data to carry on a conversation exceeds 400ms, problems arise as one person starts to speak before the other has finished speaking. If the time of transmission between VoIP packets varies by more than 30ms, there will also be perceived delays in how the listener hears the speaker. This variation, known as "jitter" is compensated for by a jitter buffer, however, if the network is poorly designed, this buffer could reset and cause audio dropouts. While the amount of data to complete a VoIP call is not huge (21-320Kbps per call), this data must be handled properly. One network configuration tool that helps VoIP function properly is QoS (Quality of Service), basically a way to reserve a portion of the bandwidth in the network for VoIP services only. This can help reduce delay, jitter, and latency. QoS may not be available on low cost network equipment, but is always part of an enterprise grade network.

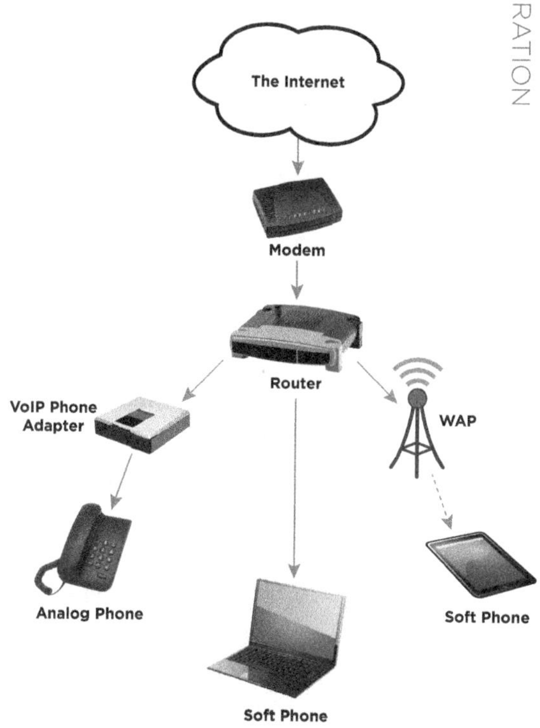

Figure 13-6 *VoIP Telephone System*

A Hybrid Solution

Finally, it might be appropriate to offer the customer a solution that includes both good old fashioned POTS and VoIP services. There are two reasons to offer this as a recommendation, first if the network goes down so does the customer's ability to communicate with the outside world. The POTS service would still likely be available. Secondly, since VoIP relies on an IP address rather than a physical location, 911 and enhanced 911 services could be compromised. POTS has a fixed location tied to a known connection, and can be located by a physical address. Emergency responders can locate the caller without being given an address by the caller. As VoIP technology continues to improve, these problems will be less of an issue, but for now a clear understanding by both the integrator and the customer is important.

DIGITAL HOME HEALTH CARE

Home Health Care (HHC) includes a broad range of health care services which can be administered in the home rather than at a health care facility or doctor's office. Digital Home Health Care is a relatively new discipline which utilizes the internet, digital media, and a variety of electronic devices to provide a range of benefits, which enhance not only the health care of the individual (usually a senior citizen), but their interaction with others. It can also do a great deal to provide peace of mind for the relatives and caretakers of the individual by notifying those people if and when anything takes place which is out of the ordinary.

For example, a person "aging in place" (living at home rather than in an assisted living environment) can easily record vital statistics like blood pressure, and report these readings when the visit the doctor. However, with wireless technologies and the internet, this data can be sent immediately to the health care professionals. Other situations which might be cause for alarm can be instantly relayed to family members or even call for emergency services. There can be sensors added to vials of medication that can indicate when they are used, and things like weight, temperature, blood sugar, etc. can be monitored when the medication is taken so that the patient's diagnosis and treatment can be improved in relation to the medication that was taken. All of this information is managed via a customized system which is designed specifically to meet the client's needs.

Benefits

The homeowner is not the only one who can benefit from the implementation of a digital Home Health Care system.

1. *User* — The primary client becomes connected to the outside world and is able to remain in the home. This is sometimes called "aging in place". This connection is not just related to health care but can greatly improve their interaction with family and friends, using telepresence applications. It is known that improving the social interaction of an aging person can have very real health benefits. This interaction may go beyond family and friends to include church, education opportunities, and more.
2. *Family* — There is a great deal of peace of mind associated with

knowing what is going on with their loved one. They know they can be alerted to virtually any kind of activity (or lack thereof) that the system is designed to address.

3. *Health care provider* — Time can be of the essence when it comes to medical issues. Health care professionals can be alerted to a number of different scenarios, and respond more quickly than they normally would be able to respond.
4. *Integrator* — most of these systems involve a Recurring Monthly Revenue (RMR) model, which is becoming a key component of many integrators' business model. In addition, providing a service of this type often leads to referrals and additional projects with friends and family of the primary client.

System Components

There are literally an infinite number of possible sensors which could be used in a system of this type, depending on the individual needs of the client. In general they will fall into these categories:

- *Motion sensors* — just as in a security system, motion sensors let the system know when the occupant is moving around, and where.
- *Heat sensors* — multiple sensors can be used in different rooms. If most of the home is 70°F (21°C) and one room is 21°F (-6°C), a window or door may be open. These sensors could also cause an alert in case of a fire or even a stove being left on past a certain time.
- *Pressure sensors* — pressure pads under a mattress can indicate if occupant is in bed. Sensors in other locations can log movement around the house.
- *Door contacts* — not just exterior doors but cabinet doors: (Did the occupant take their medicine this morning?) ... or a refrigerator door, or garage door.
- *Security system* — the sensors used in the security systems, such as door sensors, can do double duty and provide additional information about when a door is opened, closed, or left open.
- *Personal Emergency Response Systems (PERS)* — this is a device worn by the occupant. It allows for manual activation of an alert if the person has an accident. One of the main risks the elderly face when living in their home alone is the possibility of a fall. Think: "I've fallen and I can't get up."

Who Should Be Doing This Work?

It is important that the company designing and installing a system of this type have a broad knowledge of subsystems, sensors, and logic programming. For this reason, a systems integration company is a very good candidate. They already have the experience, tools, and professionalism to help the client make good decisions regarding the functionality of the system.

This skill set includes exhaustive and comprehensive client discovery as well as properly designing, installing and testing the system. There is also a lot of programming and logic involved if the system is to truly meet the specific needs of the client. CEDIA channel integrators are generally experienced in all of these.

It should be noted that a system of this type does involve a certain measure of life safety. For this reason, some jurisdictions may require security licensing to do this work.

And for the same reason, the system must have 24/7/365 dependability. Much of this will depend on a solid and robust home network and internet connection.

In conclusion, the concept of "aging in place" and digital home health care is becoming more mature and viable as the population ages, and technology advances. Systems integrators who choose to engage this new trend may find it to be a good fit in their business model and a way to generate consistent cash flow.

CHAPTER 14

THE DESIGNER AND THE PROCESS

DESIGN OVERVIEW

Design is CEDIA's middle name, and may be the single most important aspect of our profession. We pride ourselves with technical knowledge of equipment, parts and programming. Those bits are, indeed, "where the rubber meets the road". Design, more importantly, IS the road. Design describes the path we take from loosely defined client desires to brilliantly executed personal solutions for complex and unique electronic lifestyles. Understanding where you need to go is primary to how you intend to get there. In other words, designers take the time to solve the right problems. This is the essence of design for personal electronic systems integration—to uncover the spoken and unspoken true needs of a client along with everyone else who will touch the wide variety of systems CEDIA professionals provide.

Design is hard to define because it is so fundamental, often assumed, and yet rarely perfected. In this chapter, we will explore new thinking about the design process, and describe concrete tools you can use to discover essential client needs and then convey them to your team so those dreams can be fulfilled with appropriate, predictable and profitable results!

Design as a Business Model

Many integrators place too much emphasis on early-stage sales, forget the importance of design and engineering, and then try to recover from mistakes during the scramble of late-stage installation. This approach can spell financial disaster, while another philosophy can be your key to prosperity. Let's take a close look at the following diagram.

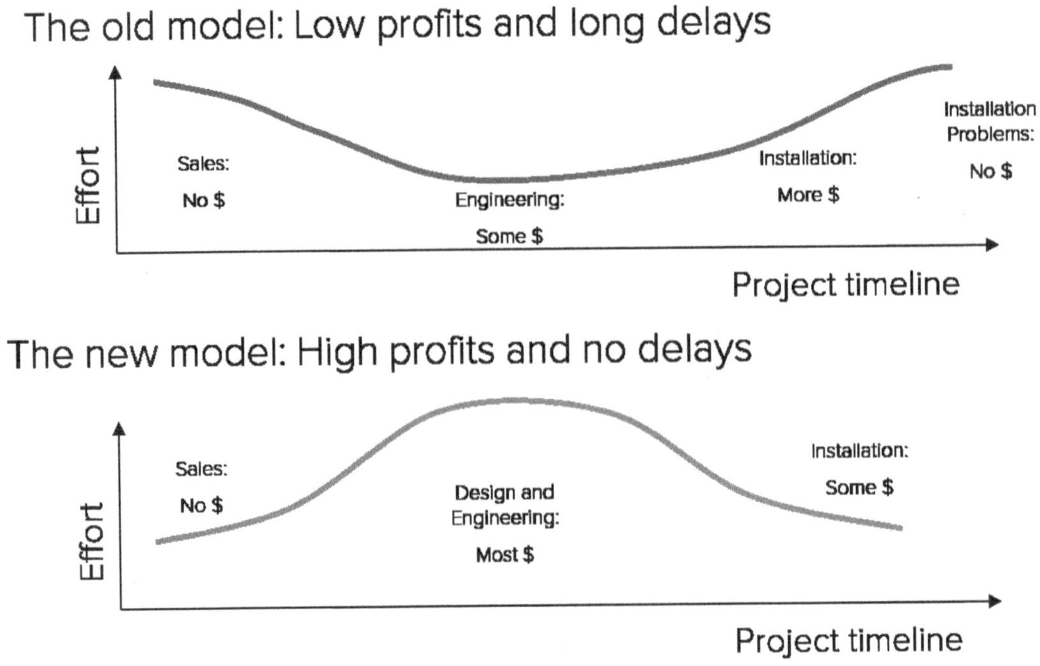

Figure 14-1 *Design as a Business Model*

Taking the time and making the effort to carefully explore client needs, then describing them in precise, measurable language to get predictable, repeatable results is the key to profitability and success. Rather than promising the world to a client you really haven't taken the time to explore options with, be smart and perform a proper needs assessment. When you begin a project, there are many unanswered questions. How can you know what your clients really need? Ask them! This is where designers can make or break the success of a project. Excellent designers know how to ask the right questions, elicit useful answers and convey them to the engineering and installation teams in terms they can understand. Take the time to get this part right.

Interaction Design

From interfaces between computers and humans, to interfaces between humans and hand tools, interaction design uses both art and science to connect people with technology. Successful interaction designs have simple, well-defined goals, a strong purpose and an intuitive interface between the user and the tool. When designing user interfaces, keep the intended user in mind at all times. Ironically, this may not be the person writing the check! Explore the needs of everyone who will touch the system, including visiting relatives and service staff.

Simplifying Design

Getting a design into its final form involves a number of steps. Whether it's the screen on a computer, app on a mobile device or a wall-mounted keypad, people are responding to products with simpler features. We often start with long wish list and "must-haves" and then narrow it down to a final design using tools such as user or focus groups to test validity. A good design is often defined by its short "learning curve". The more intuitive the design is, the shorter the learning curve, and the more easily it can be adopted by the user. Be courageous and remove all unnecessary features. If a button is visible, it must be usable, and vice versa. If a feature is needed, it must be visible. Design the interfaces with minimal button pushes and thoughtful button feedback. Try to avoid hidden buttons or features and always keep the needs of the intended user in mind.

Human-Centered Design

Human-centered design has its origins in disciplines such as computer science, ergonomics, product design and artificial intelligence.

ISO 9241-210, an International standard titled "Ergonomics of Human-centered System Interaction" defines this design process as "an approach to systems design and development that aims to make interactive systems more usable by focusing on the use of the system and applying human factors/ergonomics and usability knowledge and techniques".

All too often, complex electronic systems are created to show off the knowledge of the engineers. They bake too many features into the system and cause stress with users, who simply want to get something done. Before committing to a design, build simple mock-ups and prototypes and perform usability testing with the people who will actually use the system. This is the essence of human-centered design. Systems are created for real people with a perfect fit for their size, capabilities and desires.

One example of human-centric design is wearable technology and the way it brings technology closer to the user.

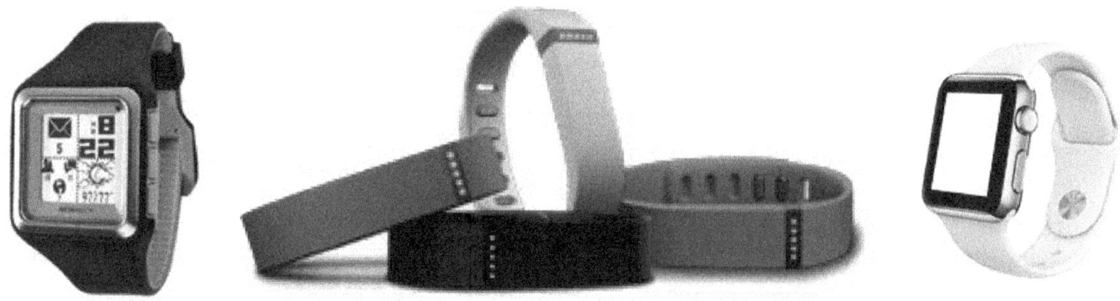

IDEO

IDEO was founded by David Kelly, who also founded the Hasso Plattner Institute of Design at Stanford University, or d.school as it is generally known. IDEO is an award-winning global design firm that takes a human-centered, design-based approach to helping organizations in the public and private sectors innovate and grow.

The d.school at Stanford champions the modern design philosophy. Students from all disciplines seek to study innovative design processes where human values are the core of a collaborative approach.

Students are taught a 5-step process.

- Empathize: Discover the needs of the user.
- Define: Understand what is unique in the user's situation.
- Ideate: Brainstom. Come up with creative ideas that fit the goal.
- Prototype: Create a physical product to test the potential solutions.
- Test: Get feedback on your solutions and refine the next iterations of prototypes. Observe and learn about possible new solutions.

The free HCD Toolkit provided by the d.school walks users through the human-centered design process and supports them in activities such as building listening skills, running workshops, and implementing ideas.

DESIGN PROCESS

Design is a process that starts with intimate awareness of the needs of the intended user(s) then continues through stages of iteration and refinement. Eventually, we discover the right answers to the right questions. Designers wear several hats during the different phases of a project.

Initially, as a communicator, you need to identify the factors that will define success with the project. Listening to others is a key component to this. By allowing other people associated with the project, initially this would be the client, to talk about their needs and desires, the information obtained will be more appropriate for them. Later, the ability to communicate will improve all phases, from engineering to project management, system verification and commissioning. Always use language that is well suited to the listener. The goal is to inform, not impress.

Another skill is acting as an anthropologist, studying people to determine their habits and traits. This, in turn, will elicit information that will be useful in determining a functional design that fits their environment and lifestyle.

Having a well-informed vision for the desired result will allow you to connect the dots. For example, realizing that a particular technology matched with the intended user's specific needs will achieve the goals of the project is a skill that will serve you well.

Engineering is an essential skill. Knowing your electronics fundamentals and understanding what can and can't be done are critical to the success of the project.

Acting as the project manager during all phases of the project is one of the other skills that is required of the designer. Ensuring that everyone involved knows what is expected of them will help them carry out their responsibilities and succeed.

It is very important to remember that you are the representative of the client. One of your major responsibilities is to ensure that the schedule is met, and if things are not on track, make changes to get them back on track. Inspect the work at regular intervals to ensure design compliance. We all make common mistakes, and the designer is the most qualified person to catch them before they escalate into huge problems.

The Five Step Process

One way to clarify client needs is to implement the "Problem Seeking Model", as described by William Pena and Steven Parshall in their excellent book "Problem Seeking: An Architectural Programming Primer". Following this process will get you much of the information you need to accurately define the project.

1. Establish Goals; Ask "why" before "how". What does the client want to achieve, and why. Your client interviews will give you an insight to their goals.
2. Collect and Analyze Facts; What do we know and what is given? Separate the facts from fiction. You must determine what is factual from the information that is given to you and that information needs to be verified.
3. Analyze and Test Concepts; How does the client want to achieve the goals? Use quick, low-resolution methods to test the concept and see if there are any obvious issues at this stage.
4. Determine Needs; How much money and space are available? What level of quality is desired? Match the budget to the highest level of quality you can attain.
5. State the Problem; What are the significant conditions affecting the design of the system? What direction should the design take? Present the needs analysis to your engineers in the form of problem(s) to be solved. Use clear, unambiguous language to state project goals.

Design Considerations

There are four primary design considerations that you should take into account when starting a project.

Function takes into account the people who are going to be using the design, their activities and relationships with other people.

Form determines the site where it will be installed, the environment in which it operates, and the level of quality.

Economy is largely associated with costs such as the initial budget. This may be difficult to determine. Clients usually don't want to tell you what they are willing to spend as they think you will maximize the budget. You may have to determine a budget based upon other information you obtain. Also consider the total cost of the system, which includes operating, and lifecycle costs.

Time could include constraints on project completion, the life of the design and past issues that could be problems. Consider future needs as well. A good design will be relevant for the long-term needs of the user. Plan for future upgrades so they seamlessly weave into the design.

Table 14-1 *Design Considerations*

Function Form	People Activities Relationships Site Environment Quality
Economy Time	Initial budget Operating costs Lifecycle costs Past Present Future

Information Index

We can now combine five-step process and the design considerations to create an Information Index. This will help you make the project more understandable from all available information.

The graphic below shows an Information Index that is filled in with some simple but effective words to describe each box.

Table 14-2 *Information Index*

	Establish Goals	Analyze Facts	Test Concepts	Determining Needs	State Scope
Function	Fun	Users, Family	Flows	Space	Performance Requirements
Form	Comfort	Site	Access	Style	Form Considerations
Economy	Value	Budget	Cost Control	Cash Flow	High Value Low Cost
Time	Growth	Importance	Phasing	Deadline	Long Range Performance

THE ROLES OF THE DESIGNER

In simple terms, the designer is a multitasker. The ability to transition into different roles is one of the key traits of a successful designer. In many cases, the designer must be aware of the role they inevitably play in sales and marketing, not just design and engineering.

Marketing, or the skill to identify what is available in terms of technology, environment and other factors is needed so that when presenting ideas to the client in response to their input, you can convey solutions that are relevant and achievable.

Sales is a combination of listening, learning and teaching. The best sales people are confident, knowledgeable and "people-oriented", they relate easily to others. Don't be a "know-it-all". If a client asks a question that you don't know the answer to, don't guess or make up an answer. Tell them you will get back to them with the correct information after doing some research. Not being empathetic to your potential customer may cost you the project.

Once you have successfully won the project, the system design must be finalized. This involves exploring possibilities in terms of technology, client information obtained from interviews, environment and other factors that determine a coherent, complete design.

After you have completely explored the needs of your client and precisely described what problems have been identified, you become the engineer, or problem solver. You determine what can or can't be done given the technical resources at your disposal. Engineering is the real world in that there may be things that are part of the design that are not achievable, either in terms of technology or budget. Any issues must be conveyed to the client as early as possible.

After you have an agreement on a final design with the client, it's time to become a project manager. Key components for this role are scheduling and keeping track of the progress of the project to ensure a successful and timely completion. Frequent client communication is required as an informed client a happy client. Even if your company has full time project managers, it is still the responsibility of the designer to manage the way the design is executed, and ensure compliance with the stated performance goals.

Experienced designers are also qualified to install, troubleshoot and complete their projects should the need arise. This experience may be what separates you from the competition. Knowledge of local codes and federal laws is essential to a project that will pass inspections and it will give the customer confidence knowing that you have these skills. Be prepared to wear multiple hats!

Needs Assessment

This section provides more detail on the first task, that of focusing on your clients, listening to their needs and inquiring into their reasons for, and uses of, the integrated electronic systems they dream of.

Such client-oriented attention sends a powerful message, namely that you intend to keep your clients in the forefront of your considerations. You should see your clients as your "bosses" to the extent that satisfying those clients with a design that addresses their expectations is your chief concern.

Here are some tips on how to actively hear and understand what your clients really want.

- Set aside generous amounts of time to spend with clients so your interviews are thorough and unrushed. Quality time spent in the initial phases of a project saves time and misunderstandings later. Make sure you have an agreed-upon budget to perform client interviews.
- Actively listen to what your clients say they want. Make good eye contact and pay attention to every word. Clients may not differentiate their needs from their wants or dreams.
- Pay attention to your clients' unspoken "messages." Are there issues they have not yet expressed or considered? Do the husband and wife concur on decisions? Are there underlying expectations or points of confusion?
- Take detailed notes and avoid presuming things about your clients. Take nothing for granted.
- Ask thought-provoking questions of your clients. Get them to tell stories. You need to know why they chose you, their intended use for an integrated system, who will be the primary operators and what lifestyle they are comfortable with.
- Encourage your clients to ask questions of you. Provide clear and logical explanations to clients' questions so that a nontechnical person can understand. Invite them to express their concerns or hesitations.
- Project a respectful, professional and honest image to your clients. You will elicit trust and confidence from them.
- Use paraphrasing to check your understanding of clients' needs by restating, in your own words, what you thought you heard and let them confirm (or clarify) your understanding.
- Document everything learned.

Identifying the Players/Stakeholders

All projects have interested parties called stakeholders. A project might have several stakeholders, including the architect, designers, builders, and contractors, but your customer is the primary stakeholder. A sponsor is the person who bears the ultimate financial burden for the project and has the most vested interests in having the project completed successfully.

Make sure that you have all of the relevant information for each stakeholder such as full name, phone number, email address, etc. and publish a contact list to the team so communications flow freely.

Evaluation/Survey

This is the stage that, if you get wrong or miss something, will cost you! Sometimes designers (or sales people) forget to ask important questions. Did you discuss lighting controls? HVAC? Communications? Content streaming? Acoustics? Design interviews should follow a rigorous process. Create a detailed client questionnaire or evaluation form as a memory aid for your design staff. It should not replace face-to-face interviews, but can help keep the conversation moving in productive directions. A written survey form can become your template for describing the initial scope of work.

Here are two excellent questions to ask, to help elicit good information during your interviews:

1) Are you the right person to answer these questions?
2) Is there anything else I should be asking you?

Existing Conditions

Certain issues can only be ascertained by being at the site. There are several major concerns when looking at the existing conditions for the project.

- Assume the measurements are not accurate. For example, are the measurements from sheet rock to sheet rock or crown molding to crown molding? Are measurements to rough or finished surfaces?
- Review architectural plans and identify what may cause problems in the design. In order to resolve this, get with the contractor and stake claim for runs. Spray paint your company symbols for cable runs on frame members.
- Verify that the plans were followed and look for framing issues such as sheer walls, fire rated walls etc. If the walls are fire rated, what are the legal requirements for penetration?
- Are there any physical constraints when reviewing the design that may have been overlooked?
- There is an old adage..."measure twice, cut once". Check and recheck all measurements on-site. This is especially important for cabinet design and dedicated home theater spaces, where accurate dimensions are critical. Don't trust the printed set of plans. It is incumbent on the designer to verify all site conditions in the field.
- Draw sketches, date them and put as much information on them as possible. Remember, when you are back at the office, this is one of the major pieces of reference information for your design and the estimate.
- Take pictures and give them meaningful titles. An example might be to number each photo and put that number on the sketch with an arrow indicating the direction from which it was taken.
- Determine spatial relationships. Make a note of openings in walls and ceilings such as ventilation vents and human factors that may determine the practical installation of the system. Keep an eye

open for sunlight, reflections, sight-lines and other potential visual hazards. Seek out potential acoustical problems caused by nearby motors or HVAC equipment or unwanted sound bleed between spaces. Printed plans don't always reveal these issues.

- Understand local wiring codes and standards, and wire types that may have to be used as a result of their location, internal, external etc. Noting wire runs that may have to be separated from existing wiring due to high power loads such as HVAC pumps etc. is another consideration.
- Be careful to verify all buildings that are included in the work scope and how each is constructed.
- Obtain feedback from anyone that is familiar with the site. Owners, builders, electricians, plumbers and other people may have pertinent information that could help.

Estimating

Projects rarely have unlimited funds and are usually constrained by a budget. Often, the budget is viewed as "huge" by the customer and "unrealistic" by the supplier. In either case, cost constraints and a cost management plan are a crucial part of a successful project. The scope plan provides the input for cost estimating. The output of the process is a bill of materials (BOM).

The BOM details the quantity and cost for each resource required during the installation and completion of the project. The BOM can take different forms depending on the intended purpose and audience. For example, customers see the BOM as the cost estimate, and some companies actually call it the proposal. Residential industry professionals see the BOM as a list of equipment and any miscellaneous materials required for the project, plus a rundown of all the necessary installation services. The document given to the customer should contain information pertinent to them, keeping the specifics for internal use.

Here is a listing of potential estimating sources:

- Credible historical data
- Published industry standards
- Cost analyses
- Value engineering
- Associated service and maintenance fees
- Schedule of labor rates
- Product-specific labor estimates

The following practices can substantially help you in estimating projects:

- Maintain a product database.
- Update labor estimates regularly.
- Use real data from completed projects.
- Use specialized software tools.

- Master the use of spreadsheets.
- Identify the correct product for the application.
- Calculate lifecycle costs.

There are considerable benefits to using specialized software tools. Keep in mind the following software assets:

- Increased accuracy and estimating speed
- Enhanced profitability
- Custom reports
- Ease of use and maintenance
- Project management assistance
- Handy template proposals
- Availability of manufacturer databases
- Tie-in to back-office systems

Emerging Technology

Designers need to stay current with new and emerging technologies. In today's fast-paced world of consumer technologies, new products come along that can have a huge impact on your design. Streaming media, new video resolutions, sustainability, mobile devices, natural user interfaces, augmented reality and virtual reality are evolving rapidly. There are several effective ways to do this:

- Stay current with industry trends.
- Attend trade shows.
- Read trade publications.
- Network with industry professionals.
- Research recent product developments.
- Monitor code changes, standards and regulations.
- Monitor product development.
- Evaluate new technologies for client applications.
- Make equipment substitutions or additions as warranted.
- Provide budgeting for research, continuing education, analysis, procurement, testing and verification.

Documentation

Documentation is created from the start to the end of a project. It becomes the history of the progress and completion and acts as the reference for each phase. See Chapter 15 for more on documentation.

Scope Statement (Statement of Work)

A standardized project scope statement explains the project details in easy-to-understand terms avoiding technical jargon. It is not designed to impress with big words and technical expertise, but rather to clearly and concisely spell out what is expected of all parties.

The project scope statement should include the following:

- Project objectives
- Product scope definition
- Project requirements
- Project boundaries
- Project deliverables
- Product acceptance criteria
- Project constraints
- Project assumptions
- Initial project organization
- Initial defined risks
- Schedule milestones
- Fund limitations

Request for Proposal (RFP)

To gather pricing information for higher-cost projects, companies usually use a Request for Proposal (RFP). In the electronic systems contracting industry, the RFP is often used to find the best solution to a homeowner's unique situation by engaging specialists and sub-contractors. The RFP must describe the products or services in sufficient detail for suppliers to provide complete and competitive information. In an RFP, the supplier or seller provides the project specifications and cost information and is responsible for meeting those specifications. An RFP may be used to solicit proposals from subcontractors, like security installation companies and electrical contractors.

Figure 14-3 *Project Proposal*

Proposal

The proposal is the document that defines the complete project. It communicates design possibilities to the client by drafting the proposed design options in order to finalize system choices. It will be used to add or delete conditions as the project progresses. The legal part of the project, the contract, will usually be based upon the contents of the proposal. I should reflect the company's level of quality and attention to detail.

While the parts may vary slightly, these are the key elements of any proposal:

- Statement of work, brief outline
- Functional descriptions
- System functionality
- Room-by-room description
- Activity-based descriptions
- Illustrations and block diagrams

- Bill of materials
- Pricing detail
- Payment schedule
- Terms and conditions
- Statement of exclusions

System Design and Engineering Documents

While there are many ways to develop and implement document management for a project, the diagram below shows a sound and practical process to ensure that the project is complete at every stage. This demonstrates how the logical procession of documents drives the process in an orderly fashion. Chapter 15 of this book dives deeper into these documents and their role in the process.

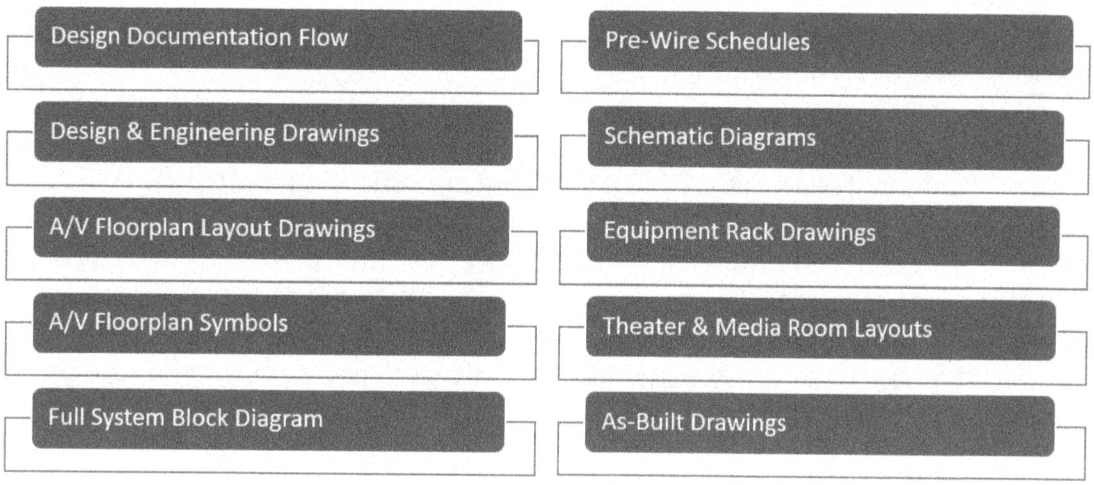

Figure 14-4 *Design & Engineering Documents*

Visualization

It is imperative that all stakeholders have the ability to visualize functionality as well as the look and feel of user interfaces. For more on these topics, see Chapter 7 Control Systems & User Interfaces, and Chapter 15 Project Documentation.

Block Diagram

The Block Diagram shows all of the system components wired together, along with the products that are needed at the head-ends to make it all work. It's the drawing that shows the complete picture, all devices, all the floors all the connections between the racks and the rooms.

Block Diagrams can be powerful sales tools. It is often much more helpful to clients to visualize their system layout in the form of an illustration or drawing than to stare at a list of equipment. The system becomes more tangible when referenced to a block diagram.

Engineering

The engineering role requires massive amounts of technical expertise. You must read prints and plans, and craft ingenious solutions to design challenges that can spring up unexpectedly.

Use flexible approaches to system integration to realize creative solutions. You must not only engineer system details, but also coordinate personalized user interfaces that allow your clients to test your work.

There are important differences between designers and engineers. Engineers solve problems; Designers create problems by discovering client goals during Needs Assessment. Designers ask WHY. Engineers ask HOW. Sometimes engineers are too caught up in the technical aspects of products to work effectively as designers. The best designers are inquisitive, open to options and new insights, offer creative perspectives and ask really useful questions.

Engineers take detailed descriptions from designers and turn them into precisely documented, buildable projects. A good team has designers and engineers working hand-in-glove.

Importance of Prototyping

Design Thinking relies heavily on early-stage mockups and prototypes. These are tangible, physical models that clients can play with and respond to. Don't get carried away here. Simple, low-resolution, low-risk models are sufficient. You can use Post-it Notes, cardboard, foam core board, even doll houses to get client feedback. By all means, get these prototypes into your client's hands as early as possible, before expensive engineering and product procurement occurs.

Appraising Prototypes

Designers assist in the appraisal of prototypes and usability testing to determine areas for improvement. If you are proposing a technology or product that is new or untested, obtain samples and experiment with them in your lab. You'll probably discover hidden details that will save time at the final installation. Invite your clients into the lab to kick the tires and try new products. Their feedback will be invaluable.

For larger, more complex projects, like motorized mechanisms or other exotic fixtures, look for infrastructure and other installation complications. Designers know the intent of the client along with architectural details and are well suited to supervise the testing of mockups and prototypes. Pay attention to architectural and logistical complications, including the following:

- Space requirements
- Power needs
- Cabling requirements
- Bandwidth and control protocols
- Ventilation
- Building materials

- Ingress and egress
- Serviceability
- Human factors and ergonomics

DESIGN MANAGEMENT

Adherence to Original Design Intent

Designers are also Project Managers. They understand the goals of the client and are instrumental in creating the scope of work. System designers should pay attention to their projects every step of the way and be in close coordination with other project managers and installation technicians on the team. Designers are responsible for Design Compliance—making sure that what is on the plan has been built exactly as described.
Make regular visits to the job site and be available as a resource to the installation teams. Designers should make regular reports to their clients to assure them that the project is going according to plan.

Value Engineering

There are times when costs escalate or budgets are reduced. Achieving similar results while reducing costs is called Value Engineering. Designers play a critical role when systems need to be re-evaluated. Value engineering is used to analyze and improve all phases of a project and is an ongoing process. While every attempt to value engineer a system is carried out initially, there are often improvements that can be achieved during later phases of a project.

Tracking Progress

Milestones

Milestones are specific points in a project that allow us to determine if we are meeting the stage goals. Milestones are monitored as project work proceeds, providing the basis for managing the project schedule. They are used as a benchmark for reporting project status.

The effects of not meeting project milestones include increased project costs and customer dissatisfaction.

There are many software packages that can be used determine if project goals are being met and even suggest solutions to missed milestones.

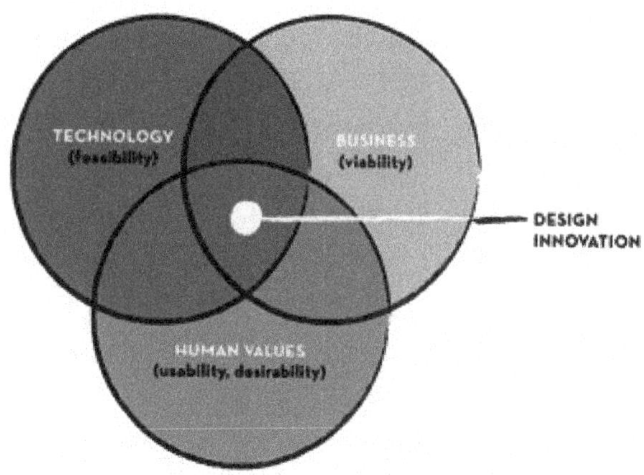

Figure 14-5 *Bringing It All Together*

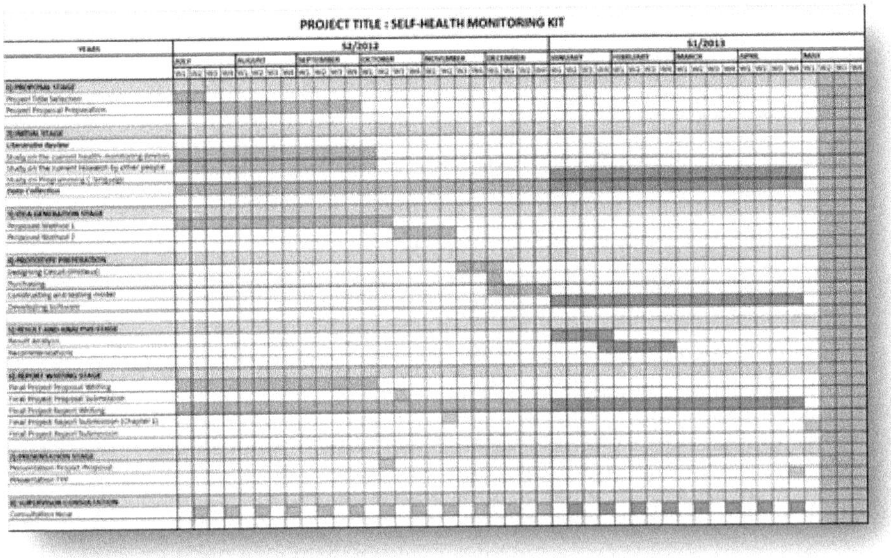

Figure 14-6 *Gantt Chart*

System Commissioning

Perhaps the single most important milestone in completing a project is System Verification and Commissioning. This is the highest expression of Design Compliance. Designers need to be on site with the final installation team to verify that all products are present, correctly installed and working according to manufacturer's specifications.

After verifying that all equipment and materials are present and accounted for, System Commissioning occurs. This includes loading software, configuring menus, setting performance parameters, and then testing the system under all possible use scenarios. Designers specify the procedures for System Commissioning early in the process so that field technicians know exactly what is expected before they start work. Create a professional company form that precisely describes the set-up procedures for all equipment and user interfaces. Be sure to include performance parameters such as maximum SPL at the seating location, projected image system contrast ratio, security passwords, network SSIDs and Wi-Fi coverage. The list is long and should be fully detailed in advance.

SUMMARY

In conclusion, the importance of a good design philosophy and rock-solid design process cannot be overemphasized. Integrators who have demonstrated success and quality of work over time have done so mainly through design excellence.

References:

d.school at Stanford
http://dschool.stanford.eduelicit/wp-content/uploads/2013/10/METHOD-CARDS-v3-slim.pdf

CHAPTER 15

DESIGN AND ENGINEERING DOCUMENTS

Documentation is an important part of any custom electronic design project. Documentation begins with the sales call and continues through planning, installation, customer training, and follow-up service. Whether the project involves new construction or retrofit, documents are the essential tools that facilitate the planning and tracking of all aspects of the project. Proper documentation provides a "paper trail"— a journal of the events that transpire during the process of the project. No matter what size the project is, proper documentation will be needed for it to be successful. In this chapter, documentation refers not only to written documents like contracts and project scope statements, but also to more technical documents like blueprints, schematic drawings, and schedules.

Architects, designers, and engineers create documents to convey the intent of the building or space design. Project managers use documents to manage time, cost, and scope. All of the design and engineering documents presented and explained in this chapter relate to one thing: Conveying all of the information needed to ensure a successful project which meets the stated goals.

DOCUMENTATION FLOW CHART

Companies should establish a documentation workflow. In the example flow chart shown, the box headings represent project phases while the smaller boxes indicate the documents needed for each of the phases.

The design process originates at the initial sales or client meetings. Sales team managers walk out of those meetings with a client's needs worksheet

PROJECT DESIGN DOCUMENTATION

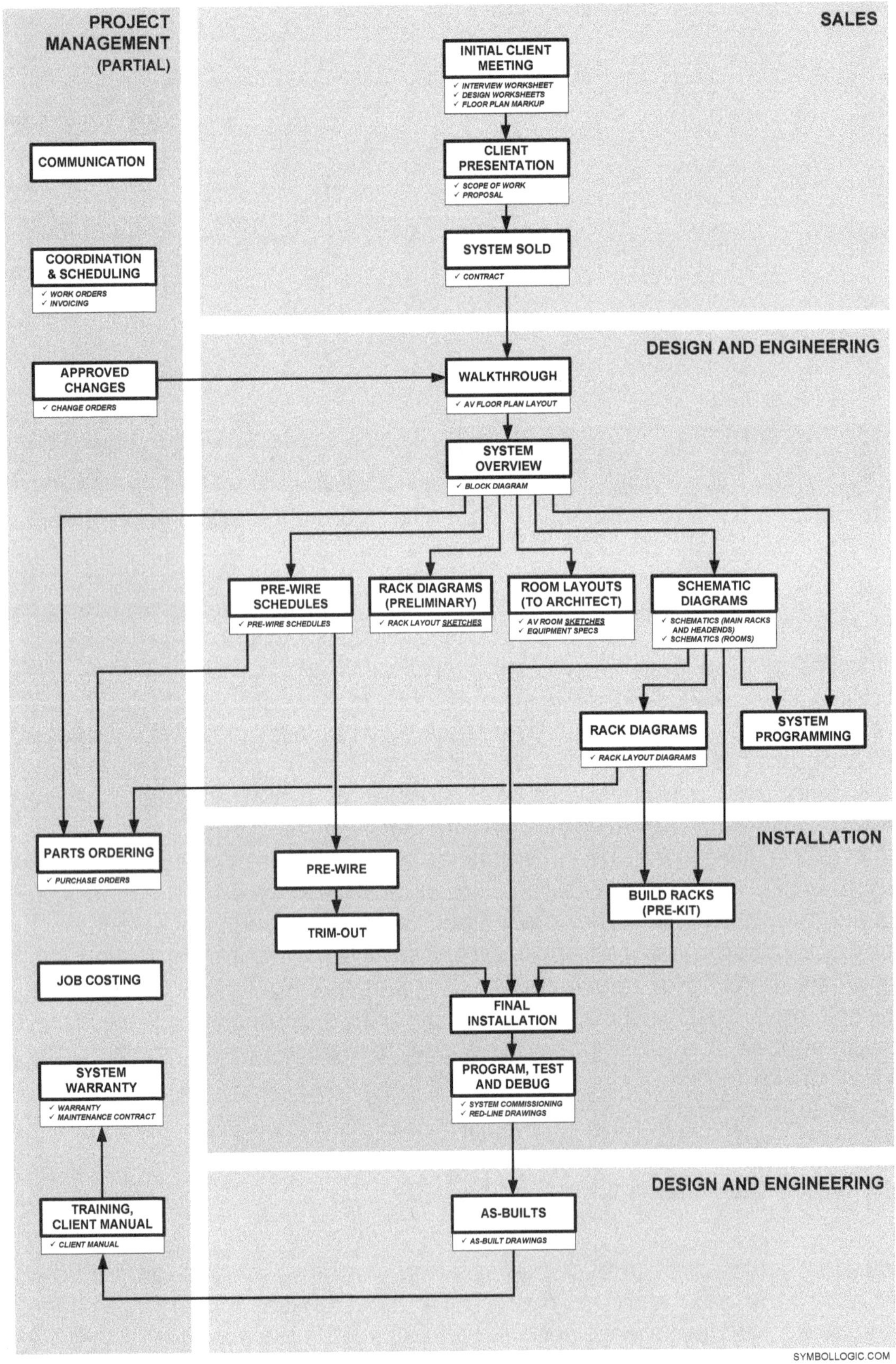

Figure 15-1 *Documentation Flow Chart*

and a marked-up floor plan of the basic physical A/V design. That information then transitions from the sales team to the design and engineering team, where the marked-up floor plans become the AV floor plan layout drawings. These help to create system overview drawings, or a full system block diagram.

The block diagram then paves the way to create the pre-wire schedules and detailed rack and room schematic diagrams. And with those documents the team can create the rack layouts, begin system programming, and finally build and test the system.

SYSTEM DESIGN AND ENGINEERING DRAWINGS

These documents are created in the order shown below by the A/V designers and engineers for the purpose of guiding the assembly and installation of the system. Both installers and designers need to know how to read and understand design and engineering drawings:

- *Drawing size and Orientation.*
  IIn the industry of electronics installation, it is vital to use proper size and orientation for the drawings so it will be more efficient to use. The most suitable sizes are 11 X 17 ("B" Size or Tabloid / A3) and 13 X 19. Also, 24 X 36 (ARCH "D" / A1) size is usable, but a bit harder to manage on the Job Site. The minimum size 8.5 X 11 (Letter / A4) is generally too small, but still can be useful on the jobsite or in a job file. It is common to use landscape orientation for plan view drawings and portrait orientation for block and schematic drawings.
- *Page Frame, Title Block, and Revision Blocks.*
  Now every page in the drawings package should have a page frame, a revisions block with revision number, a brief description, engineer's initials and date. The title block included in the document should have the company's logo, title (client's project name), description of the drawing, such as floor plan, schematic diagram, etc., beginning date, revised date, page number, and engineer's initials.

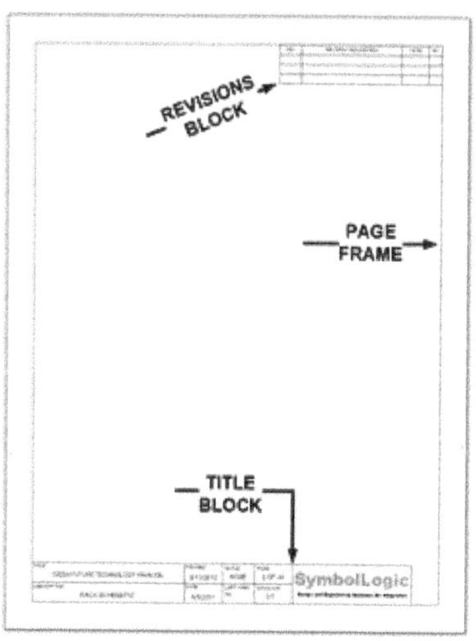

Figure 15-2.
Page Frame, Title Block, Revision Block

A/V Floor Plan Layout Drawings

These design drawings show the physical locations of all key A/V devices and confirms to the client and other project stakeholders what is being installed. Using the architectural floor plan as the background image with A/V floor plan symbols on top creates the drawing. This drawing also provides the groundwork for creating further documentation such as the full system block diagram. Creating the A/V floor plan drawing and getting it right before anything else is done is the foundation for a successful installation.

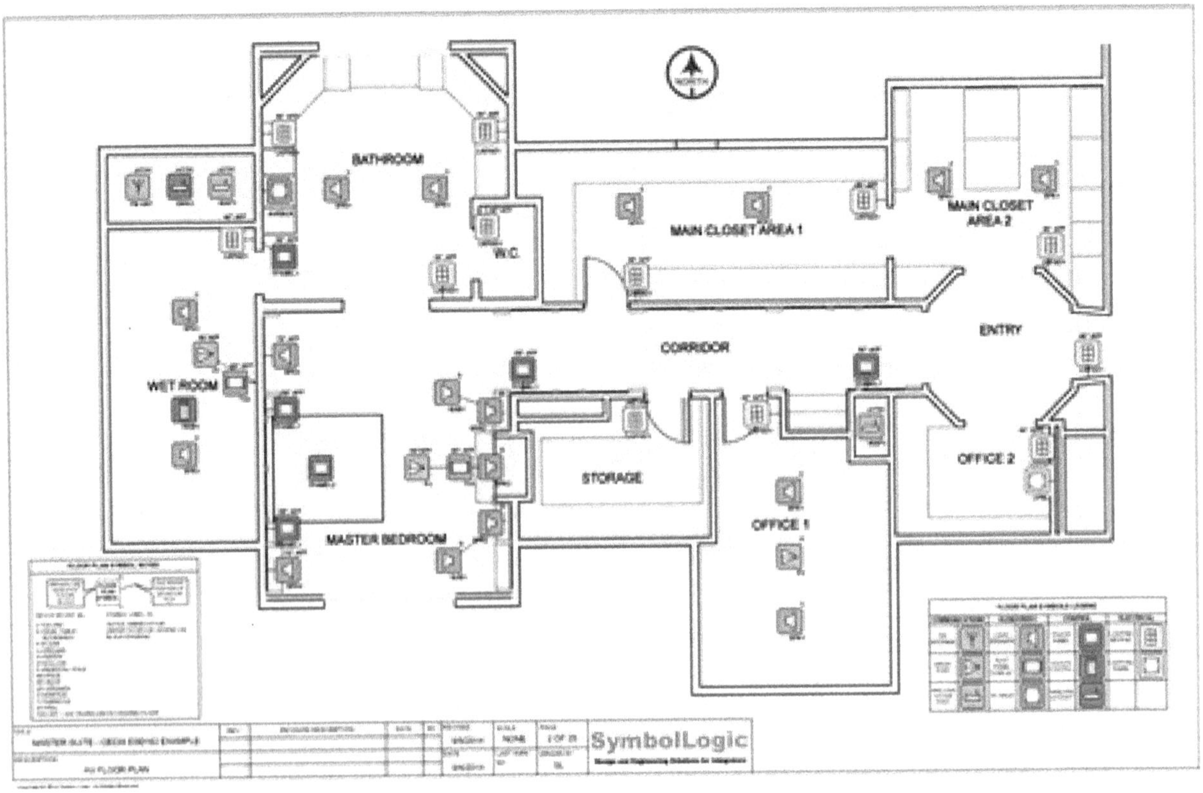

Figure 15-3 *A/V Floor Plan*

A/V Floor Plan Symbols

Symbols are graphical representations of real devices or objects. Architects, engineers, and designers use many symbols, lines, and colors to display their ideas in a drawing. Knowing some of the most commonly used symbols is important, but it is also important to know where to find other resources in books and online that show symbols used in particular disciplines. Always check with a plan's legend, or symbol key, to verify what each symbol is representing.

Figure 15-4 shows the symbols established in the J-STD-710 standard. These are the architectural A/V floor plan (and reflected ceiling plan) symbols used for audio, video, and control systems as well as environmental control and communication networks. The following section describes the details and proper use of these symbols.

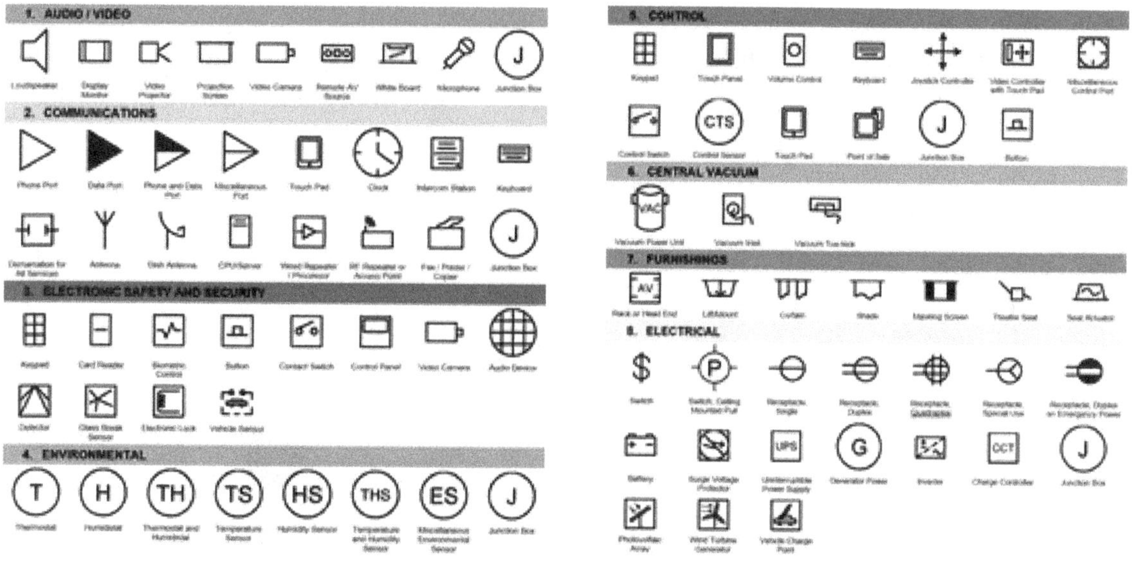

Figure 15-4 *Drawing Symbols per J-STD-710*

Optional Attributes

The symbols can have four optional attributes to indicate the mounting style of the device, primary and secondary device technologies, and a device abbreviation, which can easily be referenced to a legend or schedule on the page. These attributes were created to be very flexible and to allow any possible future device to be represented. This means even when an entirely new type of device is introduced, the system will allow the designer to tell a very complete story about it through the icon annotations. In the example shown in Figure 15-5, the device is a ceiling-mounted, L/R bar speaker, which is self-powered.

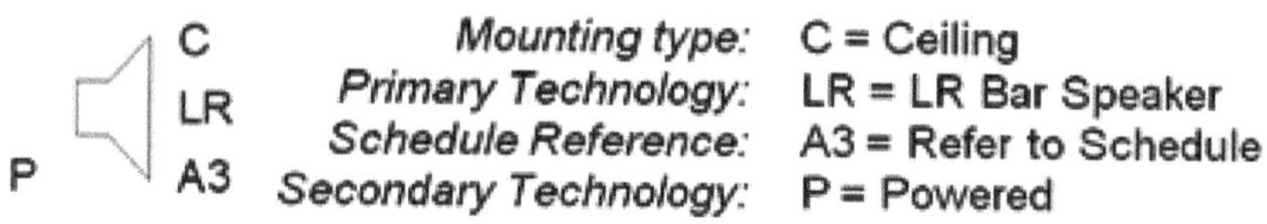

Mount Type	Abbreviation
CEILING	C
DESK/TABLE	D
FLUSH	F
FLOOR	FL
GROUND	G
HIDDEN	H
MULLION	M

Mount Type	Abbreviation
OUTDOOR	O
PEDESTAL	P
RACK	RK
ROOF	R
RECESSED	REC
SURFACE	S
WALL	W

Figure 15-5 *Optional Attributes*

The attributes are flexible and can be used in different ways, such as an engineer's own numbering scheme for product manufacturer or model. Engineers can decide to use only some of the attributes or none at all.

Optional Leader Lines

You can use leader lines to show more closely, where the device is mounted on a wall and then instead of using the "mounting type" attribute for mounting style you could use it for showing exact heights above finished floor such as shown in Figure 15-6.

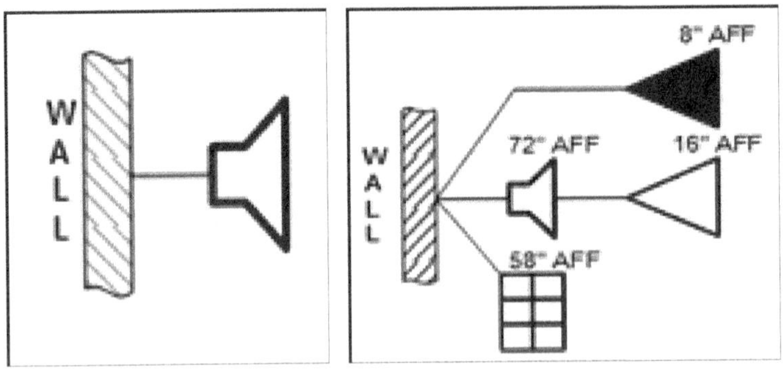

Figure 15-6 *Optional Leader Lines*

Optional Call-Out Tags

The engineer can add optional call-out tags to show even more device information like wall jack number, cable number/letter, or RF channel as shown in Figure 15-7.

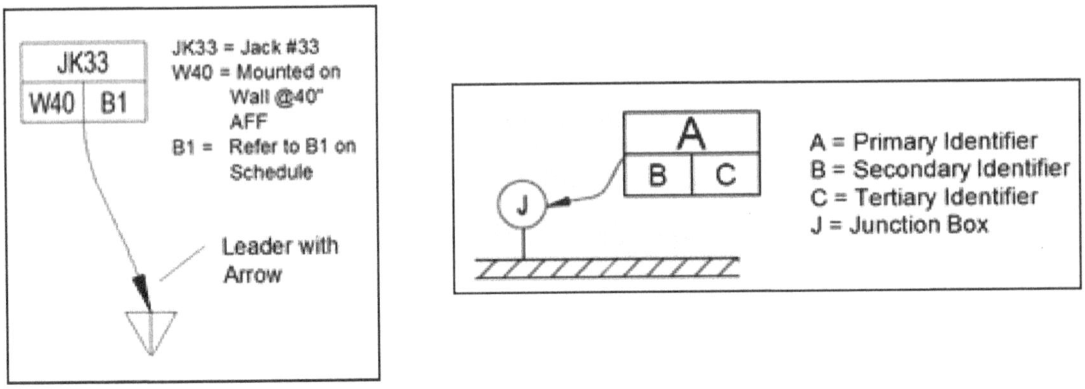

Figure 15-7 *Optional Call-Out Tags*

Optional Symbol Background Colors

The J-STD-710 symbols standard allows for the symbols to use background colors as shown in Figure 15-8. Using colors is a great way to easily distinguish the different categories of symbols on the drawings.

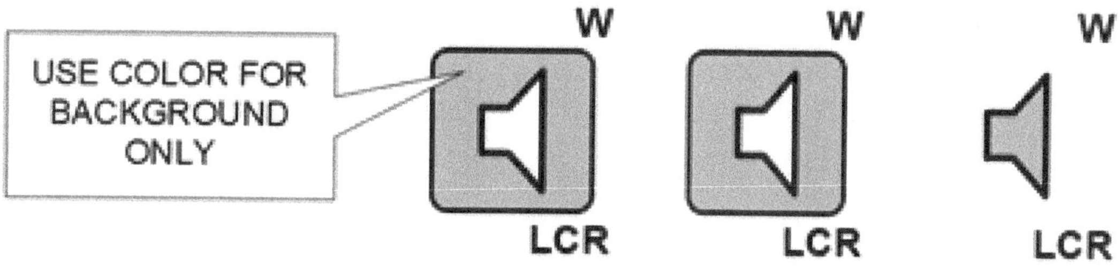

Optional Background Colors for Symbols			
Symbol Category/ Background Color	***RGB Values***	***AutoCAD 16 Color***	***AutoCAD 256 Color***
AUDIO-VIDEO/ORANGE	255,179,51	40	40
COMMUNICATIONS/GREEN	85,234,137	3	90
ELECTRONIC SAFETY AND SECURITY/RED	240,0,100	1	230
ENVIRONMENTAL/BLUE	60,197,255	4	140
CONTROL/VIOLET	213,121,236	6	201
CENTRAL VACUUM/GRAY	179,179,179	9	9
FURNISHINGS/BROWN	197,138,80	33	33
ELECTRICAL/YELLOW	255,255,0	2	2

Figure 15-8 *Optional Symbol Background Colors*

LEGEND		
REF	SYMBOL	DESCRIPTION
AV01	LAR	LINE ARRAY SPKR
AV02	LCR	LCR BAR SPKR
AV03	S	14" SUBWOOFER SPKR
AV04		NEC PROJECTOR, CEILING, NS
AV09		DRAPER 110" SCRN, REC, CEILING
C10		FW PORT, WALL
C11		IP PORT, WALL
C12		IP/TEL PORT, FLOOR BOX
S03	IR	INFRARED RECEIVER
S03		BIOMETRIC CONTROL, EYE, WALL@50"
S11		BEAM ALARM SENSOR
S15		PANASONIC HD PTZ CAMERA, WALL@90"

Symbols Legend

When using symbols it is necessary to include a symbols legend in the diagram. A legend is a table or list on a drawing identifying what each symbol represents. It explains the lines and symbols used in the drawing. Legend blocks vary depending on the type of plan. A set of plans may have more than one legend if multiple systems are shown on the plans. And legends may not necessarily be placed on the same page as the drawing. Always refer to the legend for the proper interpretation of a symbol, as a symbol's meaning can change from project to project.

Figure 15-9. *Symbols Legend*

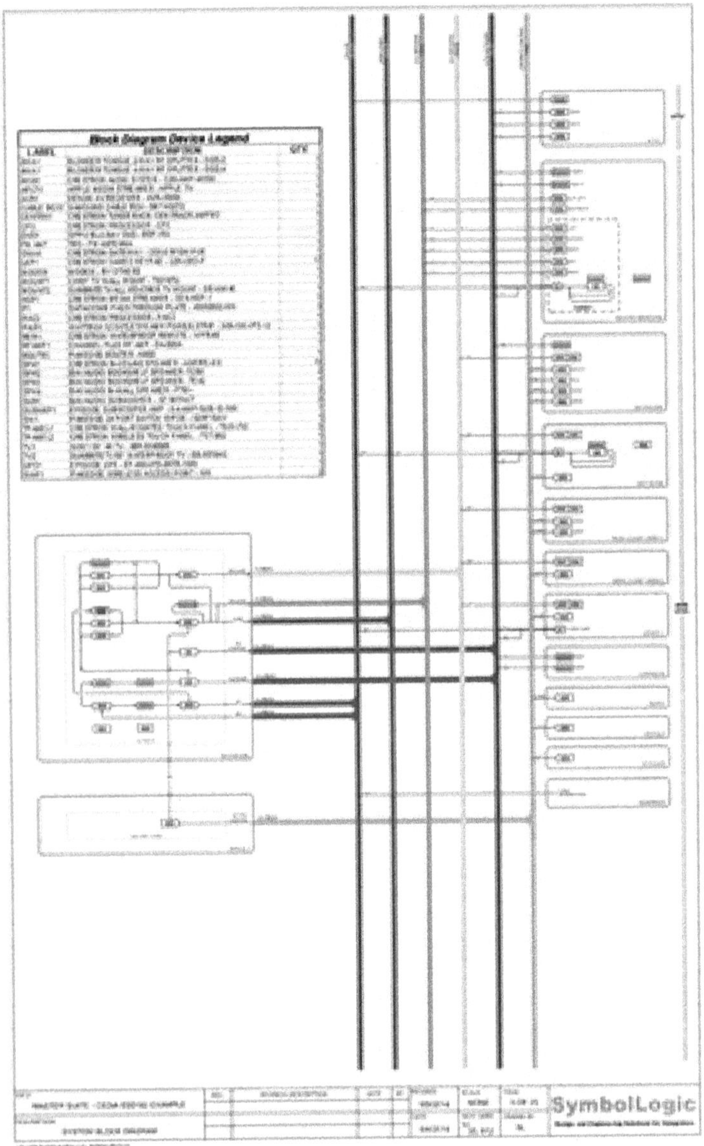

Figure 15-10 *Full System Block Diagram*

Full-System Block Diagram

A full-system block diagram reveals more information which cannot be easily shown in the floor plan layout. It is a vertical riser-style diagram showing the complete system, including signal flow and connectivity on every floor. This drawing can be very helpful in establishing a more accurate cost for the project as it displays many aspects of the system. This drawing is the basis for creating a complete and accurate prewire schedule and is the foundation for creating the detailed schematic wiring diagrams for the project. It is not intended to be a rack-wiring diagram. Specific device connection details for wiring racks are shown in the schematic diagrams.

In this diagram, your company's wire/cable types, colors and numbering sequences will be used. The block diagram is organized showing the head-end areas on the left side of the page, prewire types and colors in the center, and the rooms, areas and zones on the right. The device blocks should be labeled with abbreviated text to signify the specific devices used. Block connections are single lines with arrows showing signal flow where appropriate. Each pre-wire cable has a unique number shown. Using sequentially numbered cables in groups pulled to the various rooms can be helpful for technicians in the field.

Additionally, the full system block diagram is a great onsite tool to verify that all pre-wires have been pulled to their correct locations before the wallboard is installed.

The process used to create the block diagram begins with:

1. Knowing what pre-wire types you use in your company.
2. Rooms are broken-lined rectangles including the name of the room in the lower right of each rectangle. Devices in the rooms are simple solid rectangles with abbreviations for the device name. This is the "schedule reference" abbreviation used in your floor plan symbols. All this information is taken from the A/V floor plan drawing.
3. Attach devices to the pre-wire columns with pre-wire connections and label the cable with a number.
4. Total all prewire types and draw horizontal lines to where they connect at the head-ends on the left.
5. And lastly, draw the head-ends. This part takes careful thought and planning as you are deciding on all of the needed head-end equipment, to make the system work as planned.

Establish your Company's Wiring Philosophy

- Cable types and colors
- Numbering
- Sequences

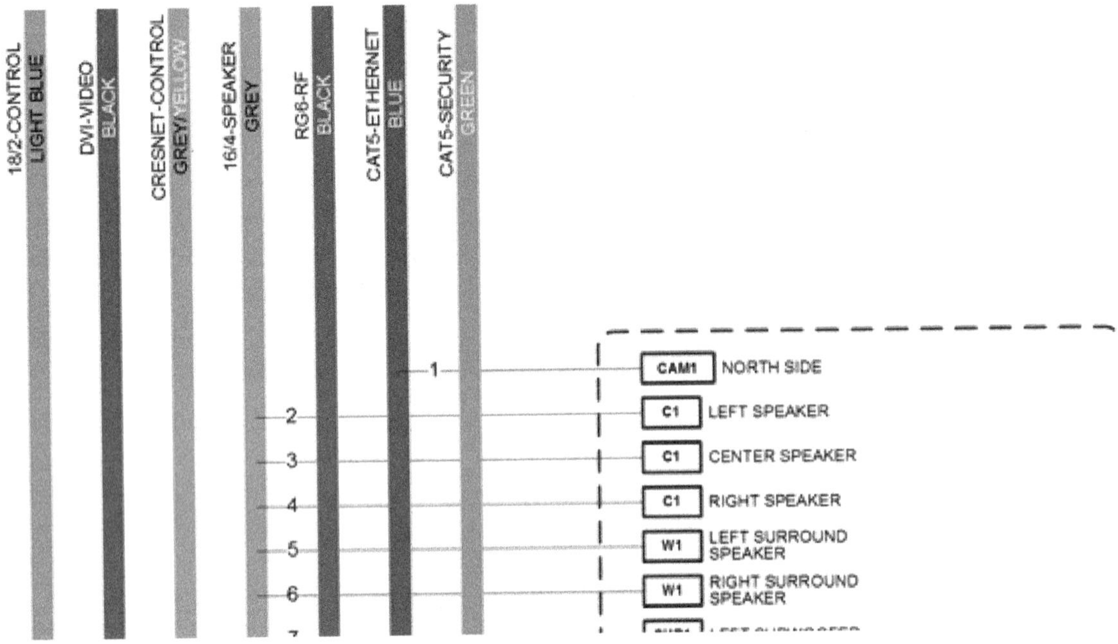

Figure 15-11 *Cable Color and Notation Philosophy*

Example

- 1 to 799 - AV, network and control pre-wires
- 800 to 999 - Lighting control
- 1000 to 1999 - 1st level head-end/racks and rooms
- 2000 to 2999 - 2nd level head-end/racks and rooms
- 3000 to 3999 - 3rd level head-end/racks and rooms
- 4000 to 4999 - 4th level head-end/racks and rooms
- Etc.

Pre-Wire Schedules

From the block diagram an accurate pre-wire schedule can be created. Pre-wire schedules are whole project planning documents, showing cable types, from and to locations, length, and labeling of cables used in the project. Pre-wire schedules can provide the basis for a pre-wire installation budget and are the documents which are used by installers to pull cable to the various areas in the project. They are not used for internally wiring racks or other head end and room electronics areas - those areas are usually wired using the schematic drawings. The full system block diagram is an important tool, which reveals the complete and accurate pre-wires needed for the project.

Pre-Wire Schedule by Area									
AREA NAME	AREA NO.	FLOOR	Wire Number	FROM	WIRE TYPE	TO	FUNCTION	NOTES	LENGTH (FT.)
BATH		MAIN LEVEL	26	AV RACK	CAT5 BLU	ROOM	TV	SPARE	50
BATH		MAIN LEVEL	28	AV RACK	CAT5 BLU	ROOM	TOUCHPANEL	NETWORK	50
BATH		MAIN LEVEL	27	AV RACK	RG6 BLK	ROOM CABINET	WALL PORT	RF	50
3									
									150
BEDROOM		MAIN LEVEL	29	AV RACK	16/4 GREY	ROOM	IN-WALL SPEAKERS		50
BEDROOM		MAIN LEVEL	30	AV RACK	16/4 GREY	ROOM	IN-WALL SUBWOOFER	ENCLOSURE MOUNTED IN OFFICE	50
BEDROOM		MAIN LEVEL	31	AV RACK	CAT5 BLU	ROOM	WALL PORT	NETWORK	50
BEDROOM		MAIN LEVEL	32	AV RACK	CNET GREY/YEL	ROOM	TSTAT		50
BEDROOM		MAIN LEVEL	33	AV RACK	CAT5 BLU	ROOM	TOUCHPANEL	NETWORK	50
5									
									250
GARAGE		MAIN LEVEL	38	AV RACK	CAT5 BLU	ROOM	VIDEO CAMERA		50
GARAGE		MAIN LEVEL	39	SECURITY PANEL	CAT5 GRN	ROOM	TOUCHPANEL	SECURITY	50
GARAGE		MAIN LEVEL	40	AV RACK	CAT5 BLU	ROOM	DATA DEMARCATION	RF	50
3									
									150
HOME OFFICE		MAIN LEVEL	34	AV RACK	CAT5 BLU	ROOM	WALL PORT	NETWORK	50
HOME OFFICE		MAIN LEVEL	35	AV RACK	CAT5 BLU	ROOM	WALL PORT	NETWORK	50
HOME OFFICE		MAIN LEVEL	36	AV RACK	CAT5 BLU	ROOM	WALL PORT	NETWORK	50
HOME OFFICE		MAIN LEVEL	37	AV RACK	CAT5 BLU	ROOM	TOUCHPANEL	NETWORK	50
4									
									200
KITCHEN		MAIN LEVEL	22	AV RACK	16/4 GREY	ROOM	IN-WALL SPEAKER	LEFT/RIGHT	50
KITCHEN		MAIN LEVEL	23	AV RACK	RG6 BLK	ROOM	WALL PORT	RF	50
KITCHEN		MAIN LEVEL	25	AV RACK	CAT5 BLU	ROOM	TOUCHPANEL WALL PORT	NETWORK	50
KITCHEN		MAIN LEVEL	24	AV RACK	CAT5 BLU	ROOM CABINET	WAP	NETWORK	50
4									
									200
LIVING ROOM		MAIN LEVEL	1	AV RACK	CAT5 BLU	ROOM	VIDEO CAMERA		50
LIVING ROOM		MAIN LEVEL	2	AV RACK	16/4 GREY	ROOM	IN-CEILING SPEAKER	LEFT	50
LIVING ROOM		MAIN LEVEL	3	AV RACK	16/4 GREY	ROOM	IN-CEILING SPEAKER	CENTER	50
LIVING ROOM		MAIN LEVEL	4	AV RACK	16/4 GREY	ROOM	IN-CEILING SPEAKER	RIGHT	50
LIVING ROOM		MAIN LEVEL	5	AV RACK	16/4 GREY	ROOM	IN-WALL SPEAKER	REAR SIDE RIGHT	50
LIVING ROOM		MAIN LEVEL	6	AV RACK	16/4 GREY	ROOM	IN-WALL SPEAKER	REAR SIDE LEFT	50
LIVING ROOM		MAIN LEVEL	7	AV RACK	16/4 GREY	ROOM	IN-CEILING SUBWOOFER	LEFT	50
LIVING ROOM		MAIN LEVEL	8	AV RACK	16/4 GREY	ROOM	IN-CEILING SUBWOOFER	RIGHT	50
LIVING ROOM		MAIN LEVEL	17	AV RACK	CAT5 BLU	ROOM	TV	SPARE	50
LIVING ROOM		MAIN LEVEL	18	AV RACK	RG6 BLK	ROOM	WALL PORT	RF	50
LIVING ROOM		MAIN LEVEL	19	AV RACK	CAT5 BLU	ROOM	WALL PORT	NETWORK	50
LIVING ROOM		MAIN LEVEL	20	AV RACK	18/2 TRAY	ROOM	SMARTGLASS	CONTROL	50
LIVING ROOM		MAIN LEVEL	21	AV RACK	CAT5 BLU	ROOM	TOUCHSCREEN WALL PORT	NETWORK	50
13									
									650
PROJECTOR ROOM		MAIN LEVEL	9	AV RACK	DVI TO HDMI	ROOM	VIDEO PROJECTOR	VIDEO	35
PROJECTOR ROOM		MAIN LEVEL	10	AV RACK	DVI TO HDMI	ROOM	VIDEO PROJECTOR	VIDEO	35
PROJECTOR ROOM		MAIN LEVEL	11	AV RACK	DVI TO HDMI	ROOM	VIDEO PROJECTOR	VIDEO	35
PROJECTOR ROOM		MAIN LEVEL	12	AV RACK	DVI TO HDMI	ROOM	VIDEO PROJECTOR	VIDEO	35
PROJECTOR ROOM		MAIN LEVEL	13	AV RACK	DVI TO HDMI	ROOM	VIDEO PROJECTOR	VIDEO	35
PROJECTOR ROOM		MAIN LEVEL	14	AV RACK	DVI TO HDMI	ROOM	VIDEO PROJECTOR	VIDEO	35
PROJECTOR ROOM		MAIN LEVEL	15	AV RACK	CAT5 BLU	ROOM	WAP	NETWORK	50
PROJECTOR ROOM		MAIN LEVEL	16	AV RACK	CAT5 BLU	ROOM	GATEWAY	NETWORK	50
8									
									310
									1910

Figure15-12 *Pre-Wire Schedule*

Schematic Diagrams

Schematic diagrams are detailed point-to-point wiring diagrams for the assembly and service of equipment racks, head ends and area electronics. They reveal special wiring details that cannot be easily shown in the full system block diagram. Each head-end rack and room electronics area can often times be shown on its own schematic drawing page. The system prewires generally enter and exit the head-end rack on the left side and right sides of the page. All input devices in the rack (or room), such as source equipment, are drawn on the left side, output devices, such as amplifiers, are on the right side, and all other equipment such as processing equipment is usually drawn in the middle of the drawing page. Power management devices are generally drawn in the lower left. Termination details are usually shown on the schematics legend page.

Taking a closer look at the devices and the wiring of the rack, one can see that each device symbol has a manufacturer and model number at the top. Device labeling has the inputs on the left and outputs on the right side of the symbol. Most cables are shown as single lines. Each individual cable has a number on the top and the cable type and color on the bottom. Each wire-end termination can be shown with a small square symbol, showing a number and letter which can be referenced to a termination legend in the drawing showing the type of connector used and its wiring details. Not all cables need to be shown, such as power, network and some control cables. Using references instead of actual lines for some of the cables can simplify and cleanup the drawing without any loss of connection information. Simply use the same shape such as a small diamond or circle and the same character inside the shape on each end of the invisible line to show a connection.

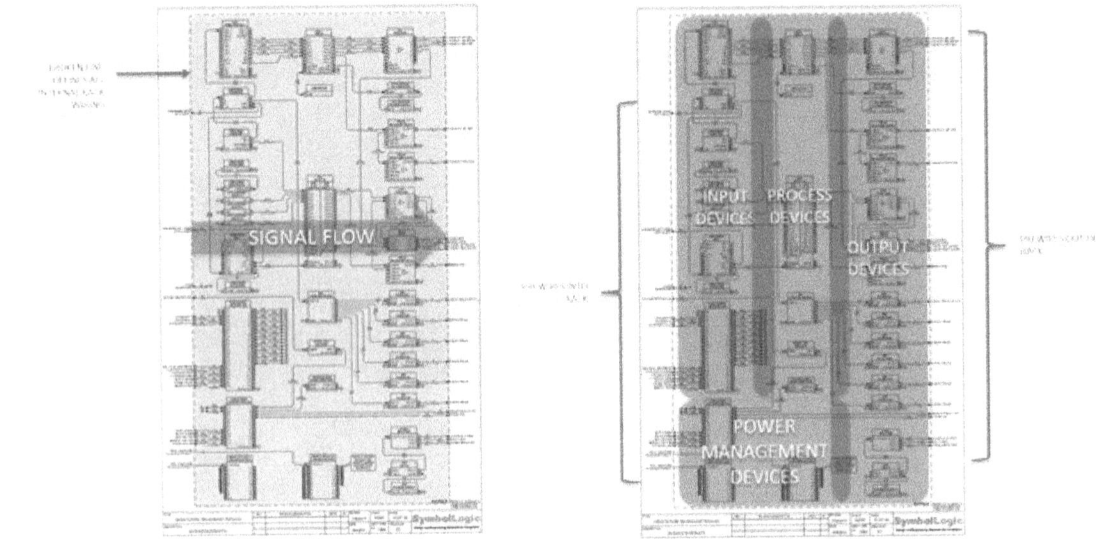

Figure 15-13 *Head End Rack Schematics*

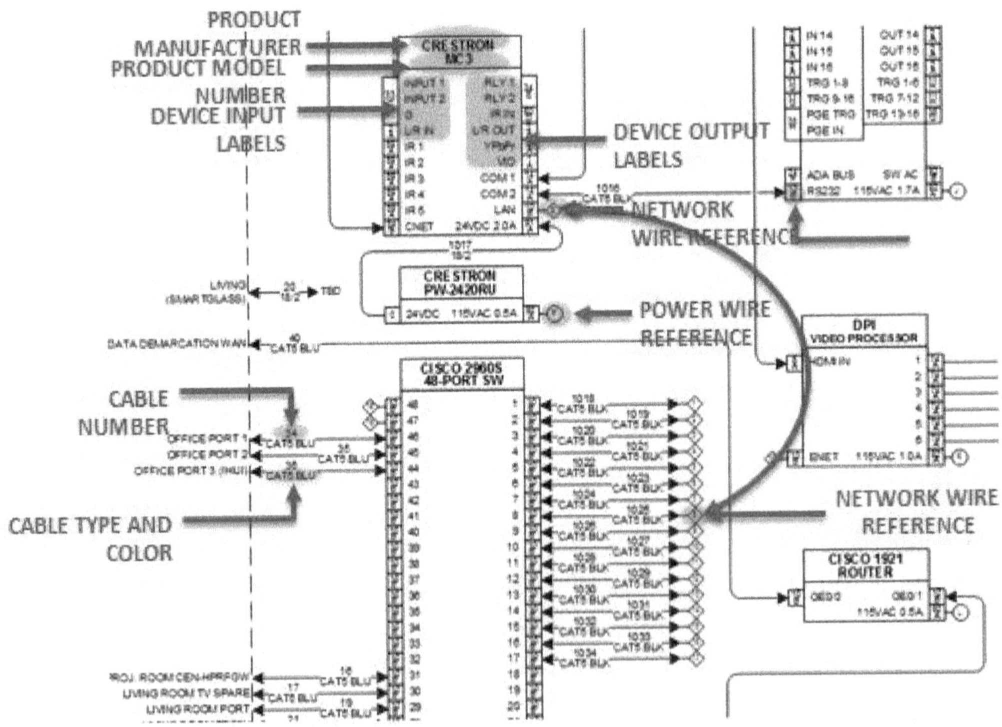

Figure 15-14 *Rack Schematic Close-up*

Schematic Diagrams: Rooms

All the same principles used in creating main rack schematics are used in room and area schematics. Generally, pre-wires enter from the head-end or main rack area on the left and exit the room or room cabinet on the right side of the page. Sometimes a broken line area can represent the complete room as shown, and a second broken lined box within the room can represent a room equipment cabinet or closet.

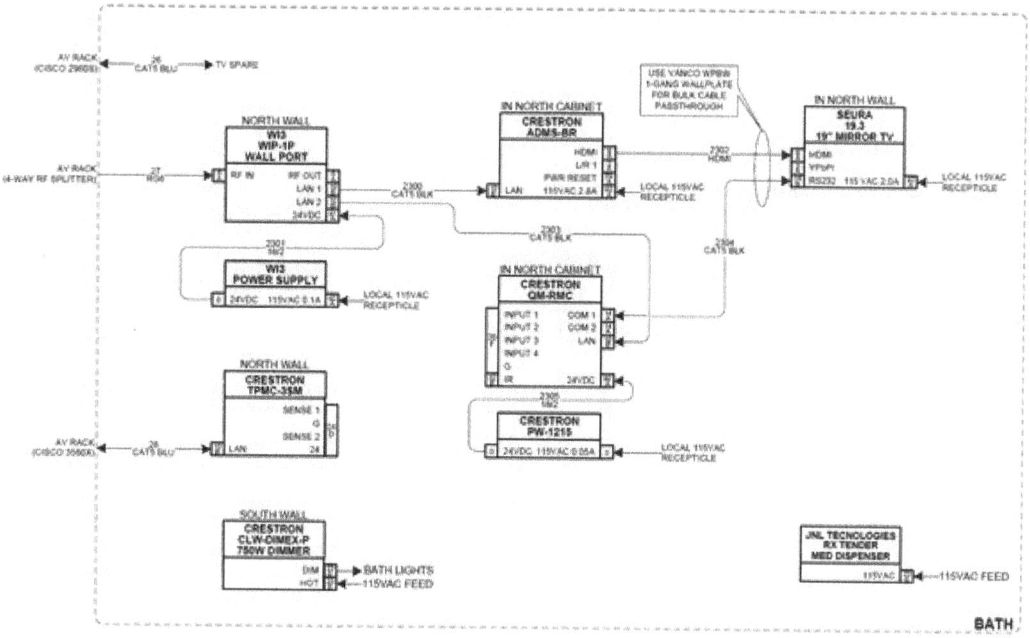

Figure 15-15 *Room Schematic*

Each schematic symbol used in your drawings should be created by first referring to the product specification sheet to be sure the product works in your design, and that you have all the appropriate input, output, control, and power ports properly labeled on your schematic symbol.

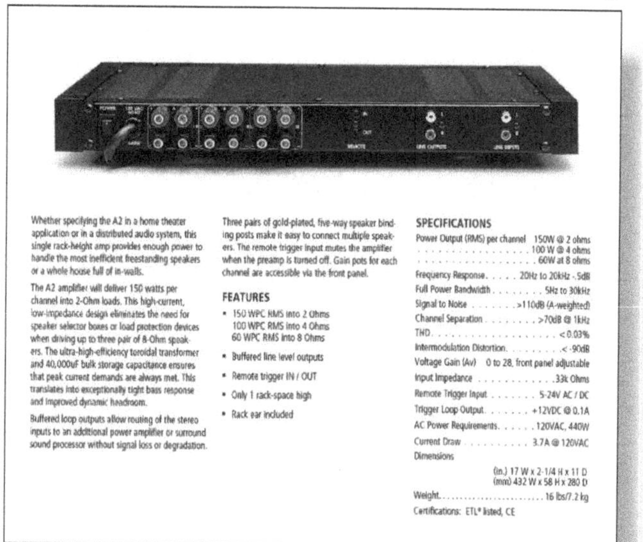

Whether specifying the A2 in a home theater application or in a distributed audio system, this single rack-height amp provides enough power to handle the most inefficient freestanding speakers or a whole house full of in-walls.

The A2 amplifier will deliver 150 watts per channel into 2-Ohm loads. This high-current, low-impedance design eliminates the need for speaker selector boxes or load protection devices when driving up to three pair of 8-Ohm speakers. The ultra-high-efficiency toroidal transformer and 40,000uF bulk storage capacitance ensures that peak current demands are always met. This translates into exceptionally tight bass response and improved dynamic headroom.

Buffered loop outputs allow routing of the stereo inputs to an additional power amplifier or surround sound processor without signal loss or degradation.

Three pairs of gold-plated, five-way speaker binding posts make it easy to connect multiple speakers. The remote trigger input mutes the amplifier when the preamp is turned off. Gain pots for each channel are accessible via the front panel.

FEATURES

- 150 WPC RMS into 2 Ohms
  100 WPC RMS into 4 Ohms
  60 WPC RMS into 8 Ohms
- Buffered line level outputs
- Remote trigger IN / OUT
- Only 1 rack-space high
- Rack ear included

SPECIFICATIONS

Power Output (RMS) per channel . . . 150W @ 2 ohms
. . . . 100 W @ 4 ohms
. . . . 60W at 8 ohms
Frequency Response. . . . . . 20Hz to 20kHz -.5dB
Full Power Bandwidth . . . . 5Hz to 30kHz
Signal to Noise . . . . >110dB (A-weighted)
Channel Separation . . . . >70dB @ 1kHz
THD. < 0.03%
Intermodulation Distortion. . . . . < -90dB
Voltage Gain (Av) 0 to 28, front panel adjustable
Input Impedance . . . . 33k Ohms
Remote Trigger Input . . . . 5-24V AC / DC
Trigger Loop Output. . . . . +12VDC @ 0.1A
AC Power Requirements. 120VAC, 440W
Current Draw . . . . 3.7A @ 120VAC
Dimensions
(in.) 17 W x 2-1/4 H x 11 D
(mm) 432 W x 58 H x 280 D
Weight. . . . . 16 lbs/7.2 kg
Certifications: ETL® listed, CE

Figure 15-16 *Component Spec Sheet*

The schematics are the actual wiring documents technicians use to wire the racks. As each cable in the rack is terminated, dressed, and labeled, the equivalent lines on the schematic pages are highlighted with a colored marker as being complete, so the technician never has to wonder where he/she left off.

Equipment Rack Drawings

Rack elevation drawings show the correct placement of all rack-mounted equipment, overall size of rack, power and ventilation requirements and rack accessories.

Double check that the drawing accounts for all the equipment shown in the rack schematics and that all equipment is appropriately positioned for its weight, ventilation and ease of installation and service. Make sure to check the overall rack size for proper on-site fit and include these dimensions on the drawing. Also list on the drawing the full electrical load, number of circuits and ventilation requirements, as well as any miscellaneous rack parts, pieces, and accessories needed to fully complete the rack.

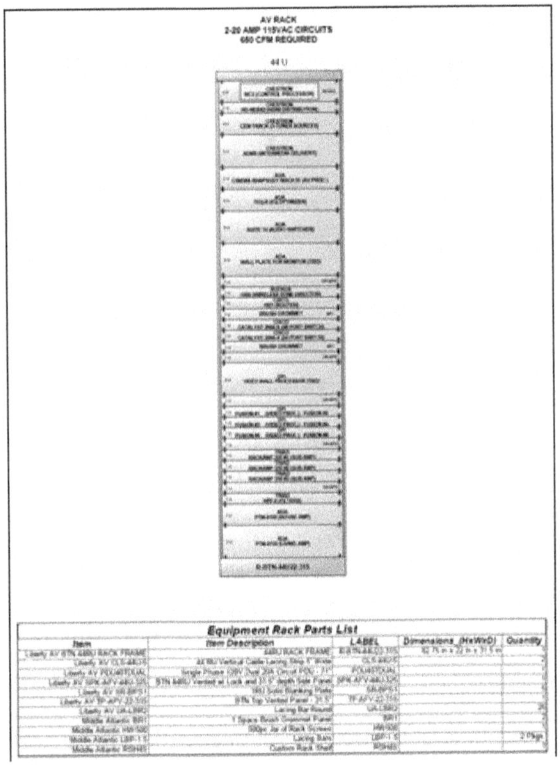

Figure 15-17 *Rack Elevation with Parts List*

AS-BUILT DOCUMENTATION

As the technician makes any and all appropriate and approved changes to the installation in the field, he or she marks-up, with red pen or pencil, the master set of drawings on the job site, reflecting what was actually done. These marked-up or redlined drawings are then handed back to the A/V engineer and translated into the final, as-built design documentation package.

Figure 15-18 shows the changes that were made to a main rack schematic from the red markings and notations.

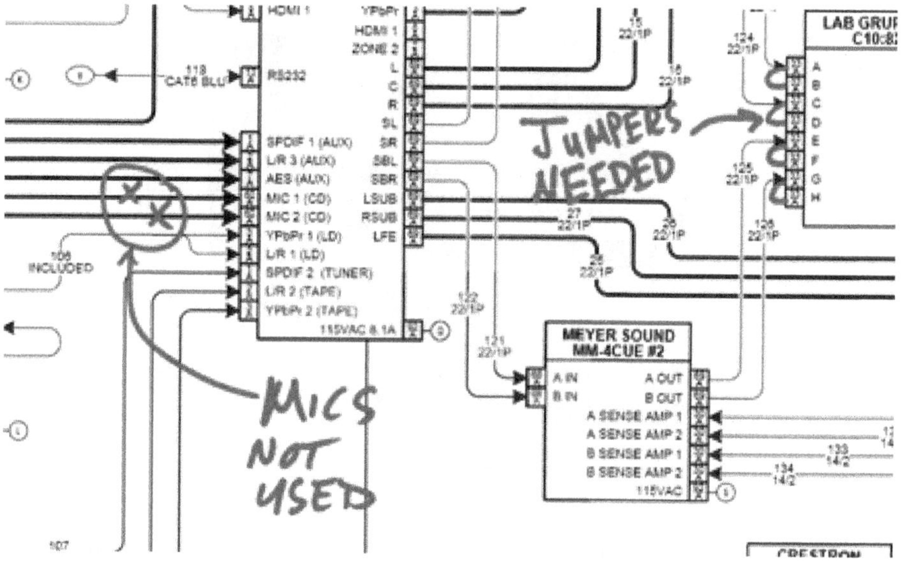

Figure 15-18 *Red Line (As Built) Details*

THEATER AND MEDIA ROOM LAYOUTS

Theaters and media rooms often require custom millwork, cabinetry, or other special buildouts. It is the responsibility of the designer to provide architectural drawings which convey the basic layout of the screen wall or other areas where the work of other trades needs to meet specific dimensions, in order to accommodate equipment, speakers, displays, or a projection screen. These drawings must include minimum required dimensions, ventilation requirements, power locations, etc.

Clear communication of these needs in advance can prevent a great deal of confusion and delay later in the project.

Room layout drawings may include:

- Floor plan view with audio and video equipment dimensions and location
- Elevation views, showing speaker locations and screen wall configuration
- Audio and video sight-lines (these should have already been done in the original theater design process)
- 3-D perspective room views

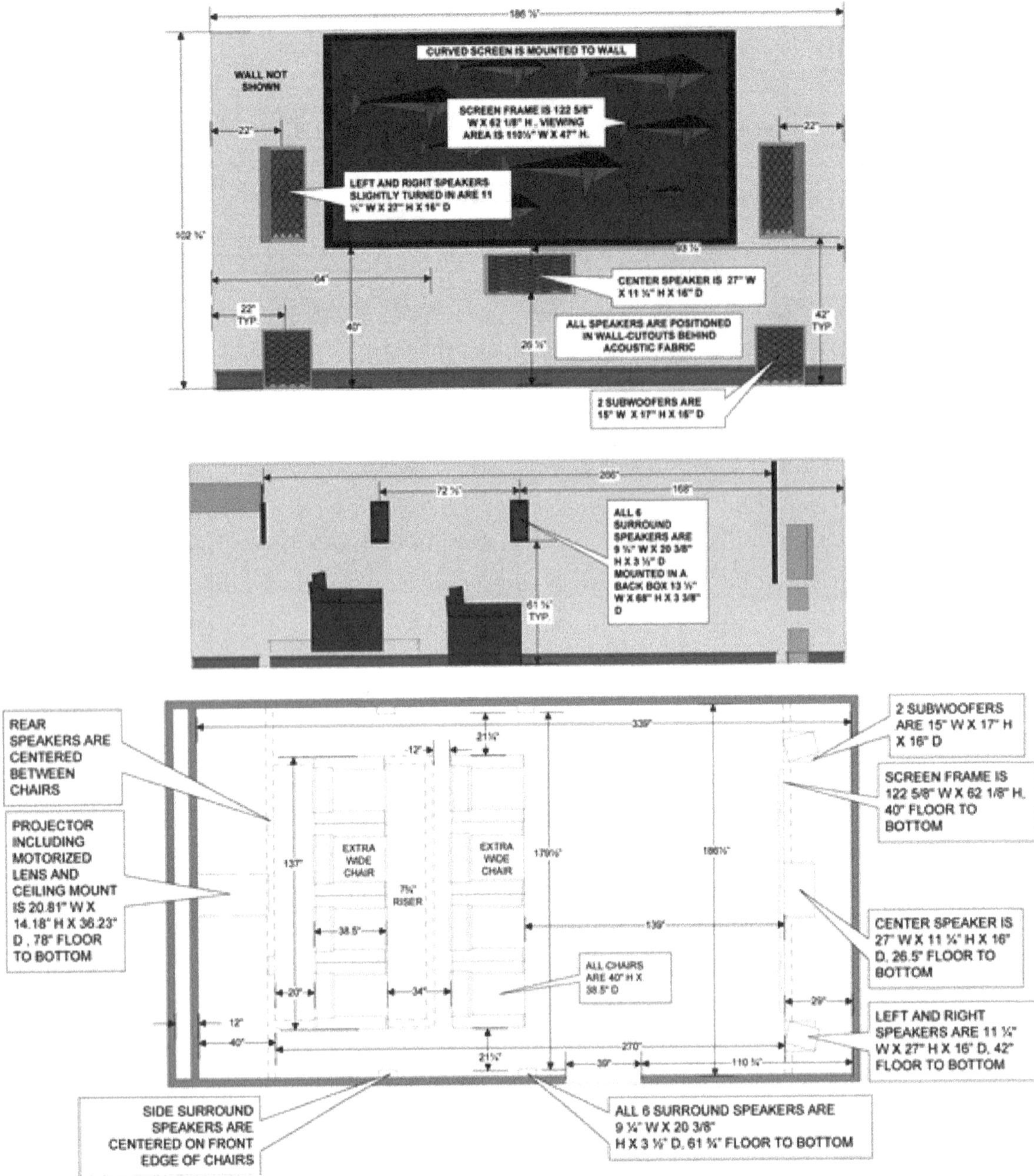

Figure 15-19 *Home Theater Design Drawings*

CONCLUSION

Not only are the drawings described in this chapter important for the proper installation of a project, but drawings such as the A/V floor plan are vital to all stakeholders such as owners, architects, builders and interior designers in helping to make decisions on how all the different technologies will affect the project from an architectural and interior finish perspective. These drawings are the visual tools needed to pull all parties together.

For young, upstart home technology companies, the thought of learning and investing in the proper tools needed to create these vital documents may be overwhelming and low on the priority list. However, the only proper way to account for the technical details and the planning of installation projects of any size is by creating these drawings and using the principles laid out in this chapter.

CHAPTER 16

PROJECT MANAGEMENT

From start to finish, all projects are managed. They may be managed formally or informally, productively or non-productively. In order to successfully complete a project, there must always be an eye toward the final product. Project management is that "eye," essentially creating a purposeful plan to use the elements of time, cost, and scope to reach the end result of customer satisfaction.

Informal project management means chaotic questioning, lack of direction, and no decisions. A formal project management structure keeps everyone on the same track by setting benchmarks, assigning tasks, and creating time frames that result in a project completed within the allotted time, cost parameters and agreed scope of work.

This chapter reviews the Project Management Institute (PMI) processes and outlines their direct application to the residential electronic systems contracting industry. It is recommended that students who wish to learn more about project management visit www.pmi.org and review the PMI publication, The Project Management Body of Knowledge.

WHAT IS A PROJECT?

The first step to successfully managing a project is to understand what a project is and how managing a project is crucial to seeing it to completion. All projects have similar characteristics.

A project:

- Is temporary
- Is progressive
- Has unique characteristics
- Requires resources
- Has a sponsor
- Should have a manager and a plan

A Project Is Temporary

A project is temporary because it has a distinctive beginning and end. The goal is to define the project, attain the project objective, and terminate the project.

Hopefully, the project terminates because the objectives of the project have been achieved, but projects might also terminate for other reasons. If, for example, it becomes clear that the objectives cannot or will not be met, or the need for the project no longer exists, then the project will come to a premature end without being successfully completed.

It is important to remember, however, that temporary does not necessarily mean short in duration. Though all projects have a definite end, that end could be in a few days or in several years depending on the scope of the project.

Temporary Surroundings

The temporary nature of projects often extends to a variety of tasks surrounding the project. For example, there may be a limited time frame for marketing activities or a limited time that a product or service is available. In addition, the lifespan of the project management team is usually temporary as well. Upon completion of the project, the team is usually disbanded or moved to the next project.

Though projects and many of the tasks surrounding them might be temporary, the results of the project are often long term. For example, the installation of a satellite dish would be an extremely short project with results that will last for many years. In addition, personal or business relationships as well as economic and educational opportunities are often long-lasting, unplanned side effects of a project.

A Project Has Progressive Elaboration

Progressive elaboration occurs throughout a project's lifespan and can be thought of as "improvements made along the way." That is to say, updates and improvements are made to the project as more detailed information (such as a more refined pricing estimate) becomes available. The result is a more accurate plan and includes several iterations within the planning process.

For example in the planning stage, the project manager or management team breaks the project down into smaller steps. These steps involve tasks (or activities) and events, as shown in Table 16-1. The steps are performed in a logical fashion until the completion of the project.

A timeline, such as the one shown in Figure 16-1, is an important component of the management plan. It will ensure that the progression of tasks and events move forward in increments and continue to follow the scope of the project. As the steps or timeline of the project progress, the tasks get more detailed and defined.

Table 16-1. *A List of Tasks and Events*

	Task or Event	Description
1	Event	Deposit Received
2	Task	Order Equipment
3	Event	Equipment Arrives
4	Task	Schedule Installation
5	Task	Perform Installation

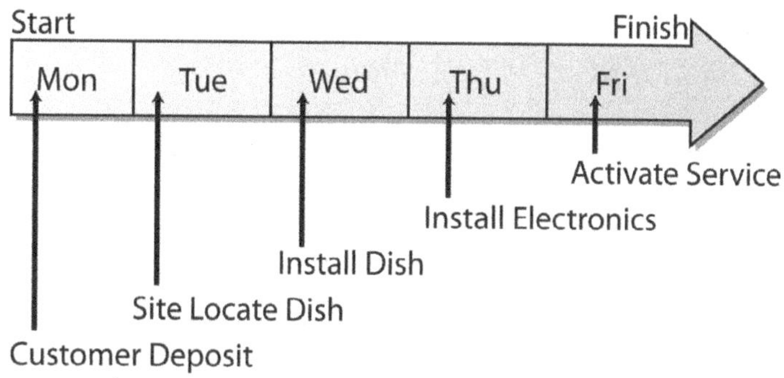

Figure 16-1. *Project Timeline*

Each Project Is Unique

A common trait of all projects is that every project will create a unique product, service, or result. In the electronic systems contracting industry, projects often include the same general deliverables. However, even projects that seem to be the same with an identical end product vary based on the location, timing, customer, or objective. Every project is unique and will most likely never again be executed in exactly the same way, by the same participants, or within the same environment. However, events and tasks can be executed in the same fashion.

This uniqueness of each project creates the challenge in project management. A seasoned project manager will always allow for the differences in personnel or environment and use past project experiences to enhance his decision making through a project.

A Project Requires Resources

Resources and their availability are critical to the successful completion of a project. Project resources include people, materials, assets, software, and other items that are needed by the project in order to achieve its goals. Managing the allocation and use of resources is an important aspect of the project manager's job and there is seldom an endless supply of money or time. Resources must be accounted for, but they must also be used in the most cost-efficient and timely way possible to achieve quality results.

A Project Has a Sponsor

All projects have interested parties called stakeholders. A project might have several stakeholders, including designers, builders, and contractors, but your customer is the primary stakeholder. A sponsor is the person who bears the ultimate financial burden for the project and has the most vested interests in having the project completed successfully.

In the electronic systems contracting industry, projects are usually customer-created and customer-driven and require the sponsor or customer's direct involvement. The customer creates the need for the project. The project manager helps the customer fine-tune his objectives.

A Project Has a Manager

A project manager is a strong leader who plans and oversees the project's flow from beginning to end. The challenges of managing a project are not always straightforward, requiring the project manager to bring in a mix of science and art. The project manager must be comfortable handling the more sensitive aspects of communication to bring out the best results in team members and contractors.

The project manager performs many tasks:

- Provides guidance to project team members
- Initiates and maintains customer contact
- Conducts site reviews
- Consults with sales representatives
- Assigns resources to tasks
- Prepares various types of documentation
- Manages the project timeline and schedule
- Ensures the scope of work is fulfilled
- Ensures the project stays on budget
- Formulates solutions to obstacles

Ultimately, project managers take responsibility for the outcome of the project. For this reason, the project manager is usually someone with experience working on a project team.

Sometimes, the project manager is chosen based on a level of knowledge about a particular area of the project. Subject knowledge and understanding the project process is critical to the success of any project manager.

Successful project managers are usually those who:

- Are comfortable with change and willing to adjust throughout a project, as needed
- Have a solid understanding of organizational structures
- Have an understanding of the company's unique product strategy and mission
- Develop strong management and communication skills
- Pursue education and training opportunities

A Project Has a Plan

The project plan is a blueprint or outline that shows the intended path of the project. It addresses all of the various needs of the project and provides an audit trail of the many tasks and events that need to be accomplished in order to complete the project successfully. A project manager is the primary position responsible for the overall project plan.

The project plan is not only important to control the current project, but it can also provide important data at the conclusion of the project. This data will allow a project manager to realize what approaches throughout the project worked or did not work and how to adjust accordingly on future projects. A project plan is a formal, approved document used to guide both project execution and project control.

A project plan includes:

- Scope management
- Time management
- Cost management
- Quality management
- Procurement management
- Human resource management
- Communications management
- Risk management

THE PROJECT LIFE CYCLE

The project life cycle encompasses the whole project from beginning to end. To manage the project more easily, the project lifecycle is further broken down into segments that are completed in sequential order to arrive at the project's conclusion. The number and function of the phases is determined by the scope and objectives of the project. Taken as a group, the phases make up the project life cycle, or process model. Although there is no specific way to map a project life cycle, always ensure that the cycle progresses sequentially from beginning to end.

Basic phases of a project life cycle include:

- Initiating the project
- Planning the project
- Executing the project
- Controlling and monitoring the project
- Closing the project

The steps may all happen in a couple of days, or they might take years to complete. There may also be many more phases and sub-phases, depending on the complexity or uniqueness of a project. The phases are generally sequential, but often to maximize time and resources, a subsequent phase is started before the prior one is finished.

Initiating the Project

Initiating the project includes the following activities and secures a willing and able customer:

- Finding the customer (lead generation)
- Determining if the customer can fund the desired plan (lead qualification)
- Determining project deliverables
- Defining the project scope, and providing initial cost estimates
- Securing the customer by signing a contract for service

These activities occur before the physical project begins and wrap up after a project is completed. During the initiation phase, the project manager will work closely with the sales representative to fully understand the desires of the customer and obtain the information necessary to develop a scope statement.

Planning the Project

The planning phase begins once the following tasks have been completed:

- Customer is secured
- Project is defined
- Contract is signed
- Initial payment is received

Planning time is a very important aspect of the project. Planning saves money by ensuring that resources and equipment are available when needed. The planning phase is crucial to keeping the project on schedule and within budget. The project manager creates the project plan by:

- Collecting preferences from the customer
- Securing adequate personnel for the various tasks
- Ordering equipment
- Planning the schedule and timeline

Executing the Project

The execution phase is where the actual technical work of the project is completed, making it the largest, most complicated phase of an electronic system project. As a result, it is also the phase that is most likely to cause the project to get off schedule or go over budget. In fact, this phase is commonly broken down into sub-phases, each having its own life cycle.

Project execution phases may include:

- Drawing/Engineering Documentation
- Pre-wire
- Trim-out
- Electronics Installation
- Programming and Testing
- Final Turnover

Each of these phases has five sub-phases. These include:

- Initiate
- Plan
- Execute
- Monitor and control
- Close

Within the phases, each sub-phase must be completed in order. However, this rule does not apply to full phases. Full phases may overlap if they are not dependent on each other. Also known as fast-tracking, this technique helps a project manager utilize time and personnel more efficiently.

The scope document is crucial to the execution phase. It is the map that the project manager uses to assign team members the tasks needed for the completion of the project. For example, it is very important that the execution phase include a requirement that all equipment is tested and is working properly. For this task to be completed properly, it must be assigned to a team member who is capable of performing the appropriate tests and evaluating the results correctly.

Monitoring and Controlling

While the project is in progress, the project manager is responsible for assuring that work is being performed in a professional manner. During this phase, the project team employs a unique set of controls to ensure the quality of the project deliverables. Work is checked for accuracy, tested for compliance, and problems are addressed. After the controls are in place and work is verified, the project manager gives permission to close out this phase (or sub-phase) and the next phase is entered.

Closing

Closing requires approval by the appropriate party, usually the project manager. This phase may include final system testing, auditing, and otherwise verifying the project deliverables. Training the customer, completing final documentation, and turning the completed project over to a support or service department is often part of this phase.

Closing the project includes:

- System testing
- Customer training
- Final documentation
- Project audit
- Turnover
- Final payment

System testing is designed to catch mistakes. When possible, testing is performed at the shop so that very few, if any problems exist when equipment is delivered to the job site.

Customer training takes place once the system is completely installed. The project manager schedules a special time to train everyone that will be using the system. If the system is large or complex, or if there is more than one system in the house, multiple training sessions should be scheduled. These should be spread out appropriately to maximize the homeowner's learning.

In small projects, the scope document may be enough for final documentation. In a larger project, documentation may include CAD layouts and other information necessary to service the system in the future.

The project audit makes sure the customer was charged correctly, charges and services are properly billed, the project was profitable, and project information is archived for future reference.

Turnover from project to service department occurs at the completion of the project, and all documentation is given to the service department as they are now fully responsible for the project.

Sometimes the project is closed before the home is completed, making a future visit necessary for final installation. In this situation, the customer must sign off on equipment and professional services delivered to date.

Both parties should then come to an agreement about how to handle the outstanding balance of deliverables. Options include moving the equipment to the site and installing later, storing it for future installation, or installing it with construction still in progress. Note that if the customer chooses to have items installed before the jobsite is actually ready, it is important to request that the customer signs a release form that absolves the electronic systems contractor of any liability should the equipment be damaged or stolen.

PROJECT CONSTRAINTS

Unlimited time and money exist only in very rare situations; almost every project has constraints. Projects are typically measured against the constraints of scope, cost, and time. Balancing these three factors is crucial to project quality.

In a given project, none of these three constraints operate independently. Rather they function as a group with trade-offs as the balance shifts to any direction from the original plan. For example, an accelerated time frame might result in an increase in cost. Any change in the scope of the project must be examined in terms of these constraints and their inter-relationships. Quality is the sum of managing cost, scope, and time.

Scope

In the electronic systems contracting industry, the scope statement is the document that details the project. This document is written for the customer in a universally understood language that is free of industry jargon. This document is usually prepared by the sales representative working with the customer, and then the project manager uses this document to create the project plan. Changes to this document, and therefore to the scope of the project, usually result in changes to project cost and time frame.

Cost

Similar to other industries, project costs in the ESC industry include direct costs (i.e.: electronics, building materials, and labor) and indirect costs (i.e.: facility rental fees, advertising, payroll, and administrative). In an electronic system project, the customer imposes the cost constraints, defines the scope of work, and conveys the timeline of the project. The advantage of having a budget is that it helps give structure to a project. Defined limits on spending result in an easy-to-establish end point.

Time

There are time constraints through all phases of a project, including subphases. The time frame is also important to help structure work. As an example, two extremely important milestones in the timeline of an electronic system project are the sheetrock installation and obtaining a Certificate of

Occupancy (CO). Recognizing the importance of these two events at the beginning of the project allows for a better timeline in which these two tasks will be given the correct attention.

Quality

The desired end result of the cost, scope, and time associated with any project is quality. Meeting or exceeding customer expectations in all of these areas result in a satisfied customer and often lead to repeat business.

Defining the Scope is Critical

The scope of the project is the basis for all of the planning that goes into a successful project. Developing a project scope statement template helps the project manager develop consistent scope statements and eliminates redundant tasks by pre-filling standardized information. Defining the scope puts the objectives in place and serves as the basis for cost, personnel, resource, and time planning. The scope is documented in the project scope statement, which, along with the cost planning document, makes up the contract with the customer.

Needs Assessment

Needs assessment is the gathering of relevant information about the three electronic system areas: the customer's desires, the site conditions and the project objectives, and translating that information into specific needs. Whether a project is in a new home, a retrofit, or a remodel, it is crucial to fully understand the desires of the stakeholders, particularly the customer. There are a variety of ways to gather this information, identify the needs, and use that information in developing the scope statement.

THE PROJECT SCOPE STATEMENT

A standardized project scope statement explains the project details in easy-to-understand terms avoiding technical jargon. It is not designed to impress with big words and technical expertise, but rather to clearly and concisely spell out what is expected of all parties.

The project scope statement should include the following:

- Project objectives
- Product scope definition
- Project requirements
- Project boundaries
- Project deliverables
- Product acceptance criteria
- Project constraints
- Project assumptions

- Initial project organization
- Initial defined risks
- Schedule milestones
- Fund limitation
- Project configuration management requirements
- Project specifications
- Approval requirements

Project Objectives

Project objectives are measurable criteria. In a project, objectives can be measured in terms of time, cost, scope, or quality.

Product Scope Definition

The product scope definition describes the characteristics of the product and services offered in the project scope statement. Defining products and services clarifies the scope of work and gives both the company and the customer a resource to answer disputed items.

Project Requirements

Project requirements are the conditions or capabilities that must be met or possessed by the deliverables of the project. A clear definition will help the project manager track and manage project requirements — many of which involve numerous tasks.

Project Boundaries

By identifying exactly what is included in the scope, project boundaries help avoid conflicts among the company, general contractor, and any sub-contractors. Changes at the worksite will require a change in the project boundaries.

Project Deliverables

Project deliverables include all the items and services listed in the product scope document plus ancillary "soft" deliverables such as accounting reports or written how-to instructions.

Product Acceptance Criteria

When a project is complete, the customer must accept and sign off on it. Product acceptance criteria is an important part of the project. It lets the customer know that the work is complete and gives the customer an opportunity to raise questions about the new system. This is also an important milestone for the electronic system contractor, signifying an opportunity to close out the project, collect final payment, and initiate the warranty period.

Project Constraints

The project constraint section should list specific constraints that might lead to extra charges. This will help avoid dissatisfaction should the situation arise.

Project Assumptions

An important part of the project scope is to spell out the project assumptions, both physical and time oriented. The potential impact to the project in terms of cost, time, and quality should also be evaluated and adjusted if they prove to be incorrect.

Initial Project Organization

The initial project organization list identifies members of the project team. Customers feel more comfortable about the quality of the project when they know the names of the people involved.

Initial Defined Risks

Spelling out possible risks in advance will prepare your customer if they occur. These risks are documented in the initial defined risks section of the project documentation.

Schedule Milestones

Schedule milestones should be included as part of the project scope statement. These milestones will identify schedule constraints and specific scheduling issues in advance. For example, all parties involved understand that plumbing and electrical work must be finished before the cabling phase can begin.

Fund Limitations

Funding for a project can be broken down and limited for the project as a whole or for individual phases. The funding structure and limitations should be included as part of the project scope statement.

Project Configuration Management Requirements

It is important to spell out payment schedules, change order policies, and other administrative issues as part of the Project Scope Statement. See Chapter 17, Customer Relations, for more information on contract types and payment schedules.

Project Specifications

The project specifications section should include any external documents including CAD plans, floor plans, or other third-party specifications.

Approval Requirements

By signing the project scope statement, the customer gives approval for the project as a whole. This section should spell out any situation that involves an additional approval process.

THE WORK BREAKDOWN STRUCTURE

The Work Breakdown Structure (WBS) organizes and defines the entire scope of the project. WBS is the document that provides the basis for planning, estimating, and managing a project. It defines the total scope of the project and breaks it into smaller, more manageable pieces called work packages.

Format of the Work Breakdown Structure

The WBS is represented in one of two ways, a flowchart (Figure 16-2) or Table 16-2). The flowchart is similar to an organizational chart and visually shows how different work packages move to the next level of assembly. The flowchart can be organized around products, phases, or a particular process.

The tabular form of the work breakdown schedule looks like an outline and works better for developing cost estimates in a worksheet format and tracking project status.

Decomposition

Decomposition is the process of breaking down each deliverable and sub-deliverable into smaller, more manageable components. Deliverables should also be defined with sufficient detail to support the development of specific project tasks, or work packages.

Verification

Verification of the output of the decomposition process determines that all project needs are met. In order to determine that the decomposition is correct, you must determine that the lower level components are both necessary and sufficient.

WBS Dictionary

Generated during the process of creating the WBS, the WBS dictionary is a detailed collection of components contained in a WBS. For each listed component, the WBS dictionary lists an account identifier, a statement of work, the team member responsible for the work, and a list of scheduled milestones. It might also include contract information, quality requirements, and technical references.

THE WORK PACKAGE

The objective of developing a Work Breakdown Structure is to break down a project into its smallest components. The work package is that smallest component. It is a deliverable or project work component at the lowest level of each branch of the Work Breakdown Structure. The work package includes the schedule activities and milestones required to complete the work package deliverable or project work component.

Cost Constraint

Projects rarely have unlimited funds and are usually constrained by a budget. Often, the budget is viewed as "huge" by the customer and "unrealistic" by the supplier. In either case, cost constraints and a cost management plan are a crucial part of a successful project.

The scope plan provides the input for cost estimating. The output of the process is a bill of materials (BOM).

Start with the Scope

The scope statement and the Work Breakdown Structure provide the input for the process of cost estimating.

The Output is a Bill of Materials

The output of the cost estimating process is a bill of materials (BOM). The BOM details the quantity and cost for each resource required during the installation and completion of the project. The BOM can take different forms depending on the intended purpose and audience. For example, customers see the BOM as the cost estimate, and some companies actually call it the proposal.

Residential industry professionals see the BOM as a list of equipment and any miscellaneous materials required for the project and a rundown of all the necessary installation services. The document given to the customer should contain only general information keeping the specifics as an internal document.

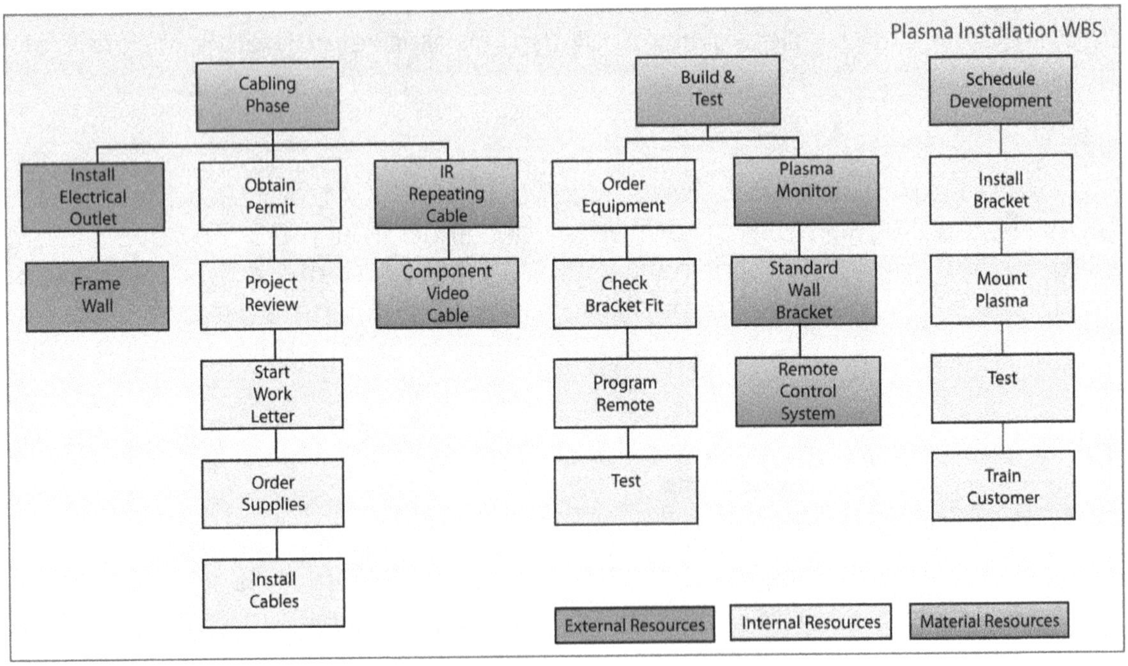

Figure 16-2. *TV Installation WBS (Flowchart Format)*

Table 16-2. *Plasma Installation WBS (Tabular Format)*

1.0 Cabling phase	2.0 Build & test	3.0 Deliver y & installation
1.1 Install electrical outlet	2.1 Order equipment	3.1 Install bracket
1.2 Frame wall	2.2 Check bracket fit	3.2 Mount plasma
1.3 Obtain permit	2.3 Program remote	3.3 Test
1.4 Project review	2.4 Test	3.4 Train customer
1.5 Start work letter		
1.6 Order supplies		

The different types of BOMs are shown in Figures 16-3 through 16-5:

- Work order view
- Purchase requirements view
- Sales invoice view

THE JOB COSTING REPORT

The job costing report, as shown in Figure 16-6, is a view of the cost estimate that summarizes the cost of products and services for the project. It includes cost, sell list, gross profit, margin, and discount figures for each phase of the project. This report should be reviewed regularly.

Industry Factors Affect Cost Estimating

Though the scope statement and defining the Work Breakdown Structure are the most important factors in cost estimating, factors within the electronic systems contracting industry are also important. These enterprise environmental factors include the external environmental factors and internal organizational factors that surround or influence the project's success.

These factors fall into two categories:

- Market conditions
- Commercial databases

Market conditions account for what products and services are available during the project life cycle, including the availability of resources and the terms and conditions of getting them.

Commercial databases track costs by collecting information on installation times and product costs from a number of different companies across the industry and documenting material costs as well as human resource costs industry-wide. These databases provide a reliable cost-estimating tool for both established and young start-up businesses.

Organizational Factors Affect Cost Estimating

Every organization has its own internal process for estimating costs. For example, are costs based on turnkey or custom systems? The company might use cost-estimating templates or it might prepare each estimate from scratch. The project manager and project team might be ultimately responsible for the estimate, but a sales engineer might actually prepare the estimates.

Cost Estimating Policies

It is important for a company to have cost estimating policies that ensure that estimates are consistent. Cost estimating policies include a checklist that identifies the people and tasks that are part of the estimating process. These include:

Who — creates the cost estimate, who reviews the work, and who is responsible for the outcome?

Travel — how much travel is involved and how will it figure into the estimate?

Project Management Factor — how much time will be necessary for project management? What is the size and anticipated difficulty of the project?

House Factors — what is the actual size and structure of the house?

Cost Estimating Templates

Templates provide a highly effective estimating tool. Using templates, a team can rapidly provide a thorough scope statement and cost estimate for the customer. On the other hand, templates do not allow for much customization. The best use is to use the template as a base but insert custom options to involve the customer in the decision process.

ABC Integrations
123 Main Street Unit 101
Anytown, FL 32966
(800) 555 - 1212

House Size: 5,100
File Code: 101ELWLV1-1
Proposal Date: May 15, 2008

Work Order

Client: Joe Builders
557 Oak Street
Anytown, FL 32966

PRODUCTS	BID QNTY	ACTUAL QNTY	DIFFERENCE
A-Cables: 1 gang low voltage bracket, Blue, Ea	21		
A-Cables: 2" flexible raceway, 50 foot length , Blue, Ea	1		
A-Cables : Cat5e, 1000' reel-in-a box, Blue, Ft	1573		
A-Cables : Cat5e, 1000' reel-in-a box, Grey, Ft	605		
A-Cables : Cat5e, 1000' reel-in-a box, Green, Ft	242		
A-Cables : Cat5e, 1000' reel-in-a box, White, Ft	1573		
A-Cables: bundled wire includes: CAT5E, 16/4, Siamese, purple , Purple, Ft	966		
SERVICES	**BID HOURS**	**ACTUAL HOURS**	**DIFFERENCE**
Installation, Cabling Phase, Mins (Converted to Hours)	23		

Figure 16-3. *BOM as a Work Order*

ABC Integrations
123 Main Street Unit 101
Anytown, FL 32966
(800) 555 - 1212

PURCHASE REQUIREMENTS

Proposal Date: 3/17/2008
Client: Joe Builders
557 Oak Street
Anytown, FL 32966

Description	QNTY	RATE	AMOUNT
A-Cables: 1 gang low voltage bracket, Blue, Ea (Part No: 1017, Purch. Qnty: 24)	21	0.92	19.25
A-Cables: 2" flexible raceway, 50 foot length , Blue, Ea (Part No: 1038, Purch. Qnty: 1)	1	67.75	67.75
A-Cables: Cat5e, 1000' reel-in-a box, Blue, Ft (Part No: 1001, Purch. Qnty: 0)	1573	0.08	120.65
A-Cables: Cat5e, 1000' reel-in-a box, Grey, Ft (Part No: 1003, Purch. Qnty: 1000)	605	0.08	46.40
A-Cables: Cat5e, 1000' reel-in-a box, Green, Ft (Part No: 1004, Purch. Qnty: 1000)	242	0.08	18.56
A-Cables: Cat5e, 1000' reel-in-a box, White, Ft (Part No: 1002, Purch. Qnty: 1000)	1573	0.08	120.65
A-Cables: ProConnect bundled wire includes: CAT5E, 16/4, Siamese, purple , Purple, Ft (Part No: 1007, F	966	0.19	182.57
A-Cables: RG6, Quad shield, 1000' box, White, Ft (Part No: 1005, Purch. Qnty: 1000)	1190	0.12	142.68
A-Cables: RG6, Quad shield, 1000' box, Black, Ft (Part No: 1006, Purch. Qnty: 1000)	1190	0.12	142.68
			-
		TOTAL	861.20

Figure 16-4. *BOM as a Purchase Request*

ABC Integrations
123 Main Street Unit 101
Anytown, FL 32966
(800) 555 - 1212

SALES INVOICE

Proposal Date: 5/15/2008
Client: Joe Builders
557 Oak Street
Anytown, FL 32966
File Code: 101ELWLV1-1

Description	QNTY	RATE	AMOUNT
A-Cables: 1 gang low voltage bracket, Blue, Ea (Part No: 1017)	21	1.20	25.20
A-Cables: 2" flexible raceway, 50 foot length , Blue, Ea (Part No: 1038)	1	88.00	88.00
A-Cables: Cat5e, 1000' reel-in-a box, Blue, Ft (Part No: 1001)	1573	0.15	235.95
A-Cables: Cat5e, 1000' reel-in-a box, Grey, Ft (Part No: 1003)	605	0.11	66.55
A-Cables: Cat5e, 1000' reel-in-a box, Green, Ft (Part No: 1004)	242	0.15	36.30
A-Cables: Cat5e, 1000' reel-in-a box, White, Ft (Part No: 1002)	1573	0.11	173.03
A-Cables: ProConnect bundled wire includes: CAT5E, 16/4, Siamese, purple , Purple, Ft (Part No: 1007)	966	0.25	241.50
A-Cables: RG6, Quad shield, 1000' box, White, Ft (Part No: 1005)	1190	0.16	190.40
A-Cables: RG6, Quad shield, 1000' box, Black, Ft (Part No: 1006)	1190	0.16	190.40
Installation, Cabling Phase, Mins (Labor Code: 101)	1358	1.00	1,358.00
		TOTAL	2,605.33

Figure 16-5. *BOM as a Sales Order*

ABC Integrations
123 Main Street Unit 101
Anytown, FL 32966
(800) 555 - 1212

Job Costing Report

Client: Joe Builders
557 Oak Street
Anytown, FL 32966

File Code: 101ELWLV1-1
House Size: 5,100
Proposal Date: 5/15/2008
Sales Tax Rate: 0%
Sales Tax Amount: $ -

Products

Phase	Cost	Sell	List	Profit	Margin	Discount
0 General	$ -	$ -	$ -	$ -	0%	*0%*
1 Cabling	861.20	1,247.33	2,350.65	386.13	31%	*47%*
2 Termination	-	-	-	-	0%	*0%*
3 Move-In	-	-	-	-	0%	*0%*
4 E. Build	-	-	-	-	0%	*0%*
5 E. Delivery	-	-	-	-	0%	*0%*
Totals	*861.20*	*1,247.33*	*2,350.65*	*386.13*	31%	*47%*

Services

Phase	*Cost*	*Sell*		*Profit*	*Margin*	
0 General	$ -	$ 281.25	$ 281.25	$ 281.25	100%	*0%*
1 Cabling	-	1,358.00	1,358.00	1,358.00	100%	*0%*
2 Termination	-	-	-	-	0%	*0%*
3 Move-In	-	233.00	233.00	233.00	100%	*0%*
4 E. Build	-	-	-	-	0%	*0%*
5 E. Delivery	-	-	-	-	0%	
Totals	-	*1,872.25*	*1,872.25*	*1,872.25*	100%	*0%*

Products & Services

Phase	*Cost*	*Sell*	*List*	*Profit*	*Margin*	*Discount*
0 General	$ -	$ 281.25	$ 281.25	$ 281.25	100%	*0%*
1 Cabling	861.20	2,605.33	3,708.65	1,744.13	67%	*30%*
2 Termination	-	-	-	-	0%	*0%*
3 Move-In	-	233.00	233.00	233.00	100%	*0%*
4 E. Build	-	-	-	-	0%	*0%*
5 E. Delivery	-	-	-	-	0%	
Totals	*861.20*	*3,119.58*	*4,222.90*	*2,258.38*	72%	*26%*

Figure 16-6. *Job Costing Report*

Historical Information

Historical information is perhaps the most helpful component of cost estimating. Whether from a commercial database or the company's project files, knowing the actual cost of a similar project is the best source for an accurate cost estimate. Maintaining a "lessons learned file" helps the company retain notes on past projects' pitfalls.

Project Team Knowledge

Team members with experience in the electronic systems contracting industry are a tremendous asset to cost estimating. Whether for the current company or another company in the industry, hands-on prior experience can filter database information to provide more accurate estimates.

Cost Estimating Gone Wrong

Poor cost estimating can undermine even the most carefully planned project. Unfortunately, there are several causes of poor cost estimating and too many causes combined together can have a negative effect on the final duration, cost, and quality of the project.

Causes of poor cost estimating include:

- Inexperienced estimators
- Low-balling

Inexperienced estimators tend to be overly optimistic about what is required to complete a project. They are prone to ignore or leave out small parts when estimating, and they are often inconsistent in their methodology.

When a company makes a conscious decision to complete a job for less than it will actually cost the company to complete the work, it is called low-balling. Though this can be an effective way to acquire customers in a competitive market, it will eventually have a negative impact on the business if continued on a regular basis.

Approaches to Cost Estimating

The electronic systems contracting industry typically uses two methods to determine the values used in a project: bottom-up cost estimating and top-down cost estimating.

Both methods are based on a detailed Work Breakdown Schedule (WBS). A good WBS simplifies creating the cost estimate, and determining which method to use usually depends on the size of the project. A large complicated, project usually uses the bottom-up approach whereas top-down estimating works well for small systems where resources required are readily accounted for. Estimated cost should be evaluated against the scope of work document by the project manager.

Bottom-Up Cost Estimating

Bottom-up cost estimating does just what its name implies. It starts at the bottom with the cost of separate individual items and works up to the cost of the finished project, a total of all the individual pieces.

Top-Down Cost Estimating

Top-down cost estimating takes the cost of the major components and the time required to complete them and breaks them down into more detailed segments to determine an overall project estimate.

Value Engineering

Value engineering involves selecting the alternatives for design, materials, processes, and documentation that will derive the best value for the dollars spent. It is not necessarily the alternative with the lowest cost, but rather the choice that gives the most return on investment (ROI).

TIME CONSTRAINT

Project time management is one of the three constraints that define and evaluate projects. Time constraints, and the time management plan, help a project team complete a project in a timely manner. The goal is a project schedule that works with the milestones in the scope statement. Though it sounds simple, making sure a project is completed on time involves more than efficient planning and execution.

Other considerations include:

- Activity definition
- Activity resource estimation
- Activity sequencing
- Activity duration estimation
- Schedule development

Activity Definition

Project managers use a technique shown in Figure 16-3, called activity definition, to identify the specific activities that the project team carries out in the process of producing the project deliverables. Activities or tasks defined in the Work Breakdown Schedule are translated into activity definition.

Some of the common activities for a work package include:

Electronics or Equipment Build — for example, receiver, DVD, equipment rack, plasma monitor, and speakers

Electronics Install — installing the system components in the home

Project Management — tracking and expediting the project and ensuring adequate customer training

Electronics Programming — getting the equipment up and ready to run

Cable Install — running the necessary cable in the home

Table 16-3. *Activity Definition*

Task
1.0 Cabling phase
1.1 Install electrical outlet
1.2 Frame wall
1.3 Obtain permit
1.4 Project review
1.5 Start work letter
1.6 Order supplies
2.0 Build & test
2.1 Order equipment
2.2 Check bracket fit
2.3 Program remote
2.4 Test
3.0 Delivery & installation
3.1 Install bracket
3.2 Mount plasma
3.3 Test
3.4 Train customer

ACTIVITY RESOURCE ESTIMATION

In this step, the project manager prepares a specific list of internal and external resources (including type, amount, and quantity) that are necessary to meet the project milestones.

The list of activity resources often includes:

- Equipment
- Materials and supplies
- Money
- People

The bottom-up accounting method is one of the best methods to approximate resources. The WBS is used to decompose project work into work packages that are small enough to reliably estimate activity duration and resource requirements, as shown in Table 16-4. This method is fairly accurate because the estimates come from the people doing the actual work.

One factor that must be considered is the use of outside contractors to do the company's business. This is called outsourcing.

Advantages of outsourcing are:

- Saves money because company benefits are not provided to the contractor.
- Allows the company to offer specialized services that it otherwise might not be able to afford.
- Allows the company to quickly expand and contract its workforce without hiring additional direct employees.

Disadvantages of outsourcing are:

- Experience and knowledge gained as a result of the project is not retained within the company.
- Quality of work may suffer if the wrong contractor is chosen.
- Company reputation may suffer if the wrong contractor is chosen.

Table 16-4. *Activity Resource Estimation*

Task	Who	Effort (hrs)
1.0 Cabling phase		
1.1 Install electrical outlet	Electrician	
1.2 Frame wall	Carpenter	
1.3 Obtain permit	PM	1.0
1.4 Project review	PM	1.0
1.5 Start work letter	PM	0.5
1.6 Order supplies	PM	2.0
2.0 Build & test		
2.1 Order equipment	PM	1.0
2.2 Check bracket fit	Lead Installer	2.5
2.3 Program remote	Lead Installer	4.0
2.4 Test	PM	1.0
3.0 Delivery & installation		
3.1 Install bracket	Installer	2.0
3.2 Mount plasma	Installer	1.0
3.3 Test	PM	1.0
3.4 Train customer	Sales Rep.	1.5

Activity Sequencing

After project tasks have been determined and resources assigned, the next step is to put the tasks in order, similar to the steps shown in Table 16-5. In activity sequencing, the project manager reviews the activities in the detailed WBS. Each task has a logical relationship with the other activities.

These relationships can be divided into three categories:

- Mandatory dependencies
- Discretionary dependencies
- External dependencies

Mandatory dependencies are tasks that must happen. For example, the delivery of sheetrock is a mandatory task for a new construction home; without it, there is nothing to build with.

Discretionary dependencies, on the other hand, may or may not happen but do not affect the successful completion of the project.

An external dependency is one that falls outside of the scope of the company's responsibilities. For example, an electrician must finish installing the wiring before the circuitry can be used to install a home security alarm.

Table 16-5. *Activity Sequencing*

Task	Predecessor
1.0 Cabling phase	
1.1 Install electrical outlet	1.2
1.2 Frame wall	
1.3 Obtain permit	1.4
1.4 Project review	
1.5 Start work letter	1.4
1.6 Order supplies	1.4
2.0 Build & test	1.0
2.1 Order equipment	
2.2 Check bracket fit	2.1
2.3 Program remote	2.1
2.4 Test	2.3
3.0 Delivery & installation	2.0
3.1 Install bracket	
3.2 Mount plasma	3.1
3.3 Test	3.2
3.4 Train customer	3.3

Activity Duration Estimation

After defining the activities and determining their sequence, the next task is to determine the time required for each activity known as the activity duration. Activity duration estimation assigns the number of workdays that are needed to complete scheduled activities. Duration is not just the work time, but the actual time spent working on the activity plus the elapsed time, as shown in Table 16-6. The people doing the actual work have a lot of input into determining the duration of each activity in the plan. In addition to personnel input, historical data is invaluable in this process.

Table 16-6. *Activity Duration Estimation*

Task	Duration (Days)
1.0 Cabling phase	
1.1 Install electrical outlet	5
1.2 Frame wall	5
1.3 Obtain permit	4
1.4 Project review	1
1.5 Start work letter	0.5
1.6 Order supplies	0.5
2.0 Build & test	
2.1 Order equipment	21
2.2 Check bracket fit	1
2.3 Program remote	2
2.4 Test	1
3.0 Delivery & installation	
3.1 Install bracket	0.5
3.2 Mount plasma	0.5
3.3 Test	1
3.4 Train customer	1

Schedule Development

Developing a project schedule allows the project manager to keep up with multiple projects and schedule the appropriate work teams at the appropriate time. The project manager takes the duration and sequence information and the preliminary planning information and blocks off time on the schedule for the tasks that must be completed. The project schedule evolves as necessary to reflect the actual work done. This schedule needs to be developed with the subcontractor in mind.

An important topic in schedule development is critical path. The critical path of a project is the sequence of activities or tasks that, when followed in logical order, take longer to complete than any other sequence in the project. The critical path is represented in the network diagram as the longest path. Figure 16-7 shows an example of a critical path. Reviewing the critical path and comparing actual work time to the critical path helps the project manager keep the project on schedule.

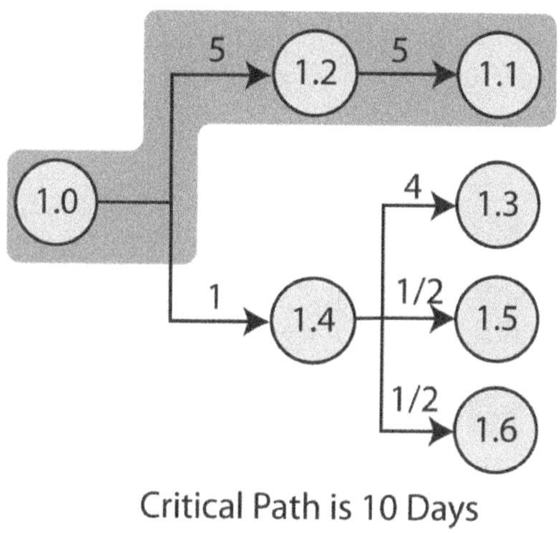

Figure 16-7. *Cabling Phase Critical Path*

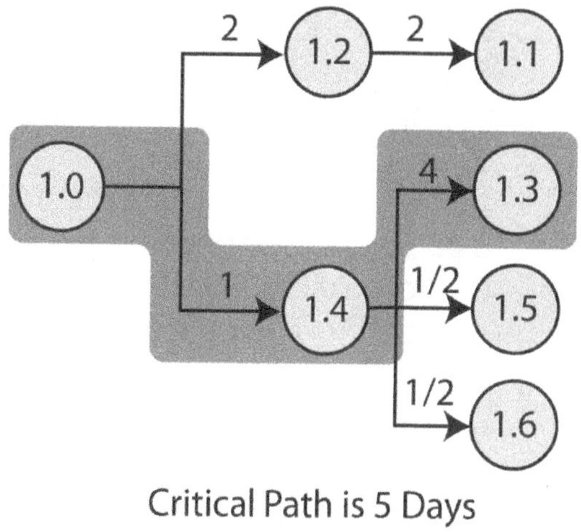

Figure 16-8. *Fast-Tracked Critical Path*

In addition to keeping the project on time, the critical path is the key to fast-tracking. When a project is fast-tracked, as shown in Figure 16-8, the project schedule is compressed and activities that would normally be done in sequence are overlapped. The goal of fast tracking is to shorten the overall project timeline.

By building the work plan for normal working conditions, the project manager leaves room to compress the critical path on occasions that circumstances require it.

Quality is a nebulous term; it is hard to define and harder to measure because it means measuring the worth of a product according to the person buying the product. Quality involves standards. Quality involves opinions. Quality means satisfaction of needs or expectations.

CHARACTERISTICS OF QUALITY

Because quality is so difficult to define, it is often defined by its characteristics. In the electronic systems contracting industry, characteristics include:

- Dependability
- Reliability
- Service
- Ease of use
- Convenience
- Respect for the customer
- Respect for the customer's property

Dependability is the ability to be trusted to deliver what is promised. Part of a project manager's job is to develop a file of vendors, suppliers, and manufacturers who have met the company's expectations on past projects.

Reliability goes hand-in-hand with dependability, and means a product or service that acts in a way that is expected or required.

Successful project managers provide quality service. Educating and certifying project team members helps them be more proficient in their area of expertise.

Well-designed systems and adequate customer training result in ease of use. Support and training are extremely important to the customer's perception of quality. The quality will remain hidden if no one knows how to use it.

Meeting the customer's expectations is the main focus of convenience. Using the system should be relatively easy for the consumer.

Good project managers respect their staff and peers and encourage them in turn to respect all customers and stakeholders. Even though these are not tangible characteristics, they provide a perception of quality that can override minor flaws.

A technician who shows respect for the customer's property, like removing shoes on a new carpet, projects an image of care and competence.

Quality Management Planning Tools

With a quality management plan intact, there are widely accepted methods for measuring quality. These include cost benefit analysis and benchmarking.

Cost Benefit Analysis

Cost benefit analysis is widely used to decide whether or not to start a new course of action. The project manager looks at the benefits of the new process and the cost to implementing it. If costs outweigh the benefits, then it should not be implemented. If the benefits outweigh the cost, then the project manager can proceed with putting it into effect. It is important to remember that the cost benefit does not have to be immediate but can be achieved over a period of time.

Cost benefit analysis is used to determine:

- Change within the company
- Cost of the change
- Benefit to the company
- Length of the payback period
- Value of tangible financial facts
- Value of intangible, non-financial facts

Benchmarking

Benchmarking is a way for companies to develop standards of quality. It compares current company processes and procedures with other projects to come up with ideas for improvements. Benchmarking is a tool to help companies stay competitive while improving quality.
Some common areas where benchmarking works well include:

Pricing — determine what is achievable and compare prices to other industry competitors. Try to set a similar level of performance or service for the same amount of money.

Surveys — use market surveys to provide information on what is being offered industry-wide. Consider a survey to identify weak areas that may need improvement.

Process — think of benchmarking as a process. Start with small areas rather than an entire system. It is easier and more manageable.

Alignment — make sure the benchmark goal is aligned with the overall strategy and goals of the company.

Service — maintain a high standard for service delivery.

Customer Satisfaction — never forget that the primary benchmark is customer satisfaction.

Other quality management tools include:

- Using checklists to keep team members on the same track and help ensure that nothing is overlooked
- Establishing brainstorming sessions to provide opportunities for everyone to share ideas and become part of the planning process
- Hiring employees with industry certifications
- Using Industry Best Practices Standards to guide company decisions

Quality Assurance

Quality Assurance is the process of applying planned quality assurance activities to ensure that the project employs all necessary means to achieve the requirements of the project. This is the responsibility of organizational leadership and should be built into the company's standard operating procedures.

Quality Control

Quality control is the process used to monitor specific project results to determine whether they comply with relevant quality standards and to identify ways to eliminate causes of unsatisfactory performance. This is the project manager's primary responsibility. To effectively manage and monitor quality, the project manager must use experience plus all of the available organizational resources, tools, and systems.

SCOPE CREEP

It is important to the overall quality and success of a project for all stakeholders to have a clear vision of the project scope and objectives. Unclear objectives lead to "scope creep." Just like it sounds, scope creep is the expansion of a project outside of planned objectives. Scope creep is usually the result of the growth or change of project requirements. It can be avoided by making sure all parties have a thorough understanding of the project goals and deliverables.

Additional ways to avoid scope creep include:

- Having approved milestones
- Reviewing budget, deadlines, and delivery during the project
- Defining deliverables
- Assigning resources as work progresses
- Assessing customer and other stakeholder satisfaction as the project progresses
- Document and get changes approved and paid for prior to completion.

Under control, scope creep is not necessarily a bad thing, but rather a normal part of the process. Changes will occur for a variety of reasons. However, the project manager can control scope creep and minimize its effect on the outcome of the project by keeping people informed and doing a careful cost benefit analysis on any proposed changes.

COMMUNICATIONS PLANNING

After a contract is signed, extensive communications and planning are necessary to move from selling a project to determining how to accomplish the project. The sales manager must communicate the customer's expectations and the details of the expected outcome to the project manager and project team.

Communications planning is the process of determining who needs to know what information, when they need it, and how they will get it. The plan guides communication throughout the course of the project.

Project stakeholders for a typical electronic system project include the:

- Customer
- Sales representative
- Executive team
- Architect
- Builder
- Project manager
- Project team members
- Outside contractors
- Property manager
- Interior designer

Though all of these parties have an interest in the communications process, the primary responsibility for communications throughout the project relies on the project manager.

Successful project managers have good communications planning skills. The project manager determines the information and communications needs of the customer, the builder, architects, other subcontractors, and the project team.

Job planning can be very technical or very simple depending on the size of your company and the demands of any given project. It is extremely important to keep all parties involved with the progress of the job and changes within the project. This can be accomplished through emails, memos, or in-person communication.

Steps in communications planning include:

- Identifying project communications requirements
- Developing communications planning policies
- Determining communications methods
- Working with outside contractors
- Running an effective meeting
- Leveraging project manager communications skills
- Orchestrating the sale-to-operations turnover

Identifying Project Communications Requirements

Project communications requirements are defined by identifying what types of information are integral to the project's success and how that information should be disseminated.

Communication requirements within the project involve the following groups:

- Project team
- Project stakeholders
- Customer
- Type of company organization and its organizational chart
- Logistics
- Vendors/Manufacturers
- External informational needs

Developing Communications Planning Policies

Like other industries, electronic system companies have a set of policies regarding how project communications is accomplished.

Determining Communications Methods

The electronic systems contracting industry uses a variety of communications methods. The method selected depends on who is sending the communication and who is receiving the communication.

Asking these questions helps project managers determine what form to use in each situation:

- What is the urgency of the communication?
- What is the availability of the form of communication?
- Who is receiving the communication?
- What is the physical environment of the project?

The end result is that everyone involved in the project should use the best available method for his situation to keep stakeholders informed and expedite project work.

Communicating with Outside Contractors

Working with outside contractors involves special attention to communication on the part of the project manager. Roles are not always obvious-who is in charge and, in turn, who is responsible must be clearly spelled out in order to maximize efficiency and minimize misunderstandings. The electronic system company's schedule is not necessarily the top priority of the builder or contractor who may have several other projects going on at the same time. It is important that they understand the integrated systems schedule and how it reflects the customer's wishes. Constant communication helps keep the plan in the forefront.

Running an Effective Meeting

Short, well-run meetings can improve communications among project stakeholders. Effective meetings don't just happen but are the result of planning by the project manager or other stakeholder responsible for the meeting. Keys to a successful meeting include:

- Thinking about scope and time
- Inviting only essential people
- Writing an agenda
- Stating meeting intentions up front
- Setting a time limit
- Always starting on time
- Using tools of the trade
- Using visual aids such as flowcharts to simplify timelines or phases
- Using Gantt charts to show potential scheduling problems
- Using network diagrams

Leveraging Project Manager Communications Skills

Communicating effectively takes time and practice. Feedback is an important part of communication because it allows for the adjustment of information that may go back and forth between parties.

Some of the other attributes of effective communication include:

- Know when to talk and when to be quiet
- Encourage open communication of ideas and thoughts
- Listen carefully to the other person in a conversation
- Provide constructive feedback
- Write notes and memos clearly and concisely
- Write technical material and reports that are clearly understandable
- Understand and respond to nonverbal communications from others
- Think and speak "in the moment"
- Determine whether others understand a message or communication
- Use language and tone suitable to listeners
- Correct others diplomatically
- Prepare a presentation and deliver it to large groups of people
- Articulate effectively when speaking with subordinates and support personnel
- Show self-confidence
- Negotiate successfully
- Articulate effectively in face-to-face and phone conversations with the company's management personnel, team members, and other staff personnel
- Avoid using technical jargon when communicating with external stakeholders

For more information on communication techniques, see Chapter 17, Customer Relations.

Sales-to-Operations

After the customer signs the contract, the sales representative institutes the process of turning over the project to the operations group. The operations turnover process helps improve communications between sales and the operations personnel staff. This also gives the sales team the opportunity to communicate and explain the customer's expectations.

COMMUNICATION DOCUMENTS

In an effective meeting, a variety of documents are used to communicate and reinforce information. In addition to the scope statement and planning schedules, there are a variety of other documents that may be used in a meeting to convey information.

These documents include:

- Cabling documentation if the home has an existing cable system.
- Installation documentation (as-built documents) for any previously installed systems.
- Floor plans for new and existing construction.
- Electrical and furniture plans help in locating speakers and TVs.
- Block diagrams detailing how the system is to be connected.
- Touchscreen layouts showing customer preferences.
- Cabinetry drawings to determine where equipment will be located.
- Cost information.

There are a variety of ways that project managers can request information from suppliers. Choosing the appropriate request format is usually based on the size of the project, the level of detail required, and who is completing the pricing.

Submittal

A submittal is a one-page document of specifications for a product or service. See Chapter 15, Documentation, for more information on submittals.

RFI

A Request for Information (RFI) is the document created as the result of an inquiry made of a contractor or vendor for a service. The RFI is used to compare various vendors on a particular project. It is critical that RFI's are approved in writing prior to execution.

The Purchase Order

A purchase order (PO) is a very important document because it serves as a contract between the buyer and the seller. Information in a purchase order is very specific and includes quantity, model number, description, unit purchase price, delivery instructions, and payment terms.

Request for Quotation

A Request for Quotation (RFQ) is a formal invitation from a buyer to a provider of goods or services to provide a quote. In the RFQ, the buyer provides project specifications. A request is usually made before a purchase order is issued to gather pricing information for comparison and eventual selection of a single vendor for the lowest-cost supplies and services.

Request for Proposal

To gather pricing information for higher-cost projects, companies usually use a Request for Proposal (RFP). In the electronic systems contracting industry, the RFP is often used to find the best solution to a homeowner's unique situation. The RFP must describe the products or services in the request in sufficient detail for suppliers to provide complete and competitive information. In an RFP, the supplier or seller provides the project specifications and cost information and is responsible for meeting those specifications. An RFP is significantly more detailed than an RFQ. An RFP may be used to solicit proposals from subcontractors, like security installation companies and electricians.

Invitation to Bid

If a company has a well-defined project and the buyer is requesting a contract price, an Invitation to Bid (IVB) is often used instead of an RFP. In this case, a variety of companies compete on price based on a proposal they submit within a given time frame.

Site Conditions

An electronic system site condition review involves several components. These include:

- Site location issues
- Existing construction
- House layout
- Equipment location
- Unusual circumstances

A site conditions survey form, as shown in Figure 16-9, is a helpful tool for documenting individual aspects of the site conditions. It documents basic information about the home; for example, what the walls are made of or whether trucks can drive close to the house.

Distance to the Site

Distance to the site is one of several site location issues. Before beginning the project and creating a time management plan, the project manager needs to know how long it will take crews to travel to the jobsite. Will overnight stay be necessary? Are accommodations readily available?

The company should also develop a general travel policy about how far away the company will travel for a job and set a policy on how to charge for travel.

Site Map and Directions

Project documentation should include a map showing the site and directions to the site location. Sometimes, this seems unnecessary, particularly when teams are familiar with the area, or if the company has just completed another project in the same neighborhood. However, areas change quickly (particularly those under construction), and it is important to remember that the time a crew spends lost or looking for a location is money down the drain.

Site Parking

Available parking at a jobsite should be determined in advance. A project cannot always assume that there is a place for worker vehicles on the property. It is also a good idea to know the location and distance to the nearest local Emergency Room.

Bringing Tools and Supplies to the Site

The location of the jobsite impacts what tools and supplies can be brought to the site. When tools are required that are difficult to carry back and forth on a daily basis, a secure site must be provided for workers to leave their tools. If the site is easily accessible by truck, the tools can go back and forth on a daily basis.

Existing Construction Projects

Projects or remodels in existing construction require special attention to planning. Older homes were built to different standards, and the project manager must be careful to pay attention to those differences. Building materials used in the home might not be available any longer, plaster walls may present costly problems when cut, or materials or construction methods might not comply with current standards.

House Layout

Detailed information about the actual layout of the house is an important component of the scope statement. Information should include each floor of the house, each room (with names), dimensions, and ceiling height. Much of this information comes from the floor plan.

It is important to check the floor plan against existing conditions. Sketch the layout and pay particular attention to permanent structures. Be sure to include utility areas (attics, crawl spaces, and basements) that are integral spaces for installation plans.

SITE SURVEY

PROPOSAL NUMBER: ______________________ DRIVING DISTANCE: ______________________

PROPOSAL DUE BY: ______________________ CUSTOMER NAME: ______________________

SITE ADDRESS: ____

PROJECT SCOPE: ____

____

BASEMENT

CEILING HEIGHT: ______________________ TYPE: ❑ OPEN ❑ DROP ❑ BOARD & PLASTER ❑ ______

SQUARE FEET: ______________________ FINISH: ❑ YES ❑ NO

CONSTRUCTION: ❑ NEW ❑ RETROFIT

ROOM NAMES:

__________ __________ __________ __________ __________

__________ __________ __________ __________ __________

1ST FLOOR

CEILING HEIGHT: ______________________ TYPE: ❑ OPEN ❑ DROP ❑ BOARD & PLASTER ❑ ______

SQUARE FEET: ______________________ FINISH: ❑ YES ❑ NO

CONSTRUCTION: ❑ NEW ❑ RETROFIT

ROOM NAMES:

__________ __________ __________ __________ __________

__________ __________ __________ __________ __________

2ND FLOOR

CEILING HEIGHT: ______________________ TYPE: ❑ OPEN ❑ DROP ❑ BOARD & PLASTER ❑ ______

SQUARE FEET: ______________________ FINISH: ❑ YES ❑ NO

CONSTRUCTION: ❑ NEW ❑ RETROFIT

ROOM NAMES:

__________ __________ __________ __________ __________

__________ __________ __________ __________ __________

____

CEILING HEIGHT: ______________________ TYPE: ❑ OPEN ❑ DROP ❑ BOARD & PLASTER ❑ ______

SQUARE FEET: ______________________ FINISH: ❑ YES ❑ NO

CONSTRUCTION: ❑ NEW ❑ RETROFIT

ROOM NAMES:

__________ __________ __________ __________ __________

__________ __________ __________ __________ __________

(Company Name):: 123 Main Street, Anytown, MA 01234:: (999) 555 - 1212:: www.company.com Page 1 of 1

Figure 16-9. *Site Conditions Survey Form*

Be sure to consider the following questions:

- Could each utility area be connected with conduit to allow for future system upgrades?
- Are there areas of the house that can't be reached from a utility area?
- Can access panels be provided to allow for future upgrades and system maintenance?

While working on a current project, try to plan for the future as well. Installing cable, conduit, and access panels now that will work for future expansions should translate into greater customer satisfaction and the reputation of being a high-quality, forward-looking business.

Electronics Location

Many times projects involve working with or around existing electronic equipment. The electronics location is where the products are located. Often, special closets are built to house the distribution panels or equipment, and special consideration for ventilation or cooling of the equipment area should be taken into effect. Existing permanent conditions should also be noted.

Unusual Site Circumstances

Unusual site circumstances are things or situations that are unusual to the area or the the typical work of the integrator. These could include a home being in a hurricane-prone area or knowing that the Homeowners Association may have restrictions that require pre-approval of site plans. Knowing this information can have a significant effect on not only the project timeline, but the bottom line as well.

Other conditions that a project manager should consider are:

Working Hours — Do local laws or a general contractor have special restrictions?

Bonding Insurance Requirements — What are the requirements for bonding, insurance, and workers' compensation?

Conduit Requirements — Are all cables required to be in conduits? What are the termination and connection regulations?

Existing Cabling — What is the inspection process for existing versus new work?

Permits — Are any special permits required for the location? If so, what is the cost and how difficult is the permitting process?

Power — Will temporary and/or permanent power be available at the site during the installation process?

Codes and Regulations

All states, cities, and even some residential communities have their own set of rules and regulations governing the electronic systems contracting industry. A residential integration company is accustomed to a set of standard methods and requirements for their area. The project manager should document any items that fall outside of those normal standards. They are important in both the cost estimating and work planning process.

System Information

Each system included in an installation has a corresponding set of instructions. A table that shows each system and which rooms get which systems is a valuable reference. This table can also include cabling information and any other installation data.

There are two kinds of systems. One is a standard system that is regularly installed by the company, and the second is a non-standard system that has never been installed anywhere by the company. Installing a non-standard system should be taken into account when estimating project costs.

CHAPTER 17

CUSTOMER RELATIONS

A company's approach to customers is a determining factor in predicting a company's success. Customers should be at the center of all activities including decisions about quality, pricing, and product differentiation. On the surface, customer relations means keeping customers informed, handling complaints efficiently, and truly listening to what customers have to say. But on a deeper level, customer relations means being a customer-focused organization.

In a customer-focused organization, activities relating to planning, design, production, marketing, and after-sales services of a product are built around the customer. As a result, every department and every individual employee understands this focus and shares the vision. Only when the entire team buys into the vision can a company deliver continuous customer satisfaction.

THE INTEGRATOR AND CUSTOMER RELATIONS

A technician or designer might be tempted to think that customer relations is the sole responsibility of the sales team. In reality, everyone who comes in contact with the customer needs to be aware of customer relations issues. In fact, in most cases, the technician and designer are the persons who interact with the customer the most, and thus their actions are vital to the company's overall image and reputation. The designer and technician represent the company's:

- Mission statement
- Level of respect
- Personality and culture
- Knowledge and technical expertise

Note that the customer is aware of much more than just the installer's technical knowledge in his interactions with technicians and designers. The level of respect for the customer's home is evident when an installer removes his shoes before walking on carpet. The company's mission statement may manifest itself in the form of a thorough follow-up to ensure the customer is satisfied. Representing the company is a huge responsibility and integrators can succeed or fail based on word of mouth alone. A good experience with an installer provides reassurance that the customer has made the right choice in selecting the right organization for his electronic needs.

Understanding the Company Mission Statement and Business Plan

A business mission statement is a short commentary that explains the company's purpose and its primary products and may describe details such as the intended customer demographic, industry influences, and more. Each mission statement is unique to the company that creates it and an example is shown in Figure 17-1. Everyone in the company should know the mission statement so that they can embrace its message in their day-to-day business activities and tasks. This helps ensure that work is completed in accordance with established company policies and procedures.

In addition to the mission statement, employees should also possess a basic high level understanding of the product mix and services that their company provides to its customers. This will be beneficial when discussing needs and expectations with the customer and in answering any questions someone might have about the organization.

ABC INTEGRATIONS' MISSION STATEMENT

ABC Integrations provides turnkey electronic systems integrating comfort, entertainment, and convenience in the modern digital home.

Figure 17-1. *Example Mission Statement*

The company's business plan describes how the company conducts business and generates revenue. It also defines how employees help to carry out the mission of the company. Not every company will share the overall business plan with every employee. However, an overview of its content in particular job descriptions and how they interrelate should be visible to each employee. The company's organizational chart is often provided so employees can gain an understanding of the various positions within the company and see how the work flows from one employee (or department) to another.

The company's marketing plan is another tool that employees need to understand in order to help the company grow and thrive. A marketing plan is a definitive guide for an organization's marketing strategies and tactics used in offering their products and services for sale in the marketplace over a defined planning period, typically one year.

With an understanding of these documents, each employee is in a better position to give customers accurate information, step in when needed to facilitate problems, explain company processes and policies, and generally represent the company in a positive and educated manner.

WHO IS THE CUSTOMER?

Essentially, anyone who interacts directly or indirectly with the company is a customer. In the simplest form, this is the homeowner; but in reality, almost everyone is a customer to some degree. Therefore, it is imperative that each employee act responsibly and professionally at all times in his dealings with people outside the company.

In addition to these external customers, employees must also remember to practice a high level of customer service when dealing with internal customers. These are the individuals within the company or project team, including subcontractors, architects, builders, interior designers and manufacturer partners, who require something even though they might not pay for that service or information.

The Requirements of External Customers typically have common needs that they expect to be met, such as:

- Providing access and information
- Demonstrating respect
- Reassuring and validating them
- Showing high-quality and efficient work

In addition, customers need to feel that they are heard and that their opinions are respected, but also that they are working with professionals who will take their thoughts into consideration while guiding them through every interaction with the company.

The Importance of Internal Customer Relations

An internal customer is a person or coworker within the company or project team who needs a service or piece of information. While external customers provide revenue, internal customers provide the resources (profit) and knowledge that keep the company producing and unique.

Internal customers have needs just as external customers do, such as:

- Faith in their competency and efficiency
- A feeling of accomplishment
- Productive days with limited hassle
- Coworkers with positive attitudes
- A feeling that they are trusted and that they can trust others

- Knowledge that their opinions are heard
- Assurance that they are involved in the decision-making process

Most of all, internal customers need to feel appreciated and valued as a resource.

AN EXCELLENT CUSTOMER SERVICE ATTITUDE

An excellent customer service attitude sets the stage for success, builds positive relationships, and even helps overcome problems more easily. Attitude is made up of several elements, including:

- Appreciation
- Confidence
- Competence
- Courtesy
- Empathy
- Honesty
- Open-mindedness
- Patience
- Reliability
- Responsiveness

Projecting Confidence

Confidence comes from knowing how to do a job well, knowing that products and services are meeting customer's needs and expectations and understanding what is expected in a given situation.

Technicians who project a confident attitude reassure customers of not only their competence, but that of the company as a whole. Confidence brings calm and a sense that things are going well, resulting in a pleasant and productive work environment. Overconfidence, however, is having a level of certainty that is significantly greater than circumstances warrant and usually leads to failed expectations because of false assumptions. Although confidence is a desired characteristic and can help customers feel secure, overconfidence can undermine a project's success.

Connecting with Customers

Customers appreciate working with technicians who make an effort to connect with them. Smiling, making eye contact, open body language, friendly tone of voice, attentiveness, listening, being well groomed, neatly dressed, and responding are all important to establishing a good relationship with the customer.

Competence

Competence means understanding the complexities of the task at hand — that the product knowledge and the skill set to perform the tasks are reasonably obtainable. Part of this means being familiar and knowledgeable about the products and services provided by the company. A competent technician is able to find information efficiently and makes staying up to date a high priority.

Appreciation

Appreciating the customers, both internal and external, means acknowledging their intelligence and sensitivities. Approaching tasks and dilemmas with a positive attitude lends a sense of respect and appreciation. Customers who feel that they are appreciated in turn have a more positive attitude about the project. Problems become opportunities to further prove that their choice of a systems integrator was the right one. Appreciation can soften rather than solidify roadblocks that are bound to come up in any project.

Honesty

Honesty is a common element to all successful relationships, both in the business world and in personal life. Many customers can detect when they are being told an untruth, and it sets up a scenario of defensiveness and mistrust. Honesty is one of the primary, fundamental moral human characteristics that can never be restored 100% once it is violated.

Having trustworthy relationships with customers fosters customer loyalty. Being consistent by stating the truth and following through on promises helps to build a solid company reputation. Even in circumstances where research must be done in order to answer a question can build credibility if done correctly. When customers feel the company is trustworthy, they will continue to purchase goods and services.

Steps to heighten the customer's perception of honesty include:

- Promising only what can be delivered — under promise and over deliver.
- Telling a customer "what she wants to hear" only when it's the truth.
- Referring them to someone else if necessary.
- Explaining actions thoroughly using layman's terms.
- Working on behalf of the customer.
- Presenting both the advantages and disadvantages.
- Clearly defining expectations and delivering on those expectations. Unclear expectations that aren't delivered on can be viewed as your having misled the client.

Emphasize Reliability

Reliability is an important aspect of customer relations because customers want products and services they can depend on. Reliability is the degree to which the results of an assessment are dependable and yield consistent results. This is more easily explained by the old adage "do what you say and say what you do." This means completing tasks within promised deadlines and clearly communicating changes in plans when they arise.

Other important traits, such as checking voice messages and e-mail regularly, responding promptly, and planning and performing work correctly, are all part of a reliable role model.

Open-Mindedness

Open-mindedness is the willingness to research actively for evidence that might go against a favored belief, plan, or goal and to weigh such evidence fairly when it is available. After various alternatives are considered, an open-minded person can objectively choose the best option and act accordingly. Demonstrating a lack of open-mindedness can result in jumping to conclusions that may be incorrect or in believing false assumptions. It can also lead to making assumptions about a problem with a system. Keeping an open mind helps the installer maintain an unbiased view of the project and the people involved.

Courtesy

Courtesy is more than just being polite. Of course, the basic courtesies of saying "please," "thank you," "I'm sorry," or "excuse me" are expected because they convey a sense of respect. But making eye contact, smiling often, and being respectful of another individual's point of view is also part of being courteous. Being courteous also means avoiding inappropriate language or having personal conversations in a customer's home.

Courtesy also includes being sensitive of another individual's time. For example, calling the customer when running late for an appointment demonstrates an awareness that he may have rearranged his daily schedule to accommodate the meeting.

Courtesy also extends to the introductions of others who may be working in the home. Taking responsibility for briefly introducing the install team to a homeowner indicates a level of respect and professionalism. Asking for permission before entering private areas of a home (such as a bedroom or office/den) also projects a courteous attitude. Although this may seem unnecessary, it may indeed be important to the homeowner who may have a sick child or relative resting nearby. It is these actions, when performed consistently and earnestly, that separates the successful, highly referred companies from the rest of the pack.

Understanding needs and expectations successful customer relations, both internal and external, rely heavily on understanding the customer's needs and expectations. This can only be achieved by understanding the project, the customer's expectations, and the company's expectations. Having a clear understanding of any given situation goes hand-in-hand with good communication skills, both verbal and non-verbal.

Asking open-ended questions, such as "What can I do for you?" or "What would you like to know about this product?" helps facilitate discussion and leads to a better understanding for all parties involved. Remembering to document any changes that affect the project scope, work plan, budget, or schedule helps keep the entire team informed.

Using Understandable Language

Using too much technical or trade-specific jargon is one of the biggest obstacles to clear communication in a technical project. Internal communications to peers and coworkers often require the use of abbreviations and terms that have no meaning (or a different meaning) to those outside the field. When those same abbreviations and terms are used with customers, confusion can happen very quickly. If this is not immediately noticed, a path of miscommunication can begin. When talking with a customer, it is the technician's responsibility to be completely sure the customer has understood any technical terms or concepts. Sometimes, even common acronyms like HVAC or ISP will not be understood by someone who isn't familiar with general technology, so a quick explanation may be required. Speaking clearly and asking for confirmation of the information given is a good way to check the level of understanding with the customer.

CONTRACTS

Proper contract management goes a long way towards establishing and communicating expectations to the customer. There are many forms of contractual agreements, but all are legal documents and, as such, should be carefully reviewed before signing. A contract spells out the project scope, timeline, expectations of the parties involved, and the cost for completing the project. A signature on the contract indicates acceptance of the terms contained within it and thus obligates the technician to fulfill the conditions agreed upon within the given parameters.

The type of contract reflects the cost estimating process used. Kinds of contracts include:

- Fixed price
- Time and materials
- Cost plus percentage
- Cost plus incentive fee
- Cost plus award

With a fixed price contract, there is a pre-determined fee agreed to by all parties. That fee includes the cost of materials, labor, and profit.

A time and materials contract sets an hourly wage, and the contractor is paid based on the time it takes to do the job. The contractor is reimbursed for materials purchased or the customer purchases materials directly.

A cost plus percentage fee contract is sometimes used in an environment where costs of materials and labor are changing. However, since this type of contract provides no incentive to control costs, it is rarely used.

A cost plus incentive fee contract contains a fee paid to the contractor based on a mathematical formula which sets a specific fee that the contractor is paid if the final cost is equal to the target cost. The fee is raised or lowered if costs are over or under.

A cost plus award contract is a fee based on performance. This can be based on different factors based on the contract needs, but it often contains a bonus offered for projects being completed early or under budget.

All contracts should have a clear scope of work defining system functionality easily understood terms.

COMMUNICATING WITH THE CUSTOMER

Communicating with a customer encompasses not only what is delivered, but how it is delivered. Though having a quality product, technical expertise, and up-to-date ideas are extremely important. Customers will often remember how a service was delivered long after they remember what was delivered.

Communication finds many ways to travel from sender to recipient, including:

- Face-to-face and active communication
- Telephone, voice-mail, and text messaging
- E-mail and written communication

Face-to-Face Communication

First impressions are important. Right or wrong, people do make judgments based on appearance. A professional appearance, a positive demeanor, and enthusiasm for the job are all basic signalsthat help set the stage for good face-to-face communication. Once these are in place, the next level of interaction becomes evident — eye-to-eye contact, body language (nodding of the head to confirm active listening, for example), facial gestures, and overall demeanor.

Active Communication

Active communication is a process used to effectively communicate to customers and coworkers. It is based on focusing on what is being said by questioning and repeating the information. This process helps make sure everyone is on the same page.

Steps in active communication include:

- Listening completely
- Restating for clarification
- Acknowledging
- Summarizing
- Follow-up

Listening completely is the first step. If there are other activities or tasks that are higher priority, then politely asking the customer for a few minutes to finish up is warranted.

Responses to explain the situation such as, "I need to finish running this cable, can we discuss this in 15 minutes?" is appropriate.

Once a dialogue is initiated, restating for clarification becomes important. Restating is the repeating of verbal conversation to be sure there is clear understanding by all parties. Phrases such as, "So this doesn't look the way you expected it to?" or "Are you saying that this is not the type of monitor you ordered?" can help to identify problems in a straight-forward and helpful manner so that they may be resolved quickly.

Acknowledging differs from restating in that the information that is repeated is not verbal conversation but non-verbal clues that the customer may exhibit. For example, the phrase

"You're saying this speaker is okay but the look on your face says you're not happy with this product," acknowledges the facial expressions of the customer and probes for more information. Acknowledging emotions happen in the same way — "I see that this situation is frustrating you, I would be happy to show you the remote control again."

Repeating the main issues of the conversation is called summarizing. Summarizing ensures that all action items resulting from a conversation are recorded properly and nothing is left to "fall through the cracks."

Not all of these steps are necessary in every conversation, but using active listening techniques helps clarify discussions and leads to better communication. The result is often a customer that feels he has been listened to and taken care of properly.

Telephone

The telephone has been around for over 130 years and it is one of the most frequent modes of communication. Certain rules apply for the use of the telephone in a business environment that help ensure customers are handled properly with this important tool:

- Answer the phone whenever possible rather than letting the call roll to voice-mail.
- Focus 100% attention on the caller.
- Identify yourself and your company.
- Be enthusiastic and speak clearly.
- If the person is already a customer, maintain a service attitude.
- Avoid using negative phrases or defensive language.
- Take good messages and repeat information to the caller to avoid mistakes.
- Transfer the call, if necessary, or request permission to place them on hold to find out additional information.
- At the end of the call, make sure the customer has all pertinent information.

- Confirm any action items resulting from the conversation.
- Say goodbye in a friendly manner.

After the call is completed, any notes taken are the only remnants of the conversation, so be sure they are complete and accurate. Perform any required actions as soon as possible (such as ordering components or re-scheduling subcontractors) to ensure all details are handled correctly.

Receiving Voice-Mail

Voice-mail is the current term for yesterday's "answering machines." In our bustling world, voice-mail messages say more than "Hello, call me back"; they are often long and detailed and contain very important business information.

The recording that plays prior to a caller leaving a message is almost as important as the message itself. The personal greeting should announce the recipient's name, the name of the company, and how to leave a message. The greeting should be changed regularly so that it is current. Many large corporations have adopted the policy for employees to update voice-mail recordings on a daily basis with their intended schedule and availability.

Employees should check for messages at least twice a day (morning and afternoon) if not several times a day and return calls within 24 hours or sooner, if possible. In today's business world, to offer a lower level of service than this is generally unacceptable.

Leaving Voice-Mail Messages

There are also rules of etiquette to follow when leaving a message on someone else's voice-mail system:

- Speak slowly and clearly but have a friendly and enthusiastic tone.
- Be sure to leave complete information including your name, company, and the reason for the call.
- Explain the purpose of the call, provide any requested information, and specify any expected actions.
- Give important information (e.g., name and phone number) at both the beginning and the end of the message.

Keep in mind that any messages on an answering machine can have an influence (positive or negative) on a potential customer. Messages may be replayed or forwarded to coworkers or supervisors, so care must be taken to remain professional at all times. A word of caution — never leave any personal or private information in a message because many people may have access to the voice-mail system.

It is also important to follow up on messages. If a message is not acknowledged in approximately 24 hours, call again. Sometimes messages are accidently deleted or don't get to the correct person and a follow-up call is necessary.

Texting

Texting has become a norm in communicating, and just like other methods of communication, you need to be sure to set boundaries with your client, such as times you are available to text. Other things to think about when text messaging include:

- Making sure that you include others who are important to the conversation to receive the message.
- Considering adding team members that may be contacted at odd hours so the client does not feel you cannot be contacted in an emergency.
- Making sure that you get the hours of availability from the client.
- Establishing an in-house policy regarding how text messages are handled (ie; forwarding to appropriate personnel as a backup, restating communication in another form).

E-Mail

Today, much of the communication with customers and coworkers is through e-mail. Understanding netiquette (Internet etiquette) rules are important when using e-mail communication regularly:

- Be concise and to the point.
- Avoid using fancy typestyles and too many colors.
- Note all attachments in the body text of the e-mail so that recipients are sure to see them.
- Always fill in the subject line, because many spam programs automatically send e-mails without a subject to the Junk/Spam folder.
- Remember what e-mails are both permanent and public.
- Be sure that e-mails reflect the correct company image.
- Consider composing e-mails offline to keep from accidently sending an incomplete e-mail.
- Add the recipient's e-mail address and subject after the e-mail is completely written.
- Be particularly careful when using the Reply and Reply All features of e-mail applications.

Dealing with Difficult Customers

Sometimes, despite all reasonable efforts to be professional, some customers remain unreasonably demanding, rude, or argumentative. Whether the customer is simply an unpleasant person or a wonderful person having an extremely bad day, the technician must attempt to resolve the situation and turn a negative situation into a positive one. In these cases, professionalism and restraint are of utmost importance. It may be helpful to enlist the customer's help by asking, "Where do you think the problem lies?" which might help the customer focus on the real issues with the project, rather than the drama of being upset.

Whether the problems are real or imagined, if a customer behaves inappropriately by yelling, threatening, or using abusive language, the situation needs to be diffused before attempts can be made to address the problem. Figure 17-2 shows common-sense steps for dealing with inappropriate customer behavior.

These steps include some active listening skills, such as acknowledging the customer's feelings, focusing attention on solving the problem, and providing positive alternatives. Additional steps that may be needed are setting limits on inappropriate actions and avoiding a response to intimidation or threats.

Most importantly, the supervisor must be notified when a difficult customer is encountered. This will not only keep the supervisor apprised of the situation but also provide an opportunity for them to provide guidance as to how best to handle the situation.

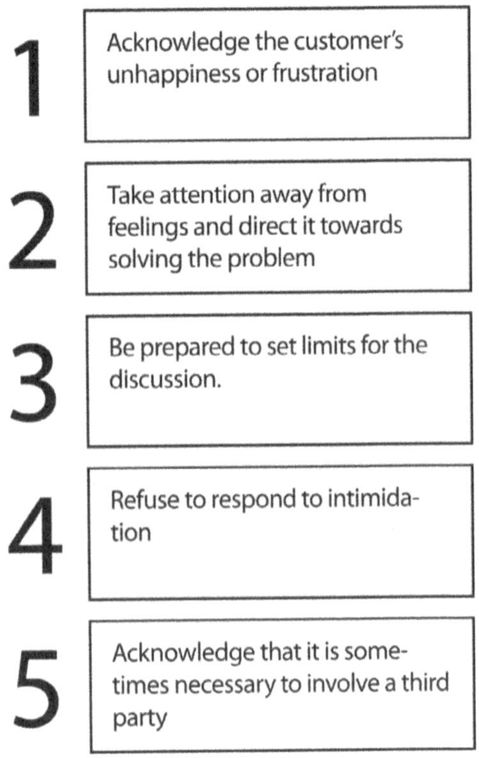

Figure 17-2. *Action Steps*

Dealing with Difficult Situations

Sometimes, customers have valid reasons to be upset; they may have had a bad experience with the company or be unhappy with the performance of a product. Sometimes, they will have difficult questions that require research, or perhaps they are irate about the fact that products needed to complete their project are backordered. In all of these cases, it is important to:

- Listen to what the customer is saying
- Respond productively
- Use calming words
- Acknowledge the problem

No customer wants to feel like he is being "handled." Avoid absolutes or unreasonable promises, but provide assurance that work will be done to resolve the issues at hand. The next step is to focus on fixing the problem. Gather the necessary information, give the customer options on how to proceed, perform the necessary work, and follow up to make sure things work smoothly.

An important part of developing a strong relationship with a customer is being able to deal with the "bumps in the road" when they arise. The result of a negative situation could end up reassuring the customer that he can indeed count on your company because you have his best interests in mind.

CUSTOMER TRAINING

Much of the success of an electronic systems contractor depends on customer satisfaction, a large part of which depends on whether or not the contractor can use the products that have been installed. If a customer can use his electronics package with confidence and ease, the likelihood of a successful project is increased. Therefore, customer training is a vital part of the entire process.

Prior to turning over the completed system to the customer, all equipment should be tested. Once verified that the equipment is working as designed, a time should be scheduled with the customer to review the operation of the equipment and provide one-on-one training. During this time, be sure to:

- Ask users if the system and the explanations of how to use the system make sense.
- Use terminology they are familiar with as a starting point to introduce new concepts to them (e.g., referring to setting the time on an alarm clock).
- Provide quick reference aides (e.g., laminated cards) to provide helpful assistance.
- Check for comprehension throughout the session, not just at the end.
- Make sure customers actually run through the controls at least once during the training session so their understanding of the process can be confirmed.

User Interface Realities

Many customers approach their home theater systems or whole house controls as they do their automobiles, they just want to get in and drive. They don't want to know how the engine works, they simply want to dim the lights, watch a movie, and enjoy the surround sound. The component that is responsible for this is the user interface.

Complicated books full of technical terms conjure up negative images for many customers who label themselves "non-technical." The documentation can make them feel overwhelmed or even ignorant. Using technical terms that have no meaning to them or talking about training in terms of hours begins to make them think twice about the wisdom of their purchase.

The challenge is to instruct them promptly, thoroughly, and painlessly. Customers may not want to be bothered with the definitions of such terms as GUIs and macros. They could have a variety of source components they want to control and there may be multiple users in the household with different preferences, capabilities and varied frequencies of use. Helping them understand how to use the system without using technical jargon is important to a successful install.

Laminated cards for basic functions Laminated cards are great for helping customers remember basic application instructions.

They are also helpful for family and friends visiting in the home and using the equipment. Laminated cards:

- Last longer than paper brochures.
- Have a professional appearance.
- Provide clear and concise operating instructions.
- Serve as inexpensive technical aids.
- Impress visitors who are trying to use the equipment.

Some important points to remember when creating these types of visual aides are:

- Be sure to include only priority uses
- Keep instructions clear, concise, and readable
- Use icons and graphics where possible
- Include a labeled picture of the remote
- Make pictures and text as large as possible
- Try to limit the information to a single two-sided card

It is also important to use a high-quality cardstock so that the information reflects positively on the company as a whole.

Designing a Standardized Instruction Template

A standardized user-instruction template is helpful for certain products that are used on a regular basis. The advantage of a template is that it saves time and guarantees that all the necessary information is given to the customer.

However, care must be taken to include information that is specific to the customer's unique situation and that irrelevant information is removed. A template document should also include a help section. Pointing a customer in the right direction helps him identify the problem quickly, reduces frustration, and cuts down on service calls.

The Customer Instruction Package

A customer instruction package is a great tool to leave with the customer once the project is complete. It can be a folder, zippered case, or binder that organizes all the important information she needs about her new system. The package should be a combination of standardized and customized material. The packet should include:

- Owner's manuals
- Warranty cards
- As-built drawings
- Business cards
- Copies of customized instructions
- Troubleshooting guides

Owner's manuals contain very detailed information about electronics products, and sometimes customers actually like to read them. They may need a manufacturer's phone number, address, or website. Many people expect to receive all owners' manuals when they purchase a home, and expect them to be available.

Warranty cards are used to register a product with the manufacturer. Having the cards in the instruction packet is a professional way to facilitate this process.

As-built drawings, including the system's rack drawings and system schematics, should also be included in the customer's instruction packet. This is a professional way of showing customers the time and planning that went into their unique, custom system. It is also helpful for the customer have on hand for review by any service personnel in the future.

Providing one or two business cards encourages the opportunity to generate new business based on the customer's referral. The best advertisement is one satisfied customer telling another potential customer of the expertise and professionalism he experienced with his new system.

Even though there might be a set with the equipment, having a backup copy of the customized instructions in the information folder is another way to show the customer that all of the bases have been covered when it comes to providing them with complete documentation.

A troubleshooting guide is the first reference the customer reaches for when there is a problem he cannot solve. When written correctly, it empowers the customer to solve small problems by pointing him in the right direction and redirecting his actions to correct the problem. It also tells him when a problem has arisen that requires the attention of a professional. The guide should be comprehensive and cover all possible scenarios that may occur with the equipment.

Training Hints

During the training session, linking written instructions to verbal explanations is another way to help customers understand the information they are being taught. Because the primary user may be an electronics whiz or a technical novice who requires a lot of encouragement, specialized instruction may be necessary. Be flexible and adapt as the circumstances dictate. Instructions may need to be geared to the use of the multiple remote controllers that came with each component, or to the use of a touch-screen that controls an entire system.

The following are some helpful hints for demonstrating the system and training customers:

- Keep explanations and terms simple. Use vocabulary customers will understand.
- Use hands-on training methods. Put the remote or the touch-screen into the customers' hands.
- Walk the customers through each system function so they get a feel for the ease of operation and gain confidence in their ability to operate the controls.
- Don't be too technical; remember that customers want to know how to operate the system, not build it.
- Show users how to press the buttons and how to give the equipment a chance to respond.
- Concentrate the training on the customized features that the customer has requested.
- Encourage customers to ask questions.
- Refer customers to your instruction materials and teach them to use those aids to solve problems and to answer questions they might have. Make sure they know they can call you with any unresolved problems.

The total training time involved will also depend on the amount of detail needed and the system's sophistication. It may be necessary to conduct multiple training sessions. Be prepared to schedule follow-up sessions, and allow the customer time to get familiar with their new system. It is very likely that they will have further questions after a short period of time.

Supplied Remote Controllers

Although it is a good idea to include a custom programmed remote system for every project, some customers may choose a system that does not provide automated control of their electronics.

In such circumstances, the original remote supplied with the equipment may need to be used instead. This may require some notes to guide the primary user through the basic functions. These instructions for basic functions might include:

- Power on/off sequence
- Input changes

- Input sources — at the receiver or head end, or at the display device
- Transport function outlines
- Icons — play, pause, stop, fast forward, and rewind
- Scanning in and overlaying the words instead of symbols into the remote
- "What if " scenarios

It will also be helpful to provide instruction sheets on what to do if certain scenarios occur. For example:

- What if during a lightning storm the surge protector goes off?
- What if the cable box or the satellite receiver needs to be reset?
- What if the remote is dropped and stops functioning?
- What if we want to operate the equipment from the front panel control?

By giving customers the knowledge to handle such scenarios in advance, they are better prepared to handle unexpected situations.

Touch-Screen Cleaning

Touch-screens seem to attract dust and debris. Even when the screen cover is faithfully used, the screen can be tracked with fingerprints and smudges. Putting a Clean Screen reminder on the menu or home page as well as instructions on how to clean it is helpful for customers in maintaining their system.

IR Line-of-Sight Disclaimer

With the advent of radio frequency (RF) distribution, infrared frequency (IR) use has declined. However, IR receivers are still used on certain jobs and in areas that have a large amount of RF interference. The line-of-sight disclaimer states that to function properly, the remote must have a clear line of sight to the component being controlled.

Furniture, pets, and people can block the IR frequency emanating from the remote. Positioning this disclaimer on the remote reduces service calls. It also gives clear directions on how the system works.

Remember that not everyone who uses the customer's interface will have received training. Even a small amount of instruction, like noting the disclaimer, will help the customer use the equipment successfully.

RF Range Disclaimer

RF technology has eliminated many IR problems and is much more user friendly than IR-based systems. But the disclaimer, written on the remote or in the instructions, must clearly note the usable distance for the remote. Be clear in the instructions on range so customers do not develop false expectations.

CUSTOMER SATISFACTION

Satisfied customers are the best candidates for the purchase of additional products. They are also the basis of referrals for new business, and referral leads are often guaranteed sales with little competition.

At the completion of a project, it is important to establish a follow-up procedure. Follow-up tells the customer that he is appreciated, provides feedback to know that the products are performing as intended, and verifies that the customer is getting the most out of his new system. Follow-up provides the opportunity to address any questions or problems before the customer calls. In addition, follow-up provides an opportunity for additional product sales or referrals.

Effective follow-up strategies include:

- Having a purpose
- Following up in a reasonable amount of time
- Checking on the status of specific problem resolutions
- Following up to check on overall status

A follow-up call is a great time to verify that a problem was solved, to provide information about an additional product, or to answer questions about equipment. Follow-up is most effective when done promptly, so ask for input about convenient times and methods to respond.

Be sensitive to the type of communication that works best for the customer. E-mail might work better than phone calls during work or the baby's nap time. On the other hand, some people don't check e-mail for several days, so a phone call would be more appropriate for them.

Complaints are opportunities to show the customer that they are valued. Effectively handling a problem or complaint will enhance the customer's image of the company. Even if there is a problem or the answer is "No," the fact that the situation is dealt with promptly and efficiently leads to increased satisfaction.

A short call to check on how things are going can make a huge impression, lead to increased customer satisfaction, and generate new business. Similarly, a postcard about upcoming service or warranty issues is a helpful reminder as well an opportunity to ask for referrals.

GLOSSARY

802.11 — a set of media access control (MAC) and physical layer (PHY) specifications for implementing wireless local area network (WLAN) computer communication in the 2.4, 3.6, 5, and 60 GHz frequency bands.

1000baseT — an Ethernet specification which transmits data at the rate of 1Gb per second over Twisted Pair Copper Cable up to 100m

100Base-T — an Ethernet specification which transmits data at the rate of 100Mb per second over Twisted Pair Copper Cable up to 100m

10GBaseT — an Ethernet specification which transmits data at the rate of 10Gb per second over Twisted Pair Copper Cable up to 100m when using CAT6A cable

110 punch tool — hand tool used to terminate twisted pair cable to modular jacks or 110 punch block

2.4GHz — An ISM (Industrial, Scientific and Medical) radio band used for wireless communications

3D Television — television display or projector which delivers a three-dimensional image using either active or passive glasses or by autostereoscopy (no glasses needed).

5GHz — An ISM (Industrial, Scientific and Medical) radio band used for wireless communications

70-Volt system — type of speaker distribution system that uses transformers at the output of an amplifier and at each speaker in order to provide a constant voltage of 70.7 volts. Typically used in larger commercial installations. (also knowns as a constant-voltage system)

A/D Converter — converts an analog signal to a digital signal.

Absorber — anything that absorbs sound and thus reduces sound reflections in a room; can be a device intended for this purpose, or ordinary objects and people in the room.

Absorption Coefficient — The ratio of the sound energy absorbed by a surface to the sound energy incident on the surface.

AC — see alternating current.

AC — Line Quality Monitor an instrument used to detect problems in the AC line; monitor the minimum and maximum frequency and voltage as well as count the number of drops and surges during the monitoring time.

AC-3 — The original lossy audio compression codec by Dolby Digital. Used prior to 1994.

Accent lighting — lighting that adds interest to a room or landscape by drawing attention to an object or architectural detail.

Access point (AP) — a wireless tranceiver connecting wired Ethernet to a wireless 802.11x network

Acoustically Transparent (AT) screen — video projection screen made with fabric mesh or vinyl with small perforations to allow sound to pass through

Active Loudspeaker — A loudspeaker which has the power amplifier(s) built in. In home theater usuall a subwoofer

ADA — see Americans with Disabilities Act.

Additive color process — photographic process in which the desired colors are produced by combining appropriate proportions of three primary colors. This the method used to create a color image in video.

ADEA — see Age Discrimination Employment Act.

Admittance — the measure of how easily an object carries AC current, usually expressed as "Y", the opposite of resistance

ADSL Asymmetric Digital Subscriber Line — A DSL connection where the upload and download speeds are not symmetrical. Usually download speeds to a customer's premises are greater than upload speeds.

Advanced Television Systems Committee (ATSC) — standards committee that addresses digital television broadcasts

Age Discrimination Employment Act (ADEA) — legislation that protects people age 40 and over from employment discrimination based on age.

Agenda — list or outline of things to be considered or done; often used to structure a meeting.

AHU — see Air Handler Unit.

Air handler or air handling unit (AHU) — component of an HVAC system that cleans, and cools or heats the air and the sends it back into the home.

Air-source heat pump — type of heat pump that uses the external outside air as a heat source or heat sink to heat or cool the interior of a home.

Alarm — a condition or state of a security or fire alarm system when triggered by a the state of a detection device. The alarm state may trigger a number of different actions, such as audible sound, phone call, lockdown, HVAC functions, or lighting functions.

Alternating Current (AC) — an electric current that changes its amplitude and reverses its direction of flow (polarity) in a sinusoidal cycle at a frequency that is measured in hertz.

Ambient lighting — overall illumination in a room or space. May include both natural light and artifical light.

American National Standards Institute — A private, non-profit organization (501(c)3) that administers and coordinates the U.S. voluntary standardization and conformity assessment system.

American Standard Code of Information Interchange (ASCII) — a character encoding scheme for computing devices. Based on the English language.

American Wire Gauge (AWG) — a system of defining the size of copper wire based on its cross-section, used primarily in US and Canada since 1857, also known as Brown & Sharpe Wire Gauge.

Americans with Disabilities Act of 1990 (ADA) — legislation that prevents employers from discriminating against qualified individuals based on certain disabilities.

Ammeter — an instrument used to detect and to measure electrical current.

Ampere (Amp, or A) — a quantity measurement combined with a time measurement to define current, the number of electrons flowing through a circuit.

Amplitude — the magnatude of an audio signal, or sound in the air

Analog — a signal in which the waveform is the same as the original sound waves

Analog terrestrial broadcast signals — see terrestrial signals.

Analog video signal — video signal that creates a picture by taking the form of continuous waves that are displayed via a series of successive scans

Anamorphic lens — a lens used in the process of modifying a wide image to occupy a narrower frame, or to reverse this process to recover the wide image

Annealing — process that restores the flexibility of a wire after it has been pulled through a die, or drawn from a larger guage to a smaller guage

ANSI — see American National Standards Institute

ANSI/EIA-600 — see CEBus.

Antivirus program — software program that works to stop viruses, worms and trojan horses; many operate on a subscription basis and run daily checks of a user's computer.

AP — see Access point.

App — abbreviation of "application". A small software application, optimized for use on mobile devices and smart phones. Usually focuses on one specific task, calculation, game, or product.

Apple — small program contained on an HTML page of a website that is written in Java and is not dependent on the operating system on which it runs.

Architect — person responsible for the design and oversight of a building's construction.

Architectural Drawings — set of drawings created by architects and engineers that tell how a building should be constructed. These can include floor plans, site plans, framing plans, electrical plans, plumbing plans, elevations, sectional drawings, and presentation drawings

As-built drawings — set of plans updated to show how the project was actually built. These drawings are the result of the field-marked, red line drawings.

ASCII — see American Standard Code of Information Interchange.

Aspect ratio — relationship of screen width to screen height

ATSC — see Advanced Television Systems Committee.

Attenuation — decrease in the value of the power of a signal or sound. Commonly measured in decibels (dB).

Audible frequency (AF) range — sound which can be heard by humans, generally considered to be 20Hz - 20kHz.

Audio Calibration — the process of evaluating, verifying, and tuning an audio system to optimize performance according to established sound quality goals.

Audio power amplifier — an audio component that receives a line level signal and increases its amplitude to drive loudspeakers

Audio/Video Receiver — a component which selects sources, processes audio and video, tunes radio stations, and provides amplified output to drive speakers

Auro-3D — an immersive surround sound format introduced by Auro Technologies

AutoCAD — Autodesk software program for creating 2D and 3D drawings.

Autoformer-based volume control — type of volume control that manage speaker-level signals by combining the primary and secondary winding mechanisms found in transformers

A-weighting — see dBA-weighting

Axial mode — acoustical resonance in a room which occur between opposing parallel surfaces (walls, floor/ceiling)

Back porch — portion in each scan line between the end (rising edge) of the horizontal sync pulse and the start of active video.

Backbone — Part of a network infrastructure that connects devices. Normally has a higher bandwidth than the individual segments connected to it.

Backup communication — any redundant means of communication in a security system which provides a link to the central station. May be a phone line, cellular telephone, internet or two-way radio.

Balloon framing — a house framing method where floors are attached to tall vertical exterior wall studs (obsolete)

Bandwidth — a range of frequencies, from lowest to highest. May apply to audio (frequency response) or networking (where throughput is directly related to bandwidth)

Base 10 — see Decimal Numbering System.

Base 16 — see Hexadecimal Numbering System.

Base 2 — see Binary Numbering System

Bass Management — A function of a multichannel surround processor that combines the low bass frequencies from all of the channels and directs this signal to the LFE output to the subwoofer(s).

Bass trap — device or structure used to absorb bass frequencies, lessening the effect of standing waves; also called low-frequency absorber. Most operate at frequencies above 80Hz.

Benchmarking — comparison of two processes or procedures in order to measure a given feature such as quality.

Bend radius — the curvature of a bend in an installed cable. The minimum bend radius is the smallest recommended curvature, beyond which performance may be compromised

Bill-of-Materials (BOM) — document that results from cost estimating process which lists quantity and cost of each resource needed for a project.

Binary numbering system — a mathematical representation of counting sequentially in which all numbers are comprised of two unique values: 0 and 1.

Binary test — logical comparison of two binary values.

Biometric identification — a way of verifying a person's identity based on unique physical characteristics like fingerprints or retinal scan

Bit — shorthand abbreviation for binary digit. Represented by a lower case 'b'

Bit position zero — least significant bit in a string of bits; right-most bit position.

Black level — a video signal level that represents the blackest intensity.

Block Diagram — diagram used to show circuits or flow by breaking the information into smaller sections or blocks to show the relationship or flow between components.

Blueprint — scale drawings of space layout, construction, and specifications needed to erect a building or home.

Bluetooth — wireless radio data transfer specification working on the 2.4Ghz band that allows for PAN (Personal Area Network) communication between devices.

Blu-ray Disc — recording format that has the ability to store several hours of high definition video signals (720p/60, 1080i/60, 1080p/24, or 1080p/60) on a disc the same size and shape as a conventional DVD, but with up to 25 GB of capacity for a single-layer disc, and 50 GB of capacity on a dual-layer disc.

Boiler — component that generates heat through burning various types of fuel and uses that heat to warm circulating water (or sometimes another liquid) in a closed system.

BOM — see Bill of Materials.

Boolean logic — a method of comparing states of logic using operators such as AND, OR, NAND, etc.

Bottom-up cost estimating — approach that compiles cost of separate individual items to arrive at a cost for the entire project.

Break lines — break lines are used to show a gap in the drawing. A long wall with no changes in structure might be shown at the corners with break lines across the construction lines to indicate missing length.

Break switch sensors — a sensor which is normally closed

British Thermal Unit (BTU) — measure of thermal energy used to heat and cool in HVAC systems; heat required to raise a one pound-mass of water (usually around one pint) 1° Fahrenheit (F). One Watt = 3.41 BTU.

Broadband Internet — Internet access that is usually provided over a cable or DSL connection.

BTU — see British Thermal Unit.

Buffer — region of memory used to temporarily hold output or input data.

Business plan — document that spells out a company's expected course of action for a specified period, usually including a detailed listing and analysis of risks and uncertainties.

BusTopology — network architecture layout based on a single main communications line (trunk) to which nodes are attached; also known as linear bus. An example would be RS485.

Buzz — an unwanted edgy tone, usually low frequency, usually caused by a defective loudspeaker

Byte — series of 8 bits. Represented by an upper case 'B'

Cabinetry drawing — drawings that show the furnishings, particularly the built in furnishings, of a home or office.

Cable — two or more wires inside a common jacket, designed for a specific application

Cable modem — device provided by cable television service companies to connect their cable network to an Ethernet network.

Cable schedule — document showing every cable run in a project, including its start point, destination, cable type, use, and termination type. Should also have a provision to check off or initial when each cable is run, terminated, and tested

CAD — see Computer aided design.

Campus Area Network (CAN) — one form of a metropolitan area network that is commonly seen in an academic setting.

CAN — see Campus Area Network.

Candela — unit which expresses the luminous intensity of a light source.

Capacitance — a measure of the amount of electric charge either stored or separated for a given electric potential.

Capacitor — device which resists changes in voltage in an electric circuit.

Card reader — a device used to provide access by means of a magnetic strip on an identification card

Cathode Ray Tube (CRT) technology — "legacy" video display utilizing an electron-beam gun at the back of a vacuum enclosure.

CEBus — communications standard released in 1992 by the Electronics Industry Association (EIA) that governs communications between consumer electronic devices, such as appliances, lighting, and HVAC equipment. Now obsolete.

CEC — specific feature on HDMI-enabled equipment that allows communication between HDMI-connected devices via simple commands (like "play") that control other devices without any special programming.

Central Processing Unit (CPU) — the "Brain" of a computer that executes all calculations and machine instructions.

Centralized lighting control system — type of lighting system where control comes from one central source rather than many individual switches.

Certificate of Occupancy — document issued by a local governmental agency that states a property meets the local building standards for occupancy and is in compliance with public health and building codes

Change order (CO) — document used to record changes to an existing agreement; becomes part of the contract when agreed upon by all parties involved.

Checksums — verify the overall validity of a packet by using a simple arithmetic sum across all bytes within a data packet.

Chiller — component of an HVAC system that removes heat from one source, such as water, and supplies that same heat to another medium such as air.

Chimney — structural component of a house that allows gases (like carbon monoxide) and other by products burning fuel to escape to the outside environment.

CIE chromaticity diagram — a method for visualizing what our eyes perceive as the visible light color space within a 2D realm without concern for luminous intensity. Created by the International Commission on Illumination in 1931.

Circuit — a complete loop through which current can flow.

Circuit breaker — a switch designed to protect an electrical circuit from damage caused by overload or short circuit. Unlike a fuse, a circuit breaker operates automatically and can be reset.

Civil Rights Act of 1964 — legislation that prevents discrimination based on race, color, religion, sex, or national origin.

Civil Rights Act of 1991 — an amendment to the Civil Rights Act of 1964 that adds the category of "disability" to the protected classes and provides for appropriate remedies for intentional discrimination and unlawful harassment in the work place.

Clamp-on ammeter — has a movable set of jaws that can open and clamp around the wires to be measured, one wire at a time.

Client-Server Network — type of network configuration in which all the computers communicate directly with one computer, known as the server. The server monitors all resources and communicates with all the computers on the network.

Closed-loop system — type of geothermal HVAC system whose heat exchanger is a loop of piping filled with fluid that is buried underground; both absorbing heat to transfer to the home (in winter) and taking heat to transfer back to the earth (in summer).

CO — see Change Order.

Coaxial cable — a type of cable used for satellite, CATV, CCTV systems, comprised of an insulated central conducting wire, a dielectric barrier, a second "coaxial" conductor, usually braided, and usually some additional sheilding. Coaxial cable is durable, withstands linear stress well, and is capable of carrying a lot of data. The most common types are RG-6 lSeries 6) and RG-59.

Codec — abbreviation for compressor/ decompressor or encode/decode; a technology for compressing and decompressing digital data.

Coil — the electromagnet that switches the state of the relay when it is energized.

Color accuracy — the degree to which a video representation matches the colors of the original image.

Color burst — signal used to keep the chrominance subcarrier synchronized in a color television signal.

Color comparator — device used in video calibration that mimicks the human eye's ability to tell the difference between two nearby colors.

Color gamut — complete subset of colors.

Color space — three-dimensional model into which the three attributes of a color can be represented, plotted, or recorded.

Colorimeter — device that provides correlated color temperature, luminance readings, and CIE x, y coordinates.

Combing — offset vertical lines resulting from a moving edge displayed at two different points of time.

Command sequence — a series of instructions that are executed one after another to perform a desired function.

Comment — documentation placed into a program that is not executable; its purpose is to provide clarification of the code to other programmers who may view the code.

Common Object File Format (COFF) — format specification used by Unix systems for executable and object code files.

Communicating thermostat — bi-directional device that both sends and receives information to allow for integration of the HVAC system with the other systems in the home

Communications plan — Written document describing a company's communications goals, the tasks involved in achieving those goals, tools and timetables needed, and how the results will be measured.

Communications Protocol — set of procedures which controls how a data communications network operates.

Company Retention Strategy — positive public relations actions aimed to improve employees' perceptions of their relationship with the company and thus reduce employee turnover.

Compiled language — a piece of code that is transformed from source code into executable binary form once, and then run in binary format thereafter.

Compiler — computer program which translates a high-level source code language into a low-level, assembly or binary language which is ready for linking and execution.

Complex waves — see Irregular waves.

Composite analog video signal — video signal which carries all image and sync information on a single coaxial cable

Compression tool — hand tool used to terminate coaxial cable with F, RCA or BNC connector

Computer aided design (CAD) — The use of computer programs to draft and/or design detailed two- or three-dimensional models of physical objects including buildings and mechanical parts.

Condensation — process by which a vapor becomes a liquid; opposite of evaporation.

Conditional logic — see Boolean logic.

Conductance — a measure of a material's ability to conduct electric charge.

Conduction — transfer of heat from one substance to another through direct contact.

Conductor — anything that electricity flows through.

Conduit — metal or fiber pipe or flexible tube used to enclose electrical cables; may be used for either high voltage or low voltage.

Conflict resolution — act of arbitrating differences of belief or opinion about a given set of conditions or circumstances.

Construction lines — on an architectural drawing, the lines used to aid the drafter setting up the drawing. Also called guide lines.

Continuity tester — an instrument that tests the ability of a circuit to conduct electrical current; does not indicate the level of performance

Contract — legally binding exchange of promises. Also, the document that spells out this promise in writing. Contracts are used as a management tool and as a safeguard for your financial interests.

Contrast ratio — ratio between peak white level and the darkest black level.

Convection — transfer of heat from one substance to another through circulatory molecular motion, the natural tendency of heat to rise

Cost benefit analysis — an analysis of the relationship between the costs of undertaking a task or project and the benefits likely to arise from the project.

Coulomb — a measurement of the quantity of electrons.

CPU — see Computer Processing Unit.

CRC — see Cyclic redundancy checks.

Critical path — series of tasks that take longer to complete than any other logical segment of the project.

Crosstalk — A magnetic or electrostatic coupling, which causes energy transfer from one wire to another. Shielding or special twisting can solve this issue.

Current — a flow of electricity through a conductor. Measured in Amperes.

Customer relations — task of keeping customers informed, handling complaints efficiently, and truly listening to what customers have to say; being a customer-focused organization

Cyclic Redundancy Checks (CRCs) — polynomial formula using all bits within a data packet and taking into account the order of these bits to create a 16-bit or 32-bit value that can verify the overall validity of the packet.

D/A Converter — A device that converts a digital signal to an analog signal

D65 — see Illuminant D.

D6500 — see Illuminant D.

Daisy chain — cabling method that connects end points directly in line without returning to a common point.

DALI — see Digital Addressable Lighting Interface.

Damper — structural component of an HVAC system which opens and closes to control the flow of air through the ductwork allowing conditioned air to various zones of the home as requested by the thermostat.

Dashed lines — marks used on architectural drawings to show elements that can not actually be seen in that particular view of the building, e.g., footings in a framing plan.

Data encryption — method of securing transmitted data through encoding algorithms.

dBA-weighting — sound-pressure levels derived using A-weighting; denoted by "dBA," or A-weighted dB levels; standard weighting curve applied to audio measurements, designed to emulate the response of the human ear at lower levels

dBC-weighting — follows the frequency sensitivity of the human ear at higher levels; noise measurements made with the C weighting scale are designated dBC.

DBS — see Direct Broadcast Satellite.

DC — see Direct Current.

Debugging — the process of identifying and fixing the causes of failures in a software program or system.

Decibel (dB) — unit of measurement which is used to measure the intensity of sound, either acoustically or in an audio signal. One tenth of a Bel.

Dehumidifier — device that removes humidity or moisture from the air.

Deliverables — tangible work products of a project.

Design diagram — visual representation of the process flow of a computer program that uses graphical icons and pathways.

Diamagnetic — substances that dilute magnetic flux and are used to keep magnetic objects apart.

Diaphragmatic absorber — sound absorber that removes energy from a sound field by moving a surface to absorb energy at specific frequency

Dielectric — continuous layer of polymeric material in a coaxial cable that separates the center conductor (found inside the dielectric) from the ground shields located outside the dielectric material. It is an insulator, and modifying its thickness in any way affects performance.

Diffuser — device which reflects sound in many directions

Digital Addressable Lighting Interface (DALI) — open standard protocol for lighting control that is contained in the technical standard IEC 62386.

Digital Direct Drive Image Light Amplifier (D-ILA) — video projection technology that uses a reflective LCD to create images by using a light source that is reflected off the LCD and sent through the lens to the screen.

Digital Light Processing (DLP) — video display technology which uses a proprietary chip with Digital MicroMirrors to create pixels on a screen.

Digital MicroMirrors (DMM) — tiny mirrors that are used in a chip design to reflect light towards a projection screen to turn a pixel on, or away from the screen to turn a pixel off. Used in DLP projection technology (Digital Light Processing)

Digital multimeter (DMM) — a multimeter or volt/ohm meter that displays results digitally. See multimeter.

Digital Signal Processing (DSP) — processing of an audio signal in the digital domain

Digital Subscriber Line (DSL) — service from a telephone company that uses a DSL modem connected a telephone line to provide Internet service, without the installation of a second phone line.

Digital Theater Systems (DTS) — a multi-channel digital surround sound format owned by Digital Theater Systems (DTS, Inc.) used for sound on film, DVD and Blu-ray formats

Digital to Analog Converter (DAC) — device or circuit which converts digital audio to analog

Digital Visual Interface — first digital connection standard for consumer devices launched in 1999 to connect LCD monitors to personal computers. Developed by the Digital Display Working Group.

D-ILA — see Digital Direct Drive Image Light Amplifier.

Dimmer — device that regulates the amount of electrical voltage sent to a luminaire. Controlled by a slider, knob or control signal

Direct Broadcast Satellite — Direct Broadcast Satellite system that sends TV broadcasts directly from a communications satellite to home antennas, or dishes.

Direct costs — expenses directly attributable to certain elements of a project, ie. electronic equipment.

Direct Current (DC) — a steady value of current that does not change direction of flow or amplitude.

Direct sound wave — a sound wave that arrives at the listener's ear (or microphone) directly from the source, without reflections

Direct Stream Digital (DSD) — a method of storing digital audio which uses an extremely high sample rate and lower resolution

Direct view TV — image viewing device in which the image is being emitted directly from the surface of the display; includes CRT "tube" sets, flat panel plasma and LCD displays

Disc — optical storage medium such as CD, DVD and Blu-ray which can be removed from the player and taken elsewhere. Some are read-only, some are re-writeable.

Disciplinary action — official steps taken to reprimand a respondent for inappropriate or impermissible behavior which has violated company policy.

Discovery mechanism — device that uses a procedure defined by the application layer protocol or one that the developer designs to detect what devices are present on the bus.

Disk — magnetic storage medium, such as floppy disk or hard drive. May be portable or built into a compuer or other component.

Display calibration — process that involves adjustment of display control parameters to ensure that the viewer sees images within the proper contrast, color, and gray scale tone range, as the content creator intended

Distortion — difference between the in the input and the output of an audio device

Distributed lighting control system — "classic" lighting system where each fixture or group of fixtures throughout the room is controlled individually by a switch on the wall.

Distribution amplifier — device that accepts and distributes one audio or video input out to 2 or more destinations.

Distribution matrix switcher — device that can take several input sources and distribute any one of them to any number of displays.

DLP — see Digital Light Processing

DMM — see Digital MicroMirror, Digital Multimeter

DMX512-A — RS-485 based communications protocol developed by the Engineering Commission of USITT that addresses the entertainment technology industry, especially stage lighting.

Dolby ATMOS — an immersive surround sound format introduced by Dolby Labs

Dolby Digital — a series of lossy audio compression technologies developed by Dolby Laboratories.

Dolby Digital Plus — a digital audio compression scheme used with HDTV and HD DVD/ Blu-ray

Dolby Digital Surround EX — a higher quality (than Dolby Digital) digital audio compression scheme used which enables the use of a surround center channel (6.1)

Dolby Pro Logic II — a surround sound processing technology used to decode Dolby Surround soundtracks.

Dolby TrueHD — an advanced lossless multi-channel audio codec mainly used for HD DVD and Blu-ray.

Domain analysis — method of researching and assessing similar software systems in a common industry or domain in order to identify their similarities and differences.

Domain Name System (DNS) — used to resolve a URL (Uniform Resource Locator) (such as www.cedia. org) to a specific IP address.

Double pole double throw (DPDT) — two SPDT switches controlled by one mechanism.

Double pole single throw (DPST) — two single pole single throw switches that are controlled by a single mechanism.

Drawing frame — perimeter line around drawing defining the limits of the drawing area.

Drop-down menu — list of choices that appear as a user either rolls over or clicks on a menu item.

Dry bulb temperature — temperature of air measured by a thermometer shielded from radiation and moisture.

Dry contact closure — condition created when two contacts close to make electrical continuity in a circuit.

DSD — see Direct Stream Digital

DSL — see Digital Subscriber Line.

DSP — see Digital Signal Processing

DTS — see Digital Theater Systems

DTS HD Master Audio — a surround sound format that supports a virtually unlimited number of channels (limited by storage medium)

DTS:X — an immersive surround sound format introduced by DTS

DTS-ES (DTS Extended Surround) — a matrix centered surround sound audio format that includes two variants, DTS-ES Matrix and DTS-ES Discrete 6.1

Duct booster — auxiliary fan located in the duct which pushes more air into an area of the house that requires a boost of conditioned air.

Ductwork — structural component of the home; airshafts (usually metal) that are located throughout the walls, attics, basements, and crawl space of the home in order to supply air to the air handler and return air to the home.

DVD — See Digital Versatile Disc

DVI — see Digital Visual Interface

DVI-A — interconnect used to carry a DVI signal to an analog display, such as a CRT monitor or low-cost LCD.

DVI-D — interconnect used for direct digital connections between source video and digital monitors

DVI-I — interconnect capable of carrying either a digital-to-digital signal or an analog-to-analog signal.

Dynamic Host Configuration Protocol (DHCP) — process that allows for allocating IP addresses dynamically by a DHCP server

Dynamic Routing — network traffic management process that uses an internal routing table to identify the most efficient path based on overall load, line delay and bandwidth and automatically reconfigures the network to take advantage of these more efficient pathways; generally preferred over static routing for handling peak traffic conditions.

Early reflections — set of reflections which have only been reflected once, arrived at the listener just after the direct sound

EER — see Energy Efficient Ratio.

Efficiency ratings — quantative measurement rating system that gives consumer information about a component or system's energy efficiency with increased efficiency as numbers increase.

EIA — see Electronics Industries Alliance

Electric radiant floors — floor system that consists of electric cables built into the floor to transmit heat.

Electrical plan — scaled drawing of a floorplan that indicates the locations of receptacles, switches and lighting fixtures.

Electricity — the flow of electrons that is produced when an electron jumps from the outer shell of its atom to the outer shell of a new atom and thusly knocks another electron out of orbit from that second atom.

Electromagnetic interference (EMI) — external inerference in a signal caused by electromagnetic induction or radiation from such sources as electrical wiring, motors, or lighting

Electromagnetic noise — imperfections in AC current.

Electron — a negatively charged particle that orbits the nucleus in concentric layers called shells.

Electron Current Flow Theory — in a circuit, current moves from the negative side to the positive side because electrons are what current measures and that is the direction they move.

Electronic documents — documents created and often communicated by computers and computer software.

Electronic Systems Technician — an individual who installs, upgrades and services electronic systems in the field (EST)

Electronics Industries Alliance (EIA) — formerly the Electronic Industries Association. An alliance of individual trade organizations that has issued several industry standards, such as EIA/TIA-232 (formerly known as RS-232). Ceased operations in 2011, but member associations continue the work

Elevation view — architectural drawing representing a horizontal view of a wall or space in a plan.

ELF — see Executable and Linkable Format.

EMI — see Electromagnetic interference

Energy efficient ratio (EER) — ratio of cooling capacity (BTU/hr) to the power input (watts) under steady state conditions (95° F outdoor, 80° F return and approximately 51% relative humidity).

Energy/heat recovery ventilators (ERV/ HRV) — system that reclaims energy from exhaust airflows through the use of heat exchangers.

Equal Employment Opportunity Commission (EEOC) — independent federal agency created in 1964 that works to eliminate employment discrimination based on race, color, religion, gender, disability, age or other criteria unrelated to job performance.

Equal loudness contours — see Fletcher-Munson curves.

Equal Opportunity Act of 1972 — legislation designed to prohibit job discrimination for reasons of race, religion, color, national origin, and sex.

Equal Pay Act of 1963 (EPA — legislation requiring that women and men must receive equal pay for equal work.

Equalization — the process of adjusting the relative energy in various audio frequency ranges

Equalizer — device used to cut or boost individual frequencies of an audio signal using a number of filters. May be analog or digital.

ERV/HRV — see Energy/heat recovery ventilators.

EST — see Electronic Systems Technician

Ethernet — a collection of technologies used for establishing connections in a network; standardized as IEEE 802.3.
Evaporative cooler device that cools by adding moisture to the air.

Event loop — a software program loop (or state) in which the application receives an event, handles the event, and then waits for the next event to occur.

Event-driven programming — software system that responds to and processes events.

Executable and Linkable Format (ELF) — common file format standard that covers executable files, object code and shared libraries that is not bound by any particular processor or architecture.

Executable file — a binary form of a program which is ready to be executed by a computer.

Execution phase — section of a project where the actual implementation or technical work is completed.

Exhaust vent — opening by which stale or air that has been inside the home is passed to the outside environment.

External customer — anyone who directly or indirectly pays for a company's product or services is a customer; this is the homeowner and/or builder.

Extranet — non-public TCP/IP network that joins together customers, suppliers and distributors that have common goals over the same infrastructure as the Internet; may have some portions that are available for public viewing.

Fair Labor Standards Act of 1938 (FLSA) — federal legislation that establishes overtime wage requirements and defines specific exempt occupations.

Family and Medical Leave Act of 1993 (FMLA) — federal legislation that provides up to 12 weeks of unpaid, job-protected leave per year for employees who have (or adopt) a child, have serious health problems or who need to care for a child or other family member.

Fast Ethernet — Ethernet standards that supports 100 Mbps using twisted pair copper or fiber optic cable. An example is 100BaseT

Fast-tracking — overlapping of tasks in a project so that some work items may be occurring simultaneously and thus the project schedule and milestones are achieved more quickly.

F-connector — coaxial connector type which uses the solid center conductor of the cable and the braided sheild as its two conductors.

Feedback — the communication of responses and reactions to proposals and changes or to the findings of performance appraisals with the aim of enabling improvements to be made.

Ferromagnetic — materials that concentrate magnetic lines of flux and can be magnetized.

Fiber Optic Cable — type of cable with a glass center core surrounded by a jacket made of layers of various forms of plastic that transmits data using light rather electricity

File extension — small number of letters (usually three) at the end of a filename that indicate the type of information stored in the file.

File Transfer Protocol (FTP) — protocol used to move files either individually or in groups to another computer on the network.

File type — format of a file, commonly indicated by its file name extension.

Firewall — security measures (hardware and/or software) that blocks unauthorized users from gaining access to a computer or network.

Fixture and finish schedules — tables or schedules that detail the type and quality of materials used in the house.

Fixture schedule — part of a lighting plan that details the power and exact fixture type of each lighting element needed in the lighting plan.

Fletcher-Munson curves — represent an average of the frequencies that the human ear perceives as loudness at different levels; also called equal loudness curves or equal loudness contours.

Floor plan — widely used drawing type which shows rooms, doors, walls, etc. as viewed from above. Allows locations to be shown for most wall mounted devices such as outlets, controls, etc.

Flowchart — a graphical representation, primarily through the use of symbols, of the sequence of activities in a system (process, operation, function, comparison or activity).

FLSA — see Fair Labor Standards Act.

Fluorescent lamp — device that is a gaseous discharge light source with a tubular electric lamp containing low-pressure mercury vapor and other gases.

Flux density — the number of changes in energy flow across a given surface per unit area.

Flux lines — imaginary curved lines that represent quantities of magnetism.

FMLA — Family and Medical Leave Act.

Foil tape sensor — a device for sensing broken glass.

Foot fall — sounds created when someone is walking on the floor above; energy from the steps is transferred to the floor and from the floor into the space below

Foot-candle — unit of measurement of illumination; 1 foot-candle equals the amount of light delivered by a 1-candela light source to a 1 square foot surface that is 1 foot away.

Foot-Lamberts — luminance unit equal to one lumen per square foot.

Forced air — type of heating system that uses a blower motor to move air through the furnace and into the ductwork.

Frame — complete image on a TV screen.

Frame rate — the number of video images captured or displayed each second.

Frequency — number of cycles completed each second by a certain AC voltage.

Frequency meter — an instrument used to measure the frequency of signals being produced by various electronic equipment.

FTP — see File Transfer Protocol.

Functional specifications — a document containing many levels of detail as to what a new (or upgraded) computer system should be expected to do.

Fundamental frequency — the initial and lowest frequency of a resonance or complex wave

Funding — the act of providing financial resources to make a project possible.

Furnace — a device used to heat a building.

Gamma — power law relationship between the electrical stimulus and the resulting light output from an imaging device.

Gamut — see color gamut.

Gantt Chart — chart that illustrates the duration of tasks as compared to the project timeframe; highlights dependencies, milestones and resources associated with particular tasks.

Gateway — hardware or software that makes it possible to maintain communication between computers or computer networks that may use different communication protocols; also called a router.

Geothermal heat pump — type of HVAC system that uses ground water at a stable temperature to moderate the temperature in the home

Glass break detector — sensor that responds to the shattering of a pane of glass. They may be either audio sensitive or mechanical.

Graphical User Interface (GUI) — a way of communicating with a CPU by manipulating buttons(icons) and windows with a mouse or pointing device (your finger or stylus)

Ground — A conductive connection between the earth or other large conducting body and an electrical circuit to form a complete electrical circuit.

Ground loop — electrical condition where two cirtuits are connected which have different potentials to ground. Can cause unwanted noise and a safety hazard.

GUI — see Graphical User Interface.

Haas effect — a psychoactoustic effect causing humans to localize a sound source in the direction of the first arriving source despite the presence of a reflected sound arriving later from a different direction

Hardwired system — a system using wires to communicate rather than through the air (or wireless).

Harmonic distortion — unwanted harmonics, or overtones, introduced into an audio signal by an audio component. Measured in %. A lower distortion specification means a more accurate reproduction of sound

Harmonics — integral multiples of the fundamental frequency of a complex wave. Harmonics contribute to the unique sound of an instrument or voice.

HDBaseT — a connectivity standard which allows uncompressed HD video signalsm, audio, and other signals to be carried and distributed over twisted pair cabling and standard RJ45 connectors.

HDCP — see High-bandwidth Digital Content Protection

HDTV — see High-definition digital television.

Heat load — amount of heat generated by things or people in a particular space.

Heat pump — type of HVAC system that is combined or a hybrid system that heats air in the winter and cools in the summer.

Heat transfer — the process in which heat moves from one substance to another.

Heating , Ventilation, and Air Conditioning (HVAC) — the system in the home which provides high indoor air quality

Heating Season Performance Factor (HSPF) 4 — quantitative measurement of seasonal or annual efficiency of a heat pump operating in the heating mode.

Helmholtz Absorber — a low- to mid-frequency absorber which is tuned to a specific frequency; also called a slot resonator.

Hexadecimal — a mathematical representation of counting sequentially in which all numbers are comprised of sixteen unique values: 0 thru 9, and A thru F.

HID — see High-Intensity Discharge Lamp.

High Definition Television (HDTV) — digital television format that provides a high-quality widescreen picture (16x9) with digital surround sound.

High voltage dimmer — traditional dimmer that works with a standard 120v house current.

High-bandwidth Digital Content Protection (HDCP) — form of Digital Rights Management developed by Intel Corporation that uses an advanced key exchange system which is highly secure

High-Definition Multimedia Interface (HDMI) — a compact audio/video interface used to transmit uncompressed digital streams, digital surround sound, control and network information and two channels of audio return signal

High-Intensity Discharge Lamps (HID) — type of lighting that provides more wattage than any other lamp type; uses mercury vapor, metal halide, low or high pressure sodium

High-level language — a programming language designed to suit the needs of the programmer; e.g., readable by humans; it is independent of the internal machine code of any particular computer

Horizontal communication — information exchange between departments or functional units as a means of coordinating their activities.

HSPF — see Heating Season Performance Factor.

HTTP — see HyperText Transfer Protocol.

HTTPS — See Secure HTTP

Hub — communication device that contains multiple ports. Each computer in a network is directly connected with each port of the hub. Also, used to describe the point on a network where many circuits are connected.

Hue — specific color classification given to an object based on the seven colors found in the spectrum; red, orange yellow, green, blue, indigo, or violet.

Hum — an undesirable noise often caused by grounding problems or leakage of AC into a signal

Humidistat — device that regulates humidity levels by reacting to changes in the moisture content of the air.

Humidity — amount of water vapor in the air.

HVAC — see Heating Ventilation and Air Conditioning

Hybrid lighting control system — combination of both distributed and central lighting control features.

Hydronic radiant heat — floor system that pumps heated water through tubing laid in a pattern underneath the floor.

Hyperlink — a text word or graphical icon or picture in an HTML document that links, or allows navigation to, another HTML document or file.

HyperText Transfer Protocol (HTTP) — protocol used to carry requests from a browser to a Web server in order to transport pages from the server back to the requesting browser.

Icon — symbol or pictogram representing a specific device in a drawing. Identity of each icon should be defined in the legend

Identity theft — process of assuming someone else's identity for illegal financial gain.

IEEE 1394 — standard developed by Apple for high speed data transmission on local cable networks (LANs) as well as home networks. Commonly referred to as FireWire.

Illuminance — method of light measurement where the light source is measured by pointing the light metering device at the source to determine the intensity of the light falling upon an object

Illuminant D3 — illuminant upon which the video industry is standardized that represents that color of white most observers perceive as the most neutral shade of white; also corresponds to a color temperature of 6500 Kelvin; also called D6500 or D65.

Image processing — manipulation of the structure or content of images with computers and special software programs.

Impact Isolation Class (IIC) — test used to measure foot falls

Impedance — the opposition that a cable, component or circuit offers to alternating current. Measured in Ohms (Ω)

Impedance meter — device used to measure opposition to AC current flow in a system

Incandescent lamp — a light device that uses a coiled tungsten-wire filament secured inside a glass bulb that glows when electricity is passed through it.

Incremental build model — see Iterative Development Process.

Indirect costs — expenses of a project not directly relatable to a tangible item; ie. rental fees or advertising costs.

Inductance — the capability of a coil to store energy in a magnetic field surrounding it.

Inductor — a device that stores electrical energy in a magnetic field.
Informal training and development   method of disseminating important knowledge through the use of natural workplace interactions and casual information exchange.

Infrared — light with a wavelength longer than visible light. Commonly used to transmit data from remote controls. An LED is generally used to emit the IR pulse. May also be sent over wire and converted back to light at the destination using an emitter.

Infrasonic — sound that is below the range of human audible range of sound.
Initial defined risks section part of a project's documentation that identifies known risks of a project.

Initial project organization list — part of a project's documentation that lists important members of the project team and their contact information.

Insulator — materials that do not carry electricity.

Intake vent — opening by which fresh air from the outside environment is passed to the heating system.

Integrated system — several sub-systems connected so that they work together and can be controlled easily

Integration — act of combining parts into a whole.

Intelligence controls — component of an HVAC system that includes algorithms, scheduling, and remote communications.

Interlaced scanning (i) — television format in which electron beams sweep the picture tube twice to create half the image on the first pass (on each alternating line) and the other half on the second pass.

Internal customer — individuals within a company or project team; e.g., subcontractors, architects, builders, and interior designers, who require information (but do not pay as an external customer does).

Internet — global network used to transmit the data/information using the TCP/IP protocols.

Internet Protocol Address (IP Address) — unique number that each device on a computer network uses for identification when using the TCP/IP communication protocol.

Internet Service Provider (ISP) — company that provides connectivity to the Internet.

Interpreted language — a programming language whose programs are turned into a binary form usable by a computer each time it is run, as opposed to a compiled language.

Interview — face-to-face or long-distance (such as by telephone) discussion between an employer and potential employee to determine the suitability of the interviewee for a job opening.

Intranet — internal network of an organization that uses Internet protocols.

Inverter — logic element that receives a single input and changes it to its opposite state.

IP Address — see Internet Protocol Address.

IR — see Infrared

ISP — see Internet Service Provider.

Iterative development process — cyclic or repetitive software development methodology that was developed to address the inefficiencies of the waterfall development process.

IVB — see Invitation to Bid.

Jargon — industry-specific terms that a person outside of the industry may not necessarily understand.

Job costing report — view of cost estimate that summarizes costs of projects and services for a particular project.

Job description — formal statement listing the elements of a particular job or occupation, e.g., purpose, duties, equipment used, qualifications, training, physical and mental demands, working conditions.

Key System Unit — central processor on a multi-line telephone system which allows users to directly dial other users on the system as well as outside lines

Keypad — a set of buttons arranged in a block with numbers and or letters used for the control over telephony, security or audio/video systems and subsystems

Keyword — an essential or definitive term that is recognized by a computer as important; whether for use in programming, searching data on the Internet, or indexing data.

Kirchhoff 's Current Law (KCL) — states that the sum of all currents entering a node must be equal to the sum of all currents leaving the node.

Kirchhoff 's Voltage Law (KVL) — states that the directed sum of all the voltages around a loop must be equal to zero (v1 + v2 + v3 + v4 = 0).

KSU — See Key System Unit

Lambertian surface — surface that disperses light evenly.

Lamp — commonly called a light bulb; a device used in a light fixture that influences the amount and type of light produced by the fixture.

Lead generation — process of making contact with potential customers through advertising and other such efforts.

Lead qualification — process of identifying whether or not potential customers have the financial ability to fund a project.

Leaders — line with arrow heads on one end that point to and label or describe particular items on a plan.

Least significant bit (LSB) — the bit contributing the least value in a string of bits; also called low order bit.

Legend — table or list on a drawing identifying what each drawing element or symbol represents

Lessons learned file — documentation of past scenarios where mistakes and corrections are noted; helps the company retain notes on past projects' pitfalls.

Letterboxing — process of adding black horizontal bars at the top and bottom of the screen to place a wide image on a 4:3 display surface

LFE — see Low Frequency Effects channel

Life cycle — see Software development process.

Lighting control system — light fixtures and associated communications hardware and software which control the lighting system

Limiter — electrica circuit or device that prevents some portion of its input from reaching the output; also called a clipper.

Link editor — see Linkage editor.

Linux — open-source computer operating system which is similar to the Unix operating system but designed to run on PCs.

Litigation — a legal proceeding in a court; a judicial contest to determine and enforce legal rights.

Load impedance test — a test that measures the opposition that a circuit offers to the flow of current

Load schedule — part of a lighting plan that details the electricity usage of the elements in the electrical plan; includes load identification, floor and room, load type, number and type of fixtures and the power consumed by each.

Local Area Network (LAN) — computer network covering a local area, such as a home, office or small group of buildings.

Logical operator — see Operator.

LonWorks — protocol created by the Echelon Corporation that allows network devices to communicate without knowing each other's network topology, names or addresses.

Lossless data compression — a class of data compression algorithms that allows original data to be reconstructed from the compressed data.

Loudness — the overall sound level as perceived by a listener

Low Frequency Effects channel (LFE) — in a multichannel surround system, the name of the audio channel designated for special sonic effects (below 125 Hz) usually reproduced by a subwoofer

Low voltage transformer — transformer that comes in two forms: magnetic and electronic.

Low-frequency absorber — see Bass trap.

Low-level language — executable language such as Assembler language that does not need a compiler or interpreter in order to be executed on by a computer processor.

LSB — see Least Significant Bit.

Lumen — international (SI) unit of luminous quantity of light that equals the amount of light spread over one square foot of surface by one candle's power when all parts of the surface are exactly one foot from the light source.

Luminaire — light fixture that holds the lamp or bulb and also the parts around it that help position, protect, and connect lamps.

Luminance — method that measures the amount of light being emitted or reflected off a particular surface. Units of measure is the candela per square meter

Lux — unit of light measurement that is equivalent to one lumen per square meter.

MAC address — Media Access Control address, globally unique 40-bit address consisting of a manufacturer's code and a serial number; a hardware address that uniquely identifies each node of a network.

Machine code — see Object code.

Macro — a file containing a sequence of commands that can be executed as one command; often built to perform frequently used, as well as complex operations.

Magnetic contact — device with two parts that hold a magnetic connection together but when moved individually, can break the magnetic connection.

Magnetic field — results when atoms in a material are aligned in a particular way.

Malware — abbreviation for malicious software.

MAN — see Metropolitan area network.

Manual backup — a way to over-ride automatic settings.

Marketing plan — written document that explains the actions needed to achieve one or more marketing objectives

Markup language — a language that surrounds pieces of text with beginning and ending tags which are typically set off in angle brackets (<>); most common example is HTML.

Mediation — negotiation to resolve differences conducted by some impartial third party.

Mesh network — network configuration where each node sends and receives its own data, plus serves as a relay for other nodes

Metropolitan Area Network (MAN) — computer network intended to serve an area the size of a large city.

Mission statement — a statement laying out the purpose of the company with the intent to keep users and members aware of the purpose

Mobile app — see App

Modem — a device which modulates/demodulates a digital signal so that it can be carried over analog infrastructure

Monitoring service — company that offers contracted services to receive information from security systems and pass on information to the appropriate people or authorities. AKA Central Station.

Most Significant Bit (MSB) — the bit contributing the most value in a string of bits; also called high order bit.

Motion detectors — a variety of technologies to sense movement.

Mouseover — text that appears when the mouse pointer is held over an active hyperlink.

MPEG-2 — software standard for the compression and transmission of digital data.

MPEG-4 — collection of methods defining compression of audio and visual (AV) digital data.

MSB — see Most Significant Bit.

Multicasting — broadcasting multiple lower resolution programs simultaneously when the channel is not used for high-definition content.

Multimeter — an electronic measuring instrument that combines several functions in one unit

Multi-mode Optical Fiber — optical fiber whose core diameter is large relative to the wavelength (see wavelength) of the light, thus allowing a large number of modes (see modes) to propagate.

Multiplexer — device that allows multiple signals to be transmitted across a single physical channel.

Multi-point standard — one transmitter and multiple receivers.

Multi-source audio — audio system which allows the user to choose between different audio sources

Multi-stage systems — type of HVAC system that has more than one stage of cooling, more than one stage of heating or both; allows switching for multiple levels of heating and cooling using a Y1 terminal to operate the compressor in the low-speed mode when needed and the Y2 terminal to boost the speed to high when needed.

Multi-zone audio — audio system which allows different sources to be sent to different parts of the home independently

Near End Crosstalk (NEXT) — a measurement of signal bleed in twisted pair cable

Negative building pressure — condition that occurs when an HVAC system draws more air from the return ducts than it expels through the supply ducts.

Network Address Translation (NAT) — Internet standard that allows a local area network to use one set of IP addresses for internal traffic and a second set of IP addresses for external traffic.

Network addressing — ability of the network to identify a node on the network.

Network communication protocols — rules that specify how computers interact and exchange messages in order to send and receive information over various communication channels.

Network Interface Card (NIC) — hardware device that is used to allow a PC to connect to a transfer medium in order to allow communication with other devices and computers.

Network Interface Device (NID) — the point of connection between networks. In a residence, the location of demarcation.

Networking — process of connecting computers so they can share information, resources and equipment.

NEXT — Near End Crosstalk

Nibble — half of an 8-bit Byte. Equal to 4 bits.

NID — see Network Interface Device.

Nits — measure of luminance equal to one candela per square meter.

Node — an end point of a network connection having a device attached to a network such as a computer, file server, printer, scanner, etc.

Noise Criterion (NC) — set of empirical curves used in United States; part of the family of Balanced Noise Criterion (BNC) curves, an almost universal approach to the critical task of selecting a noise level goal especially as related to HVAC.

Noise Reduction Coefficient (NRC) — the mathematical average of absorption coefficient values (typically 125, 500, 1K, 2K, 4K & 8K Hz) for a given material. Intended for use in the speech range.

NRC — see Noise Reduction Coefficient

Null — low pressure point of a sound wave; also called a trough.

Object — in object-oriented programming, an instance of an object class.

Object code — machine-executable instructions, usually generated by a compiler from source code and written in a higher-level language.

Object lines — lines that actually draw the visible items on the plan.

Object-oriented programming (OOP) — Class of programming languages and techniques based on the concept of an "object" which is a data structure encapsulated with a set of routines which operate on the data.

Oblique mode — a mode produced by reflections off all six surfaces of a room.

Occupational Safety and Health Act of 1970 (OSHA) — legislation that is intended to prevent employees from being injured or contracting diseases in the course of their employment.

Occupational Safety and Health Administration (OSHA) — government agency which enforces laws and regulations related to jobsite safety and health

Octave — a doubling or halving of a frequency; a 2:1 ratio of two frequencies. In music two notes of the same name, 12 semi-tones apart

Ohm — the amount of electrical resistance, or opposition, between two points.

Ohm's Law — states that the voltage (V) across a circuit is equal to the product of the current (I) flowing through it and the resistance (R) of the circuit (E = I x R).

Ohmmeter — an instrument used to measure the DC electrical resistance in a circuit or component

OOP — see Object-Oriented Programming.

Open source programming language — a language that is considered public domain and not supported by a commercial vendor.

Open-loop system — type of geothermal HVAC system that uses water from a surface or underground source (pond, lake or well) to circulate through its system.

Operating System (OS) — fundamental software layer that enables applications to run on a hardware platform.

Org chart — see Organizational chart.

Organizational chart — diagram that shows the structure of the organization, the relationships within the organization, and ranks of the jobs and positions of the organization

Oscilloscope — an instrument used to measure and display frequency-based electrical information

OSI Model — The OSI (Open System Interconnection) model describes 7 abstract layers of communication between devices. Similar functions are grouped into the same layer. A layer serves the layer above it, and is served by the layer below it.

Outsourcing — using a contractor (non-employee) to complete a project work item.

P2P — see Peer-to-peer network.

Package system — type of HVAC system where the main components (evaporator, condenser, and compressor) are all located in one cabinet.

Packet — unit of data that is routed between an origin and a destination on the Internet or any other packet-switched network.

Pan Tilt Zoom (PTZ) — a type of video camera which can be remote controlled (L/R, Up/Down, and zoom)

Paper trail — printed record or documents that chronicle the progress of a project.

Parallel circuit — a circuit with the same voltage across their ends resulting in identical polarities.

Parametric equalizer — an electronic multi-band audio processor that allows for control of amplitude, center frequency, and bandwidth

Parity — extra bit of information added to a unit of data to make the total number of 1-bits in the resulting unit either even or odd.

Particulates — unwanted contaminates; fine particles (liquid or solid) suspended in the air such as dust, smoke, fumes.

Pascal — unit of measurement used for sound pressure levels; one Pascal is equal to one Newton per square meter. Typically used as a micro-Pascal (1 millionth of a Pascal)

PCM — see Pulse Code Modulation

PDF — Portable document format; the native file format for Adobe Acrobat. PDF is the file format for representing documents in a manner that is independent of the original application software, hardware, and operating system used to create those documents. A PDF file can describe documents containing any combination of text, graphics, and images in a device-independent and resolution independent format.

PDP — see Plasma Display Panel.

Peak — high pressure point of a sound wave; also called a crest.

Peak-to-peak — the total height of a wave, from maximum positive to maximum negative

Peer-to-Peer Network (P2P) — network architecture in which each device is connected on the network, but without a central "host" computer acting as a server.

Perforated Panel Absorber — type of absorber using holes or a perforated surface to achieve sound absorption.

Performance review — an analysis undertaken at a fixed point in time to determine the degree to which an employee has met the stated objectives of his or her position.

Personal Area Network (PAN) — network of computers in immediate proximity to a person or device

Phishing — process of re-directing someone to a seemingly legitimate looking website with the purpose of collecting personal information to engage in identity theft.

Phosphors — chemical compounds which radiate light when struck by a beam of electrons.

Photodiode — device capable of converting light to voltage or current.

Picture Line-Up Generation Equipment (PLUGE) — equipment used to generate a monochrome test pattern primarily intended for proper calibration of contrast (system gain) and brightness (black level).

Pink noise — a variation of white noise that has equal energy in all octaves. Commonly used to measure the performance of loudspeakers and audio systems

Pixel density — number of pixels per square inch; higher pixel density correlates to a higher overall resolution.

Pixels — single points of color and light on a video display

Plain Old Telephone System — slang term for the traditional analog telephone system

Plan view — drawing which shows a building or room as viewed from above

Plasma Display Panel (PDP) — type of television viewing device that uses a highly ionized xenon and neon gas in thousands or millions of micro-chambers

Plenum — The cavity above a drop ceiling which is used as a air return to the air handler, primarily in commercial construction. Cabling in this space is usually required to be "plenum rated"

Plot plan — drawing wich shows buildings, roads, and other features of a project site, and other above-ground features, as viewed from above, on a scale allowing a large area of land to be covered.

PLUGE — see Picture Line-up Generation Equipment.

PO — see Purchase Order.

Point-to-point diagram — detailed wiring diagram for the assembly and service of equipment racks, head ends and area electronics. Often refered to as a schematic diagram.

Point-to-point transmission — transmission of data directly from one terminal to another without the use of any intermediate computer or terminal port.

Polarity — a description of either positive or negative applied to an electric charge, voltage, or speakers.

Polarity test — a test designed to make sure that each speaker in the system has the proper polarity

Polarity tester — a device to determine positive or negative response to signal by speakers in an audio system

Pole — a set of contacts belonging to a single circuit.

POTS — see Plain Old Telephone System

Power — the energy used to operate an electrical device or devices.

Power over Ethernet (PoE) — the ability to pass power (up to 25.5W), as well as data, over an Ethernet network. Defined by IEEE 802.3at-2009

Powerline networking — home network that uses special modules plugged into electrical outlets to connect peripherals together to form a network.

Precedence effect — see Haas effect

Pre-configuration — information that provides the addresses of available devices and any other necessary information, e.g., a device is a contact input or output.

Pre-design phase — phase of a project that is marked primarily by information gathering activities, gathering project requirements, and determining project scope.

Pregnancy Discrimination Act of 1978 — amendment to Title VII of the Civil Rights Act of 1964 to prohibit sex discrimination on the basis of pregnancy.
Pressure pad a trigger pad in the floor activated by weight

Primary listening position — the location in a home theater which the system is calibrated to for optimal performance

Primary stakeholder — specific customer that has primary responsibility for funding the project; also called a sponsor.

Procedural programming language — language consisting of programs that are organized as a set of procedures that have definite beginnings and ends.
Product mix variety of services offered by a company. Particularly refers to related services.

Programmable thermostat — thermostat with the ability to record different temperature/ time settings for heating and/ or cooling equipment and thus control the equipment by those settings

Programming — the overall concept of designing, writing, testing, debugging, and documentation of computer programs.

Programming methodology — the analysis, design and implementation of computer programs.

Programming specifications — formal document that details how and in what terms a program will address the requirements set forth in the functional specifications document.

Progressive discipline — process of using increasingly severe steps or measures when an employee fails to correct a problem after being given a reasonable opportunity to do so.

Progressive elaboration — he process of moving from the beginning to the end of the project through its various phases.

Progressive scanning (p) — television format in which information to each pixel in a frame of video sequentially, from left to right and top to bottom to create an image.

Project assumptions — physical or time-oriented factors that are listed in the project's documentation that may affect the outcome of the project.
Project communications requirements detailed documentation specifying how information will be communicated to participants of the project.

Project constraints — limiting factors of a project that fall under time, cost and scope parameters.

Project deliverables — items ultimately supplied by the project; without which the project cannot be considered complete.

Project lifecycle — timeframe encompassing the beginning to the end of the project.

Project Manager (PM) — person responsible for oversight on the project from the beginning planning stages to completion.

Project objectives — goals to be met by the project.

Project plan — outline illustrating the intended path of a project.

Project requirements — conditions or capabilities that must be met by a project.

Project resources — include people, materials, assets, software, and other items that are needed by the project in order to achieve its goals.

Project scope — extent or range of view, outlook, application, operation, effectiveness, etc.

Protocol — standard for transmitting data between two devices.

Prototype — a model of something to be further developed; a sample.

Proxy server — device that sits between an end customer application (such as a web browser) and a server on the Internet in order to "pre-process" requests from the customer to see if the request can be handled locally; if not the request is forwarded to the remote server.

Pseudocode — a type of English-like statements used to describe the algorithmic steps needed in a program, analogous to a flowchart as a planning tool for programming.

PTZ — see Pan Tilt Zoom

Pull tension — the amount of tension put on a cable as it is being installed or while suspended between two points. The maximum recommended pull tension is the amount (in lbs. or kg) beyond which performance may be compromised

Pulse Code Modulation (PCM) — a popular method of representing analog audio in digital form

Purchase Order (PO) — contract between a buyer and seller showing items to be obtained; each with an associated monetary value.

Quality assurance — systematic process of verifying that a product meets the specified requirements.

Radiation — electromagnetic emanation that requires no medium to transfer heat.

Radio frequency (RF) — radio or electrical waves in the frequency range of about 3kHz to 300GhZ.

Radio Frequency Interference (RFI) — external inerference in a signal caused by high frequency radio or television signals (RFI)

Rattle — a sound made by loose objects shaking or vibrating against one another

RCP — see Reflected ceiling plan

Reactance — a function of the inductance and/or capacitance within a circuit and their effect on the phase relationship of voltage and current within the circuit.

Real Time Analyzer (RTA) — a device which displays the frequency spectrum of an audio signal in real time.

Recording Industry Association of America (RIAA) — a trade association representing the recording industry, primarily record companies and distributors

Red line drawing — marked-up field drawing showing changes to the original documents by annotating the changes with red line markings. As-buit drawings are created from the red-line drawings.

Reflected ceiling plan — drawing which shows a building or room as viewed from above but detailing the ceiling plane rather than the floor. Includes details such as lighing, HVAC, in-ceiling speakers, ceiling tile configuration, etc.

Reflected sound wave — sound which has bounced off of a surface; arrives at the ear slightly later than the direct sound wave because it travels a longer distance.

Reflection — sound wave which reaches the ear after bouncing off a surface.

Refresh rate — rate at which the frames are displayed.

Regression testing — the re-testing of a previously valid program after modifications have been made to ensure that faults have not been introduced to the system.

Relative Humidity (RH) — ratio of how much moisture the air can hold versus how much moisture is actually present in the air at a given time expressed as a percentage

Relay — an electrical switch that is controlled (opens and closes) by another electrical switch.

Reliability — ability of a person or company to perform and maintain its functions, expectations, and responsibilities

Repeater — device used in data communication to strengthen a signal as it is passed along the network cable.

Request for Information (RFI) — a document used to solicit information from a provider regarding products, capabilities, prices, or services.

Request for Proposal (RFP) — a formal request to a vendor to submit a proposal to provide a product or service. It may include specifications which define the overall system quality, project procedures and process.

Request for Quotation (RFQ) — document used to solicit vendor responses when a product has been selected and price quotations are required from several vendors.

Resistance — the opposition offered by an electrical conductor to the flow of a current through it, resulting in a conversion of electrical energy into heat.

Resistor — an electronic component that opposes an electric current by generating a voltage drop in proportion to the current between its two terminals (based on Ohm's law) and converting electrical energy into heat.

Resolution — measurement of the quality of a video image that is directly related to the number of pixels that make up the image.

Resolution test pattern — monochrome pattern traditionally used to evaluate television system bandwidth and frequency response.

Retrofit — to install something into an existing structure

Revenue — income that a company receives from normal business activities by the sale of goods or services to customers

Reverberation — the continuing sound after the sound source has ceased to vibrate as a result of repeatedly reflecting off multiple surfaces; also called reverb

Reverse-phase control — dimming device that turns the waveform off at the end of the cycle.

Revision — change to a document usually identified by a number or letter code such as Rev.1, Rev.2, etc. Each revision should include a timestamp and the name or initials of the person making the change.

Revision block — grid-like section on a drawing which lists and keeps track of the history of changes (revisions) made to the drawing.

Revision control — the file management and storage of documents and software revisions that is primarily concerned with ensuring that previous versions of information are not lost or deleted.

Revision identifier — short segment of a file name that identifies the specific version of the file as opposed to other versions of the same file.

RFI — see Radio Frequency Interference

RFI — see Request for Information.

RFP — see Request for Proposal.

RFQ — see Request for Quotation.

RH — see Relative humidity

RIAA — see Recording Industry Association of America

RJ-31X — interface which allows security system's dialer to "sieze" the phone line and call out, even if a home phone is in use or off the hook.

RJ-45 — standard 8 position/8 contact (8P8C) type of connector used for data and telephone. May be male (plug) or female (jack).

RJ-45 crimp tool — hand tool used to terminate twisted pair cable with RJ-45 plug

RMS (Root Mean Squared) — the average power an amplifier will deliver into a specific load. The most accurate way to compare power amplifier specs
Room mode a frequency which resonates within an bounded space forming a standing wave; the rooms dimensions correlate to the range of many modal frequencies possible.

Rotary switch — works like a slide switch except that the control is a knob that rotates instead of moving in a line.

Router — a network device that connects two separate networks together. In the home, this will often serve as the 'Gateway' from the Internet to the home LAN.

RT60 — means of expressing the measurement of the reverberation time in a physical space that indicates the elapsed time required for the reverberation to decay by 60 decibels

Saturation — relative brilliance with which a film (or print) reproduces a subject's colors.

Sawtooth wave — a non-sinusiodal waveform that resembles the blades of a saw.

Scale — ratio of measuring units expressing a proportional relationship between the drawing and the full size item or space it represents.

Schedule — group or table showing details or properties of related devices, objects or materials in a plan or drawing.

Schedule milestones — instances in a project that reflect important points along the project lifecycle where goals are met or measurements are taken to assess overall project performance.

Schematic diagram — detailed diagram for the purpose of understanding the interconnection of devices and to provide graphical information for the assembly or service of a system.

Scope — objective(s) and extent of work to be accomplished by the project.

Scope creep — on-going addition of requirements to a project without corresponding adjustment of approved cost and schedule allowances.

Scope of Work document — agreement document among the project team and key stakeholders. It represents a common understanding of the project and sets authorities and limits for the project manager and team. It includes business objectives and the boundaries of the project including approach, deliverables, milestones, and budget.

Scope statement — short verbiage that addresses what a project will encompass.

SDTV — see Standard Definition Digital Television.

Search engine a program that references a database of information that contains links to website pages where the information that is searched for can be found on the Internet.

Search engine optimization — the process of designing or updating a website so that it will perform better (i.e. rank higher) in the search engine rankings results list.

Seasonal Energy Efficiency Ratio (SEER) — quantitative measurement rating system that evaluates the amount of energy a particular HVAC system delivers to every dollar spent

Secondary cell — rechargeable devices where the chemical reactions that result in the generation of electricity can be reversed.

Section view — part of a drawing that shows the vertical relationships of structural materials or a cut-view of an object.

Secure HTTP (HTTPS) — HTTP protocol which adds a layer of security encryption.

Security panel — the central processor of the security system.

SEER — see Seasonal Energy Efficiency Ratio.

Segment — an electrical connection between networked devices

Sensor — device that detects a specific condition, such as temperature, moisture, contact etc. so that another component can react to that condition

Sequence diagram — the specific scenario of execution in the system in terms of object instances.

Series circuit — wiring confitguration where loads are connected end to end and their values, in ohms, are added together to get the total resistance of the circuit.

Server — computer or device on a network that manages a network's resources.
Service Set Identification a 32-character alphanumeric key uniquely identifying a wireless LAN

Setpoint — defined indicator point in an HVAC system where a specific action takes place (turn on/off, etc).

Sexual harassment — unwelcome sexual advances or conduct on the job that creates an intimidating, hostile or offensive working environment.

Shield — a part of many cable types which reduces signal loss of high frequencies and external interference such as RFI and EMI. Sometimes also provides an electrical return path.

Shielded Twisted Pair (STP) — twisted pair cable, usually 8 conductor, which includes a foil shield to protect from EMI and RFI

Short — having a small distance from one end or edge to another, either horizontally or vertically; causing failure in an electrical circuit.

Silicon X-tal Reflective Display (SXRD) — a version of a LCoS rear-projection technology

Simple Mail Transfer Protocol (SMTP) — protocol used in the delivery of electronic mail (e-mail)

Sine wave — type of waveform signal in which the voltage or equivalent rises and falls smoothly and symmetrically; also called sinusoidal wave.

Single Mode Optical Fiber (SMF) — type of optical fiber designed to carry only a single ray of light (mode).

Single pole single throw (SPST) — a simple on-off switch.

Single-source audio — distributed audio system which transmits audio from one single source to multiple rooms at the same time.

Single-stage controls — HVAC controls that provide one stage of heat and one stage of cooling: on or off.

Sinusoidal wave — see sine wave.

Site plan — drawing that shows the location of items such as buildings, drives, parking, and water features of the property. Plot plan.

Skin Effect — the tendency of electrons to flow near the outside (skin) of the conductor at 100 KHz+ frequencies

Slap echo — the back-and-forth reflection of primarily mid-range and high frequency sound between two parallel hard surfaces.

Slide switch — switch that use a sliding button or bar to open and close the circuit

SMF — see Single-mode optical fiber.

SMPTE Color Bars — an industry standard test pattern which includes seven vertical bars of 75% intensity. Developed by the Society of Motion Picture and Television Engineers

SMTP — see Simple Mail Transfer Protocol.

Software design — one phase of the software development process where software solutions are created that address the requirements of the proposed system.

Software development — process of creating software programs to meet the necessary requirements of the end users to complete a business function or other goal.

Software lifecycle — duration of a computer program or system; typically broken down into six phases: requirements, design, implementation, testing, deployment and maintenance.

Software process — the total set of software engineering activities necessary to develop and maintain software products.

Software testing — activity that is part of the software development process whose goal is to evaluate a piece of software code to determine whether is functioning as intended.

Solenoid valve — valve actuated by a solenoid for controlling the flow of gases or liquid in pipes.

Sound isolation — process of reducing the amount of sound transmitted from one space to another.

Sound Pressure Level (SPL) — the strength or intensity of acoustic sound waves, measured in dB; a logarithmic ratio referenced to the threshold of audibility

Sound Transmission Class (STC) — method used to quantify how well a boundary such as a wall, ceiling or floor attenuates air-borne sound traveling from one space to another, measured at 16 frequencies from 125Hz to 4kHz

Sound wave — The cyclical variation of air pressure at a frequency which stimulates hearing.

Source code — form of human-readable programming statements that a program consists of before the program is compiled into machine language.

Spam — unsolicited e-mail that is sent out in bulk to many e-mail addresses at once.

Spam filtering — programs that are designed to limit the amount of spam e-mail that a user receives by identifying them and moving them to a Junk/Spam folder or deleting them entirely.

Speaker — an electromechanical transducer that converts an electrical signal into audible sound (or an enclosure combining transducers into a system)

Speaker polarity test — a test to ensure that speakers are in phase with each other.

Spectroradiometer — device that measures luminous power of a light source at many incremental wavelengths both inside and outside the visible spectrum

Speed of sound — distance traveled per unit of time by a sound wave. In dry air (68° F) the speed of sound is 1,126 ft/sec (343.2 m/sec). It travels about 4 times as fast in water.

SPL — see sound pressure level.

Split system — type of HVAC system that uses air conditioners or heat pumps with more than one factory-made assembly, such as an indoor unit and an outdoor unit which can be roof-mounted, wall-mounted, or fixed on the ground

Spyware — type of tracking software that is loaded in many cases without the user's permission in order to perform tracking activities such as recording which websites are visited, or the buying preferences of the user.

Square wave — a non-sinusoidal waveform that is squared off at the peaks of the wave resulting from regular and instantaneous alteration of the current.

SSID — see Service Set Identification

Stakeholders — interested parties in a project.

Standard Definition Digital Television (SDTV) — digital television format that includes 480-line resolution in both interlaced and progressively scanned formats in a 4:3 aspect ratio

Standing wave (room mode) — see Room mode

Star Topology — network architecture configuration in which each node on a network is connected directly to a central hub or concentrator.

State — unique combination of information in a computer program or computer machine.

State diagram — graphical representations that are used to describe the behavior of a system by showing all of the possible states of an object as events in that system.

Static Routing — network traffic management approach where the network is configured with set, defined paths between routers that are not changeable, so traffic must only use these paths; there is not automatic re-routing of network traffic if a network path experiences a failure.

STP — see Shielded Twisted Pair.

Straight heat/cool — type of split-system HVAC where the indoor unit includes a separate furnace and the refrigeration side operates to exchange heat from inside the house to outside via the outdoor unit.

Structured programming — programming methodology that utilizes a set of well-defined structures, such as condition statements and loops to produce code that is more easily understood and maintained.

Submittal — specific information about a product or service or the form that accompanies plans submitted for the approval, consideration, or decision of another; usually a one-page document of specifications for a product or service.

Subnet — smaller group or cluster of similar devices on the Internet.
Subnet mask used to determine on which network a particular IP address is located.

Subnetting — a logical division of a network into Subnets
Subtractive color process photographic process in which all but the desired colors are removed by passing the light through subtractive filters.

Subwoofer — a loudspeaker designed to reproduce the lowest audible frequencies, typically the lower two octaves of human hearing

Supervision — guidance and/or direction provided by a member of the administration.

Supervisor — person who provides guidance and/or direction to other employees in their directly controlled group or team.

Swamp cooler — see Evaporative cooler.

Switch — an Ethernet switch is a networking device that connects networked devices together.

SXRD — see Silicon X-tal Reflective Display.

Symbol — graphical representation of a real device or object used in a diagram or architectural drawing.

Syntax — rules of a programming language that determines what is and is not acceptable to the compiler.

Systems Designer — industry professional who specifies the components and configuration of integrated electronic systems

T-1 — dedicated digital communications line that supports data rates of 1.5 Megabits per second

Tag — abbreviated way to show additional properties of an item on a drawing. The tag can be a square, circle or hexagonal shape including a leader line connecting the tag to the item.

Tangential mode — a mode produced by reflections off four of the six surfaces of a room.

Task lighting — light that is directed to a specific area in order to accomplish a task

TCP/IP — collection of data communication protocols developed to standardize data transfer between systems and networks.

Telecommunications Industries Association (TIA) — an ANSI accredited trade association which writes industry standards for the telecommunication industry
Telepresence technology allowing people in different locations to see and hear each other for enhanced communication, both business and personal
Temperature the measure of the heat

Template — a pre-determined guide or format to follow typically used as a starting point before any custom work or particular project information is applied.

Termination — discontinuance of employment on the part of the employer towards an employee.

Termination — process of installing a connector or connection on a cable or wire to make it useable for the intended use. Examples; F Connector on RG6, RJ-45 or punch block on Cat5e.

Termination Checklist — pre-established list of important items to cover when an employee is being terminated from his or her position with the company.

Terrestrial signals — older source of TV signals for most home viewing; NTSC standard used for over-the-air (OTA) broadcasts.

Test pattern — special test pattern for adjusting TV receivers or color encoders

Thermostat — control unit that turns on the heating or cooling system based upon its reading from a temperature sensor.

Threshold of hearing — owest level of sound that is audible to the human ear. Typically assumed to be 0dB (much higher for very low frequencies)

Threshold of pain — point at which the loudness of sound causes pain to the human ear.

Throw distance — Length of the projection beam needed for a projector to produce image of a particular size.

THX — the trade name for a high-fidelity sound reproduction standard used in movie theaters, home theaters, gaming consoles and car audio systems.

TIA — see Telecommunications Industries Association.

Timeline — a linear representation of the progress of a project with important points marked according to when they occur.

Title Block — section of a drawing showing important project information such as company logo, clients name, project name, date, etc.

Title VII — see Civil Rights Act of 1964.

Toggle switch — electrical switch that uses a mechanical lever or handle to open or close the electrical contacts

Token ring topology — network architecture configuration where the network is a closed loop, with no beginning or end, where nodes act as repeaters along the cable to enhance a signal as it comes thru the network.
Ton term used to describe the cooling ability of an air conditioner. Equal to the cooling of 2,000 lbs. of ice melting in 24 hours, or 12,000 BTU/Hr.

Tone sweep — a test tone which sweeps smoothly from 20Hz to 20kHz; useful for finding rattles and resonances in a room

Top-down cost estimating — process of determine a project estimate by valuing the cost of the major components and the time required to complete them and breaking them down into more detailed segments to determine an overall project estimate.

Top-down design — structured program design approach that breaks up a general task into a series of more detailed subtasks, which are then further divided until small components of code can be identified.

Touchscreen — deviced used to allow control via simply touching a graphical display through a resistive or capacitive screen

Touchscreen layout — plan and organization of the items shown on the touchscreen.

Transformer — a device that moves electrical energy from one circuit to another through inductively coupled electrical conductors.

Transmission Control Protocol/Internet Protocol (TCP/IP) — set of protocols that allow communication between computers; used as the standard for transmitting data over networks and as the basis for standard Internet protocols.

Tree Topology — network architecture configuration that is similar to linear bus topology, except that tree networks can contain branches with multiple nodes.

Trigger — event that invokes a stored procedure on the basis of certain pre-determined data-related events.

Trigger event — see Trigger.

Tristimulus filter system — see colorimeter.

Tristimulus values — set of primaries (XYZ), that correspond to the way the retina of the eye behaves.

Trojan horse — malicious software that disguises itself as legitimate software, but is harmful to the infected computer.

Trough — low pressure point of a sound wave

Trunk segment — a networking cable that has one or more nodes attached to it; also called a populated segment.

Truth table — convenient row/column format to represent the comparison of logical input values and their corresponding output responses.

Tungsten-halogen lamp — gas filled tungsten incandescent lamp containing a certain percentage of halogens.

Twisted pair — two insulated copper wires twisted around each other to reduce induction (therefore interference); common type of transmission media.

UDP — see User Datagram Protocol

UHF — see Ultra High Frequency.

Ultra high frequency (UHF) — radio frequency range from 300 MHz to 3 GHz.

Ultrasound — sound that is above the human audible range

UML — see Unified Modeling Language.

Unified Modeling Language (UML) — non-proprietary, third-generation flexible convention for expressing object-oriented software design.

Uniform Resource Locator (URL) — a web address, such as http://example.com, which directs the user to the desired resource on the world wide web

Uninterruptible Power Supply (UPS) — a battery backup or mechanical device used to provide immediate power if electrical service is interrupted.

Unit testing — type of testing methodology that is used to ensure individual units of source code are working as designed.

Unshielded Twisted Pair (UTP) — commonly used cable in the electronic systems industry used for telephone and networking. Usually 8 conductor, no sheild. Includes unsheilded CAT5e and CAT6

Unstructured programming language — negative characteristic of programming code that uses unconditional branching (most commonly for exception handling) to jump to another piece of code rather than use accepted structured programming principles to modify execution flow.

UPS — see Uninteruptible Power Supply

URL — see Uniform Resource Locator

User Datagram Protocol (UDP) — an IP protocol which does not have handshaking dia-logs, but works well for some streaming content

User interface (UI) — tools or software that allow people to interact with a machine, device, computer program, or other complex tool

UTP — see Unshielded Twisted Pair

Value engineering — process of evaluating methods and/or materials to determine which have the net result of reducing costs in a project.

Variable air volume — air distribution system capable of automatically delivering a re-duced volume of constant temperature cool air to satisfy the reduced cooling load of individual zones

VAV — see Variable Air Volume

Ventilation — the exchange of air to improve air quality. May be between indoor and outdoor air or between rooms.

Vermiculite — a mineral material used in insulation. In the 1990's vermiculite from a mine in Montana was found to contain asbestos

Version — change to a project file utilizing numbers or letters to help control and keep track of the progression of the project as a whole.

Vertical communication — communication between one level of authority and another within an organization.

Vertical resolution — number of distinct horizontal lines, alternately black and white, that can be seen in a TV image.

Very High Frequency (VHF) — radio frequency range from 30 MHz to 300 MHz.

VHF — see Very High Frequency.

Video scanning — general term for the process of drawing a picture on a TV screen.

Virtual Local Area Network — a partition of a network at level at the data link layer (Layer 2) of the OSI model

Virtual Private Network — a method of extendign a private network over a public network

Virus — self-replicating program that spreads itself by inserting copies of itself into other program code or documents.

Visio — Microsoft Windows software program that uses vector graphics to create technical diagrams.

VLAN — see Virtual Local Area Network

Volt — the unit of measure for the electromotive force or EMF; the force that pushes the electrons through a wire and is referred to as electrical pressure.

Volt/ohm meter — see multimeter

Voltage — the difference of electrical potential between two points of an electrical or electronic circuit.

Voltmeter — an instrument used to detect and to measure electrical voltage

VOM — See volt/ohm meter

VPN — see Virtual Private Network

W3C — see World Wide Web Consortium.

WAN — see Wide area network.

WAP — see Wireless Access Point.

Waterfall development process — software development approach that advocates phased development from requirements definition through design, code, testing and implementation.

Watt — unit in which power is measured.

Watt meter — an instrument used to measure total power consumption in watts.

Wavelength — distance between consecutive crests of a wave. Also, the distance a sound wave travels (at the speed of sound) during the time it takes to make one cycle

WBS — see Work Breakdown Structure.

WBS dictionary — part of a WBS that defines and explains terms and segments of a WBS in more detail.

WDR — see Wide Dynamic Range

Weber — a measure of magnetism

WEP — see Wired Equivalency Privacy.

White box testing — testing methodology based on the knowledge and analysis of the internal workings of a piece of software.

White level — brightest part of a video signal

White noise — sound that includes every frequency in the human range of hearing with equal energy at each frequency

White Paper — authoratative report or guide that details solutions to specific problems

Wide Area Network (WAN) — A network connecting computers over a very large geographical area such as states, countries, and the world. The Internet can be considered a WAN

Wide Dynamic Range (WDR) — a type of video camera capable of operating with both bright and dim ambient lighting

Wi-Fi — IEEE 802.11 standard for wireless communications and products which conform to this standard

Wi-Fi Protected Access (WPA) — a Wi-Fi encryption standard. Now superseded by WPA2

Wire — a single metallic conductor, solid or stranded, with or without insulation

Wire stripper — hand tool used to remove just the insulator from a single wire, either solid or stranded

Wired Equivalent Privacy (WEP) — a Wi-Fi encryption standard. Now superseded by WPA and WPA2

Wireless Access Point (WAP) — a device that allows wireless devices to connect to a wired network. May be free-standing or part of a router which also has wired ports.

Wireless Local Area Network — network connecting two or more devices wirelessly, usually also providing access to the Internet

Wiring schedule — see Cable schedule

WLAN — See Wireless Local Area Network

Word — fixed-sized group of bits that are handled together by the particular machine on which the data is stored.

Work Breakdown Structure (WBS) — standard software project management technique of breaking the project down into a hierarchy of work tasks which represent the work to be done.

Work order — internal document used to define the exact scope of work to be done. Often specifies who is to do the work, and the time allotted.

Work package — lowest level or smallest component of a WBS that is used as a basis for cost estimating.

World Wide Web Consortium (W3C) — international governing body that addresses the development of platform-independent web standards and specifications.

Worm — malicious software that uses computer networks and security holes to replicate itself that does not need a "host" program in order to infect a computer.

WPA — see Wi-Fi Protected Access.

X-10 — open industry communication standard that is used by electronic devices to communicate with each other using the power line for communication. Developed in 1975, no longer supported.

Zone — group of lights, speakers, sensors or other devices that work together and are controlled as one group.

Z-wave — RF-based, two-way mesh networking protocol that allows for the control of many home appliances.

APPENDIX

ESC-T Job Task Analysis
ESC-D Job Task Analysis
ESC-N Job Task Analysis
HDMI
APPLICATION NOTES
    CEA/CEDIA CEB-22
    CEA/CEDIA CEB-23
    CEA/CEDIA CEB-24
ADDITIONAL RESOURCES

JOB TASK ANALYSIS (EXAM BLUEPRINT)

International (English)

For Electronic Systems Technicians with at least 3 years of field experience.

NOTE: This is the master document on which the exam is built. CEDIA resources such as classes, books, and online training are designed to support this body of knowledge. Please refer to the **ESC-T Exam Prep Resources** document to find which resources support each area of study.

CEDIA
ESC-T

Domain 1 General Technician Roles and Responsibilities

Task 1: Maintain a "safety first" mindset by understanding and following personal and property safety procedures and preventing accidents in order to prevent harm to self and others.

KNOWLEDGE OF:

1. Applicable local and regional codes/articles specific to personal safety and accident prevention (both on-site and off)
2. Applicable national/local electrical codes specific to personal safety and accident prevention
3. Applicable construction codes specific to safety and property protection
4. Motor vehicle safety and accident prevention
5. Basic first aid treatments and procedures for minor incidents
6. Emergency procedures for major incidents
7. Typical onsite safety meeting: types of information, rules and procedures
8. Company safety policies
9. Proper use and care of hand and power tools
10. Proper use and care of ladders and scaffolds

SKILL IN:

1. Interpreting applicable codes/laws
2. Analyzing a situation and choose/apply the correct solution
3. Recognizing potentially hazardous situations and react accordingly
4. Basic first aid techniques
5. Emergency procedures
6. Operating a motor vehicle safely
7. Operating job related heavy equipment (personnel lifts, etc...) safely
8. Care and use of personal protective equipment(PPE)
9. Safe use of hand and power tools
10. Safe use of ladders and scaffolds

Task 2: Represent the company by demonstrating appropriate professional behavior, reporting work activities, and engaging in best practices.

KNOWLEDGE OF:

1. Typical company reporting methods
2. Typical employment (HR) issues
3. Company management structure and chain of command (communications)
4. Timecards, work/change orders (daily, on-going personal, and project tracking reporting methods)
5. Personal/professional behavior and appearance
6. Workplace/jobsite etiquette and professionalism
7. The importance and necessity of typical employment procedures

SKILL IN:

1. Reading and interpreting common company documents
2. Using personal and project tracking/reporting methods
3. Following directions accurately
4. Using clear, concise communications
5. Handling difficult situations/conflict resolution
6. Working well with builders and other trades

Task 3: Use project documentation by interpreting, creating or modifying appropriate field documents as required, in order to confirm compliance with design specifications.

KNOWLEDGE OF:

1. Proposals, bill of materials, pick list, inventory logs
2. System overviews/summaries (functional)
3. Architectural plans (floor, elevation, detail, etc.)
4. Schedules (time, wire, materials, etc.)
5. Charts
6. Design/engineering drawings (block diagrams, line drawings, point-to-point schematics, cabinetry, mechanical, etc.)
7. Instruction and service manuals
8. Understand the importance and proper use for typical field documents
9. Basic redline procedures and document updates

SKILL IN:

1. Reading and interpreting typical field documents
2. Creating necessary documentation that is clear and concise for others to follow
3. Modifying documentation properly using approved methods
4. Assisting project supervisor in document revision (redlines) / as-built
5. Writing clearly and legibly

Task 4: Compute project related data using relevant technical and mathematical equations, terms, and principles in order to ensure successful completion of work.

KNOWLEDGE OF:

1. Algebra
2. Geometry
3. Electronics/industry specific math
4. Decibels (dB)
5. Fractions/decimal (conversion)
6. Ohms Law
7. Basic electricity and power management (i.e., high voltage types, outlets types, power supplies, power distribution, etc...)
8. Basic audio - analog & digital (i.e., signal types, levels, frequencies, noise, bandwidth etc...)
9. Basic video - analog & digital (i.e., signal types, levels, bandwidth, etc...)
10. Basic communications (i.e., telephone, intercom, signal types, signal levels/voltages, RF, etc...)
11. Basic data and networking (i.e., signal types, bandwidth, IP, etc...)
12. Basic control systems (data rates, polarity, relays, contact closure, voltage, metadata, feedback)

SKILL IN:

1. Interpreting typical industry related mathematics
2. Interpreting typical industry related terminology
3. Understanding when and how to properly use industry specific mathematics
4. Understanding when and how to properly use industry specific terminology
5. Solving typical industry related problems using proper mathematic equations
6. Converting fractions to decimals and decimals to fractions
7. Application of Ohm's Law

Domain 2 Infrastructure (Pre-wire & Trim-out)

Task 1: Pre-wire an electronic system as specified in order to facilitate proper performance of audio, video, control, and related subsystem devices.

KNOWLEDGE OF:

1. Cable/wire types, applications
2. Construction/structural techniques/requirements/issues
3. Device installation techniques ("Pre-wire/First Fix")
4. Device placement
5. Wire dressing
6. Ventilation
7. Space requirements
8. Suspended/hanging device requirements
9. Outside service provider requirements (Telco/CATV/ISP/SAT)/ Demarcation point
10. Fire rated back boxes and other special circumstance devices and provisions
11. Wire/cabling identification (types/labeling)

SKILL IN:

1. Installing proper wire/cable for a specific purpose as specified
2. Understanding of proper installation methods/requirements of cabling and devices
3. Installing mounting devices (rings, brackets, back-boxes, etc...)
4. Relating theory to practical applications
5. Deductive reasoning, problem solving, application of theory
6. Hand and power tool usage
7. Communicating with other trades proficiently
8. Understanding outside service provider requirements (Telco, CATV, ISP, SAT)

Task 2: Trim-out an electronic system by labeling, terminating, and testing cables and properly mounting and installing trim related devices in order to support installation of audio, video, control, and other subsystem devices.

KNOWLEDGE OF:

1. Termination methods of needed cable, connector and signal types
2. Types of termination tools, and their appropriate use
3. Applicable codes and standards related to "Trim-out/Second Fix" activities
4. Typical "Trim/Second Fix" related tools and their proper use
5. Test tools, verifying results

SKILL IN:

1. Properly terminating all common cable/connector/signal types
2. Identifying and using typical termination devices and tools
3. Interpreting applicable codes and standards
4. Testing/verification of terminations and signal quality
5. Troubleshooting and correcting, based on test results
6. Using label makers
7. Proper cable installation, and dressing
8. Reading/filling out cable schedules

Domain 3 Equipment Mounting

Task 1: Install equipment into a rack or cabinet while providing for proper ventilation, power management, and mounting considerations in order to facilitate ease of use and maximum performance.

KNOWLEDGE OF:

1. Cabinet design and construction
2. Proper equipment layout and mounting techniques
3. Safe and secure equipment mounting
4. Rack and cabinet ventilation (active and passive)
5. Ventilation requirements for specific equipment
6. Risks associated with improper ventilation
7. Rack construction and accessories

SKILL IN:

1. Identifying various cabinet parts
2. Laying out equipment properly in a cabinet (best practices)
3. Mounting equipment/accessories in racks and cabinets
4. Assembling rack/equipment systems
5. Identifying different rack types/specific uses
6. Installing ventilation equipment
7. Proper cable/interconnect management

Task 2: Physically mount system components such as cameras, flat panel displays and projectors by installing the proper brackets, housings and mounting hardware in order to provide proper performance and safety.

KNOWLEDGE OF:

1. Types of display mounting brackets and their uses
2. Types of projector mounting brackets and their uses
3. Types of camera mounting brackets, housings and their uses

SKILL IN:

1. Installing various types of display brackets and mounting devices
2. Installing various types of projector mounting hardware and devices
3. Installing various types of camera brackets, housings and mounting devices

Task 3: Install power management devices such as surge suppressors, battery backups, and power conditioners in order to ensure safe and maximized performance of installed systems.

KNOWLEDGE OF:

1. Basic device recognition
2. Basic device purpose
3. Basic electricity and electrical distribution

SKILL IN:

1. Properly installing power devices and equipment
2. Basic set-up and use of power devices and equipment

Domain 4 Audio/Video Systems

Task 1: Set up audio devices such as sources, amplifiers, and speakers in order to produce a desired listening experience.

KNOWLEDGE OF:

1. Basic audio device recognition (analog & digital)
2. Basic audio device purpose
3. Basic signal flow and cable characteristics (analog & digital)

SKILL IN:

1. Identifying audio devices and components, and their interconnections
2. Basic installation of audio related devices and equipment

Task 2: Set up video devices such as sources and displays, in order to produce a desired viewing experience.

KNOWLEDGE OF:

1. Basic video device recognition (analog & digital)
2. Basic video device purpose (analog & digital)
3. Basic signal flow and cable characteristics (analog & digital)

SKILL IN:

1. Basic installation of video devices, interconnects, and accessories

Domain 5 Communications (Telephony, Data, Cctv, and Rf)

Task 1: Set up basic telephony devices such as handsets and intercoms in order to establish basic voice communication.

KNOWLEDGE OF:

1. Basic phone/communication device recognition (includes doorbells, intercoms, etc.)
2. Basic phone/communication devices (purpose)

SKILL IN:

1. Basic installation and configuration of phone/communication devices

Task 2: Set up basic data network devices such as switches and routers in order to facilitate basic data communication.

KNOWLEDGE OF:

1. Basic data device functionality

SKILL IN:

1. Basic installation and configuration of data network devices

Task 3: Set up basic security and surveillance devices such as cameras and sensors in order to provide basic monitoring of secured areas.

KNOWLEDGE OF:

1. Basic CCTV/security devices (recognition)
2. Basic CCTV/security devices (purpose)

SKILL IN:

1. Basic installation of CCTV/Security devices

Task 4: Set up terrestrial antenna, cable and satellite (RF) TV systems, distribution and equipment in order to provide proper reception of TV signals.

KNOWLEDGE OF:

1. Basic Off-Air/CATV/DBS devices (recognition)
2. Basic Off-Air/CATV/DBS devices (purpose)

SKILL IN:

1. Basic installation of Off-Air/CATV/SAT related devices
2. Basic set-up and use of Off-Air/CATV/SAT related devices

Domain 6 Integrated Control Systems

Task 1: Set up basic control devices such as remotes, keypads, volume controls, touch screens in order to allow user control over electronic devices and systems.

KNOWLEDGE OF:

1. Basic control devices (recognition)
2. Basic control devices (purpose)
3. Basic control protocols and methods
4. Interface technologies (RS232, RS485, RF, IR, contact closure, relays, IP)

SKILL IN:

1. Basic installation and setup of control related devices

Domain 7 System Verification and Testing

Task 1: Review the installed system in order to confirm compliance with design specifications.

KNOWLEDGE OF:

1. All system components and how they relate to the overall system functionality
2. System wiring, termination, and signal flow
3. Proper system operation
4. Audio and video formats, resolution, data rate, surround modes
5. Basic calibration procedures and terminology (audio & video)

SKILL IN:

1. Deductive reasoning
2. Interpretation of results
3. Understanding and using equipment and all associated devices
4. Reading instruction manuals
5. Verifying component operation
6. Navigating menus
7. Systematic, methodical procedures
8. Documenting results accurately
9. Using appropriate test equipment; meters, continuity, data rate, RF, etc.

Task 2: Verify system performance by testing device and system functionality in order to confirm proper operation.

KNOWLEDGE OF:

1. Techniques and methods for troubleshooting devices/systems
2. Basic understanding of methods to correct problems
3. Commonly used test equipment
4. Common failure modes
5. Troubleshooting techniques

SKILL IN:

1. Using appropriate test equipment
2. Deductive reasoning
3. Diplomacy/tact, accountability, and patience on the jobsite
4. Basic troubleshooting

JOB TASK ANALYSIS (EXAM BLUEPRINT)

International (English)

For industry professionals with at least 3 years of experience as a residential systems designer.

This document outlines the body of knowledge on which the certification exam is built. CEDIA resources such as classes, books, and online training are designed to support this body of knowledge. Please refer to the **ESC-D Exam Prep Resources** document to find which resources support each area of study.

CEDIA
ESC-D

Domain 1 Needs Assessment

Task 1: Initiate and investigate the scope of a project using a structured information gathering methodology to obtain customer information.

KNOWLEDGE OF:

1. Customer desires and expectations
2. Expectations for reliability and usability
3. Lifestyle and day-to-day use of the home

SKILL IN:

1. Organizing and developing the content necessary to create a formal client survey
2. Clarifying requirements
3. Interviewing/qualifying a client
4. Recording pertinent information and responses accurately
5. Determining the project stakeholders and decision maker(s)
6. Communicating efficiently and effectively

Task 2: Assess the site conditions by reviewing architectural plans and/or visiting the site in order to pre-empt architectural and structural complications.

KNOWLEDGE OF:

1. General construction methods and structural issues
2. Industry installation methods (e.g., wire types and routing)
3. Local codes and regulations

SKILL IN:

1. Working with architectural and engineering drawings
2. Taking accurate field measurements (e.g., tape measures)
3. Determining spatial relationships
4. Sketching room/existing conditions
5. Interpreting codes, regulations, and local covenants
6. Working with software based drawing/estimating programs (e.g., CAD)
7. Assessing site conditions (i.e., distance to the site, site map and directions, site parking, existing and new construction, house layout, equipment location, unusual situations, etc.)

Task 3: Establish the budget requirements by setting realistic expectations of deliverables, while explaining tangible quality differences in order to deliver the optimum performance/cost balance for the systems.

KNOWLEDGE OF:

1. Estimation techniques (Bottom-Up, Top-Down)
2. Cost analysis
3. Value engineering
4. Time, cost, scope, and quality relationships
5. Installation complexities and design options
6. Life cycle costs
7. Work Package (complete package of equipment, materials, and labor for each deliverable in the system)
8. Work Package Dictionary (document that describes each component in the Work Breakdown Structure)
9. Work Breakdown Structure (deliverable oriented deconstruction of work to be executed)

SKILL IN:

1. Creating cost estimates (Bottom-Up, Top-Down, Parametric, etc.)
2. Analyzing differences in how solution options affect the design
3. Maintaining and referencing product databases
4. Applying relevant mathematical calculations
5. Identifying appropriate product(s) for each application
6. Acquiring product knowledge

Task 4: Determine internal vs. external resource requirements for the system under design for the purpose of completing cost estimation.

KNOWLEDGE OF:

1. Submittal process (RFI, RFQ, RFP, etc.)
2. Understanding terms used by associated trades
3. Trade-off analysis, including make/buy decisions, organizational limitations, and core competencies
4. Effective meeting techniques

SKILL IN:

1. Reading, interpreting, and supplying specifications
2. Setting meetings and agendas and accurately documenting the results
3. Using precise, measurable language
4. Interpreting associated trades documents
5. Defining scope of work for designated tasks
6. Communicating the design requirements effectively (written and verbally)
7. Decision making (i.e., make/buy decisions)

Domain 2 Project Design

Task 1: Create functional specifications by translating the results of the needs assessment into activity based scenarios that can be understood by all project stakeholders.

KNOWLEDGE OF:

1. Equipment functionality and technicalities
2. Cognitive principles and ergonomics
3. Designing behaviors that support the personal goals of the users

SKILL IN:

1. Describing the sequence of product touch points
2. Creating documents that communicate sequential behaviors and interdependences (i.e., flowcharts)
3. Writing scenario narratives
4. Establishing performance levels

Task 2: Create physical specifications by translating the results of the functional specifications into system requirements.

KNOWLEDGE OF:

1. Home Theater (including surround formats, screens, masking, seating, recommended practices, performance goals)
2. Acoustics, sound isolation, and acoustical treatment options
3. Audio (components, loudspeakers, speaker sensitivity, distributed audio coverage, outdoor speakers, source options)
4. Video (formats, resolution, content protection, storage, streaming, digital imaging, broadcast formats, video conferencing, IPTV, display technologies, Blu-ray, 3D, 4K, viewing distance, viewing angle, anamorphic systems)
5. Cabling standards (CEA 2030, TIA 570-C, NEC, backbone, conduit, HDMI, fiber optics, MDU considerations)
6. Communications (telecom, VoIP, cellular, PBX, internet options)
7. Networking (specifying hardware and infrastructure, defining specifications related to QoS, segmentation, and bandwidth requirements, wireless network design, alternate carriers such as Powerline, MoCa, HPNA.
8. Interactive media spaces (gaming, performance, virtual reality, telepresence)
9. Device automation (gates, gas/electric fires, spa and pool control, irrigation, smart appliances, etc.)
10. Media servers (i.e., DVR, content management, A/V Codecs, mobile devices as sources)
11. Robotics, motorization
12. Digital rights management, metadata
13. Equipment mounting (wall/ceiling mounts, racks, thermal management)
14. Power management (i.e., power conditioning, grounding, bonding, green technology, energy management)
15. Digital home health (sensors, PERS, communication options)
16. Relevant safety regulations
17. Control systems, including user interface design, mobile devices, and communications protocols (RS232, RS422, RS485, DALI, IP, etc.)
18. Other user interfaces (i.e., ambient devices, gesture recognitions, haptics, biometrics)
19. Security and fire alarm systems, knowledge of regulations and integration of same (i.e., access control, monitoring, DVRs)
20. Lighting and shade system design and control (incl. LED)
21. HVAC system fundamentals & how to monitor/control these systems
22. Architecture and interior trim (millwork, structural, finish work, etc.)
23. Central vacuum systems
24. RF/CATV/DSS/CCTV distribution systems and HD/digital signal distribution (analog, digital, camera specs and optics, HDMI compatibility, analog sunset)
25. Basic electronics (e.g., Ohm's law, etc.)
26. Design programs and other computer applications
27. 27. Manufacturing and product specifications
28. Technology trends & how to stay informed

SKILL IN:

1. Considering future design expansions
2. Reading and interpreting product specifications, choosing products
3. Documenting system specifications
4. Identifying applicable technologies
5. Performing system related calculations
6. Calculating heat, electrical, and structural loads
7. Determining ventilation requirements (CFM, pathways, penetrations, etc.)
8. Designing and balancing audio/video distribution
9. Specifying, calculating, and analyzing acoustic design
10. Specifying spatial/mechanical/mounting/installation methods
11. Establishing performance levels
12. Determining functionality and programming requirements
13. Designing for serviceability, usability, and reliability

Task 3: Define the programming specification from the functional specification in order to determine what is to be controlled, the method and complexity of control, and the operational parameters including scripts, zone maps, and input/output relationships for the full integration of the system.

KNOWLEDGE OF:

1. Product functionality and configuration variables
2. Operational requirements, method and complexity of control
3. Structured programming, programming languages
4. Flowcharts, state diagrams, and macros
5. Interface protocols (RS232, RS485, TCP/IP, IR, digital I/O, contact closure, etc.)
6. Pseudocode and conditional logic

SKILL IN:

1. Describing sequential events
2. Specifying I/O relationships between events and actions
3. Determining fault scenarios, backup, and error recovery (i.e., reboot)
4. Reading and interpreting product manuals

Task 4: Create the user interface specification by proposing physical control arrangements in order to provide control consistent with client needs.

KNOWLEDGE OF:

1. P1. Ergonomics, aesthetics, and human factors
2. 2. User interface options and applications, including mobile apps
3. 3. Graphic design basics
4. 4. Web based control systems
5. 5. Hierarchical methods of control
6. 6. Metaphors
7. 7. Limitations of user interfaces
8. 8. Defaults and usability testing

SKILL IN:

1. Communicating ideas, concepts, and necessities
2. Choosing the appropriate physical control device
3. Evaluating the user interface designs through usability testing

Task 5: Direct the creation and evaluation of prototypes and/or working mock-ups to ensure design requirements.

KNOWLEDGE OF:

1. Equipment space and load bearing requirements
2. Equipment power, ventilation, and control requirements
3. Function and limitations of the prototype and/or mock-ups
4. Client approval of UI mock-ups (touchpanel, keypad, mobile)

SKILL IN:

1. Sketching design ideas
2. Understanding and using test equipment
3. Documenting the test outcome and/or sample evaluation and obtaining signoff
4. Researching changes in codes, regulations, and standards
5. Testing the validity of new technologies in the design

Domain 3 Design Documentation

Task 1: Create a proposal (bill of material, resource list, and labor products) based on the cost estimate by generating appropriate documentation in order to communicate the requirements of the project.

KNOWLEDGE OF:

1. General knowledge of all trades, sub-contractors, and other design professionals and their responsibilities
2. Relevant product knowledge, incl. interconnection and interaction
3. Subsystem knowledge, incl. interconnection and interaction

SKILL IN:

1. Generating details related to equipment, parts, and materials
2. Describing assemblies and sub-assemblies

Task 2: Generate electronic system plans for distribution to relevant parties by preparing or modifying architectural plans in order to determine the location of devices and wire routes, including installation and construction notes.

KNOWLEDGE OF:

1. Accepted building codes (local, national)
2. Drawing legends, icon definition, and usage (ANSI-J-STD-710)
3. Fundamental ergonomics (Dreyfuss Human Factors, etc.)
4. Product placement criteria
5. Serviceability and usability
6. Drawing layers
7. Installation guidelines and criteria
8. Document revision control
9. Interior design (aesthetic considerations, furniture layout)
10. Site considerations and traffic patterns

SKILL IN:

1. Reading and annotating drawings
2. Interpreting installation guidelines and criteria
3. Creating plan drawings
4. Product placement (i.e., user interfaces, components, equipment mounting, speaker layout, etc.)

Task 2: Generate electronic system plans for distribution to relevant parties by preparing or modifying architectural plans in order to determine the location of devices and wire routes, including installation and construction notes.

KNOWLEDGE OF:

1. Accepted building codes (local, national)
2. Drawing legends, icon definition, and usage (CEA/CEDIA/InfoComm J-710)
3. Fundamental ergonomics (Dreyfuss Human Factors, etc.)
4. Product placement criteria
5. Serviceability and usability
6. Drawing layers
7. Installation guidelines and criteria
8. Document revision control
9. Interior design (aesthetic considerations, furniture layout)
10. Site considerations and traffic patterns

SKILL IN:

1. Reading and annotating drawings
2. Interpreting installation guidelines and criteria
3. Creating plan drawings
4. Product placement (i.e., user interfaces, components, equipment mounting, speaker layout, etc.)

Task 3: Generate block diagram (single-line drawing) by showing basic system level interconnection between components and sub-systems in order to troubleshoot and illustrate signal flow and functionality.

KNOWLEDGE OF:

1. Concepts of signal flow and control nomenclature
2. Flow charts in order to create block diagrams
3. Components used in system
4. Cables and terminations

SKILL IN:

1. Generating block diagrams
2. Appropriate drawing/drafting skills
3. Organizing layout and annotating for clarity of presentation

Task 4: Create cable documentation (i.e., cabling plan and schedule) by describing the origin, destination, and type of each wire along with associated devices for distribution to associated trades.

KNOWLEDGE OF:

1. Cable types, outlets/inlets, connectors, back boxes
2. Connection of all sub-systems
3. Signal types
4. Cable characteristics
5. Trades involved
6. Local codes, regulations, and standards
7. Wire management practices

SKILL IN:

1. Using electrical formulas to calculate wire specifications
2. Specifying appropriate cable types (i.e., fire ratings, class, shielding, etc.)
3. Specifying connectors and connectorization

Task 5: Generate point-to-point wiring diagram by describing the specific input-output, wire and connector types, and method of interconnection in order to document how the components will be connected.

KNOWLEDGE OF:

1. Concepts of signal flow and control nomenclature
2. Components used in system
3. Cables, connectors, pinouts, terminations, and color codes
4. Back-panel layout of all devices in the system
5. Basic point-to-point information including symbols, grounding, voltage requirements, and other safety related information

SKILL IN:

1. Generating point-to-point drawings
2. Referencing point-to-point to cable schedule
3. Applying electrical and safety codes
4. Organizing layout and annotating for clarity of presentation
5. Detailing cable connector, pinouts, terminations, and color code requirements
6. Defining drawing layers (e.g., audio, video, control, RF, power, etc)

Task 6: Compile and re-generate as-built drawings and Operations/ Maintenance manuals by updating all post-installation construction documents.

KNOWLEDGE OF:

1. Red-lining techniques
2. Change orders
3. Project history

SKILL IN:

1. Creating and managing archive files
2. Reading construction documents
3. Version control
4. Recording setup parameters

Task 7: Prepare test specifications to verify system performance and functionality.

KNOWLEDGE OF:

1. Functions and limitations of test equipment
2. Process of evaluating entire system
3. Thorough understanding of the finished project
4. Setup parameters and performance specifications

SKILL IN:

1. Verifying that the design requirements were satisfied
2. Creating a quality control and assurance checklist
3. Making qualitative assessments and inspections
4. Preparing test reports
5. Interpreting the results of the tests

Domain 4 Design Management

Task 1: Assess the impact of change orders on the overall design.

KNOWLEDGE OF:

1. Technical limitations of all associated equipment within the system
2. Comprehensive understanding of original design intent
3. Impact of industry factors (i.e., new technologies, back orders, codes and standards, etc.)
4. Impact of organizational factors (i.e., internal vs. external resources, etc.)
5. Impact of customer factors (i.e., color preference, budget)

SKILL IN:

1. Recalculating budget costs
2. Analyzing how different solution options affect the design
3. Consulting with clients, installers, and other design professionals
4. Recalculating resource requirements for impacted work packages

Task 2: Monitor and document progress of the project to ensure design compliance.

KNOWLEDGE OF:

1. Assigned responsibilities of the contractors and sub-contractors
2. Existence of key project milestones
3. Communication plan
4. Original design intentions

SKILL IN:

1. Documenting progress
2. Inspecting installation progress by conducting periodic site visits
3. Initiating periodic status reports
4. Maintaining communication log
5. Generating, reviewing, and approving submittals

JOB TASK ANALYSIS (EXAM BLUEPRINT)

International (English)

This professional certification is for an individual with 3 or more years of experience in the field; designing, configuring and troubleshooting residential computer networks.

NOTE: This is the master document on which the exam is built. CEDIA resources such as classes, books, and online training are designed to support this body of knowledge. Please refer to the **ESC-N Exam Prep Resources** document to find which resources support each area of study.

CEDIA
ESC-N

Domain 1 Network Infrastructure

Task 1: Install communications cabling in the home using industry standards and recommended practices in order to create a robust, reliable network infrastructure.

KNOWLEDGE OF:

1. ANSI/TIA 570-C
2. ANSI/TIA 606-B
3. Cable terminations: Fiber Optic, Cat6A, Cat5e (TIA T568-A&B), Coaxial
4. Alternate carrier technologies
5. Power over Ethernet (PoE)
6. Running and landing cabling in a residential environment

Task 2: Perform the required level of cabling test procedures in order to ensure system performance meets or exceeds design specifications and client expectations.

KNOWLEDGE OF:

1. Test equipment: Verification, Qualification, & Certification
2. Wire-mapping
3. Signal attenuation
4. Cross Talk: NEXT, FEXT, PSNEXT, ELFEXT, PSELFEXT, AXT
5. Skew/Propagation delay
6. Operating network/cable testing equipment
7. Interpreting the results of advanced cable testing procedures
8. Applying test results in order develop solutions for cabling issues

Task 3: Secure the infrastructure by evaluating and fortifying all network cabling locations (patch panels, wiring drops, NID, etc.) in order to ensure client privacy and information security.

KNOWLEDGE OF:

1. Outlets
2. Patch panels
3. NID/demarc/aux disconnect
4. Installing secure hardware at patch panel and outlet locations
5. Securing/protecting external cable runs

Task 4: Design a wired network infrastructure using appropriate communications cabling that meets the performance requirements of the client in order to ensure long term operation and reliability.

KNOWLEDGE OF:

1. Cable performance specifications: attenuation, bandwidth, etc.
2. Power over Ethernet devices and operation (PoE)
3. Evaluating and specifying cabling based on cable performance vs. device/system requirements
4. Utilizing new/alternative tech to distribute network communications throughout an existing home, including powerline and coaxial protocols

Domain 2 Network Configuration

Task 1: Understand the OSI model, how it applies to the network, and how to use this knowledge to efficiently and effectively troubleshoot and resolve network related issues.

KNOWLEDGE OF:

1. The seven layers of the OSI model
2. The purpose of each of the seven layers
3. Using the OSI model to understand what layer an issue falls under
4. Network troubleshooting theory and procedures

Task 2: Implement a Local Area Network using IP addressing best practices, sub-netting, and routing in order to ensure proper network functionality and long term reliability.

KNOWLEDGE OF:

1. LANs
2. WANs
3. Subnets
4. Gateways
5. System documentation
6. MAC addresses
7. IP addressing
8. Routing: Network Address Translation (NAT)
9. DHCP configuration
10. Implementing IP addressing schemes
11. Configuration of subnets and gateways
12. Documentation of system device addresses
13. Using MAC address reservation to statically assign an address through DHCP
14. Define how data packets are transmitted between LANs and WANs

Task 3: Implement a network that meets the performance requirements of all client devices in order to ensure proper functionality and long term reliability.

KNOWLEDGE OF:

1. TCP
2. UDP
3. IP
4. Common internet services: SSH, FTP, HTTP, streaming media
5. Bandwidth and throughput: bits and bytes
6. Media storage and distribution
7. Defining bandwidth as it pertains to networking
8. Determining if available bandwidth meets requirements for streaming services
9. Determining if UDP or TCP is required for a given application

Domain 3 Wireless Networking

Task 1: Survey and analyze the RF spectrum using available wireless networking tools in order to ensure performance and troubleshoot problems in a residential environment.

KNOWLEDGE OF:

1. RF spectrum
2. Available RF spectrum analysis tools
3. Performing a comprehensive wireless site survey
4. Interpreting the results of an RF spectrum site survey
5. Utilizing gathered data to design, configure, or troubleshoot a residential wireless network

Task 2: Apply knowledge of existing wireless communication protocols (802.11a/b/g/n) in order to specify the proper hardware in a residential wireless networking application.

KNOWLEDGE OF:

1. Wireless protocols: eg. WiFi - 802.11(x), ZigBee, A-wave, etc.
2. Wireless network components: router, access point, repeater, antenna
3. Installation of wireless hardware: connection, placement, and aesthetics
4. Specification of necessary hardware to meet performance and aesthetic requirements of a project

Task 3: Ensure reliability, security, and consistent performance of the wireless portion of a residential network by proper configuration of the SSID, channel, encryption standards and security settings.

KNOWLEDGE OF:

1. Wireless SSIDs
2. Available wireless channels and selection criteria
3. Wireless encryption standards
4. Configuration of wireless networking hardware
5. Creating secure network passwords

Task 4: Optimize the wireless network by implementing multiple access points and wireless network controllers in order to accommodate mobile devices as control interfaces and media streaming sources.

KNOWLEDGE OF:

1. Wireless controllers
2. Devices roaming
3. Access Points
4. Bridging techniques
5. Setup of wireless network controllers
6. Specifying the correct network topology for a large scale wireless deployment
7. Configuration of multiple wireless access points within the same network

Domain 4 Network Design

Task 1: Implement network segmentation within a residential setting through the use of VLANs and QoS in order to maximize performance of multiple client devices.

KNOWLEDGE OF:

1. Virtual Local Area Networks
2. Quality of Service:Bandwidth, ports, DSCP, Class of Service
3. VLAN Implementation: tagging, port membership, and trunking
4. Implementing QoS protocols

Task 2: Configure a home network with remote access through the use of VPN and port management in order to safeguard client information and allow interaction from external locations.

KNOWLEDGE OF:

1. Dynamic DNS
2. Virtual Private Networks
3. Port forwarding and port translation (PAT)
4. Network security: hardware, software, wetware, and other threats
5. Remote network troubleshooting
6. Configuration of VPNs
7. Setup of dynamic DNS
8. Implementation of port forwarding and port translation
9. Providing appropriate network security through the use of hardware, software and client education
10. Utilizing available troubleshooting tools to diagnose and repair client systems remotely

Task 3: Secure a home network using available hardware and software tools in order to protect client privacy and information from internal and external threats.

KNOWLEDGE OF:

1. Physical security: wiring locations, demarc, outlet access
2. Username/password (credentials) best practices
3. Wetware: viruses, spyware, client education
4. Segmentation: VLANs, port management
5. Firewalls
6. Remote Access security considerations
7. Configuration of firewall settings
8. Update and configuration of antivirus and security patches
9. Ensuring the use of strong passwords
10. Educating clients to be aware of security threats
11. Fortifying equipment locations and wiring drops
12. Applying VLAN and sub-netting configurations to segment the network for security concerns

HDMI

INTRODUCTION TO HDMI

History of HDMI

The HDMI interface has been around since early 2002 and has changed how people watch television. DVI (Digital Visual Interface) was a pre-cursor to HDMI and used in many computer displays since 1999. The HDMI 1.0 specification was designed to improve upon DVI by using a smaller connector, adding support for audio, boasting richer colors and utilizing consumer electronic control (CEC) functions. The HDMI specification describes both the physical connection, in terms of connector style and pin-outs, as well as the signals transmitted by and received by HDMI devices. The signal includes things such as content protection, resolution, colour depth and frame rate.

Overview of the Cable

An HDMI connector is shown in Figure 1. It is a "D-Sub" connector style.

The cable carries three TMDS data channels (Transition Minimized Differential Signaling – the technology that allows DVI and HDMI to send high-speed digital data), one for each Red, Green and Blue signal. TMDS data includes both video and audio information, and each channel

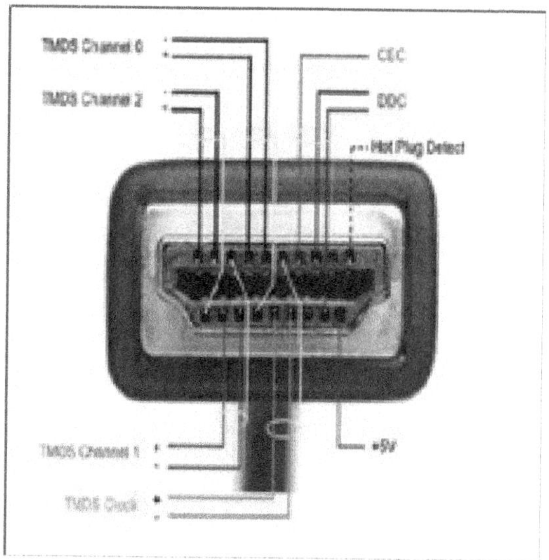

Figure 1 *HDMI Connector*

has three separate lines for positive (+) values, negative (-) values, and a ground or data shield. TMDS is a type of low voltage differential signaling (LVDS).

An LVDS carries a 300 mV signal peak-to-peak into a 100-ohm twisted-pair. It uses a twisted pair for noise reduction and a separate shield around each video pair to minimize crosstalk.

With the Hot Plug Detect (HPD) signal, the sink indicates its presence to the source device. Hot plug detect is the first step in source device recognizing a sink has been connected. The sink can toggle the hot plug detect signal to reset the HDMI connection.

Display Data Channel (DDC) is a communication interface that provides a back channel from the sink to the source to indicate events like hot plug detect. In addition, an Extended Display Identification Data (EDID) query carried on the DDC channel prompts the display to respond with its manufacturer name, model number and display capabilities to the source device. EDID describes the TV's capabilities to the source device for example audio and video formats, lip sync delays etc. The source can then select the output in accordance with what the display supports. One key area of interoperability is for HDMI devices to communicate this EDID data via the DDC channel.

The Consumer Electronics Control (CEC) channel is used for sending command and control data between connected devices, allowing a user to control multiple CEC-enabled devices with one remote. It is important to note implementation of CEC is optional on cables although wiring is mandatory.

CEC is proprietary to HDMI and communication protocols can be shared across different brands if implemented in a compliant manner.

Labeling Guidelines

All cables according to HDMI LLC must conform to one of the five types listed below. The installer and the system designer can use the labels below to procure the right cables for a job. The labels define capabilities and performance characteristics of the cable and there is no need to rely on arcane version numbers as done in the past. HDMI adopters are no longer allowed to use version numbers in the labeling, packaging, or promotion of any cable product. Effective from 2012, all non-cable products cannot make any reference to HDMI version numbers according to HDMI LLC.

Standard HDMI cables support up to 1080p 24 fps 8 bit color and have been tested to perform at speeds up to 75 MHz or 2.25 Gbps (gigabits per second). High Speed Cables are tested to perform at speeds of 340 MHz bandwidth or up to 10.2Gbps for compliant support of 2160p 24fps 8 bit color or 2160p 60fps 8 bit color at 4:2:0 Chroma subsampling. This is the highest bandwidth currently certifiable by HDMI (as of Aug 2015) on a HDMI cable. HDMI Ethernet channel was introduced with version 1.4. It can transmit data up to 100 Mbps (megabits per second) and supports all the networking formats as a normal Ethernet.

Standard HDMI Automotive cables are dedicated cables for use within automobiles and have a different type of connector but the cable construction and performance remain similar.

HDMI DESIGN AND INITIALIZATION SEQUENCE

Basic Design of HDMI

HDMI-compliant devices can be categorized into 3 types: sources, sinks and repeaters. Each device has one or more receiver(s) and/or transmitter(s), or it may contain both a receiver and a transmitter.

The source sends the content to be displayed. Examples of sources include set-top boxes, media servers, Blu-ray disc players, and computer graphic cards. A source only has an HDMI transmitter.

The sink receives the content from the source and provides it to the display so it can be viewed. Examples of a sink device include TVs and digital projectors. A sink can have one or more HDCP/HDMI receivers.

A repeater accepts content, decrypts it, then re-encrypts and finally re-transmits the data. A repeater may also perform some signal processing, such as up-converting video into a higher-resolution format, or splitting out the audio portion of the signal. Repeaters have both HDMI inputs and outputs. Examples include A/V receivers that separate and amplify the audio signal while also retransmitting the video for display on a TV. A repeater can also transmit the protected content to multiple outputs for simultaneous display on several screens.

Figure 2 *HDMI Cable Types*

HDMI Initialization Sequence

During the authentication process, a source device and a sink device - exchange their unique set of keys to determine the highest resolution (best possible format), correct audio outputs, and HDCP compliance. The connection process begins when the source outputs a +5V signal on pin 18 to the sink, which sends back the +5V signal to the source on pin 19, which is the hot plug detect pin. If the hot plug is asserted, the source will read the capabilities of the sink device (see Figure 3). The capabilities are listed in the sink's EDID, which contains a multitude of information, including the acceptable video format(s), audio formats, and lip-sync delays.

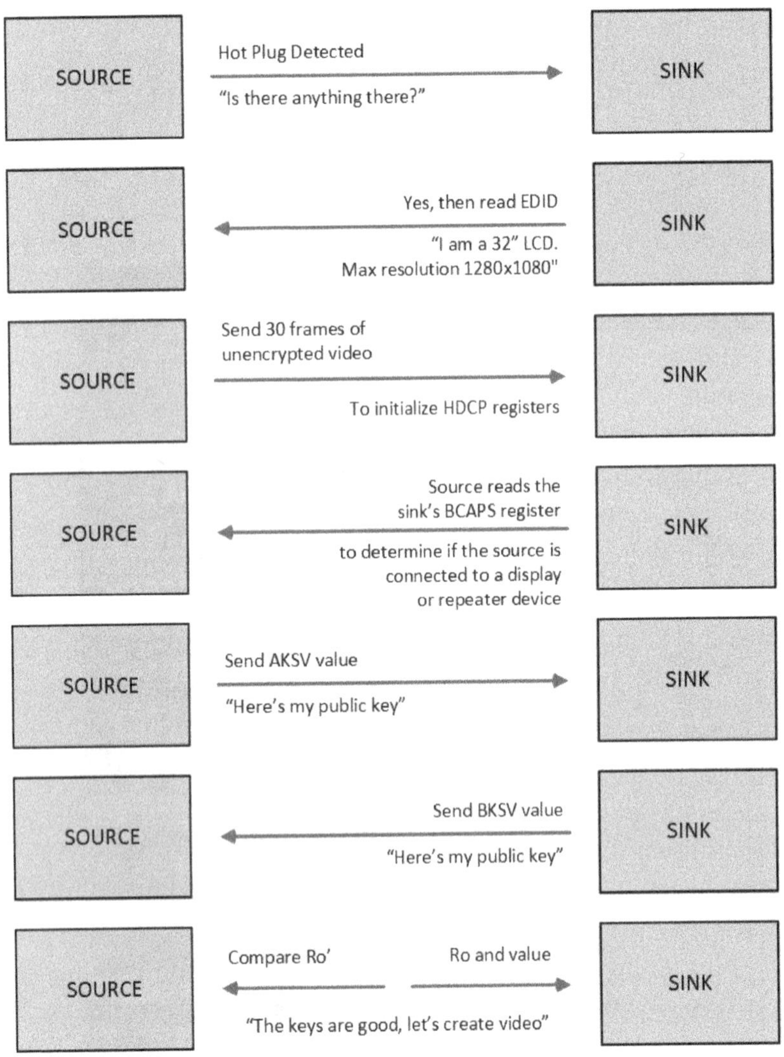

Figure 3 *HDMI Initialization Sequence*

After the EDID is read properly, the source will send about 30 frames of unencrypted video to initialize the HDCP register of the sink device. The source then typically reads the sink's HDCP BCAPS register to determine if the downstream device it is connected to is a display device or a repeater device. Reading the BCAPS register is important because the repeater bit value is used in the calculation of the Ro value. Ro is a register value used to compare the source and sink and determine whether the HDCP authentication has been completed successfully.

The source will then send its public key (AKSV) and read the sink's public key (BKSV). In addition, specific timing requirements have to be met. For example, the source has to allow at least 100 milliseconds after writing the AKSV to the sink device before reading the Ro value. The first part of HDCP authentication is completed successfully when the source reads the Ro' value from the sink device and it matches the Ro value calculated by the source. If there is a mismatch between Ro of the source and Ro' of the display device, the source will repeat the first part of HDCP authentication. The characteristic flashing seen in interoperability problems is the HDMI source sending the 30 frames of unencrypted video. The HDMI source will then set the Encryption Enable and begin encrypting the content. The source will continue to monitor encryption status using a periodic read of the Ri value.

When there is a repeater device involved in an installation, the initialization sequence and HDCP authentication is much more complex. The source has to ensure that all of the devices downstream from the repeater device are HDCP-compliant. The first part of the HDCP authentication process is the same, but the repeater device has to incorporate the public keys of all of the downstream devices into one register.

The repeater device has a maximum amount of time in which to collect the keys from the downstream devices, and some repeaters can handle only a limited number of downstream devices. If the repeater is able to handle all of the devices, it will calculate a V' value using the public keys of those devices. The source will calculate a similar V value with the same public keys. The two values will be compared, and if they match, the authentication is successful.

HDCP's purpose is to prevent users from accessing high definition content during transmission from a source device to a sink device (i.e. from a set-top box to a TV). Each HDCP-capable device has 40 keys, and HDCP allows sources, sinks, and repeaters to be connected in a tree-shaped topology with up to seven levels and 127 devices. HDCP can sometimes cause handshaking problems in which devices cannot establish a connection, especially with older high- definition displays or source devices. Problems are almost always in the source device, according to HDMI LLC, and tend to arise in one major area of implementation. Sources have to support a function called "authenticate forever," which in layman's terms means the source must consistently send a signal inquiring whether its HDMI input is selected, even while another input is in use. If a source device times out and stops inquiring, an HDCP authentication failure will most likely result.

INSTALLATION BEST PRACTICES

Distribution Best Practices

Long-Haul Cables

Before we start to discuss best practices for long-haul cabling, it is important to know how digital video signals are affected over long cable lengths. As cable length increases, image quality (signal integrity) is perceived to be perfect until a certain length. Beyond that length, the image either degrades in quality (flashing, sparkly dropouts and/or loss of sync) or disappears all together. This is known as the "cliff effect". This is depicted in Figure 4. Even before the cable length reaches the "cliff", data errors are already occurring in transmission. The reason we don't see the errors is because there is a built-in error correction technology used in digital transmission. The picture will still be corrected by the EQ in the sink device as long as the error rate is below the threshold. The signal recovery mechanism will fail once it exceeds the capability of the display.

Inter/Intra-Pair Skew

HDMI uses twisted pair cables, which are subject to two types of skews that can create timing errors and cause data drop-outs. The two types of skew are intra-pair skew and inter-pair skew. Intra-pair skew is the time differential between the two wires making up itself, while inter-pair skew is the time differential between separate twisted pair lines in the cable assembly. Total allowable intra-pair skew is only about 4.8 picoseconds, and inter-pair skew should not exceed 7.2 nanoseconds. Because of these small tolerances, HDMI cable construction is of important significance to installers. Some attributes to pay attention to include the cable gauge, cable material, and its impedance.

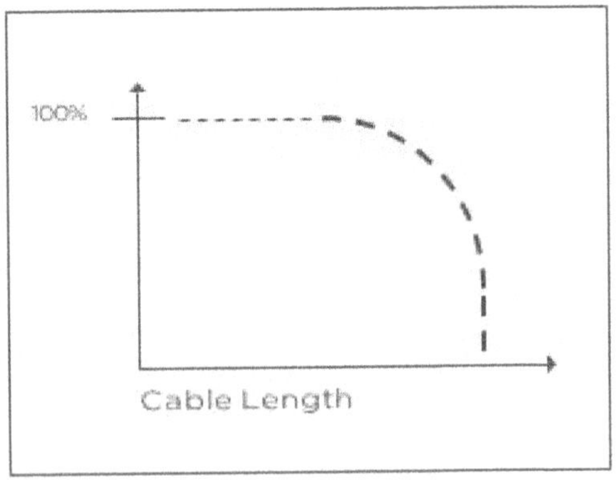

Figure 4 *Cliff Effect*

Since allowable skew is fixed and the percentage error in cables (normally measured per meter) is constant, longer cables are more difficult to manufacture. Also, it is worth noting that cabling is a component of the overall system and one has to take into account the percent error between all source and sync devices including any switches, splitters or matrix devices.

Active Cables And How To Pull HDMI Cables

Using cables with active electronics can boost and clean up the signal and almost double the range of a copper twisted cable. Cable runs of up to 30 meters are typical for this type of solution, which can either be implemented through an HDCP-compliant repeater or incorporated into the manufacture of the cable itself. Active cables embed signal-enhancement electronics in the cable itself. High speed channels in HDMI are unidirectional so care should be taken during installation to ensure proper directionality because a lossy signal will need boosting at the same end of the cable. Most of the solutions in this category require external power. In fact, HDMI Licensing recommends active (powered) extenders/boosters and recommends that they be powered by a separate power supply. It is also important to note that there are very few high- speed capable active cables in the market at this time.

When pulling HDMI cables, remember the amount of data flowing in the wire and treat it gently. Do not yank the cable or twist connectors as the tolerances are tight. It is important to note that HDMI Licensing does not currently support field terminating products because of stringent skew and timing tolerances. For in-wall installations, pull-through socks are available that will protect the connector as the cable is pulled through the wall or conduit.

If using an active cable, it is also recommended that the cable is run inside a conduit or has some future accessibility. As active cables utilize electronics, if the cable's integrated circuit fails, then the only way to repair the cable is to replace it. Conduit will enable one to easily replace the defective cable without causing unnecessary holes/damage to existing walls. Be sure to follow all state and local codes when installing conduit. Lastly, please be aware of products that draw power from the +5 volt pin of the HDMI cable. A product that draws power from the HDMI cable may fail when components and active components in the cable or extenders are all drawing from the same source.

Basic HDMI Tests

An eye pattern test is used to test the quality of the HDMI signal by the Authorized Test Centers (ATCs). The digital signal from HDMI resembles an eye pattern on an oscilloscope. The eye pattern test shows many aspects of the digital signal. Figure 5 shows a sample eye pattern test result. The following are the primary characteristics of the test:

Signal Amplitude: The height of the eye represents the signal amplitude. It should not become smaller in height than the marked diamond-shaped area in the middle. Otherwise, the signal will be too small for the display to recover.

Timing Jitter: The rising and falling edges of digital bits do not always appear at the same time. This is known as "jitter." The internal width of the eye can't become narrower than the diamond area in the middle or the display won't recover data. In other words, a wide opening, thin line, and symmetrical shape are indicators of a high-quality HDMI cable. Any area of the pattern that touches the shape inside the eye called the "mask" represents a failure.

Certain cable manufacturers include eye pattern test results with their packaging and others can provide them upon request. Installers must be careful to ensure the test results displayed are relevant – for the correct length, frequency and resolution because manufacturers do not implement HDMI the same way in their respective devices.

Bit Error Rate

Bit error rate (BER) testing shows the real number of bad bits a display could receive under a given condition. The higher the number, the worse the signal quality. BER testing uses a signal generator to output billions of data bits, sending them to the cable and receiving them from the other end of the cable. Afterward, the received data is compared bit-by- bit with the sent data. The results will show the total number of error bits in a given period of time.

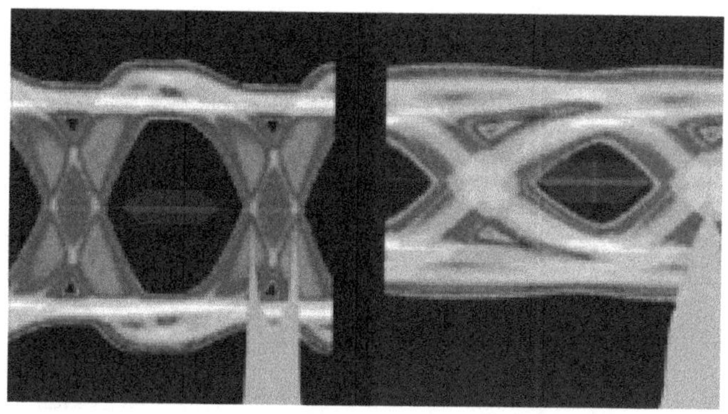

Figure 5 *The "Eye" Pattern*

Cat 5/6 And HDMI Extenders

Cable runs of up to 100 meters can be achieved by sending the HDMI signal over Cat 5/6 networking cable using specially designed adapters. Unlike HDMI cables, Cat 6 cables can be field-terminated to a precise distance. Some single Cat 5/6 solutions use compression with a sink-side box reconstituting the HDMI signal from a decompressed signal. This can result in compression artifacts and reduced dynamic range/contrast. This can be corrected by using two Cat 5/6 cables per HDMI connection. The following are some best practices to follow when considering this solution:

- A complete HDMI extender system consists of a "transmitter" and a "receiver". Both are required.
- A/V receivers that include HDMI "repeating" perform better than normal "switching" A/V receivers.
- The power supply is normally connected to the transmitter. Depending on the circumstances, better performance may be achieved by connecting the power supply at the receiver end.
- The two runs of Cat 5 must be the same length. Siamese Cat 5 cables work the best.
- Always know the gear before designing it into a system and don't try combinations on a jobsite without testing them first.
- Maintain twists as close as possible to termination (no more than .5" untwisted).
- Make gradual bends (radius should be a minimum of four times the cable diameter or 1").
- Use lubricant for tough pulls and grommets with metal studs.
- Where possible, use conduit for running cables.
- Shielded cables will minimize interference when there are many cables in a single conduit.
- Be careful and gentle when running cables for HDMI as the cable needs to carry lots of data.
- Double crimp CAT terminations.
- Use high quality cables and connectors.

Also be aware that sharp bends can cause permanent damage to the geometry of the cable and may result in transmission failure.

HDMI Fiber Solutions

HDMI over fiber optic cable offers several advantages in long-haul applications as these cables can transmit the signal more than 60 meters. Fiber is also immune to electromagnetic interference. Some of the disadvantages of fiber optic cable are that it cannot carry power and that it requires a box connected to an external power source. It is also not easy to achieve two-way communications as light travels in one direction. Some fiber solutions are also brittle and difficult to terminate. To solve these problems, manufacturers have used copper wires running alongside the fiber cables, which can weaken the fiber advantages. Some things to keep in mind when looking for fiber optic solutions are:

- Look for HDCP compliance
- Ensure that effective distance is meets the desired needs and field termination is possible
- Look for easy conduit pull (small cable head)
- Make sure the fiber system will carry the bandwidth required. Just because it is fiber does not mean it will carry the necessary data rate. This is typically due to the limitation of the electronics at either end more than the fiber itself.

HDMI Switching And Splitters

There are many types of HDMI switches available on the market. HDMI switches have multiple inputs and a single output. Longer runs are possible via active electronics. An external power supply is required by HDMI LLC, and passive switches are deemed non- compliant.

HDMI splitters mirror one HDMI source to several displays. They are primarily used in sports bars or in retail stores although they have become more common in multi-room residential installations. An external power supply is required, and it can provide up to 127 outputs with HDCP. It is important to note that this is entirely dependent on source HDCP keys supporting this number of downstream devices and splitters supporting the appropriate level of cascading.

HDMI matrix switchers combine both the switch and splitter functions. They have multiple inputs and outputs. An external power supply is required, and longer runs are possible via active electronics.

Here are some features to look for when choosing an HDMI switcher:

- Right number of ports needed for the job
- Automatic and manual switching
- Make sure the device lists the features you want it to support (i.e. 3D, 1080p). HDMI LLC has moved to labels that must list the features not the version numbers.
- HDCP Version 1.2 (or 2.2) pass-through. The higher the version supported the better.

Active switches, Cat 5/6, and fiber solutions can be chained together in combination, but doing so can significantly increase the jitter, adversely affecting the signal quality. Re-clockers can be used to increase input jitter tolerance.

Interoperability Best Practices

Interoperability issues are still plentiful and can create challenges for the installer. According to HDMI, most of the problems are limited to first-generation devices now. The most common compatibility problem is the HDCP repeater function's failure to perform reliably in all types of usage scenarios. Source devices need to properly implement the HDCP repeater function if a repeater (A/V receiver) will be installed in the system; otherwise, switching between source devices will result in an authentication failure.

HDCP can cause issues connecting multiple screens to a device. The source device creates a key for each screen, but the number of keys it can create simultaneously varies from device to device. In addition, sources need to support an HDCP function called "authenticate forever." In layman's terms, the source must consistently send a signal inquiring whether its HDMI input is selected, even while another input is in use. If a source device times out and stops inquiring, an HDCP authentication failure will probably result. Since 2006, HDMI has mandated compliance testing for all products implementing HDCP. Lastly, CEDIA recommends turning off the CEC as it may interfere with other program devices installed and is usually not cross- brand compatible.

HDCP 2.2 was released in Feb 2013 and is a newer content protection system that requires both hardware and software function. HDCP 2.2 is not limited to HDMI but can function over USB, MHL, Display port, etc.....HDCP 2.2 is required for UltraHD/4K functionality and all electronics in the chain require HDCP 2.2 authentication for the system to support UltraHD/4K resolutions.

HDCP 2.2 downstream devices (AV receiver, sound bar or display) will support earlier HDCP upstream devices (Blu-ray player) for content such as 1080p but an HDCP 2.2 source device will need all downstream devices to be HDCP 2.2 enabled for HDCP 2.2 content to be authenticated and displayed.

HDCP 2.2 requires authentication within 20ms so extra care must be taken during installation to ensure system stability and function.

Following the recommended installation practices will reduce the installer's or system designer's need to troubleshoot the system in the first place. It is recommended to pre-qualify the HDMI system prior to installation and to check specifications and compatibility with legacy equipment in the client's home. In addition, it is recommended to report installation issues to HDMI LLC as they work with manufacturers to correct compliance issues and recall non-compliant products. In the next edition of the HDMI series, we will examine EDID sequencing. EDID ISSUES

The acceptable video format(s), audio formats and lip-sync delays are listed in the sink's EDID. The source can then select the output in accordance with the best possible format the sink supports. One key area of interoperability is for HDMI devices to communicate this EDID data via the DDC channel. If the sink device has its EDID coded improperly or if a source or a repeater device fails to read it correctly, the system will fail to select the proper audio and video modes.

According to HDMI LLC, it is a good idea for installers to take a small, reliable 1080p set along on installation calls to troubleshoot for this problem. If errors are present (improper resolution etc.), the problem is most likely the source device and may be resolved with a firmware update of the device or replaced with a compliant source device.

UNDERSTANDING EDID

EDID Issues

The acceptable video format(s), audio formats, and lip-sync delays are listed in the sink's EDID. The source can then select the output in accordance with the best possible format the sink supports. One key area of interoperability is for HDMI devices to communicate this EDID data via the DDC channel. If the sink device has its EDID coded improperly, or if a source or repeater device fails to read it correctly, the system will fail to select the proper audio and video modes. According to HDMI LLC, it is a good idea for installers to take a small, reliable 1080p set along to troubleshoot this problem. If it doesn't look right, the problem is most likely the source device and may be resolved with a firmware update, or by replacing that device.

Introduction to EDID

The HDMI initialization sequence consists of three activities: connection detection (hot plug), Plug and Play (EDID), and content protection (HDCP). EDID was created by VESA (Video Electronics Standards Association) to support Plug and Play. EDID resides on a small chip called EEPROM in the HDMI sink or the input of an HDMI repeater device. All sink devices compliant with the HDMI specification are required to implement EDID. HDMI EDIDs typically have two 128-byte blocks. The second block is the CEA extension block, and is required for HDMI as it contains display- specific information.

As described previously in Introduction to HDMI and HDMI Design and Initialization Sequence, Display Data Channel (DDC) is a communication interface that provides a back channel from the sink to the source to indicate events like hot plug detect. An Extended Display Identification Data (EDID) query carried on the DDC channel prompts the display to respond with its manufacturer name, model number, and display capabilities to the source device. EDID describes the TV's capabilities to the source device – for example, audio and video formats, lip sync delays, etc.

Successful communication of the EDID data from the sink device to the source device via the DDC channel is essential for interoperability.

For a technician, having access to EDID provides two useful functions:

1. The ability to describe the supported functions of a display device.
2. The ability to use test equipment to emulate the interaction of a display with a source based on response to EDID.

The ability to describe the supported function of a display device as delivered by a manufacturer is important. While data sheets and operator manuals may be out of date, go out of print, or no longer be available, the easiest way to understand the display's capabilities is to examine the EDID. Passing the EDID into a human-readable form will give the installer an overview of any errors, for example, if a display device supports "side-by-side" 3D mode while the Blu-ray player doesn't.

Emulation of a display device using its EDID is also a useful function for installers. To determine if an A/V receiver, DVD, or HDMI switch is interoperable with a display device, using a saved EDID on the test equipment is a quick way to validate source device interoperability. This also provides a way to look for problems before a display is installed. Some set-top box (STB) manufacturers download new firmware to their equipment at midnight, and the client may find problems with the installed system the following day. Emulation of a display device with its EDID provides a way for an installer to tell the client that the display interaction was simulated with the STB originally using EDID and that the current problem is due to a new firmware download from the provider. Many manufacturers provide test equipment to emulate the EDID.

Table 1 *Sink Capabilities Read from EDID*

VESA/CEA-86 Info	HDMI Vendor-Specific Data Block
Product identification	Max TMDS rate
Product	Dual link support
Manufacturer ID Physical size of screen/aspect ratio	HDMI video timing support 3D support
Standard video timing support	3D video timing support
Custom video timing with parameters	3D structures supported
Native video timing	Separate 2D/3D video timing priorites (1st)
Video timing priorities	Deep color support
Color characteristics (XY of primaries)	Support for content types (graphics, cinema, photo, gama)
Wide gamut color	Video latency
Selectable quantization range	Audio latency

What Can Go Wrong With EDID?

Potential complications with EDID include:

- HDMI source never reads EDID, does not finish reading EDID, or does not read it properly.
- HDMI sink does not support the video format that the HDMI source is sending.
- Source may not output any video or will not output proper or optimal video.

- HDMI extender alters the downstream EDID and/or changes formats.
- HDMI source cannot read EDID and doesn't output (at least) 640x480 when EDID is unreadable.
- HDMI repeater is unable to merge a large number of EDID video timing descriptors (SVDs) from multiple downstream EDIDs.
- HDMI repeater forwards the downstream sink's EDID capabilities unmodified to the source.
- Splitter device is hard-coded with an EDID or simply takes the EDID of the first device connected.
- Sink declares a color mode of YCbCr ("color difference") in its EDID, but doesn't support both types of sampling modes (4:4:4 and 4:2:2).

If the EDID is corrupt, poorly formed, or incorrect, many audio or video problems can arise as a result. For example, the video resolution, color, or aspect ratio may not be correct. Additionally, the audio might not be in the desired format or might have the wrong number of channels.

EDID on Repeater Devices and Splitters

When an AV receiver (a repeater device) is used in a system, the EDID should show the audio from the AVR, and the video should be the "intersection" of the video data from the AVR and the sink device. The logical sequence of events when a repeater device is installed is shown in Figure 6.

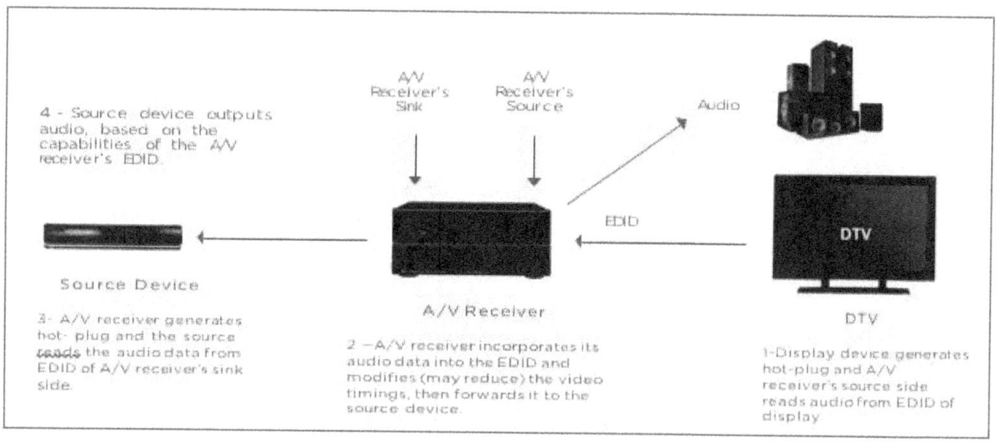

Figure 6 *EDID on an A/V Receiver*

When a splitter is used, the EDID can be one of the following: the "intersection" of the two devices, the EDID of the device connected initially, or a forced "provisioned" EDID. An example of EDID sequencing with a splitter device is shown in Figure 7.

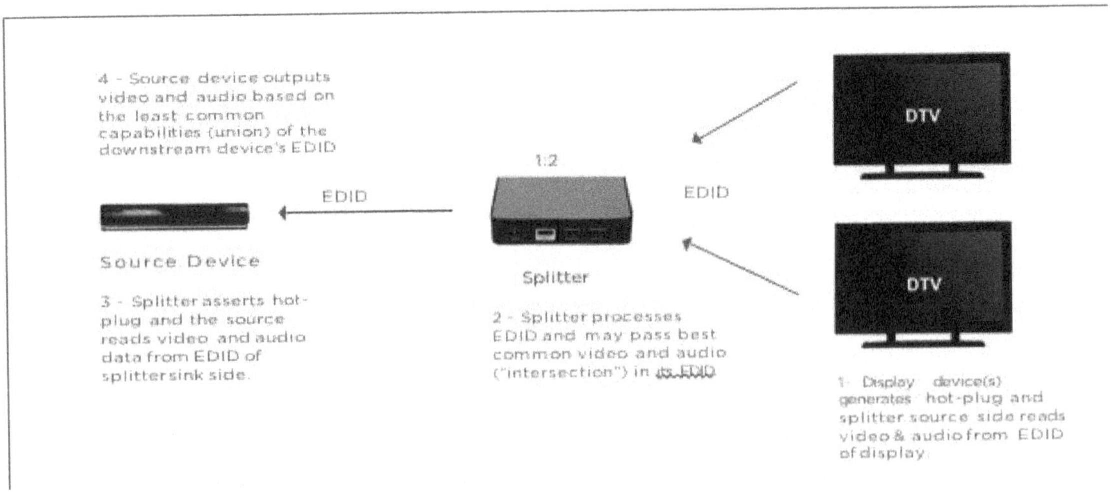

Figure 7 *EDID on a Splitter Device*

CHECKING EDID ON TEST EQUIPMENT

Connect test equipment to HDTV as shown.

- Read EDID
- Check for errors
- Verify video content
- Verify audio content
- Initiate hot plug and repeat

EDID can be loaded on a test instrument for HDMI using a computer or directly from a sink device. The EDID files are stored in XML format and can serve as a reference EDID to troubleshoot problems in the source device. For information on how to save the EDID and monitor DDC transactions, please consult the reference manual of the test equipment used. This functionality can help the technician explain to client that the display's interaction was simulated with the source using the stored EDID and the current problem is likely a result of a firmware download on the source device. It also provides a way to narrow down interoperability problems and look for faults before a display is installed. It is important to note that freeware software is available in the market that can also pass the EDID files to a human-readable form and give a description of the display's supported features.

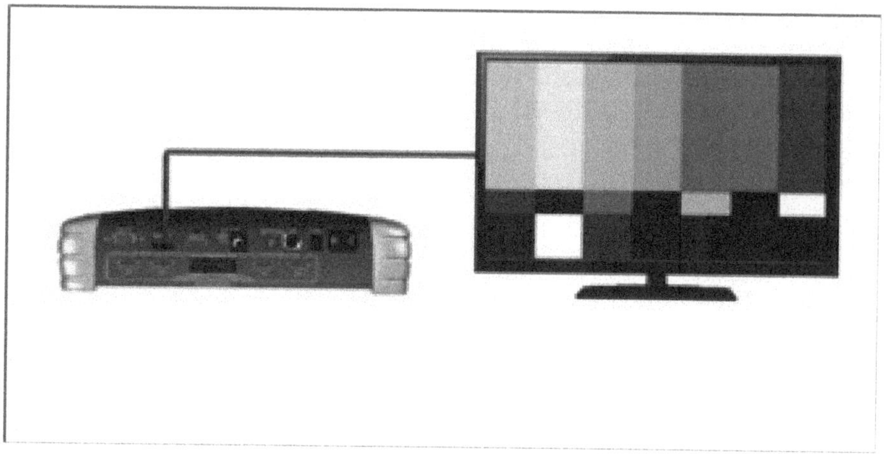

Figure 8 *Sample EDID Test Setup*

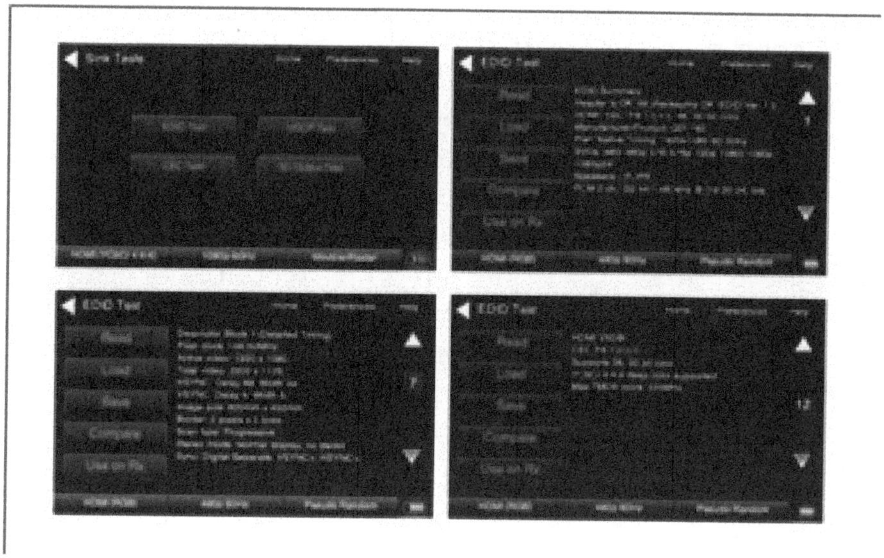

Figure 9 *Sample Screens on EDID Test Instrument*

HDMI TROUBLESHOOTING

Troubleshooting Principals

DEFINING THE PROBLEM

In order to properly identify the cause of a problem, one must first and foremost define the problem itself.

If one fails to correctly identify what aspect of a system needs to be fixed, it will be hard to get to the root of the problem. The first steps toward defining the problem include:

- Writing down the specific symptoms being observed
- Documenting all the conditions and variables that may be affecting the system

IDENTIFYING A POSSIBLE CAUSE

With a basic understanding of how an HDMI system works, the technician can make an educated guess as to the cause of the problem based upon the symptoms being observed. Listed below are four of the most common HDMI connectivity problems as well as their likely causes.

- Flashing Video - HDCP Error: If HDCP authentication fails, the source will continually attempt to authenticate the receiver device and resend the unencrypted video feed at the beginning of every attempt. HDCP handshake authentication occurs every 128 frames for HDCP 1.4 or every 20ms for HDCP 2.2.
- No Video/Hot Plug Error: If the voltage on the hot plug line is outside of the specified range (typically between 4.7 V and 5.3 V) the source will not recognize that a receiver/sink device exists and will not send any video signal.
- Incorrect Format - EDID Error: If the EDID is not processed correctly from the sink device back to the source, the source device will send an incorrect or inferior quality signal based on incorrect information about the processing capabilities of the receiver device.
- "Sparkles" or "Snow" in the Video Feed - Physical Layer Problem (Bad Cable/Connector/ Board): If an HDMI cable or a circuit board in a device is poorly manufactured or one line of the TMDS pair is a different length than the other, the information being sent will be out of sync and introduce errors into the picture.
- This situation may also occur if the system is overly complex or cables used are too long.

DIAGNOSTIC SEQUENCE

After identifying the possible causes, diagnostic procedures should focus on the cables as well as component(s) identified as a possible cause. Often there is more than one test with the test equipment that can be used to confirm that a component is the cause of the problem. Therefore, it is best to identify and use the diagnostic procedure that provides the most insight and is the most convenient to complete, as illustrated in Figure 10.

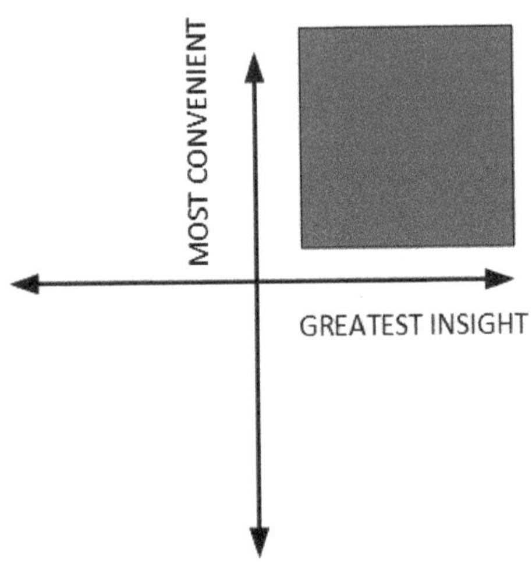

Figure 10 *Use the Diagnostic Procedure That is Most Convenient and Provides the Greatest Insight*

SIMPLIFICATION

The goal when designing an HDMI system should be to have the simplest configuration. Reconfiguring a system to a more simplified connection path will eliminate variables that can compound the problem and increase the difficulty of troubleshooting the system. As the variables (devices or cables) are removed from the signal path, remember to only make one change at a time and test the system in between the changes. If a device or cable is removed and the system begins working properly, there is a very high likelihood that the last device removed was the problem. In some cases, however, errors are additive, so there may not be a single culprit.

SUBSTITUTION AND EMULATION

Once the problem is identified, possible causes should be documented, and the troubleshooting process should be defined. At that point, actual testing should begin. When working with an HDMI system, one of the simplest ways to test the signal path is through the substitution method. Using a known good HDMI source/sink device or test equipment capable of emulating an HDMI source/sink device, by replacing components within the system, one can verify proper operation and discover the stage of the signal path where the problem is resolved.

PASSIVE MONITORING

Passively monitoring DDC (HDCP/EDID) transactions between devices in an HDMI system using test equipment will enable a technician to see the HDMI handshake between two devices without affecting it. This can be a huge advantage in identifying the root cause of HDMI handshake problems (i.e. hot plug, HDCP, and EDID problems) as well as possible permanent solutions.

CORRECTIVE MEASURES

There are a limited number of things a technician can do on-site to correct a problem. In some cases, these corrective measures only get a system working for a single instance of an interoperability problem; in other words, they are workarounds. These workarounds may not be acceptable to a client. For example, initiating a hot plug or a power cycling sequence may free up a stuck HDMI port on an HDTV, but if the HDTV exhibited that problem once, it is likely to reoccur.

Temporary Corrective Measures

- Initiate hot plug by physically disconnecting the cable and then reconnecting it. A hot plug event will cause a reread of the EDID and an HDCP re-authentication.
- Turn all devices off, then turn on equipment one at a time, starting with the most downstream sink, letting each device stabilize before turning on the next device upstream.
- Turn on repeaters only after all downstream devices have been turned on and are stable. After the repeater is stable, make sure that it is selecting an active sink before powering on an upstream device.
- Lower the video resolution to 720p or 1080i first. If this is not possible, substitute analog video or SPDIF audio cables for HDMI.

Permanent Corrective Measures

- Replace with a higher-quality cable. Make sure to choose the best cable for the client's needs. It is best to pre-test cables on the bench before installation, especially ahead of a pre-wire. Keep these new cables as short as possible.
- Add equalizer devices near the sink.
- Replace older components and devices. For example, replace an HDMI 1.3 source with an HDMI 1.4 source for pre-emphasis. Both the source and sink device may benefit from updated firmware and a newer HDCP version on later models.
- Replace HDMI extenders.
- Change HDMI ports on a component or device. HDMI ports are often not the same in terms of their transmit and receive characteristics.
- Update firmware, e.g. STBs, HDTVs, and PCs.
- Replace defective components and devices.
- Insert a switch or "correcting" device between components.

Replacing cables or equipment or updating firmware may be more involved than some of the temporary corrective measures previously discussed, but these steps are more likely to resolve the problem permanently. An important point to remember is that test equipment can confirm the root cause of a problem and verify that a solution is not simply a workaround. Test equipment can also be used to pre-qualify an HDMI system at the shop prior to an installation.

TROUBLESHOOTING WITH TEST EQUIPMENT

Test equipment can be an invaluable tool when working with HDMI systems. There are advantages to troubleshooting with test equipment which cannot be accomplished by simple trial and error. The following are some of the advantages of using test equipment

- Pre-screen products during procurement at the shop
- Pre-screen existing HDMI components in a client's home
- Pull existing device EDIDs and emulate at the shop during system prequalification
- Reduce time on-site Quick diagnosis of causes
- Higher accuracy in confirming necessity of component replacement
- Reduce the likelihood of callbacks
- High degree of accuracy in confirming reliability of solution
- Preemptively identify potential future system failures
- Test equipment may also provide the client with a test report of functionality.

The following are tests that can be performed on sink, source, or repeater device and will help to troubleshoot a system.

SINK DEVICE

- Verify if hot plug signal is high
- Verify EDID for a bad header, bad checksum, and pass/fail on compliance
- Test HDCP authentication
- Test video at EDID preferred timing with HDCP enabled
- Tests sink's support of EDID timings at primary formats:
- 1080p (24/30/50/60), 1080i (25/30), 720p (24/30/50/60)
- Test sink's handling of supported video types and sampling (YCbCr 4:2:2 and 4:4:4)
- Test for deep color if supported
- Test HDCP re-authentication following port switch Source Device
- Test HDCP authentication
- Test source's ability to respond to a known-good EDID
- Test for the maximum number of downstream devices a source can support with HDCP
- Test incoming video at various timings
- Test incoming video and verify timing, video type, and sampling (RGB, YCbCr 4:4:4 and 4:2:2)

REPEATER DEVICE

- Verify hot plug detect indication
- Verify EDID and verify whether EDID is passed through repeater and whether it is modified or not
- Test source's ability to respond to a known-good EDID
- Verify that timing (resolution) of format is passed through repeater
- If timing is passed through, verify that video is passed through without any color or sampling manipulation
- Verify HDCP authentication through repeater
- Verify whether the repeater acts as an HDCP repeater
- Verify HDCP authentication following port switch on repeater

HDMI FEATURES - INCLUDING 1.4A AND 2.0

The early HDMI specifications, including version 1.0 released in 2002 through to 1.3 in 2006, formed the basic framework for what we can call the assumed standard HDMI feature sets. It should be noted that nearly all of what is assumed as standard is in fact optional extras. Make sure the desired features are listed (I.e. 1080p, 3D, 7.1 DTS, etc.....)

Each test specification superseded the previous version and previous test specifications were no longer available. This process was changed with the introduction of version 2.0 where it runs concurrently with version 1.4.

HDMI versions 1.0 through to 1.3 supports the following features which are not listed below:

- sRGB color
- YCbCr 4:2:2/4:4:4
- 8 channel LPCM audio
- 192 kHz, 24 bit audio
- All Blu-ray Disc resolutions and Audio
- SACD with DSD support
- Deep color
- xvYCC (color support)
- lip-sync correction
- Dolby TrueHD audio
- DTS-HD Master Audio

HDMI 1.4a specification established protocols for a number of popular 3D display methods, including:

- Frame, line, or field alternative methods
- Side-by-side methods (full and half)
- 2D plus depth methods

3D video requires substantial data throughput, so a High Speed HDMI cable (with or without Ethernet) should be used, although standard HDMI cables will support the broadcast 3D formats (top and bottom, side by side).

The HDMI 1.4a and 2.0 specifications have also added support for extremely high video resolutions that go far beyond today's 1080p displays. 4K/UHD is shorthand for 4,096/3,840 lines wide by 2,160 lines high, or roughly four times the resolution of a 1080p display. Figure 11 shows the difference in resolution between common display formats and 4K/UHD.

The Audio Return Channel (ARC) in HDMI 1.4a enables a TV to send audio data "upstream" to an A/V receiver or surround audio controller, eliminating the need for any separate S/PDIF audio connection.

- An Audio Return Channel-enabled TV can either send or receive audio via HDMI, upstream or downstream, depending on system set-up and user preferences.
- LipSync functionality, introduced in HDMI 1.3, ensures that the audio stays matched to the video, automatically compensating for any processor delays whether the audio is traveling upstream or downstream.

The HDMI Ethernet Channel allows internet-enabled HDMI devices to share an internet connection via the HDMI link, with no need for a separate Ethernet cable. It also provides the connection platform that will allow HDMI-enabled components to share content between devices with speeds up to 100 Mbps.

The CEC bus is a one-wire "party line" that connects up to 10 A/V devices through standard HDMI cabling. CEC will automatically power on the appropriate products, route the DVD/Blu-ray's audio output through the A/V receiver to the attached speakers, and route the player's motion picture to the digital TV. CEC enables automatic equipment discovery and simple "one touch" operation in HDMI interfaced systems. Most installers and designers prefer to turn off this functionality, as older HDMI devices may not be cross-brand compatible. CEC however is a dedicated HDMI feature, so current HDMI devices with CEC functionality may enable a more simple solution to the use of equipment. It will not be suitable where more complex automation is required.

Figure 11 *4Kk/UHD vs Other Formats*

Additions Features of HDMI 2.0

Released in September 2013, HDMI 2.0 is an additional version to the HDMI specification. All adopter members need to agree to additional conditions as part of the HDMI 2.0 specification. HDMI adopters do not automatically become 2.0 adopters.

New features of the HDMI 2.0 specification include:

- TMDS increase from 3.4Gbps/ch to 6Gbps/ch: The increase of data rate from 3.4 Giga bits per second per channel to 6 Giga bits per second per channel allows for additional video and audio resolution.
- Rec. 2020 color: Rec 2020 is an International Telecommunication Union Standard. It offers a much wider color space than the REC 709 (HDTV) color space. Relative to the CIE 1931 color chart, REC 709 covers 35.9% of possible colors whereas REC 2020 covers 75.8%.

- Dual View: This features offers simultaneous viewing of different full screen material on the same screen. Dual view uses 3D technology with active glasses to synchronize screen data.
- 4:2:0 Chroma subsampling: This is an additional Chroma subsampling set to offer higher resolutions or frame rate at the expense of color. It takes advantage of the human eye's sensitivity of Luminance (contrast and brightness) over that of Chroma. Chroma in this instance only requires half the bandwidth of 4:4:4
- 25fps for 3D
- Up to 32 channel audio: To support immersive audio.
- 1,536kHz combined total audio bandwidth: This is actually the same as before.
- 21:9 screen ratio support
- Dynamic auto Lip-sync
- HDR Video (High Dynamic Range Video): Support allows for displaying images closer to that of the human eye. An example of this is in a situation where strong backlighting affects the foreground or subject. HDR tonally maps the image such that both the background and foreground can be more clearly seen.

HDMI Glossary of Terms

Audio Return Channel (ARC)
The audio return channel in HDMI 1.4a allows a TV to send audio data upstream to an A/V receiver, eliminating the need for a separate SPDIF audio connection. It supports the same audio formats as an SPDIF cable, which means it does not support high- definition audio or multi-channel PCM.

BCAPS Register
The source reads the sink's BCAPS register to determine whether the downstream device it is connected to is a display device or a repeater device.

CEC:
Consumer Electronics Control, One of the channels in an HDMI connection is dedicated to a set of advanced control functions, collectively known as CEC. When enabled by the manufacturer, CEC functionality allows connected devices to control each other in useful ways. For instance, a single command on a remote control can be used to play a DVD, or to launch other complex activities across multiple devices in a home theater system.

Cliff Effect
As the cable length increases, the data the cable is capable of carrying decreases. The image quality is equalized by the sink device and may be perceived to be perfect up to a certain length. Beyond that length, the image either degrades in quality or disappears all together. This is known as the "cliff effect". The cliff effect can vary based on the cable's insulation, inter/intra-pair skew, and termination of the cable connectors, among other factors.

DDC:
The Display Data Channel, one of the channels in an HDMI connection. DDC is the connection that carries the EDID signal and allows devices to assess each other's capabilities and adjust themselves accordingly. For example, a DVD player can discover the maximum resolution of the monitor it's connected to by reading the monitor's chip, and optimize its signal output to match that monitor's display capabilities. It is used for communicating EDID (Extended Display Identification Channel) information between devices.

EDID:
EDID stands for Extended Display Information Data. This is the data contained (in a small memory called EEPROM) on each DVI display or HDMI sink. The source device checks the displays DVI or HDMI port for the presence of an EDID prom and uses the information inside to optimize the output video and/ or audio format. All sink devices compliant to the HDMI specification must implement EDID.

Eye Pattern Test
Eye pattern test results graphically demonstrate transmission of a digital signal. A good test result resembles the shape of an eye.

fps:
fps stands for frames per second and is the number of individual video frames transmitted during a one second interval.

Handshake:
Handshake is the full initialization sequence used in HDMI to secure the signal prior to primary Audio and Video data being sent. Handshaking helps make clear that the intended information is both compatible and secure.

HDMI:
HDMI stands for High Definition Multimedia Interface.
HDMI is the first domestic digital transmission method to combine uncompressed Audio and Video onto one platform/standard.

HDMI Repeater:
A device that both receives and sends HDMI signals, such as an AV receiver.

HDCP:
HDCP stands for High-Bandwidth Digital content protection. This is one of the protocols used within HDMI to protect the high resolution Audio and Video signal and is vital software being available at near broadcast quality.

HPD (Hot Plug Detect)(:
HPD stands for Hot Plug Detect. This is the initial signal sent to initiate the HDMI signal.

Inter/Intra-Pair Skew
Variations in the twist of the cable, overall length of the copper cable and variations in the dielectric to insulate the wire can create an error such that positive and negative signals are skewed in time to one another.

Jitter
Deviation in or displacement of some aspect of the pulses in a high-frequency digital signal such as HDMI. This can be in terms of amplitude, or the phase timing etc.

LVDS:
Low voltage differential signaling, an electrical signaling system that can run at high speeds and carries a 300 mV signal peak-to-peak into a 100-ohm twisted-pair.

Matrix Switcher
Matrix switchers route multiple audio/video sources to multiple audio/video destinations.

Public Key(s)
The public keys (AKSV and BKSV, contained in the source and the sink respectively) are used to calculate the Ro value.

Ro Value
Ro is a register value used to compare the source and sink and determine if the HDCP authentication has been completed successfully.

Ri Value
Ri value is the recalculation of the cipher between source and display.

Sink
A device that receives an HDMI signal, such as an HDTV.

Source
A device that sends an HDMI signal, such as a DVD player or set-top box.

TMDS:
Transition-Minimized Differential Signaling, a technology for transmitting serial data at very high speeds. TMDS is a core technology used in both DVI and HDMI.

4K Resolution
Defines an image which is 4096 pixels wide by 2160 pixels high, and used in the HDMI 1.4 and 2.0specification. It is approximately 4 times the resolution of 1080p.

UHD
Commonly known as Ultra HD or Ultra High Definition. UHD defines an image which is 3860 x 2160 pixels or 7680 x 4320 pixels.
3860 x 2160 is exactly 4 times the resolution of 1080p.

V' Value
V' value is calculated when a repeater is involved in an installation. If the repeater is able to handle all of the downstream devices, it will calculate a V' value using all of the public key values of the downstream display devices. The source will calculate a similar value using the public keys. The V and V' values will be compared, and if they match, the authentication is successful.

XML
Extensible Markup Language. XML is a set of rules for encoding documents in machine-readable format.

Home Theater Recommended Practice: Audio Design

These points represent only the key elements of CEB-22 and are intended only to be a quick reference. For a complete understanding of the Recommended Practice, refer to the full original document. Also see CEDIA courses ESD131, ESD232, ESD301, ESD302, and ESD303

The Goal of Home Theater Audio is to faithfully reproduce the audio content of the source material, whether it is cinema, television, or a video game, by adhering to motion picture industry standards and making well informed decisions when dealing with design compromises.

General Performance Objectives

1. No audible coloration of the sound
2. A smooth and balanced front soundstage
3. A surround system that provides convincing envelopment
4. Intelligible dialog
5. No perceivable distortion
6. Performance consistent across entire seating area, best at primary seating
7. Accurate low frequency performance which is consistent seat to seat
8. Inaudible background noise
9. Sound isolation from adjacent spaces; both egress and ingress

Design Fundamentals

1. The room size and shape, image size, sight lines, speaker location, and seating configuration are all part of an overall system which must be designed simultaneously for best results.
2. There should be one prime seating location, optimized for both audio and video. The best seating location is on the center meridian of the room.
3. Other seating locations should all provide good overall performance. The number of seats must be appropriate for the room size.
4. Loudspeaker type and location, acoustical treatment, and room décor should be designed to complement one another and deliver the stated objectives.

Loudspeaker Objectives and Placement

1. All speakers should have a similar timbral signature (same manufacturer/series)
2. L, C, R at approximately seated ear height (no more than 15° above)
   a. If L,C,R are higher, aim to cover smoothly
3. An unobstructed path from all full range speakers to all listeners
   a. Especially critical for Center speaker
4. Center speaker on center line of room
5. Speakers mounted in baffles or cabinets should be decoupled and damped to reduce resonances.
6. L and R speakers at an angle of 45-60° to each other, not too far from screen. L and R speakers toed in toward primary listening position.
7. Surround speaker placement for optimal envelopment and accuracy
   a. In 5.1 configuration, Surround Speakers at 110-120° off center line (A)
   b. In 7.1 configuration, Surround Speakers at 60-100°,
      Rear Speakers at 135-150°. (B)
   c. In larger room, multiple Surrounds to ensure envelopment. (C)

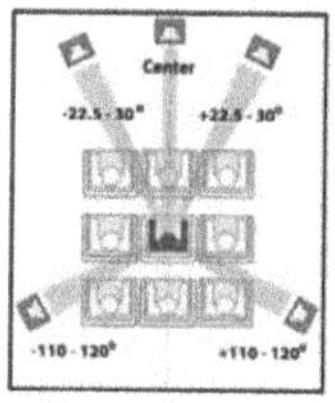

A

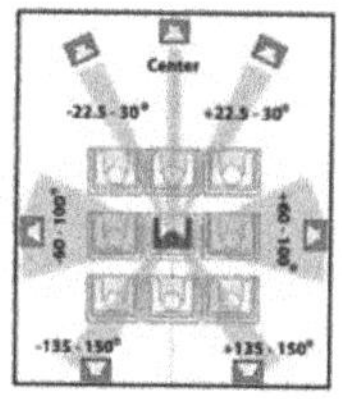

B

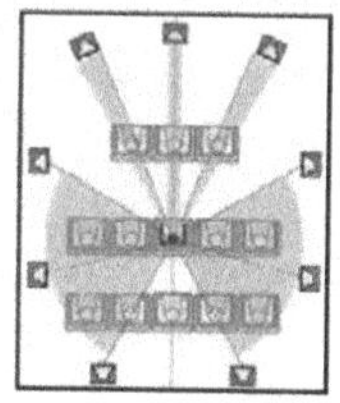

C

Subwoofer Guidelines

1. For reduced seat-to-seat variation, multiple subwoofers are ALWAYS better than just one.
2. In a closed rectangular room, using 2 or 4 subwoofers in certain configurations will yield predictable modal behavior, allowing for changes in dimension or seating to provide even response at several seating locations.(D)

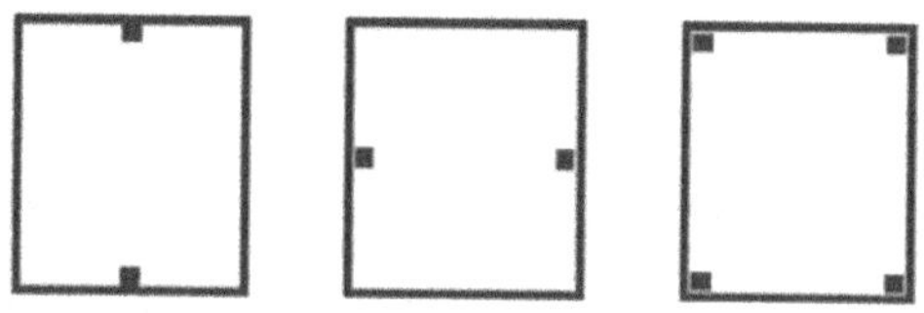

D

Seating Guidelines

1. Prime location at geometric center of speaker layout
2. Use center line for seating, not for an aisle (E)
3. No seating too close to any speakers
4. Avoid seating in 2nd order modal null points of room - 1/4 in from each wall (F)

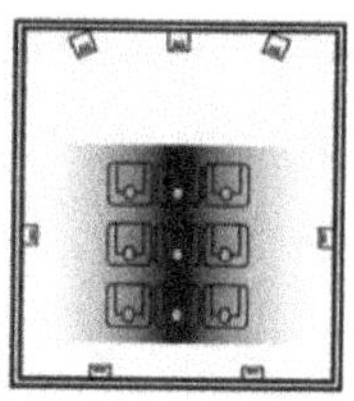

E

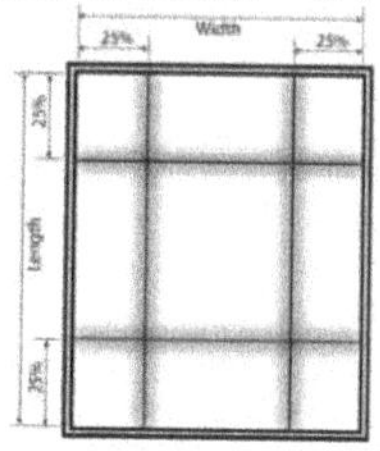

F

Acoustical Treatment

1. Reverberation Times (RT) at 500Hz should be in the range of .2 - .5 seconds.
2. Shorter RT may make room too "dead" and adversely affect the experience.
3. A typical room can achieve good sound with;
   a. Wall to wall carpet
   b. A combination of absorption (3"minimum) and diffusion, not to exceed 50% of wall area, placed to control flutter echoes between parallel walls near listening area, and control first reflections (optional)
4. All materials should be Class A fire rated.
5. There should be no audible rattles in the room.

Background Noise should be ≤ 30dB/A using RC mk II criteria. Ideal is ≤ 20dB/A.

1. Utilize oversized HVAC ducts
2. Specify low noise lighting dimmers
3. Acoustically treat nearby plumbing
4. Isolate HVAC equipment, lift pumps, etc.

Home Theater Recommended Practice: Video Design

These points represent only some of the key elements of CEB-23 and are intended to be a quick reference. For a complete understanding of the Recommended Practice, refer to the full original document.

The Goal of Home Theater Video is to faithfully reproduce the image which was painstakingly crafted by the director and to allow the viewer to "suspend disbelief" and become fully immersed in the program material. This is best accomplished by designing, installing, and calibrating the system to be consistent with established industry standards.

RECOMMENDATIONS:

General Design Considerations

1. Entire system to meet or exceed local codes
2. As energy efficient as practicable, while meeting performance goals
3. Signal processing and scaling taking place only the one optimum place in signal path

Room Layout & Installation Guidelines

1. Primary viewing position
    a. 3 X Image Height (Figure B)
    b. On the horizontal centerline of the screen
    c. Vertical angle ≤ 5° from orthogonal axis (dead center) (Figure C)
2. All other viewing positions
    a. Vertical angle ≤ 15° from orthogonal axis
3. Projector location - as far back in the room as possible (within throw range)
    a. Minimal fan noise
    b. Use of "sweet spot" of lens
    c. More accurate image geometry (minimal pincushion/barrel distortion)
    d. More efficient use of angular reflective screen (gain greater than 1.0)
4. Room lighting and décor
    a. No external light leaking into a dedicated theater
    b. Entry and egress lighting subdued and controllable by viewer
    c. All lighting must meet local codes
    d. Minimum of three lighting scenes
        i. Entry/Exit - approx. 50% dimmed
        ii. Watching - all off except path and exit
        iii. Cleaning/Task - All on
    e. Wall and ceiling finishes
        i. Dark and neutral
        ii. Non-reflective as possible
5. Source location
    a. Convenient for users
    b. Accessible for servicing
    c. Minimal cable run lengths

Projector

1. Fan noise
    a. Overall background noise at primary position ≤ 30dB/A (CEB-22)
    b. Fan can be a major contributor to this noise
    c. Maximum recommended projector noise (dBA) shown in Figure A

16 Hz	-	55dB
31.5 Hz	-	48dB
63 Hz	-	43 dB
125 Hz	-	30 dB
250 Hz	-	22 dB

A

2. Thermal issues
    a. Operating temperature should be no more than 10°F (5.55°C) higher than ambient room temperature
    b. Ventilation should remove hot air and draw in room air
    c. Uninterrupted Power Supply (UPS) recommended to ensure proper cool-down of lamp

Power & Cabling

1. Dedicated AC circuit for theater video system, on same phase as rest of theater (US)
2. HDMI or DVI is preferred interconnect
3. Interconnect attenuation ≤ 3dB (1dB ideal)
4. Strain relief where cabling connects to components
5. All cabling labeled and secured with Velcro™ when possible
6. No zip-ties or mechanical fasteners
7. Service loops where appropriate
8. Flexible conduit (minimum 1.5") from equipment to projector for future use

Image Performance Objectives

1. Luminance
    a. Minimum 14 foot lamberts (1 candela/ft^2 or 3.425 candela/m^2)
2. Contrast Ratio
    a. Sequential Contrast Method = ≥ 2,000:1 (minimum ≥1,200:1)
    b. Intra-Frame Contrast Method = ≥ 150:1
3. Calibration - for all inputs and viewing modes permitted by display device
4. Gray Scale - calibrated across entire IRE range
5. Chroma Uniformity = ≤ 20% variance between any two points on image
6. All calibration and measurements documented

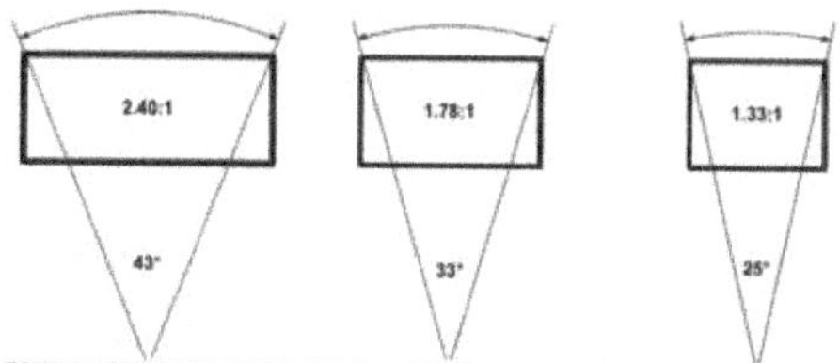

Screen Height	2.40:1 Width	Diagonal	S_v
23	55	60	69
27	65	70	81
34	82	88	102
38	91	99	114
42	101	109	126
46	111	120	138
50	120	130	150
55	132	143	165
60	144	156	180
65	156	169	195

Screen Height	1.85:1 Width	Diagonal	S_v
23	43	48	69
27	50	57	81
34	63	72	102
38	70	80	114
42	78	88	126
46	85	97	138
50	93	105	150
55	102	116	165
60	111	126	180
65	120	137	195

Screen Height	1.33:1 Width	Diagonal	S_v
23	31	38	69
27	36	45	81
34	45	57	102
38	51	63	114
42	56	70	126
46	61	77	138
50	66	83	150
55	73	92	165
60	80	100	180
65	86	108	195

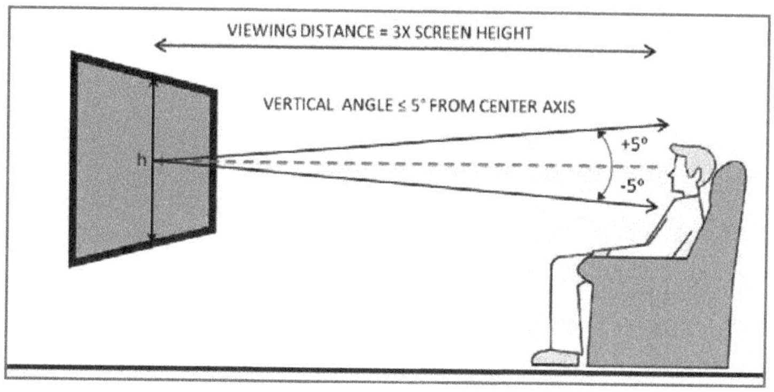

Home Theater Recommended Practice: HVAC

These points represent only some of the key elements of CEB-24 and are intended to be a quick reference. For a complete understanding of the Recommended Practice, refer to the full original document.

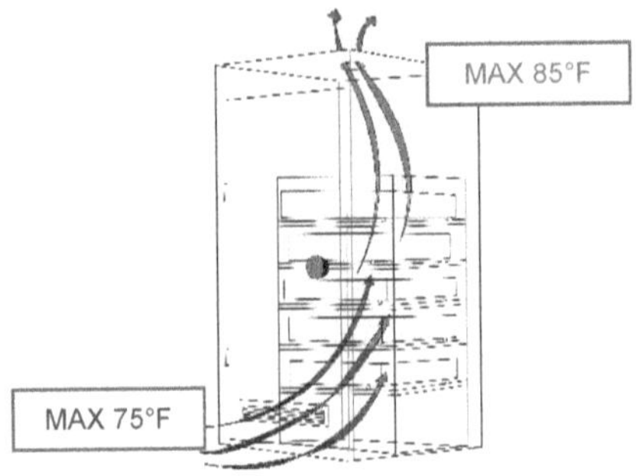

The Three Goals of Home Theater HVAC Design

1. Occupant Comfort
2. Acceptable Equipment Environment
3. Acceptable Noise Floor

RECOMMENDATIONS:

Ambient Room Conditions

1. Temperature: 68°-75°F (20°-23.9°C)
2. Relative Humidity: 30%-60%

Note; Lower humidity causes static electricity, higher can cause condensation in equipment.

Equipment Conditions

1. Operating Temperature: ≤ 85°F (29.4°C)
2. Fresh Air Inlet to Rack/Cabinet: ≤ 75°F

Note A; 99.6% of all power (electricity) going into a rack is converted to heat.
Note B; for every 10°F above 85°F, reliability of equipment drops 50%.

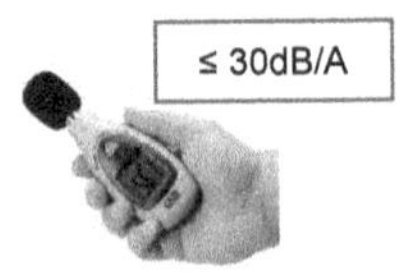

Noise Floor (at primary listening position)

1. Noise Generated by HVAC: RC(N) < 25
2. Total Noise: ≤ 30dB/A (also noted in CEB-22)

Noise Egress to Adjacent Spaces via HVAC

1. Maximum ≤ 30dB/A - measured 1m from any duct in the home

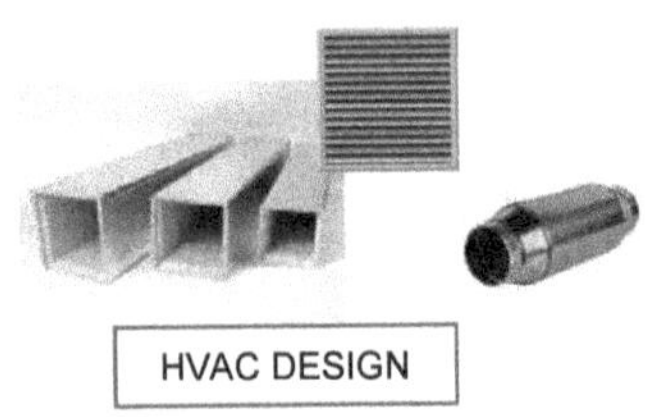

HVAC Recommendations

1. Air handler located far from theater
2. Ductwork of Non-metallic Construction (fiberglass)
3. Radiused elbows vs. mitered elbows
4. Oversized ductwork to reduce velocity
5. Dampers located far from terminal outlets
6. Ductwork with minimum 1" Wall Thickness / 3lb/ft^2 material
7. Multiple Gradual 90° Bends

ADDITIONAL RESOURCES

CEDIA Training: : available online, at EXPO, and at local training events - a wide variety of topics at all learning levels - including technical, business, and emerging trends. www.cedia.net/train

CEDIA Resource Library - over 100 documents, drawings and other resources to improve the quality of your projects www.cedia.net/train/resources

CEDIA Fundamentals of Residential Electronic Systems - this book provides the foundation for virtually all content in the Advanced book. It covers the entire industry at a more introductory level, and is perfect for anyone who is new to the industry or preparing for CEDIA's ESC (Electronic Systems Certified) credential. The two books together provide a comprehensive body of knowledge for anyone, especially those seeking CEDIA's higher certifications (ESC-T, ESC-D and ESC-N).

Standards and Recommended Practices - technical documents intended to help establish functional goals and standardized practices in the industry.

CEA/CEDIA CEB-22	Home Theater Recommended Practices: Audio Design
CEA/CEDIA CEB-23	Home Theater Recommended Practices: Video Design
CEA/CEDIA CEB-24	Home Theater HVAC
CEA CEB-29	Installation of Smart Grid Device
ANSI J-STD-710	Architectural Drawing Symbols Standard
ANSI/CEA/CEDIA 2030-A	Multi-room Audio Cabling
ANSI/CEA/CEDIA 863B	Connection Color Codes for Home Theater Systems
ANSI/CEA/CEDIA 897	F-Connector Color Coding for the Home
EIA/TIA 570-C	Residential Telecommunications Infrastructure Standard
ITU 775-1	Multi-channel Speaker Configuration
UL-1678	Mounting A/V Devices

CEDIA White Papers and Other Reference Documents - More than 40 topic-specific publications aimed directly at the residential industry

Technical White Papers

Dimming CFLs
Dimming LED Lamps
HDMI Fundamentals White Paper Compilation
Mobile Devices Pt.1 - The Business Case
Mobile Devices Pt.2 - Ten Steps to Creating a Robust Wireless Environment
Mobile Devices Pt.3 - Using Mobile Devices as a Control Platform
Network Security Best Practices
Safety Tips and Regulations
Selecting Display Size Based on Room Size and Seating
Telepresence Opportunities
Ten Steps to Creating a Robust Wireless Environment
Troubleshooting for the Home Technology Professional
Ultra HD-4K Industry White Paper
Wireless Audio Solutions: Technologies and Best Practices

Business White Papers

- Inbound Marketing
- Increasing Profits: How to Best Utilize Subcontractors
- Increasing Profits: How to Create Job Cost Reports
- Increasing Profits: How to Measure and Track Employee Productivitiy
- Managing Cash Flow
- Markup vs. Margin

Other Documents

- CEDIA Recommended Wiring Guidelines (US)
- CEDIA Recommended Wiring Guidelines (Europe, Middle-East, Africa)

Publications

US and Canada

CE Pro - www.cepro.com
Residential Systems - www.residentialsystems.com
Technology Integrator - www.technologyintegrator.net

UK and Europe

Inside CI - www.insideci.co.uk
Hiddenwires - http://hiddenwires.co.uk
SVI - www.svimag.com
Essential Install - www.essentialinstallive.eu/magazine

Mexico

HomeTech Magazine - http://musitech.com.mx/hometech/

Brazil

Home Theater and Casa Digital - www.hometheater.com.br
AVI Latinoamerica - www.avilatinoamerica.com

Columbia

AXXIS - http://revistaaxxis.com.co

Australia

Connected Home - www.trade.connectedhometechnology.com

Index